Biology

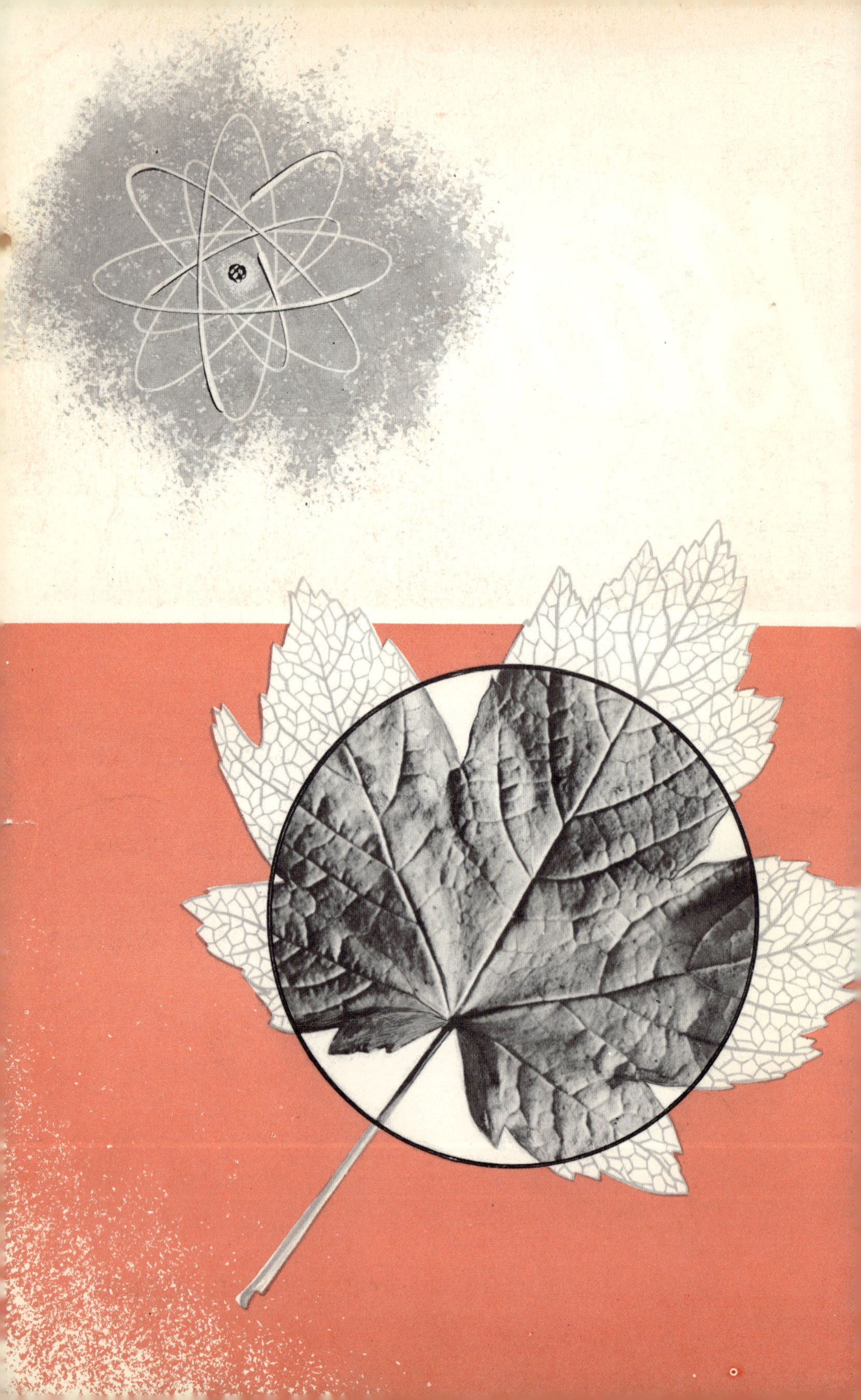

Biology

ELSBETH KROEBER

WALTER H. WOLFF

RICHARD L. WEAVER

D. C. HEATH AND COMPANY BOSTON

The Authors

ELSBETH KROEBER was formerly First Assistant in Biological Science and Administrative Assistant at Midwood High School, Brooklyn, New York. She has also been Chairman of the Department of Biology at James Madison High School, Brooklyn, New York.

WALTER H. WOLFF is Principal of the William Cullen Bryant High School, Queens, New York. Among his former positions are the following: Instructor, School of Education, The City College of the City of New York, and Chairman of the Department of Biology and General Science, DeWitt Clinton High School, Bronx, New York.

RICHARD L. WEAVER is Associate Professor of Conservation, Conservation Department, School of Natural Resources, and Associate Professor of Conservation Education, School of Education, University of Michigan, Ann Arbor, Michigan.

Cover design and many drawings by R. Paul Larkin. Credit for photographs used in unit openings: Unit Two — South African Railways, Unit Three — H. Armstrong Roberts, Unit Four — Meisel from Monkmeyer, Unit Five — Three Lions, Unit Six — National Foundation for Infantile Paralysis, Unit Seven — Lew Merrim, Unit Eight — Ewing Galloway, Unit Ten — U. S. Forest Service. Credit for composite photograph on page nine — Cruickshank-National Audubon Society, National Zoological Society, Tyrell-National Audubon Society, Philip Gendreau, Ralph Anderson, and Museum of Natural History.
Photograph on title page by Martin Bovey, Jr., from Massachusetts Audubon Society.

COPYRIGHT, 1957, BY D. C. HEATH AND COMPANY

No part of the material covered by this copyright may be reproduced in any form without written permission of the publisher. Printed in the United States of America. (5 C 8)

Preface

WE ARE CONVINCED that the study of biology is an exciting adventure for boys and girls. All young people are interested primarily in themselves and in everything related to themselves. They want to know how their bodies work, how bacteria and infectious diseases affect them. They are interested in their behavior and how they change as they mature. They want, of course, to understand reproduction and how characters are, and are not, passed on from parent to child. All this constitutes a large part of the book.

But young people with imagination and a spirit of adventure want, too, to go farther afield. They wish to become acquainted with the world around them, the great outdoors, the vast number of interesting living things. They are interested, also, in the world in its beginnings, how the earth changed in past ages, and what lies ahead. In two hundred years from now will people live as they live now? Will there be food enough to go around in another hundred years? Will we still be dependent upon green plants as we are now? Even in urban schools it is easy to arouse the pupils' interest in questions such as these. But to appreciate the role that plants and animals play they must learn these subjects at first hand. They must get out-of-doors.

To help the teacher stimulate an interest in outdoor biology, field trips have been described. These are grouped into one section at the front of the book for ready reference. If pupils can be made to feel the need for studying some biology out-of-doors, they will be better prepared for the last unit, Conservation. So that pupils may be ready in interest and understanding for this important topic, it is placed at the end of the book; but references to ecology and conservation are made again and again in the earlier units. No pupil should be permitted to complete his biology course without help in developing an interest in conservation and an appreciation of its importance.

In the experience of many teachers the objective of developing scientific attitudes and habits is best achieved if the subject is not didactically presented and belabored. The text and exercises, therefore, have been carefully written to incorporate consistently the scientific attitude of mind and scientific methods of arriving at conclusions. There is no chapter on scientific attitudes and scientific methods.

Great care has been taken, also, to achieve simplicity of expression. Difficult nonscience words have been excluded; only the essential technical terms have been included and these have been listed at the end of the chapter to help the pupil master them. The glossary at the end of the book is designed to assist the student further. Much thought and labor has also been expended to avoid abrupt transitions from idea to idea. The treatment of content carries the student forward gradually from each sentence and idea to the next.

Because illustrations are almost if not just as important as words in developing ideas and teaching facts, they have been made an integral part of the text. Nearly all illustrations are referred to, and their legends often ask pertinent questions. Many of the illustrations may be used as a basis for questions and exercises.

End-of-chapter materials were designed to be of maximum help to both the teacher and pupil. Here are: (1) a series of questions which will indicate to the pupil whether or not he has achieved an understanding of the subject, not merely the memorization of the words of the book; (2) a minimal list of technical terms essential for discussion of the topic and further reading; (3) a small number of exercises or experiments which can be easily carried out by all pupils (The *Teacher's Manual* includes further suggestions for exercises for those teachers who have the time and necessary equipment for further experimentation); and (4) a short bibliography. Aside from an occasional reference work only books and articles of proved interest to the pupil have been included.

An appendix, consisting of details of a number of type forms, will be useful to pupils who are preparing for college entrance examinations. Others, also, will find this section useful.

A few words are pertinent concerning the *Teacher's Manual* and the introductory section of the text titled "Biologists Study Living Things." The *Teacher's Manual* includes in some detail our aims in teaching biology and the methods of presentation which have been found useful by us in our many years of biology teaching. We wish, therefore, to recommend this to the teacher's attention and to say no more on these subjects here. We wish, however, to recommend for pupils' use the introductory section of the text. In it are useful hints to the student on how to study biology and how to study from a text. It is hoped that students will read those pages, especially at the beginning of the course, and at other times as need for such help is felt.

We wish to thank the many users who sent in helpful criticisms of the predecessor of BIOLOGY. These suggestions were all taken into account in preparing the manuscript for this text. We particularly want to thank Mr. Rex Conyers, University City High School, University City, Missouri; Miss Katherine Hertzka, Atlanta Public Schools, Atlanta, Georgia; Mrs. Charlotte O. Wolff and Mrs. Richard L. Weaver.

ELSBETH KROEBER
WALTER H. WOLFF
RICHARD L. WEAVER

Contents

Introduction:	Biologists study living things	1
	Field trips	10

Unit One — How living things are alike — 28
CHAPTER	1	What cells are	30
CHAPTER	2	What cells do	40
CHAPTER	3	Tissues and organs	49

Unit Two — The many kinds of plants and animals — 56
CHAPTER	4	A third of a million kinds of plants	58
CHAPTER	5	A million kinds of animals	80
CHAPTER	6	Classifying plants and animals	127

Unit Three — Plants the world's food makers — 138
CHAPTER	7	Leaves	140
CHAPTER	8	Roots and stems	151

Unit Four — How our bodies work — 168
CHAPTER	9	The foods we eat	170
CHAPTER	10	Digestion and absorption	190
CHAPTER	11	Blood and circulation	205
CHAPTER	12	Lungs and breathing	225
CHAPTER	13	Excretion	235
CHAPTER	14	Ductless glands	242

Unit Five — Why we behave as we do — 254
CHAPTER	15	The simplest kinds of behavior	256
CHAPTER	16	Our nervous system	270
CHAPTER	17	Changes in behavior	279
CHAPTER	18	Growing up	290

CONTENTS

Unit Six — Bacteria and health — 298

- CHAPTER 19 — Bacteria and disease — 300
- CHAPTER 20 — Body defenses against disease — 310
- CHAPTER 21 — Some recent discoveries — 324
- CHAPTER 22 — Stopping the spread of disease — 331
- CHAPTER 23 — Building health — 346

Unit Seven — Reproduction — 360

- CHAPTER 24 — Reproduction in some simple organisms — 362
- CHAPTER 25 — Plant reproduction — 370
- CHAPTER 26 — Animal reproduction — 386

Unit Eight — Heredity and environment — 402

- CHAPTER 27 — Why offspring resemble their parents — 404
- CHAPTER 28 — Why offspring differ from their parents — 411
- CHAPTER 29 — How characters are changed — 422
- CHAPTER 30 — Improving plants and animals — 434
- CHAPTER 31 — Human heredity — 447

Unit Nine — The history of living things — 458

- CHAPTER 32 — Fossils and their history — 460
- CHAPTER 33 — From simple organisms to complex — 471
- CHAPTER 34 — Theories to explain change — 488
- CHAPTER 35 — History of man — 495

Unit Ten — Conservation — 506

- CHAPTER 36 — Materials used and re-used by living things — 508
- CHAPTER 37 — The tangled web of life — 515
- CHAPTER 38 — A bountiful future — 528

Appendix — The structure of some animals other than man — 556

Glossary — 569

Index — 589

Biologists Study Living Things

What is biology? You have been studying biology for many years. You probably never knew it, but you have been studying biology ever since you were a baby — ever since you were able to use your eyes and your ears and your other sense organs and were able to use your mind. All your life you have lived with yourself, with other people, and with other living things. You already know a lot about living things. And that's *biology* — the study of all living things. The dictionary calls it "the science that deals with living things."

Although you already know something about yourself and perhaps some other living things, you will be astonished to discover how many exciting things in biology you had never heard of before or had never guessed would be possible. Exciting discoveries are being made all the time. Perhaps the most interesting of these will be the discoveries that are about you yourself and other human beings — discoveries about our diseases, how the parts of our bodies work, how children get to be like and different from their parents, and so on.

As you read, you will discover that biology covers an enormous field. And you will see opening up to you one occupation after another and one interesting hobby after another. There are so many interesting hobbies and jobs connected with biology that we could not

Some biologists care for animals in zoos. This girl is feeding a reindeer, *Orlando*

This New York City biology student is doing an experiment in his study of plant diseases. *Wide World*

name them all in these pages. Whether you enjoy being out-of-doors or in a laboratory; whether you enjoy working with people, with experimental animals, with plants, or mostly with chemicals; whether you enjoy settling down or exploring the ends of the earth; whether you are interested in looking into the past or looking into the future, there are jobs or hobbies for students of biology.

Science. Since biology is a science, you ought to know what a science is. The dictionary tells you "a science is a large body of knowledge based on facts or truths known by actual experience or observation." Notice that the knowledge is based not on guesses or suppositions, but on facts. The knowledge is gained by systematic study through the use of scientific methods. And it is important to know that there are many scientific methods. What a biologist does depends on what he or she is trying to find out. Sometimes this means just going out to look and listen, as when a biologist is learning about animals and plants out-of-doors, or when he hammers rocks, or studies how chickens act in a farmyard. Close observation is necessary to the biologist and to every other kind of scientist.

BIOLOGISTS STUDY LIVING THINGS

This biologist works in a trailside museum. She takes care of some of the animals, conducts field trips, and answers questions that come by mail. *Trailside Museum, Chicago*

Sometimes the scientist plans and carries out an experiment and makes observations under special conditions which he has set up. He plans the experiment in order to answer a definite question which he wants to have answered. He calls this a *problem*. Very often before beginning an experiment the scientist makes a careful guess as to the answer. The guess is called a *hypothesis*. The experiment is planned to test this hypothesis. Sometimes several hypotheses are made. Often many experiments must be performed. It is only by using controls that the experimenter can be sure the results he gets will be correct. You will learn about using controls in experiments as you study this book. Perhaps you already know something about the use of controls. Of course, the biologist is not finished when he records observations on his controlled experiments. He must draw conclusions from these observations. For that reason, careful and clear thinking is as much a part of any scientist's work as observing or experimenting. Sometimes the conclusions show that the guess or hypothesis was wrong. The biologist must face this honestly and start over again with a new hypothesis. He may have to do this many times before he meets with success in solving the problem.

BIOLOGISTS STUDY LIVING THINGS

Even when the ground is covered with snow there is much of interest out-of-doors. These skiers in New England may see deer and rabbits, such birds as grouse, pheasant, chickadees, and nuthatches, and of course, the shrubs and trees. *Eames Studio*

Off the Maine coast ornithologists study the nesting places of the double-crested cormorant.
Allan Cruickshank

As you study this book, you will learn more and more about the ways in which biologists learn about living things, how they are formed, how they live, what keeps them alive, how they may become sick, what makes them die, how they reproduce, where they came from, and how we may use other living things for our benefit. All the carefully worked out methods of discovering such facts are the scientific methods of biologists.

How you can be a biologist. You, too, can experiment; you can perform controlled experiments, observe closely, and draw your own conclusions. Perhaps your school has a laboratory. Or some of you may have your own small laboratory at home.

Before you can do much experimenting there are some things you must learn from books. We can help you learn about biology from this book by giving you some hints. This book is divided into ten large topics or Units. Be sure you know the title of the unit before you begin it; and know the chapter title before you start reading it. If you do this, you will have some idea of what you are about to study. No one would start off in a car without knowing where he wants to go. And it's just the same in reading. You must know where you

BIOLOGISTS STUDY LIVING THINGS

are trying to get when you start reading some unit or some new chapter in your biology book. The titles are like road markers pointing the way. Don't overlook them if you want to be a good biologist.

To make things still easier for you the chapter is broken up into short sections with a few words in boldface type at the beginning of each section. After reading these words in boldface carefully, think over their meaning and ask yourself what you already know about that subject. If you know something about the subject to begin with, as you study the section, the new ideas and facts can be fitted in with what you already know; in this way the reading will be more interesting and you will remember better what you read.

A good way to read a text. It is a good plan to read a whole section through to the end quickly to get a general idea of what it is about. But you must not stop with that one quick reading. A very few people, after a great deal of practice, learn to take in everything from one quick reading of a textbook; most of us cannot do it. After your quick reading of a section, go back to the beginning and read each sentence carefully so that you can understand and remember it. If you don't understand a sentence, read it again; often a second reading will make the sentence clear. But if it is still not clear or if any question arises in your mind, make a note of this and ask to have it explained in class. Of course, if there is a word you do not understand, look it up or ask someone or be sure to ask about it in class the next day. This kind of study is slow, but it certainly pays in the end. *Never pass over anything that you do not understand* without making every possible effort to have it explained.

This South Carolina class, interested in conservation, has gone out-of-doors. They are examining farm land ruined by erosion. *Soil Conservation Service*

BIOLOGISTS STUDY LIVING THINGS

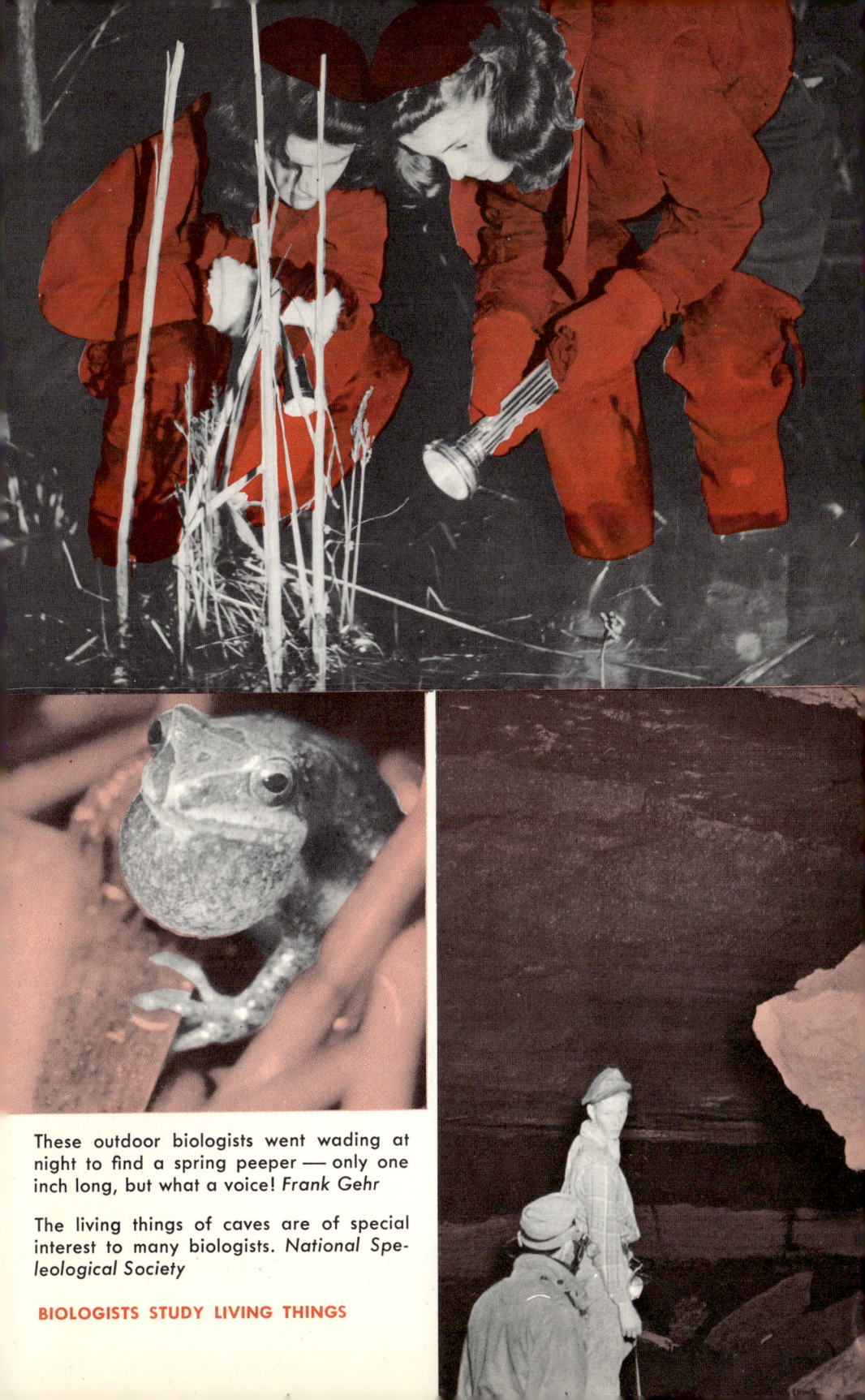

These outdoor biologists went wading at night to find a spring peeper — only one inch long, but what a voice! *Frank Gehr*

The living things of caves are of special interest to many biologists. *National Speleological Society*

BIOLOGISTS STUDY LIVING THINGS

The beaver trapped by this biologist will be taken to another stream where a beaver dam will be useful. Three Lions

Often a close look at the pictures will help you understand what you read; but only if you read the statements and questions under the picture. This is just as important as reading the text itself.

Of course, you can never understand what you are reading in biology, unless you learn to speak the language of the biologist. That means that you must know the meanings of certain biological words. The important words are printed in boldface type. They are listed at the end of the chapter to help you. If a biological term has been used before and you have forgotten its meaning, look it up in the glossary (not the index) at the end of the book.

Now if you are studying the book carefully, your mind will be active. You will be thinking about the subject as you read. Many questions and problems will arise in your mind. This may not happen with every section but it will happen with some. The more you are thinking, the more questions will arise. Be sure to jot down your questions and bring them to class. This will lead to interesting class discussions.

Learning in other ways. Biology is different from most other subjects you study in school. Besides learning from books, seeing moving pictures, listening to recordings, and having class discussions you learn in other ways. As you know, you find out some things for yourself by experiment. And you find out much for yourself through observations out-of-doors. Get out-of-doors and observe. This is one very important way of studying biology. Become acquainted with plants and animals. Find out where they live, how they live, and how they live together and depend on one another. If it is not possible for you to go as a class from school, go out with friends. You will want to take many field trips this year: to the woods, to the fields, to a pond or marsh, to the seashore if you live near the coast, to the desert if you can. If you live in a large city, you will be surprised how much biology you can learn in a city park or even in a city lot. This book suggests a number of field trips. You will want to take more on your own. And the better acquainted you are with the out-of-doors the more you will enjoy your trips. You may even see things that have never been seen or described before. Exploring is fun. Pack up what you need for your trip and get started. You will find suggestions for your first trip on page 10.

BIOLOGISTS STUDY LIVING THINGS

(Above) From May to June over much of northern United States, marsh marigold blossoms in wet places. *Shostal*

(Below) In October the leaves of many deciduous trees in Logan County, Ohio, take on fall colors. *F P G*

(Upper left) A school of blue-striped grunts found in British West Indies. (Upper right) Sea fans are found in shallow places in the South Atlantic. They are made by colonies of small coelenterates. (Left) Angel fish are common in the warm seas around the Bahama Islands. (Lower left) A sea anemone with tentacles and a needle-spined sea urchin. (Lower right) A sea feather, unlike the rigid sea fan, is capable of independent movement. *Pat and Nat Bartlett*

(Above) The flowers of prickly pear cactus brighten southwestern deserts in the spring. V. L. Finne

(Below) Beautiful flowers of hedgehog cactus blossom in low clumps in California deserts. V. L. Finne

Wildflowers grow in a mountain meadow high in Gunnison National Forest, Colorado. Patches of snow are seen on the upper slopes. *Shostal*

Field Trips

(Photo from H. Armstrong Roberts)

SEEDS

- Oak
- Milkweed
- Shagbark hickory
- Beech
- Witch hazel
- Beggar's-ticks
- Butternut

FIELD TRIPS

OUT-OF-DOORS IN THE FALL

Perhaps this is your first field trip to study living things. What will you take? A knife, of course, perhaps a trowel if you want to dig, jars of various sizes with screw tops, a pail, and boxes or other containers for collecting, perhaps a butterfly net, perhaps a dredging net or instead just a large strainer from the kitchen, and a knapsack for holding all your materials. If you have not already visited a pond, include a pond or small stream in your trip.

You will want your camera, of course. Possibly you can slip in one or two field books, depending on what you want particularly to study on your first day out-of-doors. And certainly you will want to have a small notebook and a pencil in your pocket.

In many regions fall is the season of many colors—the blues and purples of asters, Joe-Pye weeds, and ironweeds, the yellow of the goldenrods along the edges of the road or in fields. Many of the trees, too, are changing color before they drop their leaves. The red and yellow in the leaves which had been hidden all summer by the green, now begin to show.

This is a good time to start a collection of leaves of trees. Be sure to notice how they grow on the stem, opposite to each other, alternately, or in clusters called whorls. You will need to know this to find the name of the trees you see. And take a good look, too, at the shape of the tree, and its bark. After a little study you can recognize many trees even after they have lost their leaves.

As you collect leaves, look for seeds and fruits. Hickories, oaks, walnuts, butternuts, beeches, and many evergreens bear seeds in the fall. Others, like the elms, maples, birches, and poplars, produce their seeds in the spring or early summer. Take home some seeds to plant indoors or out.

Look for seeds of smaller plants, too. Many of these plants are completing their growth and producing seeds. You may not have to look very far for some of these seeds; they may already have discovered you and have attached themselves to your clothes by their hooks: the burs, the beggar's-ticks, and sticktights are getting a free ride. They cling so firmly that they will be carried far from the parent plant before you pull them off or they drop to the ground. Other seeds, like those of the dandelions, asters, milkweeds, and hawkweeds, are very light; and their tufts of silky hair keep them afloat in air or water for a long time. Collect as many different kinds of seeds as you can. Some seeds, like those of the wild cucumber, the witch-hazel, and the jewelweed, are shot from the seed pods when they are ripe.

There are many other things for you to notice on this trip. Notice which plants are found growing together and in what kind of ground they grow—hilly, flat, low and marshy, or rocky? What kinds of animals live with these plants? And then look at the soil. Is it dark or light, sandy, closely packed?

Fall is not the best time to begin a study of birds because many of those you may see are youngsters; they may not look just like their parents. And if you live in the more northerly regions, many birds have already "migrated" south by the time school begins. But even so, much can be learned about birds in the fall. If you are up early you may see large companies of swallows strung out on telephone wires, like beads on a string. They are probably getting ready to start south in large flocks. In nearly all parts of the country, wherever you may happen to live, some birds are probably arriving from farther north. Some may stay for only a day or a week, then go on farther south. Some that have just arrived may stay in your neighborhood until next spring. These are the winter residents. Keep a careful record of the date and the kinds of birds you see.

This is a good time to look for nests as the leaves thin out. Many nests can be identified by the materials used, by their size and shape, by their location—on the ground or how high above the ground—and by the way they are attached to tree or shrub. Look closely to see what materials have been used. Collect nests at this time of year if you wish. They would not be used again. And look for feathers. Most birds molt or shed some or all of their feathers during the late summer and fall.

When you come back your containers will be filled with specimens you may want to examine more closely and identify. Some of them might be kept as the beginning of a home or school museum.

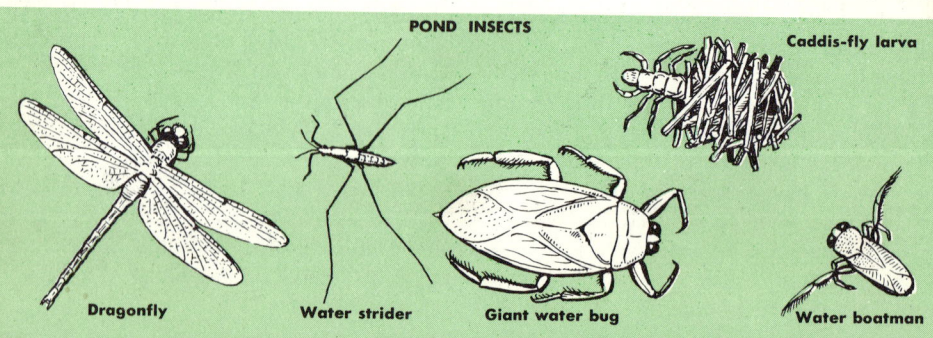

(Photo from H. Armstrong Roberts)

POND INSECTS

Dragonfly Water strider Giant water bug Caddis-fly larva Water boatman

FIELD TRIPS

A TRIP TO A FRESH-WATER POND

All of you except those who live in the desert will not have to go far to reach a fresh-water pond or marsh or stream. Even a ditch along the roadside is interesting to study, although, of course, you will see here a different collection or "community" of animals and plants, and a much smaller one.

On the lowlands bordering streams and ponds the water often is unable to drain off and a marsh or a swamp is formed. In wooded areas we usually call the wet ground a swamp. If there are no trees we speak of it as a marsh. These swamps or marshes are interesting because they steadily change. But they change so slowly that you will note the change only over a period of years. Look at the edges of the marsh. You may see cattails and rushes, tall grasslike plants. Cut some; you will see that the stems are hollow. If you try to pull them up you will discover that they have strong roots. They grow in clumps. In the fall the tops die and in the spring new plants grow out from these clumps into the deeper water. Thus the shore moves out into the water and the pond grows smaller. The land that was the edge of the pond originally dries up. Then flowering shrubs such as alders appear; even trees appear, such as maples in many parts of the country or cypresses in southern swamps. If you are visiting a pond do you see signs of the land moving out into the water?

Of course, you have brought the necessary things with you, a small pail, small glass bottles with stoppers, perhaps a strainer from the kitchen, and some larger containers. The little field book *Beginner's Guide to Fresh Water Life* by Leon A. Hausman (Putnam, 1950) will be helpful to you.

If the pond is not disturbed by wind or waves you may find a green scum on the water. You will read more about this scum in Chapter 4. It is a mass of simple plants (algae), plants that are eaten in vast numbers by water animals. Scoop up some of these plants and take them home in water. If you have a microscope in school you may wish to get a close-up of them. You can see a picture of some of them on page 60.

Darting in and out among the plants are tiny animals too small to be seen as anything more than whitish specks in a jar of water. But with a magnifying glass you can watch their rapid, jerky movements. Some of them are Cyclops, very small, one-eyed creatures named after the one-eyed giants in Greek mythology.

If you are lucky you may find a crayfish, walking on its long jointed legs along the shallow edge of a pond or stream or striding over the rocks in somewhat deeper water. A full-grown crayfish is about four inches long.

If you are looking at a backwash in a stream or the quiet water of a small pond do you see "water striders" in search of food? They are well named, for their six legs stretch wide in different directions; and they are insects so light in weight that the thin surface film of water supports them. They actually walk over the top of the water. Look too for backswimmers, fierce little insects one-fourth to one-half inch long. Their back is shaped like the keel of a boat. They swim rapidly on their backs and attack even much larger animals with their strong jaws.

And you may see a dragonfly dip into the water for an instant and depart. It has wide-spreading lacy wings and often a brightly colored and shining body. It may startle you if it whizzes close to your head, but it never lights on you. It is in search of food in the water or it may be flying over the water, touching the surface lightly and depositing its eggs. These eggs soon hatch into water forms which feed on microscopic plants and animals. When they are ready to leave the water, they crawl up a plant stem.

Look on the soft bottom of the pond where the water is shallow. Do you see snail shells? Pick some up and look underneath. Is the shell empty? The animal that once lived in it died and became the food of other animals or of decay bacteria. Sometimes you find the animal's soft body within the shell and the opening tightly closed. Take some snails back to school in a little water. If you have an aquarium put the snails in with your fish; they will help keep the water fresh and clean since they will feed on tiny green plants that grow on the sides of your aquarium and on decaying matter.

Your boxes and bags and bottles will all be well filled soon. Back at school you can observe your specimens more closely.

(Photo from Charles Phelps Cushing)

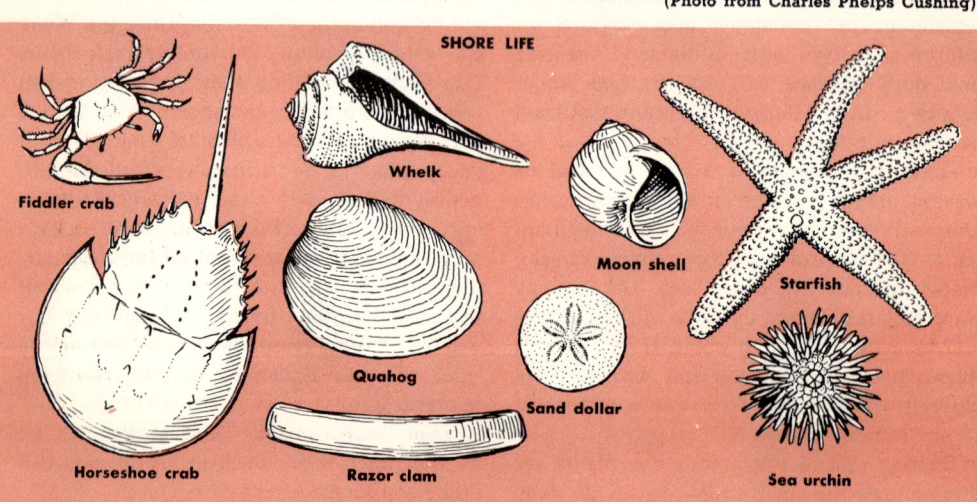

SHORE LIFE

Fiddler crab

Whelk

Moon shell

Starfish

Horseshoe crab

Quahog

Sand dollar

Sea urchin

Razor clam

14

FIELD TRIPS

A TRIP TO THE SEASHORE

If you live inland you may have to miss this exciting trip, one of the most interesting trips you can take, for here you can see living things like some of those that appeared very early in the history of the earth—strange living things. You will want to take a magnifying glass, some jars, and certainly if you live in the East, the little *Beginner's Guide to Seashore Life* by Leon A. Hausman (Putnam, 1949), or if you explore the Pacific coast, take *Between the Tides* by Ricketts and Calvin (Stanford University, 1939).

You know that twice in every twenty-four hours the ocean waters rise over the shore until the tide is high. The rising tide brings many living things onto the shore. Then the tide goes out. Some plants and animals are left stranded on the wet sands or rocks, perhaps in the glaring sun, until the tide turns again.

Let's explore the rocky portions first. Here, as the tide goes out, small tide pools are left among the rocks. Settle down beside one of these pools and quietly watch this little world in miniature. Don't touch the water. Gradually, one animal after another will come to life. Watch the small white barnacles, opening up—tapering little mounds of limestone shell. (See Figure 5.44 on page 106.) Take notes or make sketches to show how they open. Can you see the tiny "legs" kicking food into the large opening or mouth? The legs cannot be used for any other purpose; the barnacle is grown to this one spot for life. And as you watch, tiny sea anemones may blossom out with waving tentacles. (You can see large anemones on page 85.) Twisted snail shells may begin to glide slowly as the animal within explores the rocky bottom. You may see the common urn sponge (*Grantia*). Look for the waving, treelike *Obelia*, less than an inch in height, yellowish or grayish in color. It's an animal, or rather a colony of animals, in spite of its plantlike appearance. The treelike growth is really a skeleton made of lime. With a magnifying glass you can see the animals themselves; they are Coelenterates, related to the jellyfish, with waving tentacles. You may see "moss animals," too (*Bryozoa*). Look them up in your guide. Now put your hand into the pool to feel the various living things. And pick up some of the loose rocks (in the pool) to look for small flatworms or the wriggling thread worms.

When you have made a census of the living things in your pool explore a portion of flat sand beach. Examine the tangles of seaweed washed up and left by the tide as it went out—the common rockweeds (Figure 4.4, on p. 61), pieces of sea lettuce, and pieces of Irish moss or pudding plant of many colors. Perhaps you have eaten fluffy, gelatinous puddings made with Irish moss. Look for snails caught in the seaweeds. Are they all of the same kind? You will probably find, too, strings of thick, leathery, yellowish disks about an inch across. These are the egg cases of the whelk. Tear or cut open some of the disks to look for the little whelks, perhaps no larger than a grain of sand. How many do you find in one disk? Equally common is the black leathery egg case of the skate, with a long point at each of the four corners. Open this, too, and look inside. Then there are the many shells of clams, mussels, oysters, whelks, pieces of the outside skeleton of crabs and lobsters, perhaps the shell of a sea urchin, a dead starfish, a jellyfish drying up. Bring home your many treasures to be examined and identified in school; it will take you a long time to identify them all.

You will also want to explore the mud flats. If you're lucky you may find a hermit crab in shallow water, the "street cleaner" of the mud flats. This crab finds itself an empty snail shell and backs its soft, twisted body into the shell. All that can be seen of the crab is the head, the large claws, and some walking legs. When it outgrows its house it moves into a larger one. If it finds nothing suitable "for rent" it dispossesses another crab and moves in. On the mud flats near the sea you may take another crab by surprise—the fiddler crab. As you appear it scuttles off sideways to its hole, backs in and disappears. But not for long. A claw almost as large as the crab itself soon appears; then the crab crawls out cautiously, waving its big claw as though it were a fiddler's bow.

You will want to return some other day to look for these crabs and to walk along the beach and poke among the seaweeds where so many treasures are hidden. And when you come again be on the lookout for sandpipers, gulls, and terns.

(Photo from U. S. Forest Service)

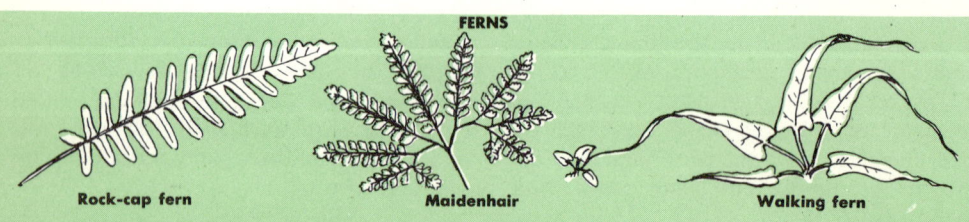

FERNS

Rock-cap fern   Maidenhair   Walking fern

16   FIELD TRIPS

A TRIP TO THE WOODS

Today let's go to a forest if there is one near by. You will probably not do much collecting on this trip, but take a few small jars in case you find a new kind of beetle or other insect, and, if you can, take your bird guide and a small book for identifying trees. Unless you live in the Far West you are not likely to visit a virgin forest—one that has never been lumbered. In most forests you would visit, the trees are second growth. About how thick are the trunks of the largest trees you see? What is the thickness of the majority of trees? How old are these trees? Perhaps a large tree has been cut down; if so, you can count the annual rings of the stump. This gives you the age of the tree when it was cut. If no stump is available, a small core of wood can be removed with an increment borer and the rings of the core can be counted. You can borrow an increment borer from a county farm agent or a forester.

Are you in a forest of hardwood trees, that is, trees that shed their leaves in the fall, or are you in a forest of cone-bearing trees (conifers)? Perhaps you are in a mixed forest. In any case, if it is a real forest and not just a grove of trees, when you are deep in the forest look straight up. Can you see the sky? Not much, if any. Here and there, where a tree has fallen the sun shines through a chink. But little direct sunlight reaches the lower branches and the ground. The lower branches, therefore, grow only a very little each year; those lowest down die and break off, one by one. The tree continues to grow taller at its top; it grows tall and slim.

You will find few shrubs (smaller woody plants). In more open spots perhaps you will find a hobblebush, a striped maple, a dogwood, or a hornbeam. Smaller flowering plants are few and inconspicuous in a hardwood forest. The time to look for them is in early spring, before the trees get their new leaves. Then the sun strikes the ground, and for a short time patches of such spring flowers as arbutus, hepaticas, and violets can be found. You can see these flowers on page 551. When these go, there will be left the mosses and ferns and gray-green lichens (lie′kens). And poking out between the soft greens are toadstools, bright orange or yellow, and whitish puffballs—all plants you rarely find in a field.

The ground here is moist for the most part. Why? Look up again. Do you see how the branches come in layers or shelves? When rain falls it drips from one layer to the next, runs off gradually, and reaches the ground slowly. Here it sinks drop by drop into the spongy forest floor, where it is held. There is no run-off from this soil. Feel it. It feels cool and moist, quite different from the ground in a field. And this soil is loose, not packed down. You can dig it with your hands. In it you find leaves and twigs in various stages of decay. It consists largely of decaying plant parts; this is what makes it such rich soil. If you have a large enough container take home some of this soil, called humus. Mix it with the soil of some plant that has not been doing well and see how the plant soon begins to grow. In a forest of cone-bearing trees, such as pines, spruces, and firs, the needles, as they fall, pile up in a thick layer on the soil; needles decay and disappear far more slowly than the leaves of broad-leaved trees.

Be on the lookout for birds and try to identify them with your bird guide. Some will be high in the treetops, others on the trunks of the trees. Insects, of course, are plentiful; look for them in dead stumps, in holes in trees, on the bark, and on leaves. Perhaps you will find some beetles and bring them home to add to your collection.

Most of the mammals in the forest will keep out of your sight. But you may hear a squirrel scolding. You may even see one if you sit or stand quietly. And as you dig up the soil with your hands you are likely to find the tunnels of mice and shrews.

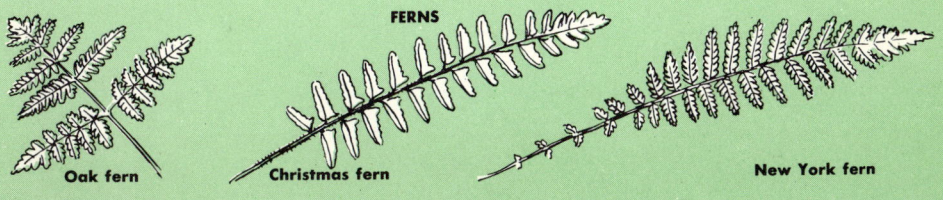

FERNS

Oak fern   Christmas fern   New York fern

FIELD TRIPS

(Photo from R. Paul Larkin)

CITY BIRDS

Starling

Pigeon

English sparrow

18

FIELD TRIPS

EXPLORING A CITY LOT

Perhaps you live in a big city and you cannot take trips to fields or forest or seashore. You can still study biology out-of-doors. If you learn what to look for and how to observe you can learn much in a half hour or an hour trip around a city block, or the school grounds, or even a vacant lot. Let's begin with a vacant lot.

Begin by walking over the entire lot. Note bare spots, if any; note whether the parts not bare have the same kinds of plants everywhere. Try to explain the variation if you find any. Then select a very small area, about one square foot. How much of the ground is actually covered by plants? Which of the plants do you recognize? Do you find ragweed? (There is a picture of it on page 351.) Uproot it and let it die. Why should it be destroyed? Examine these and other weeds closely—their stems and roots and leaves and seeds; and try to discover why they can grow here where other plants fail to grow. Are there trees in this lot? What kind? How did the seeds from which they grew get here?

With a shovel or trowel dig down ten or twelve inches to see how far plant roots extend. As you dig look for a difference between topsoil and the soil underneath; or is there no "topsoil," dark rich soil? Compare this soil with soil from the forest floor, if you can. Perhaps you will find clover or some other legume. If so, dig it up with plenty of soil around the roots and at home wash the soil from the smaller roots to find little swellings (nodules). These contain bacteria that help to make the soil fertile. As you dig keep a sharp lookout for all signs of animal life—insects or earthworms—underground. Look for little mounds of earth left by the worms. What insects do you find above ground? Do you see spiders or their webs?

If you found any bare areas in the lot, examine them more closely and try to explain why plants are not growing there. Is the soil being washed away or eroded? Why isn't the soil being washed away where plants are growing? The erosion you may see here may be of little importance, but many thousands of acres of farm land are being eroded in this way over the whole country. What can be done to stop erosion? Seeds must be planted. You could perhaps try it here and at the same time improve the looks of this city lot. What would be good seeds to plant? But before you plant you will want to loosen the soil so the seeds will get air. And if the ground is sloping what can you do to keep the soil with its freshly planted seeds from being washed downhill? For the farmer whose fields are on the slope of a hill this becomes a serious problem.

Somewhere in the lot you may find a depression in the ground filled with water if there have been heavy rains; this should be filled up. Or there may be a tin can half filled with water. Empty the can and put it where it will be hauled away with other junk. Mosquitoes lay their eggs in quiet water and even a small tin can may contain dozens of young mosquitoes.

Perhaps you will see birds. In a city starlings and English sparrows are most abundant; but don't be too surprised to find a chipping sparrow, a song sparrow, a catbird, or a robin. And if you are far enough south you may see a mockingbird. What can they find to eat? Compared to the woodland and the field and the tide pool in the rocks, the city lot offers few opportunities to animals to make their homes and find food. The number of different kinds is small. But even this soil contains some minerals; there is sunshine, water, and air. That's all a plant needs. As seeds fall here some will sprout; the young plants will grow, blossom, form seeds, die, decay, and turn back into soil and air.

CITY BIRDS

Robin　　　　Catbird　　　　Song sparrow

FIELD TRIPS

(Photo from W. G. Sargent)

COCOONS

Luna   Cecropia   Cynthia

20   FIELD TRIPS

A TRIP IN THE LATE FALL

Those of you who live where there is a cold winter season had better get out now before the ground begins to freeze. Take a trowel and various small containers for the specimens you may want to bring home.

Aside from some belated flies and mosquitoes most adult insects have disappeared, but almost all insects are still with us in one form or another or there would be none next spring. They manage to winter over in a great variety of ways. Look under boards and at the base of trees for hiding beetles. If you are fortunate you may come upon ladybird beetles —hundreds and even thousands of them in a colony. Search in the deep cracks in the bark of trees for a mourningcloak butterfly which rests during the winter; we say it hibernates (high'ber-nates) until the first warm days of spring. If you take home these insects that are resting for the winter, they will die.

Examine the inside of tall stalks of weeds like goldenrod, burdock, and mullein. Try cutting open the canes of raspberries or blackberries. Here you may find chambers containing the eggs or caterpillars (larvae) of moths or butterflies. And on the berry canes you may be lucky enough to find an egg case of the praying mantis. On page 99 is a picture of an egg case being made. Since they are such helpful insects it would be better to leave the egg case in place; make a note of where it is so you can go back to it in the spring. If you should take one home you would find it difficult to raise the many young when they hatch. Search deep in the dead portions of a tree trunk for the young stages of wood-boring beetles or for adult carpenter ants. Try to find what the woodpecker overlooked.

Examine shrubs and small trees carefully for cocoons attached to the twigs. Bring these home, but make a note of the kind of plant to which they were attached. Perhaps you can recognize the plant by its twigs and buds. Early in the spring, if the cocoon has been kept indoors, you can watch the adult come out. Other cocoons will be found in the dead leaves and other plant parts on the ground. See how many kinds you can find.

Turn over or break open some rotting logs in the woods to see what is there. You may find some adult beetles, wasps, and perhaps the large brown and black woollybear caterpillar hibernating in the logs. Have you made a list of the different insect hiding places you found?

Use your trowel to find out what is in the ground. Bring back for identification whatever you may find—earthworms, pillbugs, millipedes, the larvae of the maybeetle, ants, and a large variety of other insects. Consult Laurence Palmer's *Fieldbook of Natural History* or Comstock's *Handbook of Nature Study*.

And this is a good time for you to study soil—before frost gets into it. As you get to know more about soil you will begin to think of it almost as though it were alive. The various animals you find in the soil are as much a part of it as are the lifeless (inorganic) particles of mineral compounds. Plant parts in various states of decay also go to make up soil. And very active in the soil, although you can't see them without a microscope, are the countless soil bacteria. Dig up some soil in the woods, in a field, along the road, and examine it closely. What differences do you notice?

Of course, if you can include a pond or marsh in your trip you will have a chance to see much more insect life. Insects like dragonflies, mayflies, and stoneflies spend many months in the shallow water near the shore. With your strainer scoop up some of the mud or sand from the bottom of the pond or marsh. Look carefully through it for "hidden treasures." You may not recognize what you find now but in the early spring, if you keep the mud wet and in the dark, you may see the insects as they emerge, this time with wings.

So you see there are many interesting things to look for out-of-doors even when winter is on its way.

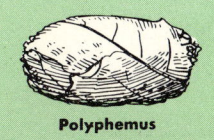

COCOONS

Polyphemus   Imperial   Io

FIELD TRIPS

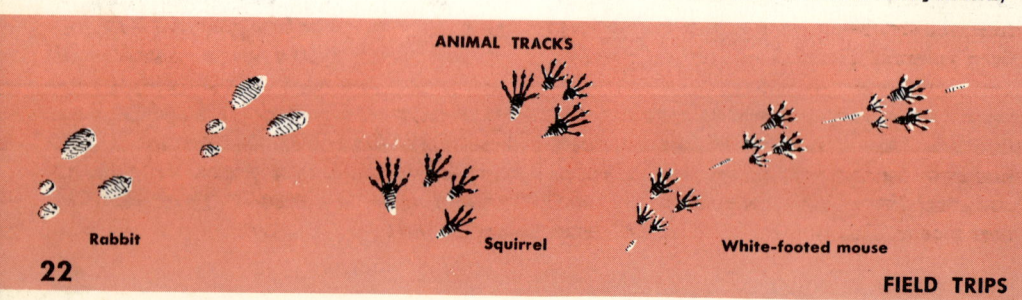

(Photo from H. Armstrong Roberts)

ANIMAL TRACKS

Rabbit   Squirrel   White-footed mouse

FIELD TRIPS

A TRIP IN MIDWINTER

Many animals do not shut up shop in the colder regions as some people think. But it is true that it is mostly mammals and birds that remain active in this season. Insects are out of sight, as we have learned; amphibia are buried in the mud; snakes and turtles are hibernating in caves and holes.

A winter trip is fun, so let's start. If there is soft snow on the ground you will enjoy playing detective. Follow the animal tracks; you can learn much from these tracks about the activities of some animals. A Cornell Rural School Leaflet or one of the many excellent books such as *Tracks and Trailcraft* by Ellsworth Jaeger (Macmillan, 1948) or *Animal Tracks* by George F. Mason (Morrow, 1943) will help you become an expert. Tracks of squirrels, rabbits, cats, dogs, and mice are usually easy to find. Sometimes you can follow the trail of a fox through fields and woodland as it hunted smaller mammals or birds. And occasionally there will be signs of a struggle; you may see where an owl or hawk has swooped down and picked up a small animal.

A few mammals, like the woodchuck, jumping mouse, some kinds of chipmunks, and some kinds of bats do shut up shop; they hibernate and live on the body fat they have stored. Bats often find a dark corner in an attic, a barn, a cave, or sometimes in a hollow tree. Some other mammals—some kinds of rats, white-footed mice, and squirrels—often move indoors for the winter and eat whatever they can find. Others, like raccoons, many squirrels, skunks, and some kinds of bears may sleep for days at a time, eat briefly, and again go to sleep; they are not true hibernators. Look for concealed spots among rocks and for holes in trees which these animals might choose for their winter sleep.

But what do animals eat when there is snow on the ground? Look around the base of young trees and shrubs. Do you see how the bark has been gnawed? Farmers are often obliged to use wire fencing to protect their fruit trees against the rabbits and field mice that come to feed. Look also in hollow logs; there you may find an odd assortment of cherry seeds, grains, and other bits of food collected by the small deer mouse. This practical little mouse sometimes takes over a bird's nest on the ground and roofs it over as a winter home.

It's a hard life for mammals in winter in cold climates, but they are adapted to it. And it's often hard, too, for the birds that do not migrate. Food and sometimes water, too, are hard to come by. Some insects can be found, as you know, in holes of trees and tucked away in the bark. And even when there is snow on the ground, in most parts of the country, seeds can still be had. If you are out in the snow, just count the number of kinds of weeds sticking up through the snow. Which of these can you find: wild carrot, yarrow, mullein, burdock, goldenrod? Which others? Laurence Palmer's *Fieldbook of Natural History* will help you identify some of them. It is fun to make a collection of these weed tops in the snow. And look well under the weeds to see under which ones you can find bird tracks and perhaps the remains of a bird's recent "lunch."

But when the snow is deep some birds have a hard time. If, therefore, you have not put up bird feeding stations on window sills or in your schoolyard it is high time for you to do it. See that they are kept supplied with sunflower seeds, millet, corn, peanut butter, suet, apples, or raisins. With such a variety you should be able to attract different kinds of birds. Be sure to keep a "guest book" of your visitors, and try to learn something of each one's habits. Some birds do not come to feeders readily. To help them out you may have to scatter their food at some distance from the feeder and protect it with evergreen boughs. In northern states sweepings from barn floors can be scattered about fields to attract snow buntings. Try to find out from your bird guide which of the birds you see are winter residents, which permanent residents. Some may be "winter visitors"—birds that do not come every year or remain for the whole winter season. Draw maps to show where the winter residents and winter visitors spend the rest of the year. Your bird guide will help you.

Christmas bird censuses are made in all parts of the country and published by the National Audubon Society (1130 Fifth Ave., New York 28, New York). You may want to join one of the census groups. Or you can make up your own group and take your own census during the holidays.

(Photo from R. Paul Larkin)

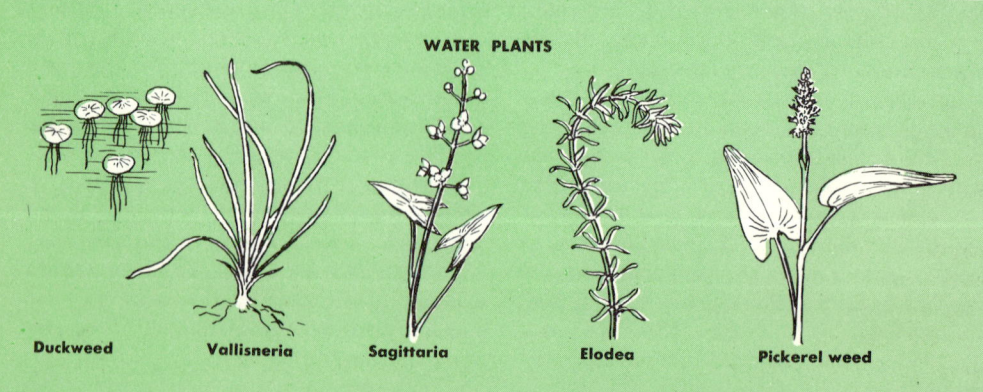

WATER PLANTS

Duckweed   Vallisneria   Sagittaria   Elodea   Pickerel weed

24   FIELD TRIPS

A TRIP TO A MARSH IN EARLY SPRING

A pond or marsh is interesting at any time of year but especially in early spring. Prepare yourselves as you always do and remember to take a dredging net or strainer and certainly a field book on amphibia. A very good and inexpensive field book is *Reptiles and Amphibians* by Zim and Smith (Simon and Schuster, 1953). As we approach the marsh we know that spring has come from the loud shrill chorus of the spring peepers and the other frogs and toads. This is their breeding season. And we should find near the surface of the quiet water their gelatinous clumps or strings of eggs. Salamanders, too, lay their eggs here, sometimes coming long distances from the woods.

If there are beavers and muskrats around you can't miss their dome-shaped houses along the banks. The muskrats use smaller branches and grasses for building theirs. Here the young are born in the spring. And on the mudflats along the shore you may find footprints of the muskrats or of raccoons or mink which have been searching for insect food. There may be footprints of herons, too, or of other birds looking for amphibia.

Among songbirds, the first to arrive are probably the red-winged blackbirds. You can't help seeing the bright patch of scarlet as they start up from the dead cattails, which sway and bend under their weight. Birds that nest in the marsh grasses or sedges in many parts of the country are the bitterns, marsh hawks, and rails. Of course, you have your bird guide with you. Swamp sparrows and yellow warblers may be examining the shrubs and trees along the shores of the pond or marsh, looking for nesting sites.

If you are lucky you may arrive on a day when thousands of mayflies, dragonflies, or stoneflies leave the water in large swarms, spreading their wings and taking flight. You found their larvae or nymphs in the mud at the bottom of the marsh in the late fall. They have had a long winter rest. As it gets warm they climb up on the water grasses or sedges, burst open their skins, crawl out, and fly away. They leave the skins attached to the grasses.

Along the shores examine the buds on shrubs and trees. Notice how they differ in color, and size, and shape. Cut off some small twigs and when you get back place them in water. Watch for developing leaves and flowers. One of the first shrubs to begin growing in the spring is the pussy-willow, which you will find in clumps at the edge of the pool or marsh. Each "pussy" is made up of many small flowers. If you keep the twigs in water the flowers will develop and the "pussies" will disappear. Leaf buds may open and roots may sprout. Then you can set the twig in the ground where it is moist and grow your own pussy-willow shrub. Maybe in the moist ground on the shore you will find the blossom of a skunk cabbage inside its purplish hood.

Now look out across the marsh or pond. Do you see that the plants grow in definite zones? In the center is open water; nearer the shore are floating plants, perhaps so many that the water is covered with them—tiny plants such as duckweeds (small green ovals floating on the surface), each less than one-fourth inch across. These are the smallest of the flowering plants. Then there comes a zone still nearer the shore where float the leaves of the water lilies. These plants are rooted in the mud. Other plants in this zone may have leaves that do not quite reach the surface; they are less conspicuous. (*Vallisneria* and *Sagittaria* are two of these.) In the next zone still nearer shore, in shallower water, grow the bulrushes, other sedges, cattails, and grasses. As some of these plants along the shore die, their leaves, stems, and roots build up soil in which shrubs and trees can grow—alders, willows, and poplars.

If you visited a pond or a marsh on one of your trips in the fall you may have noticed that the plants are marching out from the shore toward the center; the pond is shrinking. In time there will be no open water. It is easy to see how this would happen. As plants die and more and more materials pile up on the bottom of the marsh or little pond, the water becomes shallower. The marsh fills up from the bottom. At the edge, where the water was shallowest and the grasses and sedges grew, there will sometime be dry land with shrubs and trees. The grasses and sedges gradually invade the zone of the water lilies; these, in turn, invade the zone of the floating plants. This happens to all small ponds and marshes.

(Photo from H. Armstrong Roberts)

VENOMOUS DESERT ANIMALS

Rattlesnake

Sidewinder

Centipede

Tarantula

Gila monster

Scorpion

Black widow

26   FIELD TRIPS

A TRIP TO THE DESERT

Many of us live too far from a desert to be able to study its extraordinary plants and animals firsthand. We can enjoy reading about them and how they manage to get along for months or years without rain, then rain in torrents, then brilliant sunshine and hot, dry winds. If you can take a trip in a desert, take plenty of water and wear clothes that will protect you from not only the heat but thorny, prickly plants and an occasional rattlesnake. A camera, notebook, and appropriate field guide are always handy. And if you plan to collect desert plants and animals you will usually need a strong knife or machete, baskets, and jars.

In Lower California and in nearby parts of California, Arizona, and New Mexico, you can find large areas of sandy soil with relatively little life; here only three to ten inches of rain fall in a year and some years the rain doesn't come at all. Cactuses rise out of the ground, sometimes forty feet in height. Some are straight columns, some have a few branches. Their roots are shallow and widespread, holding these monsters in place. These cactuses are huge water tanks, which absorb and store water when it rains.

But over thousands of square miles from Idaho to Central Mexico and from eastern California eastward to Colorado you find so-called desert where a surprisingly large variety of plants and animals live. These deserts in early April are carpeted with blossoms of brilliant yellows, reds, and purples. The winter rains have soaked into the ground. Seeds hidden there for almost a year now sprout. The desert evening primrose, the prickly poppy, verbenas, violets, anemones, and desert lilies shoot up almost overnight. The soil is fertile and in the warm sunshine the seedlings form leaves and blossoms—most of all blossoms. These plants live for only one year; they are able to produce blossoms and seeds in a few weeks while the moisture lasts. With the blossoms come bees and other insects in search of honey and pollen. In a short time all the color is gone; the plants wither and die; only the seeds live on in the ground, dormant (resting) until the next spring; they need no moisture. Now when you look across the desert you see no gay colors, not even bright green. You see only the gray green of the sagebrush and the dull-colored creosote bush growing in scattered clumps. In part of this desert a Joshua tree may be seen stretching its arms toward Heaven like Joshua of old. Large patches of ground are bare. Here ants are building their nests in sandy mounds. Tightly coiled corkscrews lie on the ground. You wonder what they are until you look up and see they are the beans of the screw-bean mesquite (mess'-keet), a very common desert plant of the pea family. The beans don't look tempting as food but they can be eaten by man; insects known as bean weevils eat them, too.

You will see lizards of various kinds darting about and hunting insects on the hot sands during the day. Here you find the strange horned toad, in shape somewhat like a toad but not a toad at all. It is a kind of lizard. And you can see chameleons, also a form of lizard, "shooting" and catching flies with a long tongue. As fast as a flash of lightning, this tongue can be stretched out almost a foot. The chameleon's eyes move separately; its vision is acute and its aim perfect. And if one hunts among the rocks one may detect a chuckwalla (another lizard) crawling between two rocks and blowing itself up until it is wedged in tight.

And, of course, snakes live here—red racers and rattlesnakes. Probably hidden among the rocks, the rattlers will startle you now and again with their characteristic rattle, just a warning that you don't belong here and they do. But they don't strike unless you seriously disturb them. Now where there are plants and insects and reptiles there will be food for some kinds of birds, even though water is scarce. Some birds, such as doves and quail, may have to fly many miles each day for a drink. And mammals, too, live here without water—desert squirrels, rats, mice, and prairie dogs. The desert is still, very still, during the day—no creaking limbs or fluttering leaves, few bird calls, few buzzing insects. But the silence is broken now and again by a shrill whistle and as you turn to look you may see a prairie dog sitting bolt upright as it gives its warning call. It then disappears into its tunnels underground. It, too, has enemies, such as the desert fox.

Unit One

How living things are alike

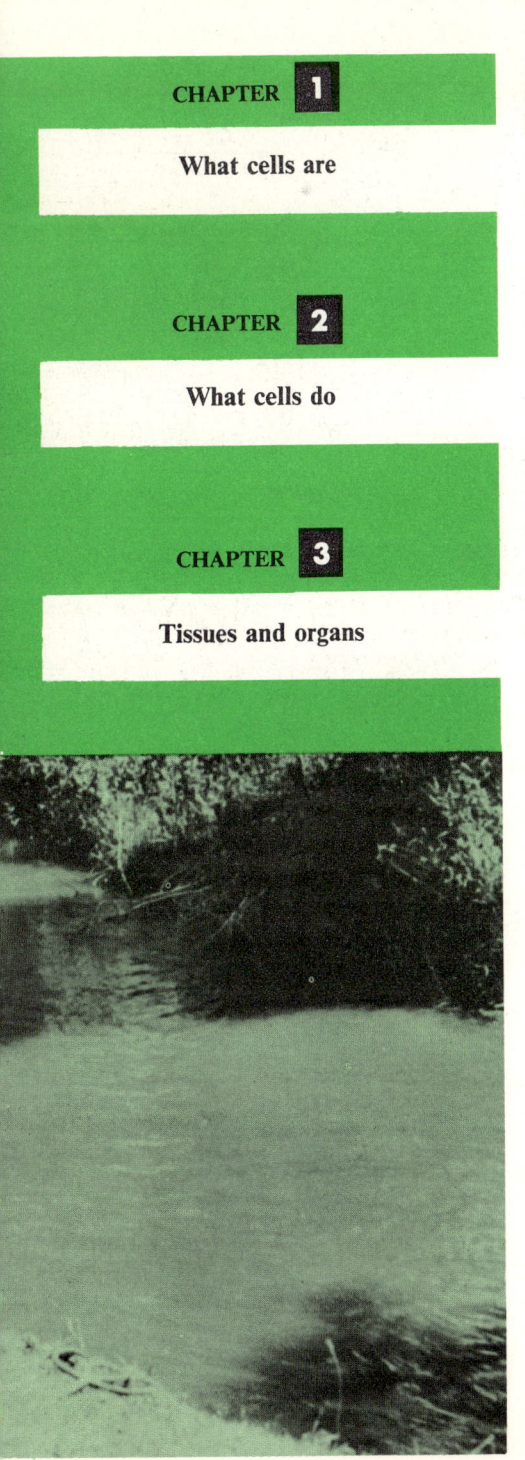

CHAPTER 1

What cells are

CHAPTER 2

What cells do

CHAPTER 3

Tissues and organs

When you turn this page you will enter a new world; you will explore the "invisible." This had remained hidden from men's eyes for many thousands of years until someone made a simple microscope. Then more and more people began to explore the invisible — the inside of plants and of their own bodies, drops of water from the rain barrel and from the pond. What they found was very exciting!

Men found much the same thing in all the objects they examined. Wherever there was life they found "cells." They discovered that some kinds of plants and animals were made up of only one cell. Other kinds were made up of millions or billions of cells living together. Look again at the picture of the sheep grazing on the banks of the stream. There are countless billions of cells in the sheep and in the plants around them. In fact, you and I, the sheep, the trees, and the grass are made up of much the same kind of cells. That's an important idea, isn't it? This idea came only after many years of study and experiment.

Of course, this is not the first time you have heard of cells, but there are still many interesting things for you to learn about them. Many biologists are still studying cells and discovering more and more about them. The first three chapters will give you something of what is known; you will find more in later chapters. But even there you will not find an explanation of the great mystery: what is it about living matter that makes it different and that gives it "life"?

Chapter 1

What cells are

Seeing the invisible. In some trip to a pond you may have brought home some of the pond water. If you were fortunate enough to look at a drop of this water through a microscope you probably saw cells, the tiny bits of living matter of which all living things are composed. More than two hundred years ago, a Dutchman, Anton van Leeuwenhoek, did the same thing, only he didn't bother to go to a pond; he dipped water out of his rain barrel. He had no good microscope such as you may have. He used a simple microscope like the one shown in Figure 1.1. Leeuwenhoek held a minor governmental position in Delft, Holland. This took so little of his time that he was able to devote himself to his one great hobby, grinding beads of glass into lenses. With these he could magnify objects until he saw even the "invisible." He studied stagnant water, parts of insects, his own blood, and lots of other things. But his microscopes were not good enough to show very much.

At about this time, however, two Dutch spectacle makers, the Jannsens, father and son, hit on an idea: to magnify an object with one lens, let us say ten times, and then magnify that image with a second lens which also magnifies ten times. The object is then magnified 10×10, or 100 times. The early compound microscopes, naturally, were very simple, not at all like our modern microscope, Figure 1.2.

Robert Hooke. Robert Hooke (1653–1703), an English botanist, made a number of compound microscopes.

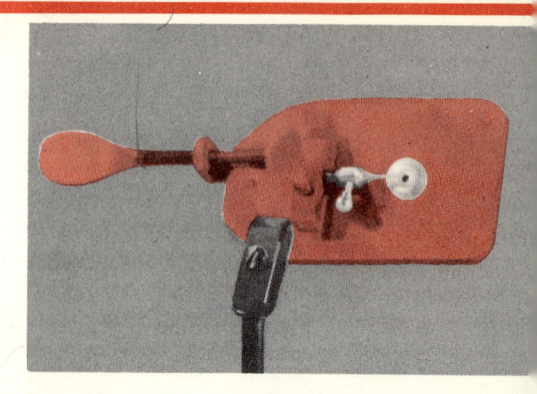

1.1 One of Leeuwenhoek's many microscopes. A lens was fastened into the metal plate. The rest of the microscope is the object holder which, by the use of screws, was used to place the object in proper position. *Bausch and Lomb*

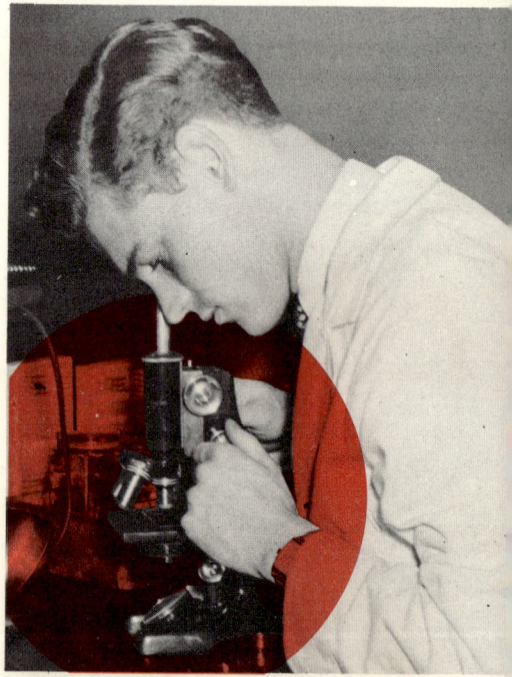

1.2 A modern student microscope. When you look through the microscope, you use two sets of lenses. Each set consists of two or more separate lenses. *Bausch and Lomb*

UNIT ONE — HOW LIVING THINGS ARE ALIKE

1.3 A section through cork as seen under the microscope. Since it is a section, you can see only the sides of the boxes. Do the boxes seem to be filled or empty?

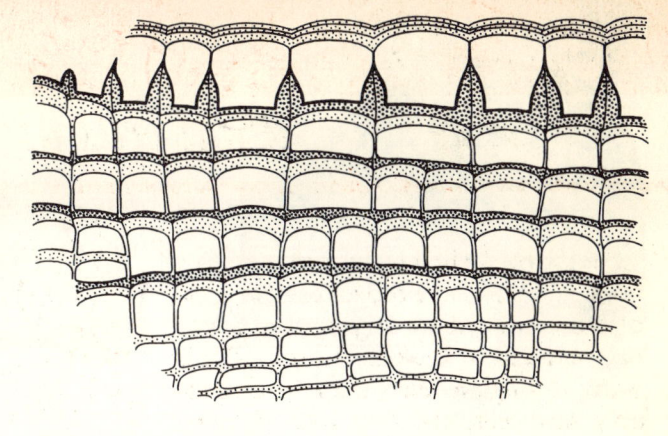

1.4 Cells like these are found in the lining of your mouth. What are the three parts of such cells? (See also Figure 1.5)

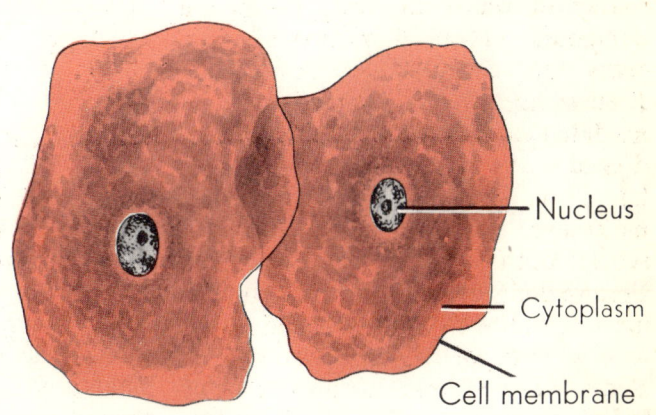

Nucleus
Cytoplasm
Cell membrane

Among the things that he looked at were very thin slices of cork from the bark of the cork oak. What he saw was tightly packed little boxes with thick walls. He drew them, and they are shown in Figure 1.3. These boxes seemed to be empty. That is why Hooke called them **cells.** They reminded him of empty prison or honeycomb cells. But nowadays we think of a cell as something very different from the empty boxes Hooke saw. You see, Hooke was looking at dead cells, and the important part of the cells had disappeared. But the name "cell" has been kept.

What is a cell? You are made up of billions of tiny bits of living matter called **cells.** So are all other animals and plants, too. And the interesting thing is that the cells of all animals — the earthworm, the frog, the fish, the dog, and so on — are almost exactly like yours; and they are basically like the cells of a plant.

Every cell is just a drop of living matter, called **protoplasm.** But it has three parts. The main part is the **cytoplasm** (sigh'toe-plasm). Find it in Figures 1.4 and 1.5. The **nucleus** (new'klee-us) is a small body of denser protoplasm lying within the cytoplasm. A **cell membrane** (also called the **plasma membrane**) surrounds the cytoplasm. The cytoplasm, the nucleus, and the cell membrane are all living matter, or protoplasm. All cells are alike in

CHAPTER ONE — WHAT CELLS ARE

31

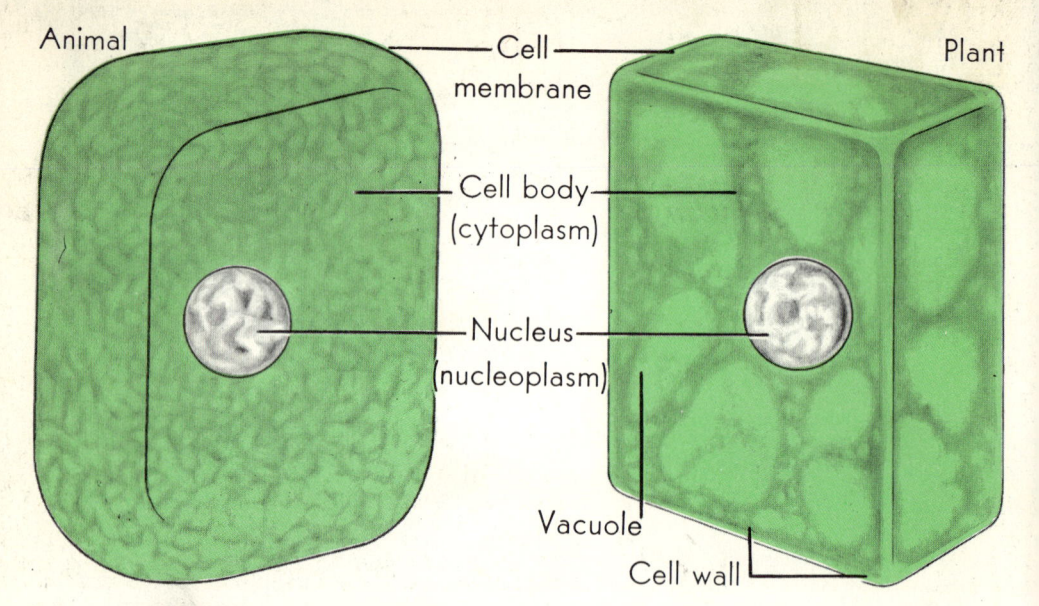

1.5 All cells have three dimensions. In the animal cell, as in the plant cell, there are two kinds of protoplasm. What other parts does the plant cell have?

this; but, of course, cells come in different shapes and sizes.

You have probably known for a long time that cells are tiny bits of living matter, or protoplasm, making up the bodies of all living things. But this answer to the question "What is a cell?" came slowly, step by step, during almost two centuries of study.

Plant cells. Plant cells have the same three parts: cytoplasm, nucleus, and cell membrane. But plant cells, generally, are surrounded by a firm **cell wall**, lying outside the cell membrane. The wall consists mostly of a tough substance, **cellulose** (cell'you-lohs). Some plant cell walls contain a substance (**lignin**) that makes them hard as well as tough. How does the wall get there? Of course, it must be made by the living protoplasm.

Plant cells often have parts not found in most animal cells. Usually, they have one or more large bubbles of liquid (called **sap**) lying in the cytoplasm. These are called **vacuoles** (vak'you-ohls). A third difference between plant and animal cells is that some cells of green plants contain small living bodies called **chloroplasts** (klor'oh-plasts). These contain a very important green substance, **chlorophyll**. It is the chlorophyll that makes plants look green, and you may already know why it is important to the plant and to us.

Nucleus and cytoplasm. Nuclei are likely to be spherical (like a ball) in shape. In general, a nucleus lies near the center of the cell. But in some plant cells where there are large vacuoles the nucleus may be crowded against the wall, and then it is flattened on one side. The protoplasm that makes up the nucleus is denser, or less liquid, than the cytoplasm. The nucleus can be pulled out of a cell by means of micro-needles used with the aid of a powerful microscope. That shows how dense and firm it must be. It also shows that it has a

6 ELECTRONS
6 PROTONS
6 NEUTRONS

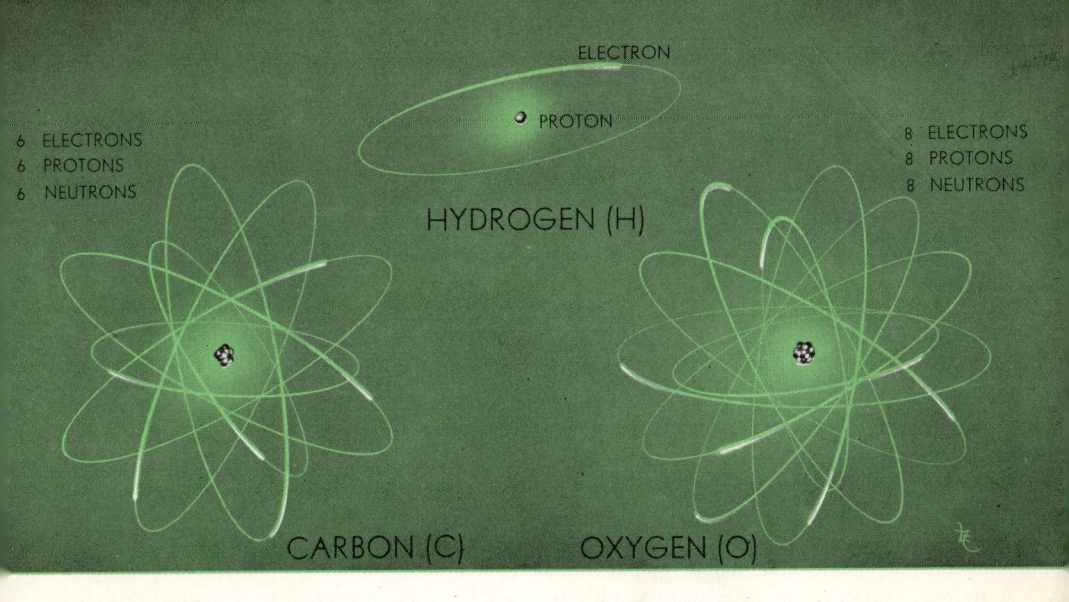

ELECTRON
PROTON
HYDROGEN (H)

8 ELECTRONS
8 PROTONS
8 NEUTRONS

CARBON (C)   OXYGEN (O)

1.6 Diagrams of hydrogen, oxygen, and carbon atoms. Of what are these atoms composed? How do these atoms differ from one another?

nuclear membrane which separates it from the cytoplasm.

The pictures on these pages all show cells that have been stained. In an unstained cell the nucleus is usually difficult to see. The reason it shows up so clearly in stained cells is that it contains a special living substance that readily takes certain dyes. This living substance is called **chromatin** (crow'-ma-tin). The word comes from a Greek word meaning color.

A thickish liquid, transparent, practically colorless, with small specks or granules in it — that is protoplasm. Protoplasm has a very definite and complicated structure. Moreover, the protoplasm of each kind of plant or animal is somewhat different from that of every other kind. In general, high or very low temperatures, dryness, or other changes in the surroundings change the structure of protoplasm and kill it. Let us now review the chemistry you studied in general science.

Atoms and molecules. Chemists, as you know, study the make-up or composition of things. They have learned that the substances are made up of **molecules.** A molecule is the smallest particle of any substance that can exist by itself. Many molecules are made up of two or more smaller particles called **atoms.** Molecules are very small, though some are much larger than others; some are large enough to be seen with an electron microscope. Some molecules are made up of thousands of atoms.

Atoms, of course, have never been seen. But small as they are, they can be "smashed" into different kinds of particles, as you may know. In the center of the atom is its "nucleus" with one or more **protons** and sometimes one or more **neutrons** (new'trons). Spinning around the nucleus are **electrons.** The smallest and the simplest atom is the hydrogen atom. It has only one proton and one electron. The uranium atom

CHAPTER ONE — WHAT CELLS ARE

1.7 When sulfuric acid (H₂SO₄) was added to the sugar, the dark mass of carbon was produced. What does this tell us about the composition of sugar? *Sullivan*

is a very large atom with 92 protons, 146 neutrons, and 92 electrons.

Chemical elements. You have often heard of elements. Now, long before scientists talked about atoms, they said that everything in the world, living and lifeless, is made up of simple substances which they called elements — the paper of this book, the air, water, you, everything. We still believe that; and we define an element as a substance made up of only **one kind** of atom. Hydrogen is an element. Uranium and plutonium are elements. You know the names of many of the other elements: carbon, oxygen, iron, helium, gold, iodine, and many others. As this is being written, we know of one hundred and one elements. Eleven of these have been made in laboratories. And it is quite possible that several more elements will be made in laboratories as research in all parts of the world continues.

To make things simpler for themselves in speaking and writing, chemists use a symbol or abbreviation for each element. This is often the first letter of the word. Oxygen becomes **O**; hydrogen is **H**; iodine is **I**. But what about iron? Since there can't be another I, the Latin name is used and shortened to **Fe**.

Atoms join together. When we define an element as a substance that contains a single kind of atom, we are not saying it contains a single atom. Not at all. Often the atoms of an element join together to make a molecule of that element. Two hydrogen atoms become attached and form a molecule of the element hydrogen. Chemists write it H_2. Atoms unite in forming a molecule of oxygen, O_2. Also atoms unite in forming a molecule of nitrogen, N_2.

Chemical compounds. Atoms of *different* elements also unite, forming molecules. The atoms become closely attached; we say they unite chemically. Then the molecule that is formed is something new. For example, two hydrogen atoms may become attached to an oxygen atom, making a molecule of water. Water is something quite different from either hydrogen or oxygen, which are both gases. Such a substance, made up of two or more different elements chemically united, is a **compound.** Chemists have a way of showing all this very briefly by using the **formula** H_2O, the shorthand for water. This formula, H_2O, tells you at a glance that water is a compound and that it is made up of 2 parts hydrogen and one part oxygen.

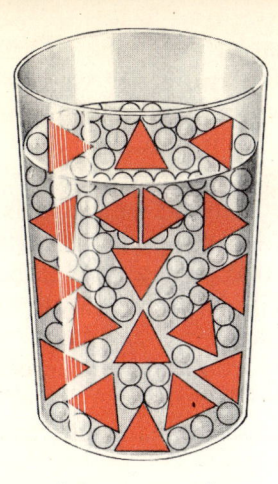

1.8 Atoms of sugar are shown as triangles, particles of water as circles. According to this picture does sugar water seem to be a compound or a mixture? Explain.

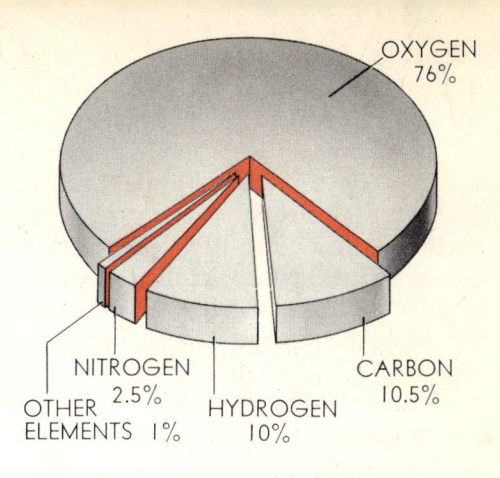

1.9 This "pie" shows the proportion of the elements in protoplasm. Percentages are calculated by weight. Which four elements are present in the largest amounts?

You can imagine that with so many elements an enormous number of compounds is possible. And the compounds are seldom much like the elements which make them up. For instance, atoms of the metal sodium (Na), that burns your skin when you touch it, will unite with atoms of chlorine (Cl), a poisonous gas with a strong odor. The compound formed is ordinary table salt, sodium chloride, or NaCl. And so with other elements; when two or more of them unite chemically, they lose their characteristics and something new appears as the compound. Figure 1.7 may have a surprise in store for you, too.

Not only do elements combine with each other; compounds themselves may combine. When they do, the same thing holds — new substances are formed. And often when two compounds are brought together, the elements of which they are made shift partners. Chemistry is an exciting business.

Mixtures. On the other hand, it happens often that when two or more substances are brought together, their atoms do not unite chemically; they do not form a compound. They simply form a **mixture**; this is not a new substance. Figure 1.8 should help make this clear. There is another thing to remember about mixtures and compounds. In a compound the substances are always present in definite proportions; in a mixture they may be in any proportions. It has no formula.

The chemistry of protoplasm. Now we'll study the make-up of protoplasm. There isn't any element in protoplasm that isn't found also in nonliving matter. And there is probably no element in nonliving matter that doesn't now and then appear in plant or animal protoplasm. Even gold, silver, and arsenic are found occasionally in plants! Figure 1.9 is a pie graph that shows you the principal elements in protoplasm. Notice how very large a proportion of protoplasm is oxygen. But carbon and hydrogen are also well represented. The proportion of nitrogen seems to be small, but compared to nonliving

CHAPTER ONE — WHAT CELLS ARE

substances this proportion is large. The smallest slice of the pie shown in the graph consists of many elements, all of them in very small amounts. Some of these elements are spoken of as **"trace elements"** because only the smallest trace of each is needed. In the list below are shown elements in your protoplasm. If we were listing the elements in the protoplasm of green plants the list would be similar but would include manganese.

TABLE 1

Sulfur	(S)	Sodium	(Na)
Phosphorus	(P)	Chlorine	(Cl)
Potassium	(K)	Iodine	(I)
Iron	(Fe)	*Copper	(Cu)
Magnesium	(Mg)	*Zinc	(Zn)
Calcium	(Ca)	*Cobalt	(Co)

Those marked with a star (*) are trace elements.

Carbon, oxygen, hydrogen, nitrogen, and the other elements are not found in protoplasm as elements. They are united into a variety of compounds, and the compounds are mixed together.

The mixture that we call protoplasm is the most complex substance known. Since it is a mixture, protoplasm does not always have exactly the same make-up. Your protoplasm is different from mine. Our protoplasm differs even more widely from the protoplasm of the cow we eat, and still more widely from that of the beans. Furthermore, the protoplasm in the various parts of your own body is not the same. The protoplasm that makes your muscles, for instance, is different from the protoplasm that makes up the cells of your blood. And yet there are certain compounds that seem always to be present in active protoplasm. Water is always present and in very large amounts. The proportion of water in cells varies from 70–90 per cent of their weight. Water is used in many different ways by active cells.

Look at the list of compounds that make up protoplasm. Notice that all, except water and minerals, contain the same three elements: carbon, hydrogen, and oxygen. Some, of course, contain one or more elements besides.

The carbon compounds. The carbon compounds are the **sugars, starches, fats,** and **proteins.** Sugars and starches are much alike. They are both **carbohydrates.** All carbohydrates contain only three elements — carbon, hydrogen, and oxygen. And the hydrogen and oxygen are always in the proportion of two to one, as they are in water. Cellulose, the material in plant cell walls, is also a carbohydrate. And there are hundreds of others.

Fats, too, contain carbon, hydrogen, and oxygen. But they have fewer

TABLE 2

A protein	$C_{2952}H_{4664}O_{832}N_{812}S_8Fe_4$	Found in your red blood cells. (Hemoglobin)
A fat	$C_{57}H_{110}O_6$	One of the common fats in your cells. (Stearin)
A vitamin	$C_{17}H_{20}N_4O_6$	Vitamin B_2. (Riboflavin)
Two sugars	$C_6H_{12}O_6$	Glucose — in many plant and animal cells.
	$C_{12}H_{22}O_{11}$	Sucrose, table sugar — in cells of some plants.
Starch	$(C_6H_{10}O_5)_n$	Found in plant cells. A similar compound (glycogen) is found in animal cells.
Minerals	A variety of compounds containing Na, K, Ca, Cl, and so on.	Widely distributed in cells.
Water	H_2O	In all cells — plant and animal.

TABLE 3

TESTING FOR SOME COMPOUNDS IN CELLS

Compound	How to test	Result, if present
Starch	Soften up; add iodine solution.	Blue or bluish black
Glucose	Add Benedict's solution; heat.	Greenish or orange
Protein	Add nitric acid; heat; then add ammonia.	Yellow or orange
Fats	Rub on paper.	Translucent spot
Minerals	Burn.	A residue that will not burn
Water	Warm; hold glass or spoon over vessel.	Film forms on cool surface

oxygen atoms in proportion to the hydrogen atoms; fats are very different from carbohydrates.

One great difference between proteins and all the other compounds is that proteins always contain nitrogen. And did you notice how very large the protein molecule is? You are not expected to remember this formula. But it would be worth your while to learn the formulas for starch and the sugars glucose and sucrose. You will use the formulas again. There are many, many different kinds of proteins. Each one has a different formula but always a very large one. The sugars, starches, fats, and proteins are never found in nature outside of living things or their remains. They are made by protoplasm out of simpler compounds. They are all carbon compounds and are often called **organic** compounds.

Testing for compounds in protoplasm. Chemists have learned to test quickly for several of the compounds in protoplasm. Probably you have already tested for starch and remember that it turns blue or bluish black when iodine is put on it. But before chemists could say that this was a test for starch it was necessary for them to make sure that no substance other than starch changes in this way. You can see that it took a long time to find the tests. But now that they have been found, it is easy for you to make the tests shown in Table 3.

What have you learned?

1) All matter, living and lifeless, is made up of molecules. A molecule is the smallest bit of matter that can exist by itself. It is made of atoms.

2) Sometimes atoms of the same kind unite to form a molecule. This results in a molecule of an element. An element is a substance that contains a single kind of atom.

3) Sometimes different kinds of atoms unite chemically; then you get a molecule of a new substance called a compound.

4) A mixture differs from a compound in that the elements or compounds that make it up are not chemically united.

5) All plants and animals are made of cells and materials produced by cells.

6) A cell is a tiny mass of living matter called protoplasm.

7) The cell, normally, consists of cytoplasm, a denser part (the nucleus), and a cell membrane. All three are living matter.

8) Plant cells have besides: a cell wall (often cellulose), usually one or more vacuoles, and in many cells chloroplasts containing chlorophyll.

9) Protoplasm is a mixture of these compounds: proteins, starches, sugars, fats, minerals, water.

10) In the various compounds that

CHAPTER ONE — WHAT CELLS ARE

make up protoplasm; the following elements are always present: carbon, oxygen, hydrogen, nitrogen. Sulfur and phosphorus are often present, and so are potassium, magnesium, calcium, and others.

elements are found in each compound, giving the exact formulas of the simpler compounds.

11. Tell how you could test for each of the common kinds of organic compounds found in protoplasm (proteins, starches, sugars, and fats) and what results you would get if the compound were present. When these tests were first established, why was it necessary to try the protein test, for example, on all the other food substances?

USEFUL WORDS IN BIOLOGY

cell
protoplasm
cytoplasm
nucleus
cell membrane
cellulose
vacuole
chloroplast
chlorophyll
chromatin
element
compound
mixture
atom
molecule
proton
neutron
electron
carbohydrates
glucose
proteins

TEST YOURSELF

1. How does a compound microscope differ from a simple microscope?
2. Show that you know what a cell is by describing its structure briefly and by making a large labeled diagram.
3. What are the structures or parts usually found in plant cells but not usually found in animal cells?
4. Describe the cell nucleus, giving as many of its parts as you can.
5. Explain, as you might to a friend who had missed the lesson, what protoplasm is.
6. Describe the relation to each other of atoms, protons, electrons, and neutrons.
7. (a) Explain what is meant by a chemical compound. (b) Give the formulas of several compounds.
8. How is a mixture different from a compound?
9. Name the elements found in the mixture called protoplasm; include the names of the trace elements.
10. (a) What are the common organic compounds found in protoplasm? (b) State which

DO IT YOURSELF

1. Learning to use a microscope. If microscopes are available you will enjoy learning how to use them. Study first a small piece of newsprint containing the letter "e." Place the small piece of paper on the glass slide so that the letter is upright, as it is when you read the paper. Add a drop or two of water with a medicine dropper and put on the cover glass. You may have to press the cover glass gently to force out the larger air bubbles. Now look at the letter through the low-power lens, focusing exactly, and draw the "e" as it looks through the microscope. Move the slide to the right while your eye is at the eyepiece; then move it to the left; then move it toward you and away from you. Write a report in your notebook of all your observations and the conclusions you draw about a microscope. When the object is in perfect focus and exactly in the center of the field of vision, you can use the high-power objective to give you greater magnification. Under high power the field of vision is so much smaller that if the object is not well centered it will disappear from view. Of course, this applies to small objects.

2. Study of cells from your own body. Gently draw the blunt end of a toothpick across the inside of your cheek. Then rub the toothpick on the center of a glass slide. Add a drop or two of dilute iodine solution and a cover glass. After you have focused under the low power, move the slide about until you find single cells. Under high power the three major parts of these

UNIT ONE — HOW LIVING THINGS ARE ALIKE

cells show up well. (These cells are called mucous membrane cells.) This is a good time to learn to make labeled drawings of what you see under both the low and the high power of the microscope. Are the cells all the same size and shape? How big is the nucleus by comparison with the rest of the cell?

3. Study of plant cells. Strip off a small piece of the skin on the inside of one of the layers of an onion and mount it on a slide with dilute iodine. How do these cells differ from the cells of your mouth? How big is the nucleus in comparison with the rest of the cell? Do you see the cell wall? Draw and label three or four cells; your drawing must be large enough to show all the parts clearly.

4. Testing for compounds in protoplasm. Even though in general science you may have tested for the organic compounds in protoplasm, it is worth while doing these tests again. Test pure starch, sugar, protein (white of egg is practically pure protein), and fat, as indicated in the table on page 37. Try each test on all four kinds of compounds. Write up your results. The tests for starch, sugar, and fats can be done at home.

ADVENTURES IN READING

1. *Atomic Science—Bombs and Power* by David Dietz, Dodd, Mead, 1954. Contains a clear explanation of the structure of the atom and the history of its discovery.
2. *Microbe Hunters* by Paul H. de Kruif, Harcourt, Brace, 1939; also Pocket Books. Has an interesting life of Leeuwenhoek.
3. "Robert Hooke" by E. N. da C. Andrade in *Scientific American,* December, 1954. This article makes more than a name of this early microscopist and experimenter in physics and chemistry.

Chapter 2

What cells do

How do living and lifeless things differ? In general, you know which things are living and which are lifeless. When something uses food, grows, breathes, makes more of its own kind, you say it is living. These activities go on in plants as well as in you and other animals. It is true even of tiny microscopic forms. However, since the electron microscope has come into use, very much smaller forms known as **viruses** have been discovered. The viruses act like living things in some ways and are like lifeless things in other ways. Are they perhaps halfway between living and lifeless matter? We don't know. But, for the most part, there is a sharp distinction between living and lifeless.

Then, too, as you know, living things are made up of protoplasm, the most complex substance known. Lifeless substances are far less complex chemically. The most complex of lifeless substances are the proteins. They are part of that far more complex substance, protoplasm.

Protoplasm, partly because it is so complex, is constantly changing chemically; its atoms and molecules are forever rearranging themselves. These changes show themselves as the activities of living things. Before we look more closely at these activities of protoplasm some review may be in order.

Oxidation. You may have learned in general science that oxidation is the chemical union of a substance with oxygen. It may be a slow or a rapid union. When it is rapid, it may be

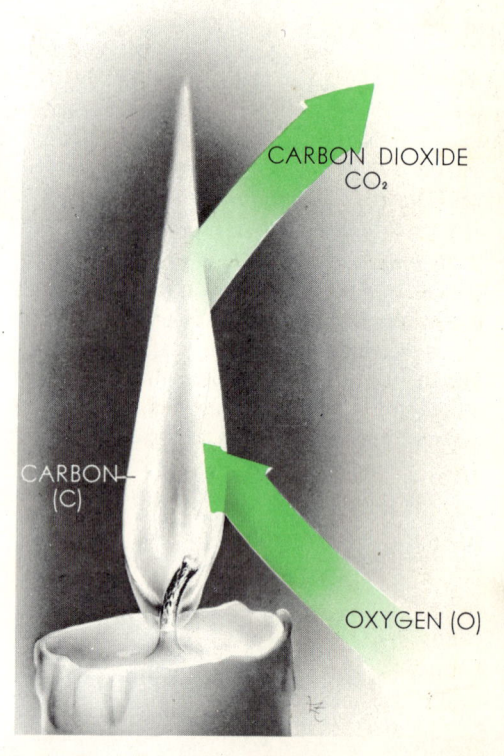

2.1 Here is rapid oxidation, or burning. Oxygen is used. It unites with carbon, and carbon dioxide is formed. Compare this with the slow oxidation that occurs in protoplasm.

called burning or combustion. Most substances burn only when they are raised to a higher temperature, called their kindling temperature. That is why you touch a match to paper or to wood if you want them to burn. The higher temperature causes the atoms and molecules of the wood or paper to fly apart. In oxidation the atoms and molecules rearrange themselves. Carbon atoms unite with oxygen atoms, forming an oxide, carbon dioxide.

2.2 Breaking up a log jam. There are active cells in the men and in the trees along the bank. What activities are being carried on in these cells? In which cells is there the greatest amount of oxidation? *American Museum of Natural History*

Hydrogen atoms also unite with oxygen atoms, forming another oxide which is water, H_2O. In this rearrangement heat is released and light appears. Heat and light are both forms of energy. Now, one of the chemical changes constantly going on in protoplasm is slow oxidation of carbohydrates and other compounds found in the cells. This oxidation is much more complicated than the burning of wood or paper. The protoplasm must first make substances, called **oxidases** (ox-i-day′ses), which make it possible for the carbohydrates or fats to break up and begin their union with oxygen. There are many steps in this rearrangement of molecules. But the end result of all the many changes that go on in the slow oxidation of carbohydrates is the formation of the oxides CO_2 and H_2O.

This complicated process of oxidation in the protoplasm of our cells is called **cellular respiration**. The word respiration is sometimes also used for ordinary breathing. But let us use cellular respiration to describe the taking in of oxygen by a cell, oxidation, and the release of carbon dioxide and water from the cell.

In cellular respiration as in all oxidation there are important energy changes. Let's look at these.

Release of energy in respiration. You probably remember that energy is defined as the power to do work. And you may remember that energy takes many forms and that one form can be changed into another. For example, substances like coal or sugar contain stored energy. Since this energy lies in the chemical make-up of the sugar it is called chemical energy. When coal is used for making steam in an engine its chemical energy is changed into heat energy; the heat energy can be changed into electrical energy and then turned into light energy in your light bulbs or into mechanical energy in your washing machine.

Now in cellular respiration chemical energy stored in carbohydrates and other compounds is changed into heat energy. It is this that gives you a normal temperature of 98.6° F. even when the surrounding air has a much

CHAPTER TWO — WHAT CELLS DO

2.3 This resting cow is doing work, and so are the trees in the background. What kinds of energy are being released in the cow? *Schneider and Schwartz*

2.5 Year after year the pieces of rock are pushed farther and farther apart by the growth of the tree. If you had to push the rocks apart, would you call it work? *American Museum of Natural History*

2.4 Mechanical energy is being used. What kind of energy was it before? Before that?

business or going to school. Moving your eyes across this page or across a television screen is also work and takes energy. Even when you sleep, your heart keeps working regularly; so do the chest muscles and other parts of the body. Millions of cells are always carrying on respiration, releasing energy, and doing work. Even in plants, the living cells are carrying on respiration, releasing energy, and doing work, although not so rapidly as the cells in animals. See Figures 2.3 and 2.5.

How respiration can continue. If you want your house to stay warm there must be some arrangement for stoking the furnace. As long as you supply fuel and a good draft (oxygen) the fire goes on and heat energy is released. Each cell is a tiny furnace that needs a constant supply of fuel and oxygen. Under normal conditions there is a steady procession of food and oxygen molecules into each living cell and a steady procession of oxides out of every cell. These molecules move in and out by the process of diffusion.

Diffusion. When people put sugar into their coffee, they often stir it

lower temperature. Some of the energy is immediately used by the protoplasm for carrying on other of its activities. And much of the energy is changed into other forms (look at Fig. 2.4) which make it possible for you to do all the work you do. Whatever you do takes energy, whether it is earning your living by moving logs in a stream or going to

UNIT ONE — HOW LIVING THINGS ARE ALIKE

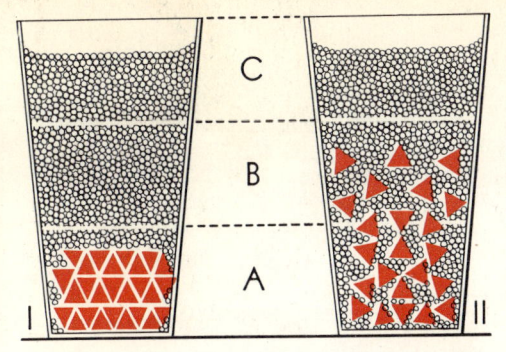

2.6 Sugar molecules are shown as triangles, water molecules as circles. In I, sugar molecules (molasses) have just been put in with a dropper. II shows what has happened after a short time. Why have sugar molecules appeared at level **B**? Compare the number of water molecules at level **A** in I and II. Explain. Draw the tumbler as it would look after longer standing.

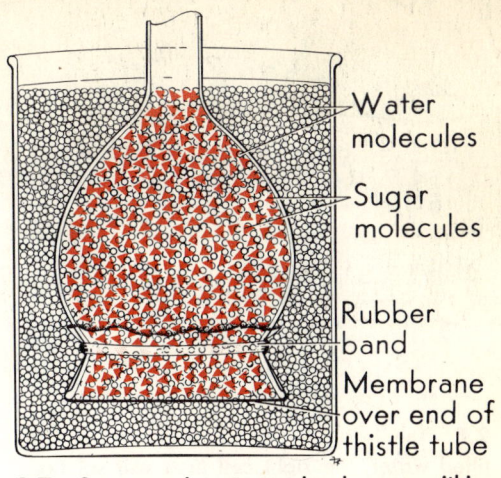

2.7 Sugar and water molecules are within the thistle tube. Only water molecules are outside it. In which direction will many water molecules move? What will happen to the amount of liquid in the tube?

because they are in a hurry. But if they'd wait a little, the sugar would move up from the bottom and spread all through the coffee without stirring. You may know that all molecules are constantly in motion. In liquids they bounce about very actively, though not quite as actively as they do in gases. As the sugar and coffee molecules bounce about they intermingle as shown in Figure 2.6. This intermingling of substances through the motion of their molecules is called **diffusion**. Even in solids molecules move about, but very, very slowly indeed.

Try putting some warm molasses with a medicine dropper into the bottom of a tumbler of warm water. Molasses contains dissolved **glucose** (glue'cose), one of the sugars. Allow the tumbler to stand quietly. You will soon see these liquids intermingling. Higher temperature makes them intermingle more rapidly. Of course, you cannot expect to see the molecules bounce around; they are much too small.

Each substance diffuses from the region where its molecules are close to one another (highly concentrated) to where its molecules are farther apart (less concentrated). Soon the molasses molecules are no longer close together at the bottom; they have spread and become less concentrated. The same is true of the water molecules; they have also spread from where they were most concentrated. Both liquids have diffused. Eventually, the molecules of the two liquids will be completely intermingled.

Diffusion through a membrane. Here is an experiment you can try for yourselves, too. Sausage casing, which is the wall of a pig's or sheep's intestine, is a good membrane to use. Even a sheet of cellophane will do. Fill the bowl of a thistle tube with a mixture of water and molasses. Tie the membrane over the large mouth of the tube. Put the tube upside down into a jar of plain water. Figure 2.7 shows you how to do it. Let it stand for a couple of hours.

CHAPTER TWO — WHAT CELLS DO

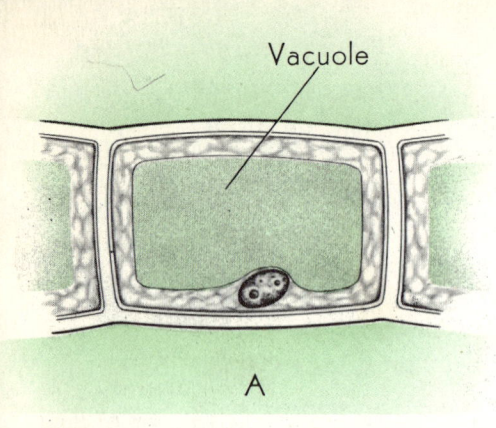

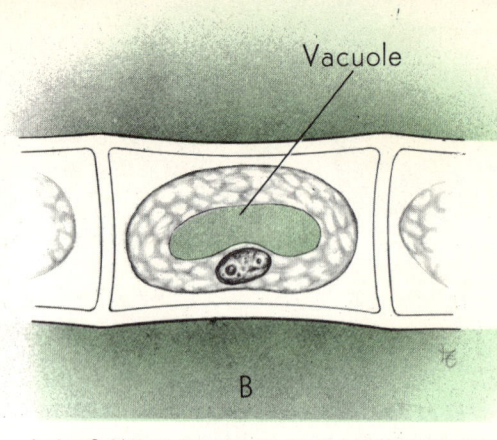

2.8 The left cell has been placed in distilled water, the right cell in a salt solution. Why does the cell wall in the left cell bulge? What has happened to the contents of the right cell? Why did water diffuse out of it?

At that time you will see that there is more liquid in the tube than when you set up the experiment. Water must have passed from the jar through the membrane into the tube. The membrane has no holes, to be sure; but molecules are so tiny that they can get through a membrane without holes. Knowing that molecules can pass through this membrane, it does not surprise you, does it, that water entered the tube? Where are the water molecules less concentrated when you start this experiment, in the jar or in the tube? Of course, they are less concentrated in the tube; the tube contains, besides water molecules, large molecules of sugar and coloring matter in the molasses. These keep the water molecules apart. The water molecules are more concentrated in the jar, which contains pure water when you start. They bounce and push each other out of the jar into the tube. And they continue to bounce from the region of greater concentration to where the molecules are less concentrated. They diffuse through the membrane. In the meantime, molecules of sugar and coloring matter diffuse from inside the tube, where they are concentrated. Even these larger molecules can diffuse through the membrane. You can actually see that the water has become brown in the jar. But to make sure that sugar has diffused out, you can test the water in the jar for sugar.

Diffusion through a living cell membrane. With the aid of a microscope you can see that water diffuses into and out of plant cells. You can mount some living plant cells in this water and take a good look at them under the microscope to see their shape. Then mount some of these same cells in distilled water (water without minerals). On a second slide mount some of the cells in a very strong salt solution. After a few minutes can you see that the cells in distilled water look swollen? Evidently on that slide the water molecules outside the cell were more concentrated than inside; therefore, water entered. On the second slide the protoplasm has shrunk away from its cell wall, forming a smaller mass in the middle. Its vacuole has grown much smaller. See Figure 2.8. The cell vacuole was a weak solution of water and minerals, a much

2.9 Three amebas photographed through a microscope. You can see many pseudopods. The protoplasm streams in all directions. Can you find food vacuoles in the ameba on the right? They are present in all the animals. *General Biological Supply*

weaker solution than the salt water on the outside. Since water molecules are more concentrated in a weak solution than in a strong one, water molecules diffused out. The diffusion of water through a membrane because of differences in concentration is called **osmosis**.

Can all substances diffuse through a membrane? Oxygen, sugars, and many salts diffuse readily through a cell membrane. These substances all dissolve in water; they are **soluble**. But substances that are insoluble in water cannot diffuse through a membrane. Many of the compounds found in a cell, such as the starches, fats, proteins, and many others, are insoluble and therefore do not diffuse. You could set up an experiment such as that shown in Figure 2.7. But this time put starch or white of egg (protein) into the thistle tube. By testing the water you can convince yourself that these substances do not diffuse out.

Cell membranes differ. Some cell membranes allow only certain soluble substances to diffuse through. We say these membranes are **permeable** to these soluble substances. They may be less permeable, or not permeable at all, to other soluble substances. And what is more, cell membranes change in their permeability. Variations in light and temperature or the presence or absence of certain substances in or around the cell makes the membrane more or less permeable. Cell membranes, like all other kinds of protoplasm, are complex substances.

Cell activities in an ameba. And now that we have learned how substances can get into and out of a cell let's find out what goes on inside a cell. A good cell for this purpose would be a particularly large cell that carries on by itself. Many microscopic animals living in water consist of a single cell. The **ameba** (a-mee′ba) is one that is especially large; it lives in pond water. You can study ameba under a microscope or on a moving picture screen if your school has a film showing this animal.

CHAPTER TWO — WHAT CELLS DO

An ameba is nothing more than a drop, or blob, of protoplasm. It has a nucleus and a cell membrane. Much of the time the protoplasm is streaming, now in one direction, now in another. As it flows in one direction it forms a projection called a false foot, or **pseudopod** (siu'doe-pod). It is a temporary foot which can form on any part of the body; in fact, ordinarily the ameba has several pseudopods sticking out in several directions at the same time. Sometimes, however, the soft protoplasm keeps on oozing in one direction; in this way the ameba crawls along over the surface of some leaf or stem under water. **Locomotion** (moving from place to place) is a very important life activity of this single-celled animal. Figure 2.9 shows you three amebas. You can imagine that a good deal of energy is needed for this locomotion. Now in plants and in our bodies there are trillions of cells packed together. Most of our cells, of course, don't carry on locomotion, although certain cells in our body do move about. And they do it in just exactly the same way as the ameba.

The false feet in the ameba are used for feeding as well as for locomotion. If some smaller single-celled animal or plant lies in the ameba's path, false feet flow out above, below, and on all sides of it and join together on the other side. The food particle is then inside the ameba; or, more correctly, the food particle is inside a little drop of water which is inside the ameba. That is a simple way of eating. If the animal picks up some worthless particle like a grain of sand, the animal simply flows away from the particle, leaving it behind.

But the ameba is not yet ready to use the food which lies within the enclosed drop of water, called a **food vacuole**. The food must be chemically changed into simpler compounds to make it usable. This is called **digestion**. But first, the protoplasm around this particle of food makes certain substances that do the digesting. This making of special substances by living protoplasm is called **secretion**. Then as the food is digested into simpler substances, they diffuse into the surrounding protoplasm. This diffusion can be called **absorption**. The lifeless compounds that are absorbed are made into living protoplasm by the protoplasm of the ameba. This is often called **assimilation**. Thus the ameba grows. A good deal of energy is used up in changing lifeless food into living protoplasm.

But where does the ameba get the energy that it needs for secretion, digestion, locomotion, and so on? Through **respiration**. Oxygen diffuses from the surrounding water into the cell. The oxygen unites with substances in the cell, and energy is released. Carbon dioxide and water and other substances are formed in this oxidation. These diffuse out of the cell. And the getting rid of these wastes formed in oxidation is called **excretion**. In the meantime, we saw that the protoplasm was growing. When it reaches a certain size, the cell with its nucleus goes through a complicated cell division. Thus two amebas are made; the animal has **reproduced**. While the ameba has been carrying on these many complicated activities, its protoplasm is sensitive to its changing surroundings. A bright light may have struck it; this made it move away. The water may have turned cold, and it stopped sending out pseudopods. Being sensitive to the surroundings is spoken of as **irritability** of protoplasm. You read above that protoplasm is always changing. It is very sensitive to its surroundings.

Activities of all cells. Describing and naming the activities of an ameba takes long even when it is done in as simple a way as it is done above. You read about irritability long after digestion. But you must think of these activities as going on all at one time within the ameba. Are you convinced that protoplasm is a very complex substance that is constantly changing?

The heading of this chapter is "What Cells Do." If you can remember the activities of an ameba you will know pretty well what cells can do. The activities of every living cell are for the most part the same as the activities of an ameba or the activities of any larger animal. As you read further, this will be brought home to you again and again. Both the animal and the individual cells that make up the bodies of animals perform the following activities: secretion, digestion, absorption, assimilation, respiration, excretion, reproduction, sometimes motion and locomotion. Irritability is the quality of protoplasm that makes all these various activities possible.

The cell doctrine. All that you now know about cells took a long time to discover. In 1665 Robert Hooke described what he called cells. It was some hundred fifty years later that a French physician and biologist, Dutrochet (Dew′tro-shay), wrote that all living things are made of cells and that whatever activities go on in an animal or plant are performed by its cells. But scientists were not ready to accept this.

However, shortly after this, in 1838 Mathias Schleiden said that plants are made up of cells throughout; in other words, plants consist of nothing but cells and the substances made by cells. Schleiden's friend, the zoologist Theodor Schwann, came to the conclusion that the same thing is true of animals. Both men were so well known in their fields and so highly thought of that their statements impressed other biologists.

This Schleiden-Schwann theory became known as the **cell theory.** The idea that living things are made up of cells throughout seems like a simple idea to us now. But it took almost 200 years to develop this one idea.

But Schleiden and Schwann still had very wrong ideas about what a cell is and what a cell can do. Another German biologist, Hugo von Mohl (1805–1872), had seen something in the cell that he named protoplasm; but he, too, had entirely mistaken ideas about this protoplasm. Some years later, however, an English biologist (Thomas Henry Huxley, 1825–1895) spoke of protoplasm as the "physical basis of life." What he meant by this was that wherever there is life there is protoplasm. This was an important contribution.

Then another idea was added to the original cell theory. Not only are living things made up throughout of cells and their products, but all activities of living things *are made possible by the activities of their protoplasm.* Nowadays there is so much evidence for these two beliefs that we no longer speak of the cell theory. We call it the **cell doctrine.**

What have you learned? Read again the last three sections, and you will get some idea of the activities of living protoplasm. It took scientists several centuries to formulate the cell doctrine, the doctrine that the cell with its protoplasm carries on the activities shown by the animal or plant as a whole. Do you know what these activities are, and can you explain each new term you use?

USEFUL WORDS IN BIOLOGY

virus	permeable	assimilation
oxidation	ameba	excretion
oxidase	pseudopod	reproduction
respiration	digestion	irritability
diffusion	secretion	cell theory
osmosis	absorption	cell doctrine

TEST YOURSELF

1. How do living things differ from lifeless things?
2. Explain oxidation and respiration, showing how they are alike and different.
3. Tell what energy changes take place in respiration.
4. What is meant by diffusion?
5. Describe an experiment which illustrates diffusion through a membrane, showing how it is like diffusion in general.
6. Explain why respiration would stop if diffusion through a membrane did not take place.
7. Using the word permeable, discuss under what conditions substances diffuse through a cell membrane.
8. List, and then explain the activities that an ameba performs.
9. What activities must a cell in your body perform if it is to remain alive?
10. Explain the "cell theory" or "cell doctrine."

DO IT YOURSELF

1. **Evidence of cellular respiration in you.** Breathe out for a few minutes through a tube leading into clear limewater in a stoppered bottle. What does the appearance of the white substance (precipitate) show? To arrive at conclusions what will you have as a control?

2. **Can an insoluble substance diffuse through a membrane?** You can easily try this for yourself. Boil a small amount of starch in water until you get a thin starch paste. Half fill a test tube with this starch paste and fasten a membrane securely over the open end of the tube. Invert the tube into a jar of water and let it stand for some hours. You can test for starch in the jar in the usual way. If you are not sure that this membrane would have let simple sugar through, wash everything when this experiment is finished and repeat the experiment using a solution of molasses, instead of starch.

3. **Living protoplasm.** Biologists have spent endless hours examining the mystery of protoplasm as it can be seen in an ameba or in a slime mold. Use both a bright light and a dim light with both low and high power of the microscope to see the endless flow and movement of the living material. Warm the slide in your hand to see whether that makes a difference. Try cooling the slide. Prepare a full report on what you did and what you saw.

4. **Streaming of protoplasm in plant cells.** The common aquarium plant, Elodea, shows streaming of protoplasm in the leaf cells. Mount a fresh-looking green leaf. Warm the slide slightly. (The palm of your hand will do.) Examine the cells at the edge of the leaf and in the middle. Do you see motion? In at least some of the cells you should see chloroplasts being carried along on the streaming protoplasm.

ADVENTURES IN READING

1. *The Private Life of the Protozoa* by Winifred Duncan, Ronald, 1950. Describes activities of protozoa and thus gives you an idea of cell activities in general.
2. If you want more information on the *microscope*, your class secretary might write to the nearest biological supply house that deals in microscopes for a booklet on the care and use of the microscope.

Chapter 3

Tissues and organs

Tissues. Look at the cells in Figure 3.1. They are the cells you have in your own body. Some of them may not look like cells to you. Look, for example, at the strange nerve cell and the muscle cells; how different they are from bone cells or fat cells.

But when you consider that each kind performs some very special activity in your body, it is not really surprising that cells should differ in shape and size. You know that muscle cells contract, nerve cells send messages through the body, fat cells store fat (or oil), and so on. We sometimes speak of such a special activity as the cell's special **function**.

You must not get the idea that these many kinds of cells are scattered hit or miss through your body. Each different kind is found with others like itself in groups or masses. Such a group of similar cells which do the same kind of work in the body is called a **tissue**. We have nerve tissue, muscle tissue, fat tissue, and so on.

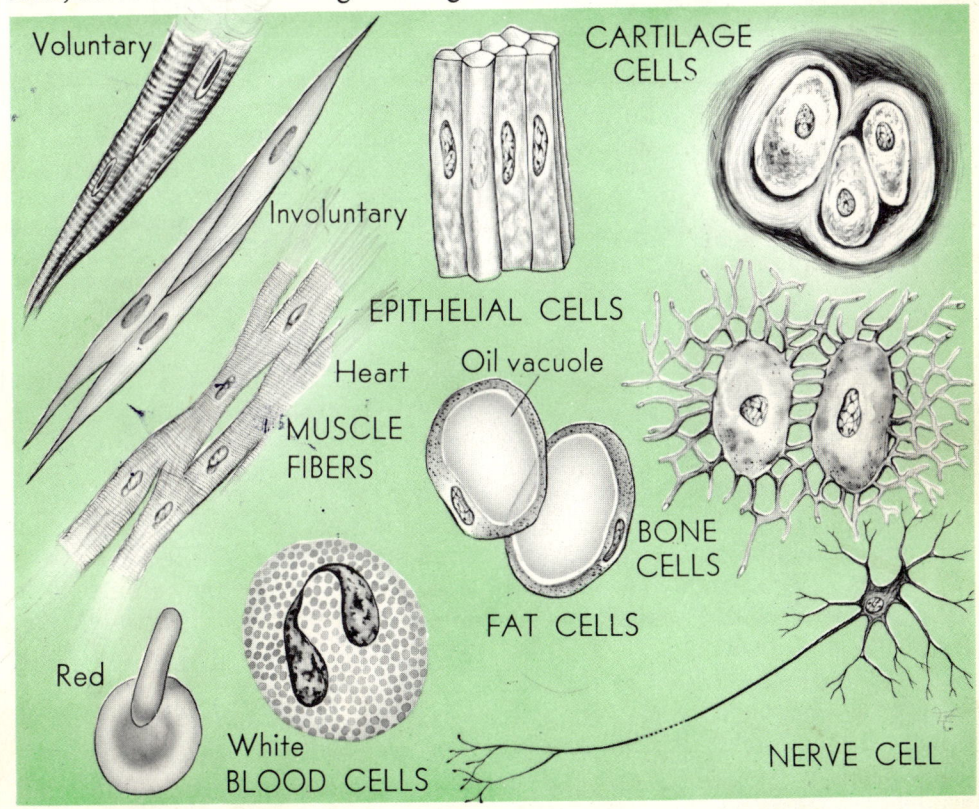

3.1 These are all cells and they are all found in your body. Note the many kinds of cells. What name is given to a group of similar cells?

CHAPTER THREE — TISSUES AND ORGANS

49

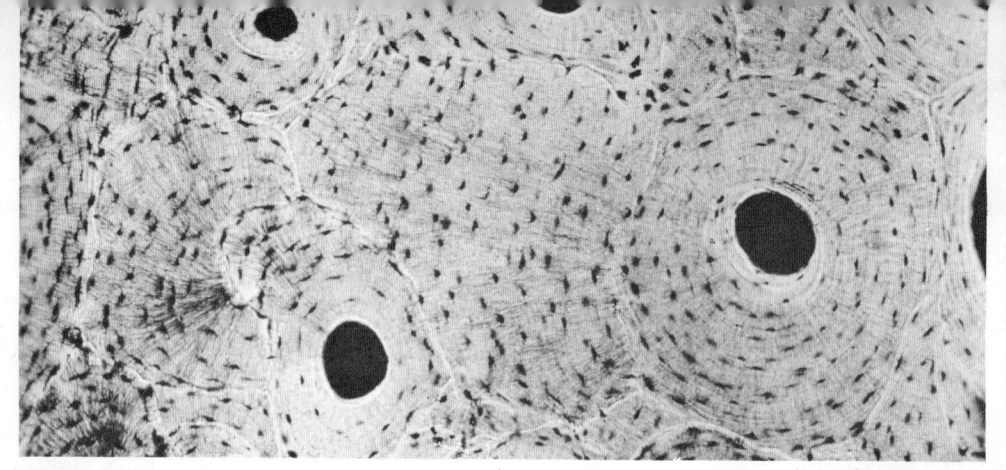

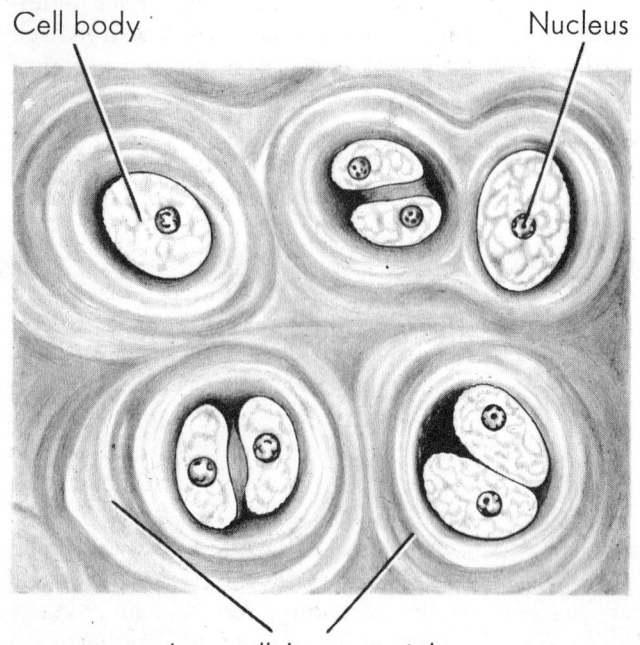

3.2 A small part of an old bone, magnified. The small dark spots are spaces where bone cells used to be. What makes up the large spaces between? The large dark spots are the holes through which blood vessels and nerves pass.

3.3 Cartilage tissue. Like bone, this tissue has a large amount of intercellular material.

Intercellular matter. Now some of the cells shown in Figure 3.1 secrete and pile up nonliving material around themselves. This nonliving material is called **intercellular matter,** which means "matter between cells." Bone cells, for example, as long as they remain alive, surround themselves with more and more lifeless mineral matter. They make it from the food that is brought to them. The intercellular matter, in fact, becomes the important part of the bone tissue. Figure 3.2 shows you how large a part of bone tissue is intercellular matter and how far apart the bone cells lie. The hardness of the bone is due entirely to the intercellular matter. Evidently, then, we must add a new idea to our definition of a tissue. We say that a *tissue is a group of cells similar in structure and function along with more or less intercellular material produced by the cells.* Some tissues have no intercellular matter whatever. Another tissue that is largely intercellular matter is **carti-**

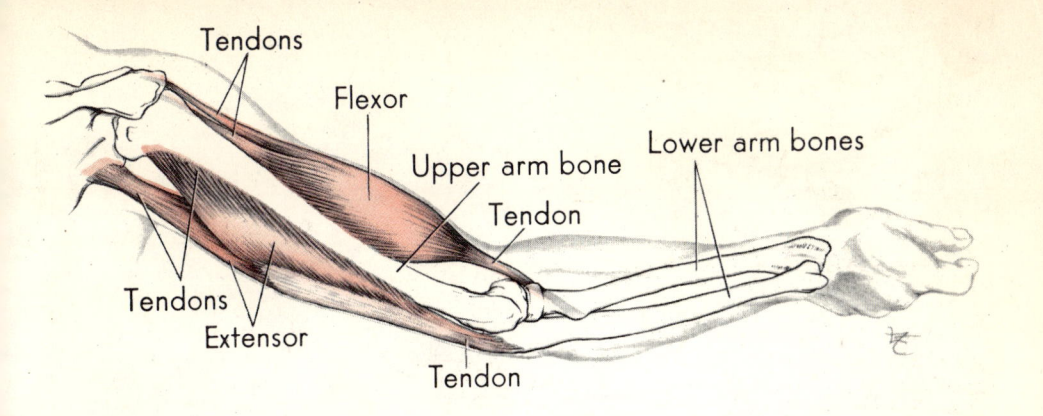

Diagram labels: Tendons, Flexor, Upper arm bone, Lower arm bones, Tendon, Tendons, Extensor, Tendon

3.4 Is the flexor contracted or relaxed in this diagram? Which muscle lies opposite the flexor? Does a muscle move a body part by contracting or by relaxing?

lage, which is shown in Figure 3.3. Cartilage is the smooth, firm tissue covering the ends of some bones; you have seen it on the end of a drumstick when you had chicken for dinner. You can feel cartilage tissue at the top of your nose and in your ear. It is stiff, but not hard like bone.

Organs. Tissues, too, like cells, don't occur hit or miss in the body. They are grouped together and make **organs.** Perhaps you already know many of the organs of the body: the heart, the stomach, the lungs, and so on. We know that most of the body's organs do some special work necessary to the body. The heart, for example, pumps blood by contracting. In the heart there is muscle tissue, but there are other tissues, too. In some organs there are many kinds of tissues. Besides the internal organs we have external organs such as the arm, the foot, the leg, and so on.

But don't confuse organ with organism. An **organism** is a living thing, either a plant or an animal. Some organisms, like the ameba and paramecium, are so simple that they consist of a single cell. But most organisms are many-celled; in these the organism is made up of organs.

Muscle tissue. A large muscle like the biceps muscle in your arm can really be thought of as an organ, too. It consists of a number of tissues, although it is mostly muscle tissue. In our bodies are three kinds of muscle tissue. Figure 3.1 shows cells from **voluntary** and **involuntary** muscle. The third kind shown is found only in the heart (**cardiac** muscle).

The voluntary muscle fiber is really a number of cells joined together; one fiber has many nuclei. Look again at Figure 3.1. These voluntary muscle fibers show crosswise stripes. (They are striated.) The involuntary fibers are not striped, but smooth. The voluntary muscles are attached to the bones and are called **skeletal** muscles. The involuntary muscles are found only in internal organs.

How voluntary muscles move bones. The name voluntary means that one can decide whether or not that muscle should contract. For example, when I

CHAPTER THREE — TISSUES AND ORGANS 51

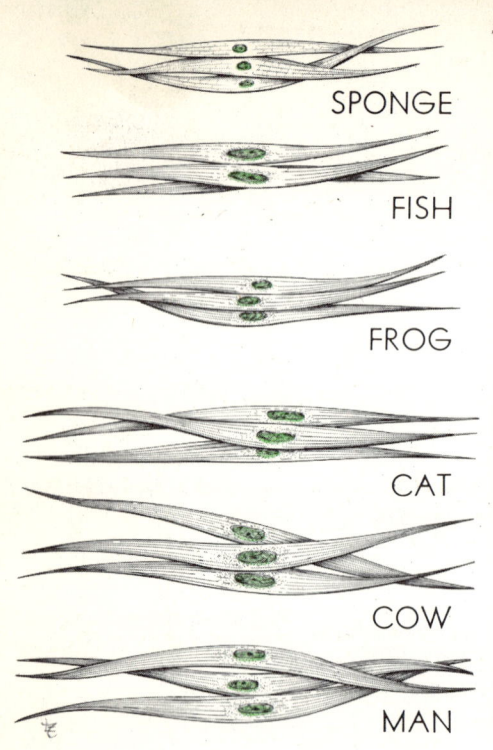

3.5 Involuntary muscle cells of different animals. Which animals? Could you tell which was which if they were not labeled?

3.6 Which of the plant organs can you see in this photograph of geraniums? Which can't you see? *Sullivan*

say "let me feel the muscle in your arm," you decide to contract the large biceps muscle in your upper arm so that I can feel it bulge. As you contract your biceps muscle, your forearm comes up. But why does the forearm come up when the large biceps muscle contracts? The muscle ends in a **tendon**, a cord of tissue which attaches the muscle to a bone in the forearm. At the other end is a tendon fastened to the shoulder. As all the fibers contract, each one gets shorter and thicker; you can feel the muscle bulging. As it gets shorter, it pulls the forearm up, as in Figure 3.4. The muscle bends the arm at the elbow. Therefore this muscle is called a **flexor**. (Flex means bend.) Now you want to let your arm down again. You have another muscle that runs along the back of your upper arm. Its lower tendon runs on the outside of your elbow joint and is attached to the bone in the forearm. When this muscle contracts, it pulls the forearm down; it is, therefore, called an **extensor**. At the same time the biceps, the flexor, stops contracting; it just relaxes. Thus, muscles in pairs extending across joints (where bones meet end to end) can move parts of the body. One muscle contracts while the other relaxes.

Tissue cells in other animals. You will be interested to know that the tissue cells in your body seem to be almost exactly like the tissue cells in other animals. Figure 3.5 shows you how similar muscle fibers are in different animals. Even in size, elephant cells are similar to mouse cells. To see variety in cells you need not go from

3.7 Cells of onion skin. This tissue somewhat resembles the epithelial tissue of animals. Which parts of the cell do you recognize? *Richard St. Clair*

animal to animal; just examine the cells within your own body.

How tissue cells arise. Most organisms start life as a single cell. This cell divides and gives rise to billions or trillions of cells making up the body. Gradually these cells become different from one another, taking on some special function. We say they become **differentiated** in structure and **specialized** in function. How do some become muscle cells, others bone cells, and so on? Biologists have asked themselves this question, and they are still trying to answer it. Only now they are beginning to find an explanation.

Organs and tissues in plants. Plants, too, have organs and tissues, but fewer of them. The plants you see in gardens, in woods, and in fields have root, stem, and leaf. Other organs appear at certain seasons: the flower, fruit, and seed. Look at Figure 3.6. These organs are made up of tissues; but as you might expect, the tissues are, for the most part, quite different from animal tissues. Only a few plant tissues closely resemble any animal tissues. One of these is the skin of onion leaves, Figure 3.7. You will learn more about plant tissues in Unit Three.

What have you learned? Living things, or organisms, are made up of cells. In most organisms there are many kinds of cells, each doing some special kind of work. The cells that are alike in structure and in their activities are grouped together; they form a tissue. There are many tissues,

CHAPTER THREE — TISSUES AND ORGANS 53

each with its special function. Organs are made up of groups of tissues. Each organ also does a special job or jobs of benefit to the organism. The grouping of animal tissues in the table may be helpful to you.

TABLE 4
ANIMAL TISSUES

Four groups of tissues	Some kinds of tissues in each group	Where found; what it does; or description
1. Epithelial tissue (covering and secreting)	A. epidermis B. mucous membrane C. serous membrane D. gland tissue	A. covers body B. lines organs; moist membrane C. covers internal organs; smooth D. makes sweat and other liquids
2. Muscle tissue (contraction)	A. voluntary or skeletal B. involuntary C. heart muscle	A. attached to bones B. found in internal organs C. a cross between A. and B.
3. Nerve tissue (sending messages)	A. all one kind of tissue	A. but cells vary slightly
4. Connective tissue (the catch-all for all other tissues)	A. bone tissue B. cartilage C. fat tissue D. yellow elastic E. white fibrous F. blood	A. gives support; levers for muscles B. support; smooth surfaces at joint C. stores food; makes cushions D. connects parts E. in tendons and many other parts F. some people put this in a class by itself

USEFUL WORDS IN BIOLOGY

function
tissue
intercellular matter
cartilage
organ
organism
voluntary muscle (striated)

involuntary muscle (smooth)
flexor
extensor
differentiated
specialized
epidermis
mucous membrane

serous membrane
gland
nerve
connective tissue

TEST YOURSELF

1. In your own words, give a complete definition of a tissue.
2. Using an example or two, explain how organisms are composed of tissues.
3. Make a list of the tissues you would expect to find in a mouse's body.

UNIT ONE — HOW LIVING THINGS ARE ALIKE

4. Give the function of each tissue in the list you made in number 3.

5. (a) Name six organs of a plant. (b) Which plant tissue resembles somewhat an animal tissue?

6. (a) Name the four main groups of tissues found in the bodies of complex animals. (b) Name the tissues put into each of these four main groups.

DO IT YOURSELF

1. The study of an organ. A bone, being a collection of many tissues, is an example of a simple organ. Get a fresh leg bone of a lamb from the butcher; have him saw it down the middle. You will be interested in finding the tissues. Feel the cartilage at the ends of the bone, and the marrow (yellow fat) in the inside of the shank of the bone. You can see the fibrous tissue that covers the bone if you prick it with a pin or dissecting needle. Are there signs of blood in the bone? Of course, a large part of the bone is bone tissue itself. Describe everything you saw.

2. The study of some animal tissues. It is possible to buy prepared, stained slides of human tissues but you will find it far more interesting to prepare slides of tissues from a freshly killed frog. Cells of a frog are very much like your own cells. Before you begin, look ahead to see what materials you will need.

Epithelial or covering tissue. (a) Flat (squamous) cells. Because frogs shed their skins continuously you will find some small pieces in the water in which the frogs are kept. Stretch a small piece on a slide; stain it with iodine solution; put on a cover glass. Examine with the low power of the microscope and draw two or three of the flat skin cells. (b) Epithelial cells with cilia, or hairlike projections from a cell. Remove a small piece of skin from the roof of the mouth of a freshly killed frog as follows: make a cut with a scalpel in the region near the eyeball and peel off the epithelium with your forceps. Mount the skin on a slide in a salt solution made by dissolving 0.3 ounce of table salt in almost 50 ounces of water (49.7 oz.), or mount the skin in Ringer's solution, which you can often buy at a drug store. Ringer's solution is a mixture of salts resembling body liquids. These solutions keep the cells alive and active. Through a microscope you should see cilia on these cells beating. You may have to use the high power. You have such epithelial cells with cilia lining the top of your windpipe.

Muscle tissue. (a) Voluntary or *striated*. Cut out a small piece of a leg muscle of a freshly killed frog. Place it on a slide in salt solution and tease it apart with dissecting needles. Press gently on the cover glass to flatten the tiny muscle fibers. You can see individual muscle fibers with their light and dark bands even under low power. To stain the nuclei add a drop of acetocarmine stain* at one edge of the cover glass. The stain will be drawn under the cover if you touch the opposite edge with a blotter. How many nuclei do you find in a fiber? Make and label a drawing of several fibers as they look under the high power. (b) Involuntary, or smooth. Cut out a small piece of the stomach wall. Separate the outer layer from the inner and tease apart the cells in the outer layer. Mount these on a slide, add some acetocarmine stain, and press gently on the cover glass. You can see that these fibers differ from the voluntary muscle fibers. Draw and label two or three of these fibers.

Blood tissue. Place several drops of frog's blood on a slide. To prevent air bubbles from forming as you cover it, touch the edge of the drop with the edge of your cover glass and then let it down gently. What color are the "red blood cells"? What shape are they? Do they contain a nucleus? Except in their color, they differ from ours. Draw two or three.

3. Plant tissues. You have seen onion skin tissue under the microscope. If you have a fleshy leaf, such as a sedum leaf, peel off some of the skin (epidermis). Hold it up to the light. Spread it over a printed word. What do you discover? Tease apart a "string" from a stalk of celery. You will find tissues there quite different from any you have seen in animals.

---

* If you do not have acetocarmine stain on hand, you can make it as follows. Heat 20 milliliters of 45% acetic acid (Chemistry Department) to boiling. Add carmine dye (any biological supply house) until some is left undissolved. Cool and filter. Will last for several years.

CHAPTER THREE — TISSUES AND ORGANS

Unit Two

The many kinds of plants and animals

CHAPTER 4

A third of a million kinds of plants

CHAPTER 5

A million kinds of animals

CHAPTER 6

Classifying plants and animals

A third of a million kinds of plants; more than a million kinds of animals; and more of each being discovered every day! We are just one of these kinds of living things; the world is theirs as much as ours. Let's look in briefly on this world of living things. We can meet only a very few of them in the next chapters.

For centuries scientists felt the need for grouping or classifying the many, many living things, but could find no satisfactory method. And then at last, in about 1750, Carolus Linnaeus devised a simple scheme for grouping and then naming living things. He explored the countries near his home in Sweden, journeying almost 5000 miles on foot and horseback, collecting plants mostly, but animals, too, and taking notes on all he saw. He classified and named thousands of animals and plants brought to him from many parts of the earth. Thousands more have been found and named since his day, as exploration continued all over the earth. Some African animals are shown on the page opposite.

You already know that Leeuwenhoek discovered how to study the "invisible" animals and plants. For hundreds of years people have studied the living things in the sea. Only recently, however, explorers wearing diving suits have described and photographed the wonders of the shallow ocean floor. Here can be seen undersea gardens of animals and plants as bright with color as the gardens you know on land.

Exploration is not at an end. Much still remains to be learned about animals and plants. You, too, can go out of doors and fill your notebooks with facts that have never been recorded. But let's first get acquainted with a few of the many kinds of living things.

Chapter 4

A third of a million kinds of plants

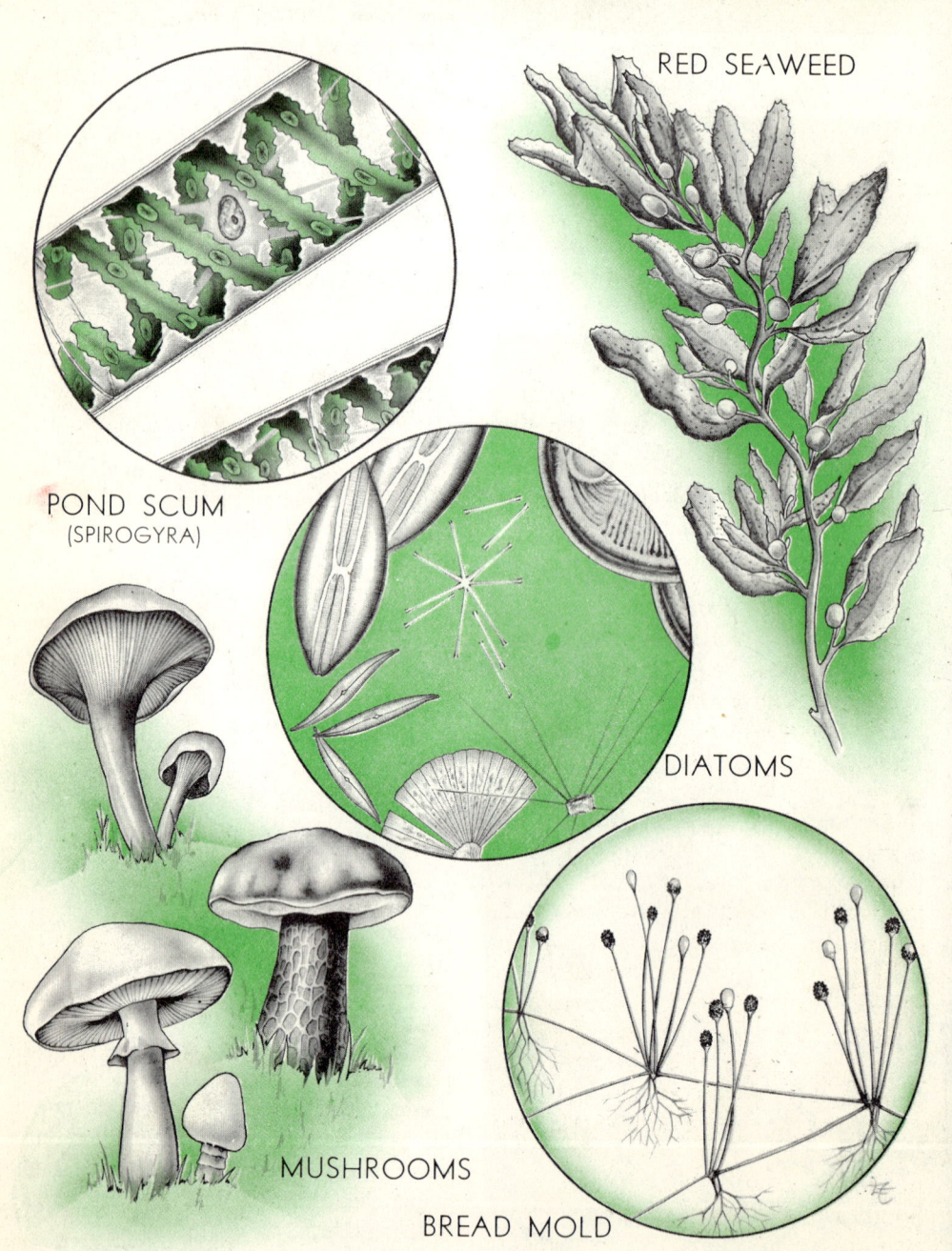

RED SEAWEED

POND SCUM
(SPIROGYRA)

DIATOMS

MUSHROOMS

BREAD MOLD

4.1 All these plants are Thallophytes—the Group that includes the simplest plants.

UNIT TWO — THE MANY KINDS OF PLANTS AND ANIMALS

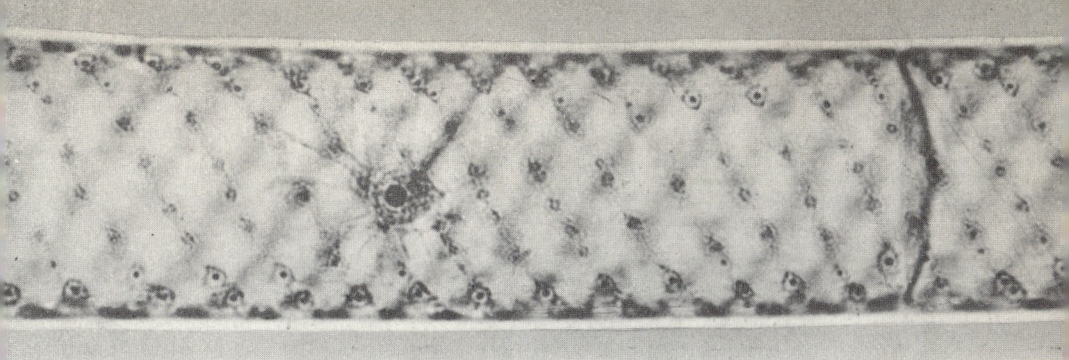

4.2 Part of a single strand of Spirogyra, one of the pond scums. Do you see the spirals? They are bright green. Spirogyra lives in fresh water. *General Biological Supply*

THE SIMPLEST PLANTS — THALLOPHYTES

The simplest green plants. If you can find a slowly moving stream or small pond, scoop up some of the water from the top and take it home to examine with a microscope or magnifying glass. Do you see any tiny green plants? There may be animals, too, but right now let's examine the plants. Perhaps in the spring or early summer you saw a scum on this same water. When you poked a stick into the scum and lifted it there was a mass of green, tangled threads hanging from the stick. These threads are simple plants known as **pond scums.** By the fall most of them have disappeared. Among them is the many-celled SPIROGYRA (spy-ro-jy'ra) shown in Figure 4.2. It is a particularly beautiful plant under the microscope. Each cell has one or more long green spirals containing chlorophyll. The plant never has flowers, and it has neither root, nor stem, nor leaves. It is just a living green thread which floats and grows on quiet, sunlit water.

Besides the several kinds of threadlike plants, there are many other kinds of simple green plants in the water. Some are single celled, others live in small colonies. Some can move about. Yet they are called plants because each cell has a wall of cellulose or a similar substance, and they have chlorophyll. We call these simple green plants without root, stem, or leaf, ALGAE (al'jee — singular alga, pronounced al'guh). See page 60. Most algae live in water. But some grow in the soil; and you may see PLEUROCOCCUS (plu-ro-cok'us), a single-celled alga growing in a flat green mass, on the bark of trees where there is shade and moisture. You might think it was a moss, but it is a much simpler plant than a moss. Scrape some off with a knife and examine it under a microscope. Algae grow all over the world, even on arctic summer snows. Others can live in hot springs at temperatures up to 170° F. All algae are important in the world because they are the food of many kinds of small water animals.

Algae at the seashore. In a trip to the shore you will see many other kinds of algae, most of them larger plants. Some, like the common brown seaweed or **rockweed,** FUCUS (few'kus), are fastened to the rocks between the tide levels. They can hold much moisture and are tough enough to stand the

CHAPTER FOUR — A THIRD OF A MILLION KINDS OF PLANTS

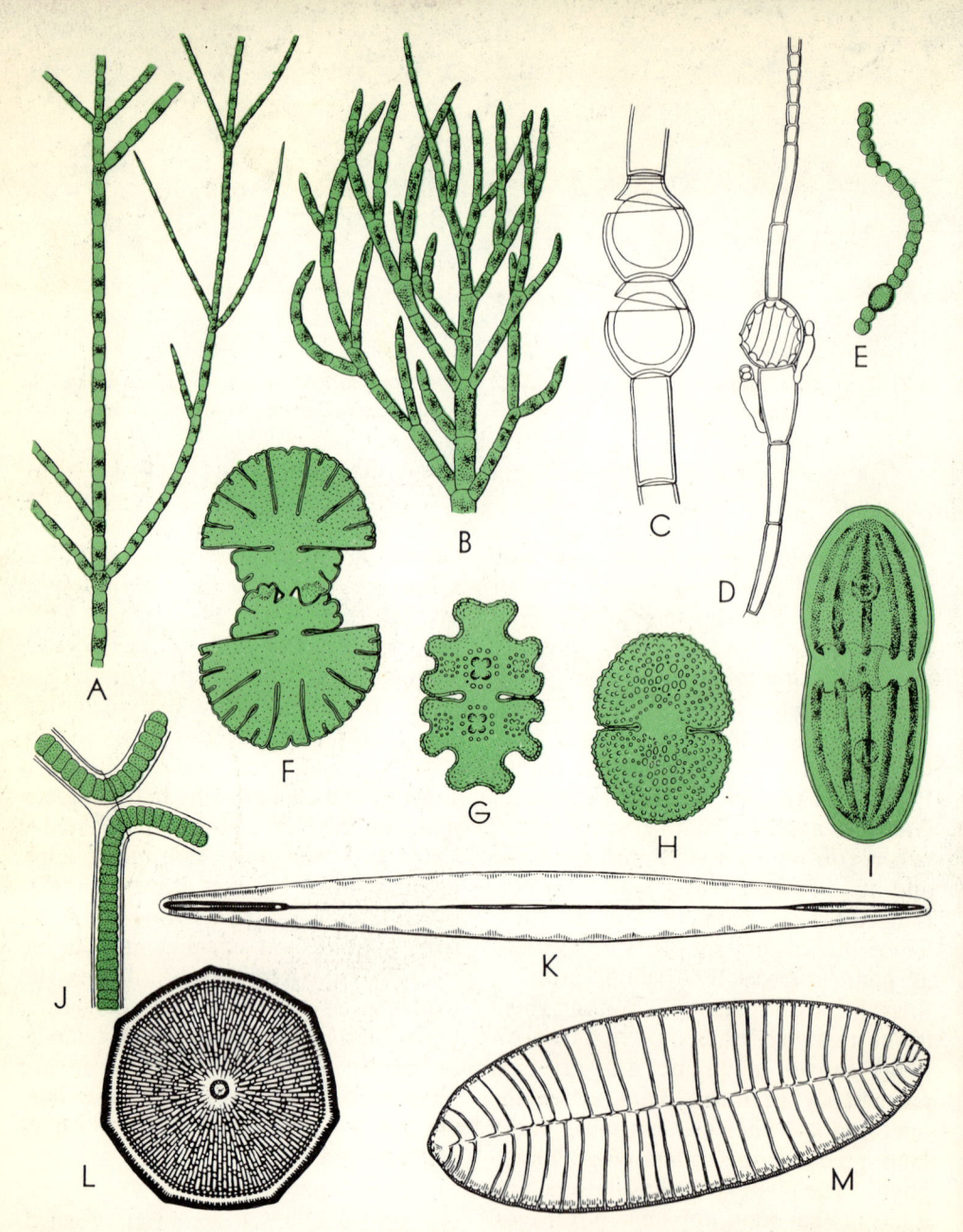

4.3 Drawings of several kinds of freshwater algae. Hundreds of kinds of algae are found in lakes, streams, ditches, swamps, and some on soil and on the bark of trees. Note that some algae are branching threads (**A** and **B**), some single celled. **C** and **D** show Oedogonium, a common alga often used for study. **K**, **L**, and **M** are examples of diatoms, which you will read about. Study of algae is the life work of some people.

UNIT TWO — THE MANY KINDS OF PLANTS AND ANIMALS

4.4 Life in salt water. This is a common sight for those who live near rocky ocean shores. Do you see the strands of rockweed? Do you recognize any animals? Note how closely plants and animals live together in this underwater community.

pounding of the surf. Here they give shelter to many small animals as shown in Figure 4.4. Some brown seaweeds, like the kelps, may be fifty yards long. Formerly kelps were gathered and burned to get the iodine they contained.

Large green seaweeds float near the surface of the open sea. Pieces of the sea lettuce (ULVA) are often washed ashore and caught on the sand or rocks. Deep down live red seaweeds. They, too, are sometimes washed up on the beach. They are usually smaller plants and delicately branched. But, like all the other algae, they have neither root, nor stem, nor leaves. Agar-agar, sold at drug stores, and used in some

CHAPTER FOUR — A THIRD OF A MILLION KINDS OF PLANTS

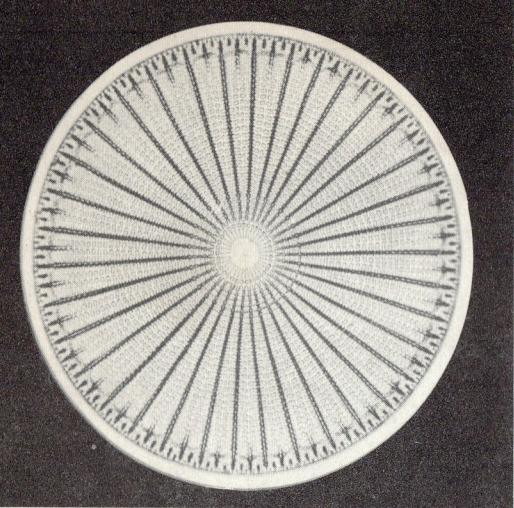

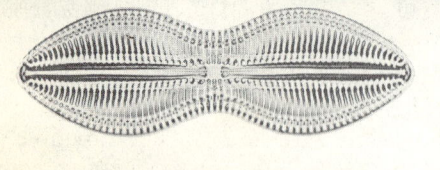

4.5 Two diatoms. Note the ornamental design on the glasslike shells. Diatoms are important to everyone who makes a living by catching animals that live in the sea, for diatoms are their basic food. How are diatoms useful to man? *Eastman Kodak*

4.6 Most of the bracket fungus (above) is under the bark. It gets its food from the tree. The Amanita looks much like our common edible mushroom, except for the veil under the cap. Beware of mushrooms with this veil; the Amanita is poisonous.

laboratories for experiments, comes from a red seaweed found off the coast of Japan and our own West Coast.

Diatoms — algae with glasslike shells. Thousands of kinds of these algae with glasslike shells live in both fresh and salt water. Most of them are single celled and all contain chlorophyll, though it may be hidden by yellow or brownish substances. Their wall consists of two parts, one overlapping the other, as a lid fits on a box. And the shell is ornamented with various designs (Fig. 4.5). These are **diatoms** (die'eh-tomes). At certain times of the year they live in enormous numbers. In the oceans they make up the most important part of the floating mass of tiny living things, known as **plankton.**

Plankton is the principal food of many animals in the oceans, from the smallest animals to the largest, such as whales.

As diatoms died throughout the ages, the "glass cases" piled up on the bottom of the seas, forming large deposits. On the California coast, land that was once at the bottom of the sea, 100,000 tons of it is dug up every year to be used in many ways — for insulating boilers, for polishes and soaps, even for toothpowder.

Fungi — simple plants without chlorophyll. Some of the simple plants have no chlorophyll; they are called FUNGI (fun'jeye — singular fungus, pronounced fun'gus). Like the algae the fungi have no flowers, or stems, or leaves, or roots. You know some of the larger fungi. The mushrooms you eat with steak are fungi. You have seen mushrooms on the ground, on old stumps, on the trunks of trees, especially in the woods where it is moist. The plant is just a mass of threads, called **hyphae** (high'fee). About one half of the many kinds of mushrooms can be eaten by man. Some are too tough and a few are definitely poisonous. Those we don't eat we often speak of as toadstools.

The molds. We know of about 75,000 different kinds of fungi. You have often seen some of the smaller kinds — the molds. Next time a mold appears on your bread or cheese or other food, don't throw it out. Give it a chance to grow in a covered glass dish, and examine its delicate hyphae. The commonest mold on bread is called RHIZOPUS (rye'zo-pus) or "bread mold." It is a miniature jungle of very fine, shiny, white threads.

Little black balls soon appear at the tips of the threads (hyphae) that stand up. These balls are cases filled with a mass of black **spores.** A spore acts like a seed; it grows into a new plant. But it is much simpler than a seed; it is a single cell with a thick wall. Hundreds of spores are formed. When a spore case is filled with ripe spores it bursts and the spores are carried far and wide by air currents. Wherever a spore settles on a piece of bread or other food, a new mold plant may appear, if the temperature is right and there is enough moisture.

Some molds are salmon pink; others look like a piece of blue-green felt. It is usually the spores that give the color to a mold. The drug penicillin is prepared from some of the blue-green molds. In these the threads are so short that without a strong magnifying glass you cannot see separate threads at all. There are many kinds of molds. Millions of bushels of stored fruit and vegetables are spoiled each year by molds.

Many fungi cause disease — parasites. Other fungi are much more important to us than those that spoil some of our food. Many kinds grow on living plants, causing serious plant diseases. See Figure 4.8. The hyphae grow into the plant and use its food, weakening and often destroying the plant. Fungi that cause plant diseases do enormous damage both on farms and in forests.

Living things that get their food in this way are called **parasites.** The organism that supplies the food is called the **host.** When you have ringworm you are the host to a special fungus that lives as a parasite on you. But not many kinds of fungi are parasites on animals; they are mostly parasites on plants. However, **parasitism,** the method of getting food from another living thing while living in or on it, is very common. You will read much more about it.

Fungi that cause decay — saprophytes. Countless fungi get their food from dead plants and animals. Organisms that get their food in this way are called **saprophytes** (sap'row-fites). Note that this is different from parasitism. In feeding, saprophytes help to break down and decay dead bodies of plants and animals. They are the earth's cleanup squad; they help to dispose of dead bodies of plants and animals and, in doing this, they put simple food materials back into the soil.

This activity of saprophytes, helpful as it is, causes us lots of trouble, too. For example, wood used for telephone poles, fence posts, railroad ties, and houses, and for all other purposes needs protection against decay fungi. That's why we paint wood regularly if we want it to last. If we didn't do that we would need an even larger supply of wood than we do at present.

An alga and a fungus may live together. Sometimes an alga and a fungus live together so closely combined that they make a single plant. The alga, having chlorophyll, makes food; the fungus holds the water and minerals that the alga needs. Such a plant is called a **lichen** (ly'ken). This kind of close partnership between two organisms, where each organism is helped by the other, is called **symbiosis** (sim-by-oh'sis). You will read later that some animals have partnerships like this, too. Figure 4.9 shows some lichens growing on the bark of a tree. Some, like the "reindeer moss" which is not a moss at all, grow on the ground; others grow on rocks and help us by breaking the rocks into soil. Lichens are eaten by some animals.

Some fungi help us bake and brew — yeasts. The **yeast** plant is a tiny, colorless, egg- or rod-shaped cell. You need a microscope to see it. It floats about in the air, settles and feeds on sugar. In feeding, yeasts change sugar into alcohol and carbon dioxide. This change is called **fermentation.** Yeast is a very useful fungus. In wine-making, yeast is permitted to ferment the sugars in grapes. In the making of other alcoholic beverages yeast ferments other sugars. Sometimes yeasts are specially raised and packed in a mass. As you may know, millions and millions of one kind of yeast plant may be pressed into one yeast cake, usually to be used for baking. When yeast is added to flour and sugar in bread dough, fermentation of the sugar takes place. The carbon dioxide gas forms bubbles in the mass of dough. These "raise" the dough and make it light and porous. The alcohol formed evaporates during the baking; you never taste it.

Bacteria. You have heard of **bacteria** often, perhaps by the name of **germs.** Most germs or bacteria are much smaller than yeasts. Even the giants among them can be seen only with a very good microscope. And then there is not much to be seen in them, not even a nucleus. To get an idea of their small size imagine a pneumonia germ magnified to the size of a tennis ball. A man magnified in proportion would be about twenty-five miles tall!

Thousands of kinds of bacteria are known. Some are parasites and live in animals or plants, causing disease; others are saprophytes and cause decay. Still others are useful to us in a number of ways; some make vinegar from alcohol, and others are used in curing tobacco and making rope from hemp.

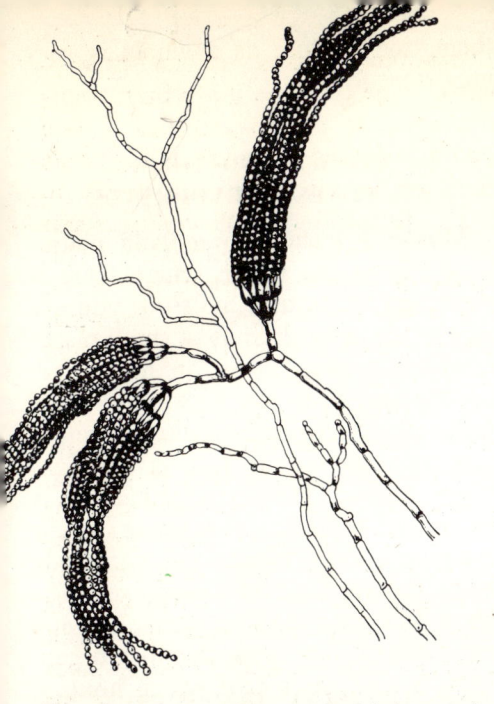

4.7 (Right) Penicillium, a mold that makes penicillin. (Left) Branches of Penicillium, as seen with a microscope, with strings of spores. (Bottom) Bread mold as seen with a microscope. Spores in cases. *Left and right above courtesy Lederle Laboratories.*

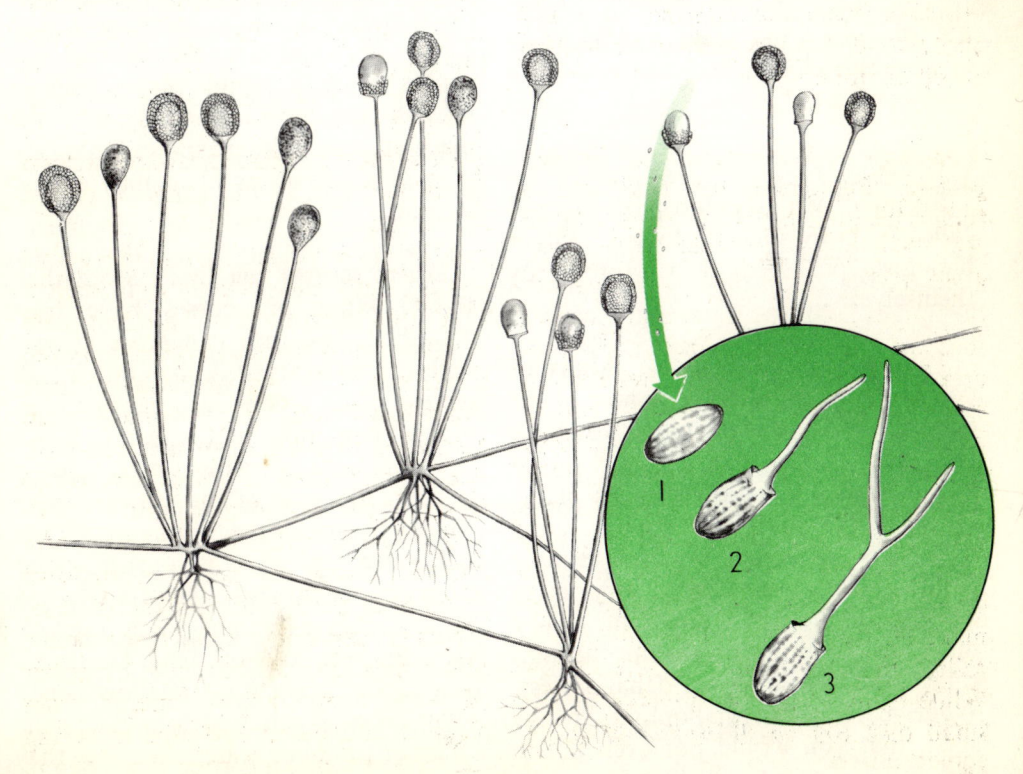

CHAPTER FOUR — A THIRD OF A MILLION KINDS OF PLANTS

4.8 This smut is one of the fungi that lives as a parasite on corn. Each ball shown here contains billions of spores.

Bacteria have no chlorophyll and are called fungi by some biologists. Other biologists put them into a group by themselves.

The phylum Thallophytes. Many of you probably did not even know of the existence of some of the plants you have just been reading about; nor would you probably think of them as plants at all. But there are many, many thousands of kinds of these simple plants. They form one very large division of the plant kingdom. They make up the group or **phylum** (fie'lum) called the **Thallophytes** (thal'o-fites). While many of the thallophytes are so small that you would not even notice them, the phylum as a whole is very important to us.

MOSSES AND THEIR RELATIVES — BRYOPHYTES

Mosses — common woodland plants. In a trip to the woods where there is plenty of shade and moisture you are sure to see several kinds of small plants known as **mosses.** Look on the ground, on stumps, even on rocks for small green plants growing so close together that all you see at first is a bright green patch. Press your hand on a patch and feel the soft cushion. Now examine a single plant; you can study many mosses with the naked eye. The plant has tiny leaflike parts growing out from a very thin stemlike organ. Then it also has a part which holds it to the ground, but this, too, is no real root. Mosses never have flowers but you may see a tiny cap or boxlike part on a stalk. Look at them in Figure 4.10. In these are the microscopic spores which, in simple plants, such as mosses, molds, and others, take the place of seeds. Where spores fall on the ground a new moss plant may appear in time.

Where mosses can live. More than 10,000 kinds of mosses have been described, and they can grow in very different **habitats.** A habitat is the kind of place where an organism lives. Mosses can grow in the Arctic Zone, on mountaintops where it is equally cold, in the heat of the tropics, or in the dry deserts of the Southwest. They stay alive for months buried under snow and ice or where they are so dried out that they will break when touched. Most mosses live on land but some live at the bottom of shallow freshwater lakes or attached to rocks in the midst of tumbling waterfalls. But they

UNIT TWO — THE MANY KINDS OF PLANTS AND ANIMALS

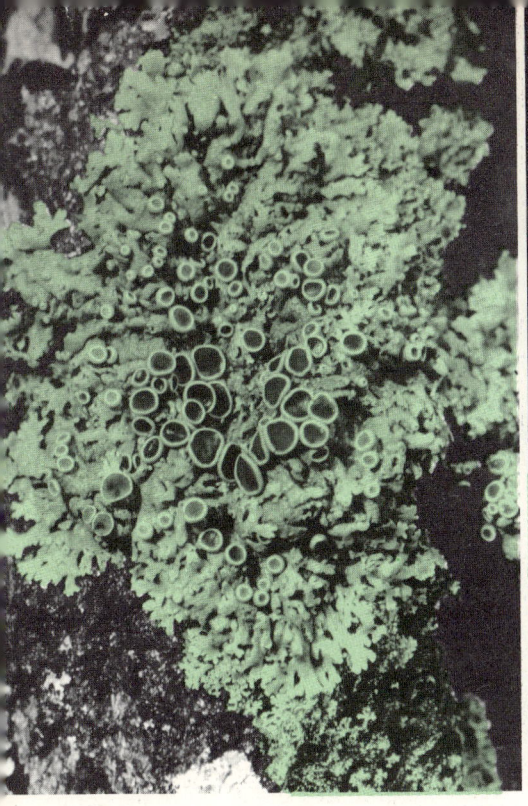

4.9 A common gray-green lichen, which grows flat on a rock. This lichen is a partnership between a fungus and an alga. What does each contribute to the other? *Hugh Spencer*

4.10 A tiny moss (Physcomitrium) that you may find in your garden. It is less than one-half inch high. What would you find in the big containers on top? Of what importance to man are mosses?

never live in salt water with the seaweeds you read about. A trip to the woods will be best for a study of mosses, but you will surely find some on an old shaded lawn or an abandoned farm, even on a bit of soil along a sidewalk in a big city. Farm land which was originally wooded turns to woodland again very quickly when no longer cultivated. Plants from the forest move in or "invade" fields and meadows. Mosses are among the early arrivals.

Importance of mosses. Mosses supply food and moisture and shelter to many small insects, worms, and other animals. Perhaps you will find some. By growing so close together, moss plants hold back water which would otherwise run down hillsides. And their rootlike structures hold the soil and keep it from washing and blowing away.

If you visit a swamp or a bog you are likely to find a moss called **sphagnum**. It is a large plant, as mosses go, with a stemlike part several inches long. When animals and plants die in a bog they don't decay as they do in other moist habitats because such quiet water contains very little dissolved oxygen. Here the sphagnums pile up gradually through the centuries and form a mass of plant remains called **peat**, many feet deep. When the bog is drained the peat

CHAPTER FOUR — A THIRD OF A MILLION KINDS OF PLANTS 67

Female organs

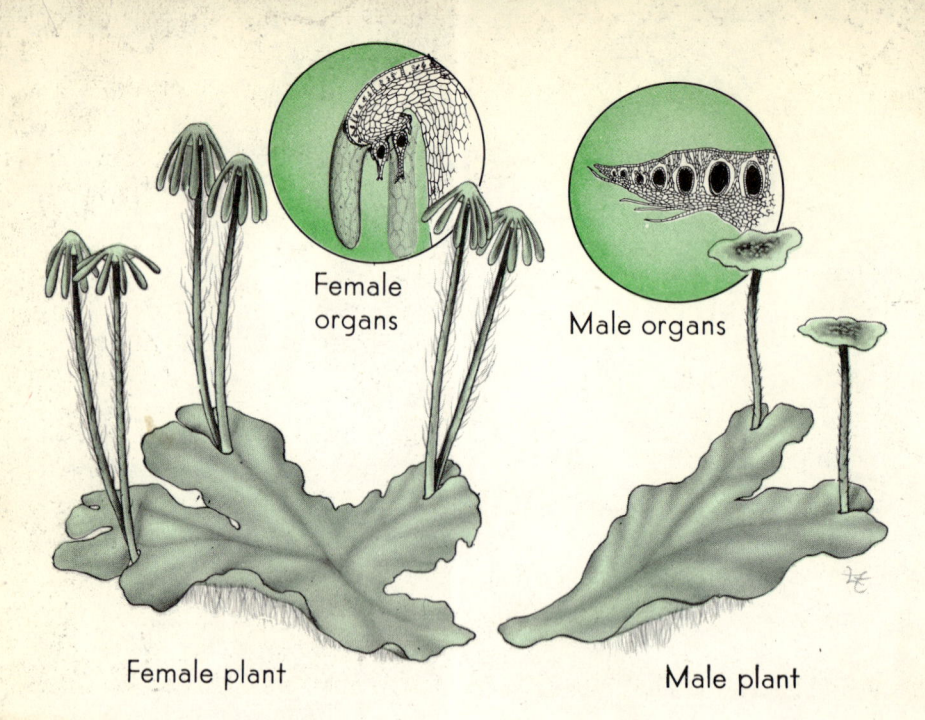

Male organs

Female plant

Male plant

4.11 One of the larger liverworts, Marchantia. The upright branches you see in this picture arise from flat portions of the plant that are attached to the soil. Spores of two kinds are produced at the top of the upright branches. *Paul Voth*

can be dug out and dried. In some parts of the world peat is still burned instead of coal or wood. And those of you who raise flowers out of doors may well have used sphagnum for mulching your flower beds. But all in all mosses are not nearly as important to us as the thallophytes.

Phylum Bryophytes. Mosses belong to a phylum called **Bryophytes** (bry′o-fites). See pages 133–136. They look more like plants to you than do the Thallophytes. But they differ from higher plants, too. They are always small and they have no real leaves or stems or roots; and they never produce flowers. Mosses have some close relatives, called **liverworts,** which you are much less likely to find. They are even simpler than the mosses. Have you ever seen them? See Figure 4.11.

THE FERNS — PTERIDOPHYTES

Ferns grow where mosses grow. If you take a trip to the woods you will doubtless find a number of different kinds of ferns. You will know them by their leaves, called **fronds.** The frond is usually divided and often finely subdivided. See Figure 4.12. Ferns have a woody stem, but in most ferns the stem runs along underground close to the surface, sending roots downward. Now look on the underside of the leaf for brown spots or ridges on each leaflet. These contain the spores which in a complicated way can produce new fern plants. You can see some in Figure 4.13.

Most kinds of ferns, like mosses, live in rich soil in the shade of the woods. Some grow on rocks. But the bracken fern, or brake, grows in sunny fields.

UNIT TWO — THE MANY KINDS OF PLANTS AND ANIMALS

4.12 The hay-scented fern. Not all ferns have leaves (fronds) as finely divided as this. *Schneider and Schwartz*

4.13 The lower side of a small piece of a fern frond. Each dark spot contains many tiny spore cases. *Brooklyn Botanic Garden*

So does the hay scented fern. One kind grows floating on water. Ferns cannot live as far north as the mosses. But as you go south toward the equator you find not only many more different kinds of ferns but much larger ones. In some regions, such as in Hawaii and in South America, ferns grow as trees. The upright woody stem of these tree ferns may be three feet thick.

Close relatives of ferns. Horsetails are relatives of ferns. They grow in very different habitats, often in the poor soil along railroad tracks, sometimes in the wet soil along streams. One is shown in Figure 4.14. And there are creeping plants that grow close to the forest floor called "club mosses" or "ground pines." But don't be misled by the names; they are neither "mosses" nor "pines." They are relatives of ferns and together with them they belong to the third phylum we have met so far — the phylum **Pteridophytes** (ter-id'o-fites). All the plants in this phylum have true roots, stems, and leaves; but they never have flowers and they do not make seeds. Modern ferns and their relatives are the descendants of similar plants that grew more than 250 million years ago. The remains of these ancient fernlike plants now make up the coal beds found in so many parts of the earth from Alaska to Antarctica.

PLANTS WITH FLOWERS AND SEEDS — SPERMATOPHYTES

More than 150 thousand different kinds. Almost all the kinds of plants you know well are flowering plants,

CHAPTER FOUR — A THIRD OF A MILLION KINDS OF PLANTS

4.14 The "scouring rush" is a relative of the fern. It is harsh and gritty to the touch. *Brooklyn Botanic Garden*

4.15 Look closely and you will see why the barrel cactus of the desert is considered a spermatophyte.

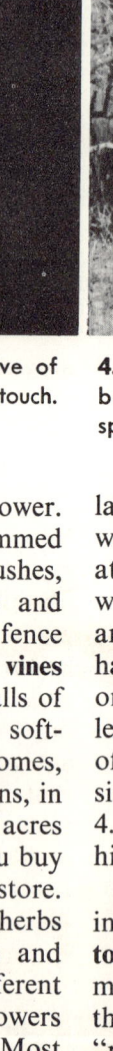

even if you never see them flower. You know **trees** and woody-stemmed **shrubs,** which you may call bushes, that decorate parks and homes and roadsides and grow wild along fence rows or in forests. You know **vines** that climb on trees or cling to walls of buildings. You know the **herbs,** soft-stemmed plants that grow in our homes, in our flower and vegetable gardens, in fields, and on farms — millions of acres of them. It is herbs, too, that you buy as vegetables at the grocery store. These trees, shrubs, vines, and herbs are all plants that bear flowers and seeds. More than 150,000 different kinds are known. All bear flowers which turn into fruit and seeds. Most are green because they contain chlorophyll, and almost all of them have true roots, stems, and leaves.

Nearly all flowering plants live on land, rooted in soil. A few live in fresh water, floating on the surface or rooted at the bottom. Only a few can live where salt water floods the soil. Some are fitted for desert life; most of these have thorns or stiff spines. Some grow only in shade. Some have delicate leaves, some leathery leaves, leaves of all sizes and shapes; some have simple leaves — as shown in Figure 4.16 — or compound leaves — like the hickory shown in Figure 4.17.

All of these plants are put together into one very large phylum, the **Spermatophytes** (sperm'at-o-fites). The word means "seed plants." Have you noticed that the name of each phylum ends in "phytes"? That makes it easy to remember the long names. You have Thallophytes, Bryophytes, Pteridophytes, Spermatophytes. "Phyte" means "plant" in Greek.

70 UNIT TWO — THE MANY KINDS OF PLANTS AND ANIMALS

POPLAR

OAK

MAPLE

4.16 Simple leaves. *Brooklyn Botanic Garden and American Museum of Natural History*

4.17 This shagbark hickory leaf is a compound leaf. *Brooklyn Botanic Garden*

How long do flowering plants live? The oldest living things are trees. The cypress tree of Figure 4.18 is fifty feet across and may be nearly 4000 years old. Some of our giant sequoias of California grow to a height of 300 feet and live 4000 years. Most kinds of trees, however, live less than a hundred years. Oaks can live up to 500 years, and the western Douglas fir and arbor vitae up to 800 years.

All trees and other plants that live for years are called **perennials** (per-en'ee-als). Some perennials, even though they live long, do not grow large. They may die down to the ground every winter and come up again in the spring, year after year. Among cultivated plants, asparagus, sugar cane, and tulips are examples of small perennials. Many plants live no more than a year. In that time they produce

CHAPTER FOUR — A THIRD OF A MILLION KINDS OF PLANTS   71

4.18 This famous cypress tree of Tule, Mexico, must be between three and four thousand years old. Can you estimate the diameter of the trunk by comparing it with the human figures at the left of the photograph? *Annette H. Richards*

their flowers and seeds. These are called **annuals**. You know many of the farm and garden crops that are annuals: buckwheat, oats, corn, spring wheat, soybeans, lettuce, string beans, and peas. Thousands of wild plants are annuals, too.

But some kinds of crop plants, such as winter wheat, cabbage, and carrots and many wild plants produce their flowers and seeds in the second year of their life and then die. These are called **biennials** (by-en′ee-als).

Two large groups of seed plants. Because of the different way in which their seeds are borne, seed plants (spermatophytes) are divided into two subphyla, **Gymnosperms** and **Angiosperms**. Both are of great importance to us.

Gymnosperms. Let us look at the gymnosperms first, those with naked seeds. If on one of your trips or on your way home from school you can find a cone of a pine, or spruce, or some other conifer, break off some of its scales. Can you see on the inside of the scale at the bottom two uncovered or "naked" seeds? The seeds may have fallen out but you will see the places where they lay.

Gymnosperms differ from angiosperms in other ways, too. Their leaves are needles like those of the pine

4.19 Pine. How do these leaves differ from those of the red cedar? *Brooklyn Botanic Garden*

4.20 Red cedar. Note the tiny scalelike leaves crowded together on the twigs. *American Museum of Natural History*

which are shown in Figure 4.19. Or the leaves are tiny and scalelike as in the red cedar shown in Figure 4.20. The leaves of almost all conifers stay on the plant for two, three, or several years before dropping off. Since the living tree is never without needles at any time of the year these plants are called evergreens. Not all evergreens are gymnosperms, however.

Gymnosperms are perennials; they grow as trees or shrubs, never herbs. The wood of conifers, in fact of most gymnosperms, is softer than the wood of most angiosperms. We call them "softwoods."

Gymnosperms grow all over the world, mostly in vast forests, from the tropics north to the treeless arctic plains. And they grow to the very edge of the tree line on mountainsides.

They are very valuable to us for their wood, which is used for lumber and for making paper. Some pines, too, have a valuable sticky sap which is made into turpentine and other products.

Angiosperms. Among the angiosperms, there is great variety. Whether you know prairies or desert, grasslands or woodland, from the tropics through the north temperate zone, most of the kinds of plants around you are angiosperms: trees with leaves instead of needles or scales, like oak, eucalyptus, poplar, and palm; the shrubs like azalea, blueberry, or manzanita; and all the many, many herbs. They all form flowers which change into structures holding seeds.

But look at the leaves of flowering plants and you will see that they fall

CHAPTER FOUR — A THIRD OF A MILLION KINDS OF PLANTS

4.21 This lady's slipper, an orchid, has the typical parallel-veined leaves of monocots. *Gehr*

4.22 An elm leaf (dicot) treated to show the netted veins. *American Museum of Natural History*

into two groups. Some are parallel veined, like the leaves of the lady's slipper in Figure 4.21 or the leaves of any kind of grass. These are **monocotyledons** (mono-cot-i-lee′dons), or **monocots**. Other leaves are net veined. In these, connected to the principal veins, you can see a large network of very small veins. See Figure 4.22. Have you ever found such a skeleton of a leaf — a leaf in which the softer green tissues have disappeared? That shows the network very clearly. The plants with the net-veined leaves are called **dicotyledons** (dye-cot-i-lee′dons) or **dicots**. But dicots and monocots differ from one another in other ways, too. They differ in the kind of flower and in the kind of seed, as well. These differences between monocots and dicots you will learn about later.

TABLE 5

SPERMATOPHYTES — SEED PLANTS

Subphylum 1
Gymnosperms
(*jim-no-sperms*)

This word means that they have naked seeds. The gymnosperms you know best are the cone bearers, or *conifers*, such as the pines and spruces.

Subphylum 2
Angiosperms
(*an-jee-o-sperms*)

These are the plants with covered seeds, seeds found in a fruit which has grown from a flower. The angiosperms are further subdivided into:
  a. Monocotyledons, or monocots
  b. Dicotyledons, or dicots.
You are familiar with so many angiosperms that we cannot begin to list them.

4.23 These are coconut palms growing in Hawaii. These trees, like the date palm, too, are among our large monocots. They are important to us for the food they supply. Dried coconut meat is used to make soap and oil. *A. Devany.*

Monocots. Banana plants, all the palm trees, sugar cane, and bamboo are among the large monocots; most of the monocots, however, are small plants. Important monocots are all the grasses, which include the cultivated grasses of lawns, the small wild grasses of meadows, and the cultivated grains like oats, wheat, barley, rice, and corn. The flowers of the grasses are small and hard to see but they grow into the cereals or grains that feed the world. More than a thousand million bushels of wheat and a thousand million bushels of oats are raised in the United States each year. And the grasses in pastures are food for grazing cattle, sheep, hogs, and goats. Add to this the food we get from bananas, dates, coconuts, pineapples, onions, and sugar cane. No matter where we live we depend largely on monocots for food.

We depend on them now for food. Can we count on them in the future? The grain crops, especially, remove large amounts of minerals from the soil. Wise farmers, gardeners and ranchers replace the minerals as they cultivate and harvest crops and graze cattle on the grasses of prairies and pastures.

Dicots. The only trees we see if we live north of tropical or semitropical areas are all dicots or conifers. These dicot trees, such as oaks, elms, birches, poplars, and so on, are all "hardwoods." Most of them shed their leaves once a year; they are **deciduous** (de-sid′you-us).

But not all dicots are trees. In the woods and fields are many dicot shrubs and herbs. In fact, there are so many

CHAPTER FOUR — A THIRD OF A MILLION KINDS OF PLANTS

4.24 The wild rose. How does it differ from all the many cultivated roses that you have seen? *Brooklyn Botanic Garden*

4.25 Each blossom in a head of clover is not unlike a pea blossom. To what family does clover belong? *Root.*

4.26 The potato plant has white or pale lavender flowers. But the farmer plants pieces of potato, not seeds. *Blakiston*

4.27 Wild carrot. Another name is Queen Anne's lace. This is a member of the parsley family. *Brooklyn Botanic Garden*

4.28 Camomile is a common composite. About how many ray flowers surround the yellow disk? *Brooklyn Botanic Garden*

different kinds of dicots, and of monocots, too, that botanists put them into groups which they call families. There are about 300 families. Here are some of the dicot families: the **rose family** (see Fig. 4.24), which includes, besides the roses, apples, peaches, pears, raspberries, blackberries, and strawberries; the **legume family** including peas, beans, clover, and alfalfa (the blossom of one legume is shown in Figure 4.25); the **potato family,** which includes the tomato and tobacco, and the poisonous nightshades, Figure 4.26; the large **mustard family** containing turnips, cabbages, cauliflowers, and others; the **parsley family** (one of the parsleys is shown in Figure 4.27); the **mint family,** including many square-stemmed and strong-smelling herbs; the **cactus family;** the extremely large group of **composites,** an example of which is shown in Figure 4.28. What looks at first glance like the flower of a composite is really a bouquet of many tiny blossoms. Surely you have pulled apart a daisy. The yellow center is a mass of tiny yellow flowers, and each white part is a flower in itself. In some composites these outer, "ray," flowers are missing. The stickers and cockleburs you find in uncared-for fields and city lots, the goldenrods and asters are all composites, as are the dandelion and the thistle. Of course, all the families have Latin names, but you can learn to know many common flowers without bothering with the Latin family names.

Dicots are useful, too. You know that conifers supply us with wood and paper and that monocots supply us with most of our food. Dicots are useful, too. Think of the apples, pears and berries, the vegetables we serve at meals (except onions; they are monocots), the coffee, tea, and chocolate we drink, the spices and flavoring substances we use in cooking. Think of the cotton and linen (from the flax plant). But more important, think of the hardwoods used for poles, and posts and ties, for building, for furniture making, and for fuel. Some of the most important problems faced by the world today are how to use to the best advantage and **conserve** our plants for future generations, and how to improve the kinds of plants on which we depend.

Plants in review. In this chapter you began with the simplest plants. You learned about algae, simple water plants that never bloom and that have no root or stem or leaf. You learned about many simple plants that were not even green and often did not grow in the soil. These were the fungi, the microscopic plants like bacteria and yeasts, the many molds, and the much larger mushrooms. Later you studied the more complex mosses and then the larger ferns. You found the ferns have leaves and stems and roots, but bear neither blossoms nor seed nor fruit. Finally you studied two large groups of plants that looked like plants. First you looked at the gymnosperms that bear naked seeds and then at the angiosperms with covered seeds. You read about monocots, the grasses, orchids, lilies, and palms and about the dicots. Many angiosperms are useful to us. There were tall trees, and tiny herbs. At first glance these seemed to differ much among themselves but practically all of them were alike in having root, stem, and leaves and blossoms which developed into seeds.

USEFUL WORDS IN BIOLOGY

algae	symbiosis	biennial
plankton	fermentation	perennial
fungi	thallophyte	spermatophyte
hyphae	habitat	gymnosperm
spore	bryophyte	angiosperm
parasite	pteridophyte	monocot
parasitism	frond	dicot
host	shrub	deciduous
saprophyte	herb	composite
lichen	annual	

TEST YOURSELF

1. Copy into your notebook only the following phrases or sentences that correctly describe algae. (a) Live both in fresh and salt water. (b) Some kinds live on land. (c) Some are single-celled, some many-celled. (d) Cell walls are of cellulose. (e) Cells have no nucleus. (f) Some kinds can live in hot springs. (g) Some kinds can live on snow. (h) May be brown, green, or red. (i) Some are colorless. (j) Have no roots, stems, or leaves. (k) Have small flowers.

2. (a) What is plankton? (b) Of what importance is it?

3. (a) Describe diatoms. (b) State several ways in which diatoms are of importance to us.

4. (a) How do fungi resemble algae? (b) How do they differ from them? (c) Give an example of a common fungus. (d) To what group of plants do algae and fungi belong?

5. Using the names of the parts of a mold plant, explain how it gets its food and how it reproduces.

6. Explain the difference between parasites and saprophytes.

7. Of what great benefit are saprophytic fungi to us? How are they harmful?

8. A lichen is a good example of symbiosis. What is meant by symbiosis?

9. Explain fermentation and show how it is helpful in (a) baking, (b) brewing.

10. (a) To what group of plants do mosses belong? (b) How do these plants differ from thallophytes?

11. Describe the most common habitats of mosses.

12. Ferns belong to the Group Pteridophytes. How do they differ in structure from Bryophytes?

13. Probably most of the plants you know are spermatophytes. What is the striking characteristic which makes botanists call a plant a spermatophyte?

14. Describe spermatophytes as to (a) size and general appearance; (b) parts of a typical plant; (c) method of reproduction; (d) variety of habitat; (e) length of life.

15. Into what two large groups are spermatophytes divided? Give a common example of each group.

16. Answer these questions about gymnosperms. (a) Do they grow as trees, shrubs, or herbs? (b) Are they annuals or perennials? (c) What kind of flowers do they have? (d) What kind of leaves? (e) What kind of wood?

17. Arrange the following under the proper heading of monocot or dicot: potato, parsley, oats, banana, sugar cane, blackberry, alfalfa, wheat, onion, tomato, cactus, corn, pea, date. On what basis did you group these plants as monocots or dicots?

18. State all the ways you can think of in which angiosperms are of importance.

DO IT YOURSELF

1. Exploring for microscopic water plants. Study plants of both fresh and salt water under the microscope. Even a magnifying glass will show up much of interest. Or try two magnifying glasses held the right distance apart. Of course, you will examine and draw the animals you see as well as the plants. A college botany such as *Textbook of Botany*, by Transeau, Sampson, and Tiffany, Harper, 1953, will be of help in identifying the plants you find. See also the fieldbooks mentioned under Adventures in Reading.

2. Study of pleurococcus. This alga sometimes grows in large green masses on the bark of trees in the shade. Scrape off some and magnify it. Do you see cells? Draw what you see.

3. Experiments with yeasts. Use wild yeasts from the air and yeast from yeast cakes. Learn all you can about their activities. Microscopes are not needed.

4. A close-up of molds. You have seen them often and probably have been annoyed at them. Now raise some molds on moist white blotting paper in covered bowls by placing a small piece of bread, cheese, lemon, or apple in the bowls. Expose the food to the air for an hour or more before you cover the bowls. Keep the food moist and at room temperature. If no mold appears on the bread, try again, but also read the label on the wrapper to find out why. Examine the foods every day; use a magnifying glass. You will be surprised at the beauty of these molds when you look at them closely and you no longer think of them as objectionable things that spoil your food. Do you see hyphae, spore cases, and spores? Transplant some of the spores into new surroundings and see how soon they grow into new plants; but, of course, you must give them food.

5. Making your own tree book. Collect and press leaves of trees, or better still, make blueprints or spatter prints of the leaves. (*Plants:* *A Guide to Plant Hobbies* by Herbert S. Zim, Harcourt, Brace, 1947, gives directions on page 83.) With each leaf include a description of the bark and the general form of the tree.

6. Useful plants. Look up and report on some industry dependent on trees or other forms of spermatophytes. You will find *Plants for Man* by Robert W. Schery, Prentice-Hall, 1952, very helpful for this.

7. A nature trail. If there are grounds near your school that you can use, start a "nature trail" by laying out a trail along which you label all the common plants and point out things of interest in both plant and animal life. In this way you will not only teach others but you will learn a great deal yourself.

8. If you live in a town and if you know your trees you may want to make a tree map of the streets. This can be very helpful to others.

ADVENTURES IN READING

1. *Plants: A Guide to Plant Hobbies* by Herbert S. Zim, Harcourt, Brace, 1947. Not only suggests hobbies and experiments with plants but also describes and helps you identify plants in the various groups. A most useful book.

2. *Plants for Man* by Robert W. Schery, referred to above, has a wealth of information of interest to you.

3. "The Land of the Sun" by Lincoln Barnett, *Life*, April 5, 1954. Most interesting!

4. *Forest Trees of the Pacific Coast* by Willard A. Eliot, Putnam's, 1948.

5. *Tree Trails and Hobbies* by Ruth C. Cater, Doubleday, 1950. Is packed with interesting information and is delightfully written.

6. *Algae, the Grass of Many Waters* by Lewis H. Tiffany, Thomas, 1938. The excellent pictures will help you identify many forms.

7. Fieldbooks published by Putnam's include the following titles: *Field Book of Common Mushrooms, Field Book of Common Ferns, Beginners' Guide to the Wild Flowers, Field Book of American Wild Flowers, Field Book of American Trees and Shrubs,* and others. Send for a list of titles.

Chapter 5

A million kinds of animals

5.1 Read on to learn about the things this diver will see. *Nate and Pat Bartlett*

Exploring the oceans. You may join exploring biologists in imagination, if you wish. Would you care to stroll through a garden in the warm seas twenty feet below the surface? Get into your bathing suit, make sure your diving gear is adjusted, and climb down the ladder that hangs over the side of the boat. Let yourself sink gently to the bottom, looking about you for the seaweeds you read about. Take care not to scratch yourself on the corals that are part of the lovely undersea gardens. Perhaps you will take your underwater camera, and surely you will take a zinc pad and a lead pencil to make a record of what you see. You will need to take notes, for you will meet many kinds of animal life from the very simplest forms to the more complex ones. Except for the fish darting by, you will see only invertebrates — animals without backbones. There is such great variety among invertebrates that **zoologists** (zo-ol'oh-jists — biologists who study animals) have agreed to put them into nine large groups, or phyla. See Figure 5.2.

80 UNIT TWO — THE MANY KINDS OF PLANTS AND ANIMALS

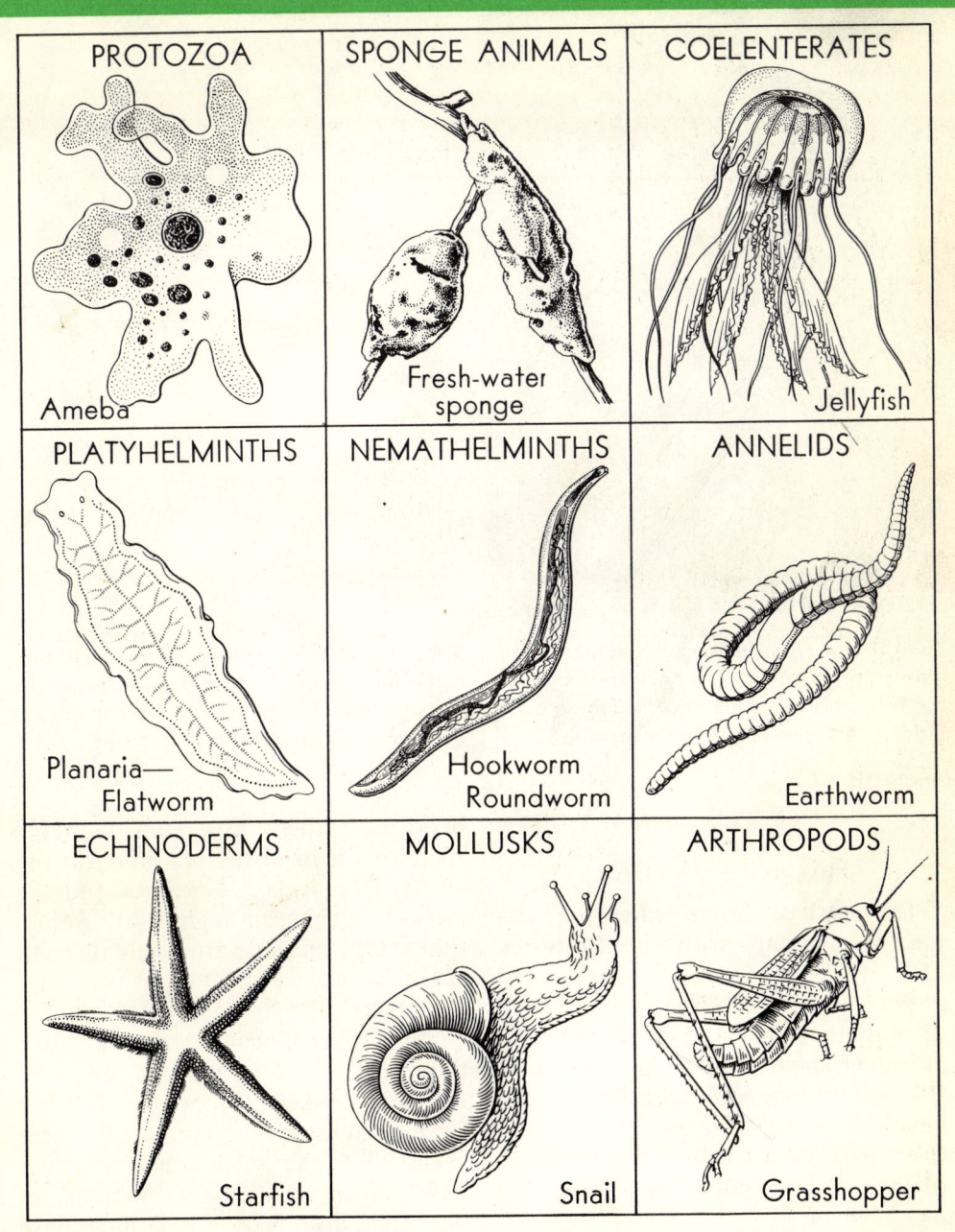

PROTOZOA	SPONGE ANIMALS	COELENTERATES
Ameba	Fresh-water sponge	Jellyfish
PLATYHELMINTHS	NEMATHELMINTHS	ANNELIDS
Planaria—Flatworm	Hookworm Roundworm	Earthworm
ECHINODERMS	MOLLUSKS	ARTHROPODS
Starfish	Snail	Grasshopper

5.2 One member of each of nine phyla of animals is shown above. The animals in all nine phyla are invertebrates—animals without backbones. Could you make a second page like this one but showing some other member of each phylum? What, for instance, could you draw as an example of a protozoan? And so on for each phylum.

CHAPTER FIVE — A MILLION KINDS OF ANIMALS

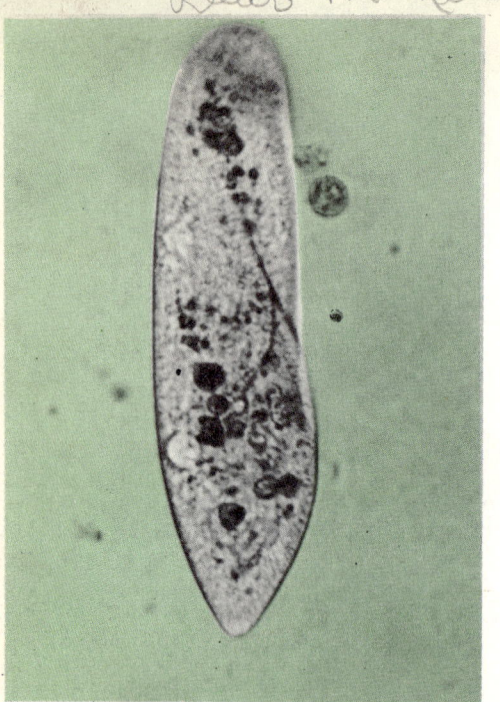

5.3 Living paramecium photographed through a microscope. The outline is blurred by the movement of the cilia. Find the groove leading to the mouth. *Hugh Spencer*

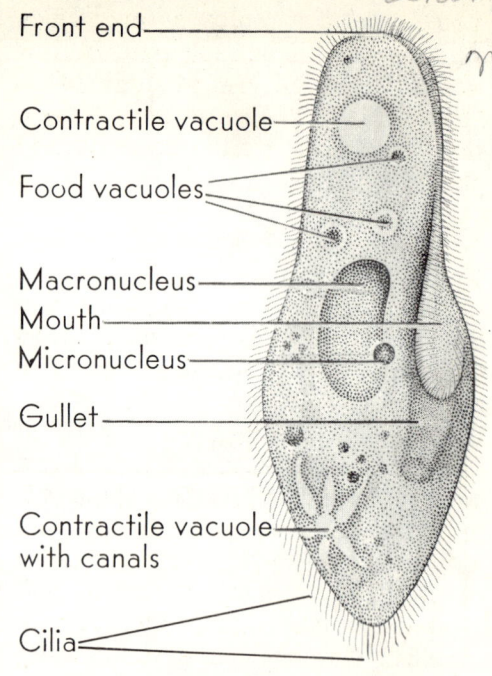

5.4 This drawing of a paramecium shows the groove through which food enters. How does the food get to this spot? What does a paramecium eat? How does it move?

ONE-CELLED ANIMALS

Phylum 1 — Protozoa

The smallest invertebrates — Protozoa. Let's start with the **Protozoa.** This is the phylum of single-celled animals, and you will need a microscope to study them. It's a big phylum, too, including some 15,000 different kinds. It's hard to believe that cells could have so many different shapes and sizes, making so many different kinds of animals! Figure 5.3 shows you one of them.

Most protozoa live in water, usually fresh water. Some live as parasites in the intestines of many kinds of animals. Other kinds are parasites in us, causing serious illness, such as malaria. Some kinds live in the ocean, billions and billions together. One kind of protozoan that lives in the sea glows in the dark; it is called **Noctiluca** (nok-ti-loo´ka) which means night light. Sometimes ships sail mile after mile through sparkling waves lighted up by these tiny protozoa.

Some other kinds of protozoa which float near the surface of the sea build complicated shells of lime around themselves. When the animals die, these shells fall to the ocean floor. So many have fallen throughout millions of years that deep beds of lime shells have formed at the bottom of the sea in many places. The chalk cliffs of southern England are limestone rock made up largely of such shells made thousands upon thousands of years ago. How the cliffs later rose out of the water to make

82 UNIT TWO — THE MANY KINDS OF PLANTS AND ANIMALS

the shores is another interesting story! You can see that protozoa, tiny as they are, play an important part in this world, which we always think of as "our world." We are in some ways a small part of the world of animals and plants.

A close-up of a paramecium. Perhaps you can keep some new pets, microscopic pets. At home or in school you can easily raise a protozoan called **paramecium** (par-a-me'see-um). You can keep it in what is called a **hay infusion.** All you need is a handful of hay and several wheat seeds boiled in a couple of glasses of water. Leave this in a glass jar for a few days; then add a little pond water; this is sure to contain some protozoa. They will grow and multiply on the food you have supplied. In about ten days the water should be swarming with protozoa. Among them will probably be some paramecia. They are large enough to be seen with the naked eye as white specks moving about in the water. Examine some on a slide under the microscope; they are cigar-shaped little animals. Figure 5.3 gives you a good idea of what you will see except that the protoplasm is colorless and transparent, not dark as in the picture. The cell is covered with tiny hairlike projections called **cilia** (sil'ee-a). These cilia are shown in Figure 5.4 but only around the edge. Actually they stick out in all directions. The cilia can beat very fast. This beating pushes the animal through the water. And it moves so fast you will have a hard time keeping up with it on a slide. When the cilia lash in the opposite direction the paramecium goes into reverse. The cilia are arranged in rows, not lengthwise or crosswise, but diagonally. For this reason, as they beat, they make the paramecium roll over and over at the same time that it is moving forward or backward. As it rolls over you can probably see a groove, as though part of its soft protoplasm had been scooped out. The groove leads to a spot, the mouth. Longer cilia line the groove; their beat is inward so that any smaller organism may be caught in a water current and swept to the mouth and into the soft body. Here, lying in a drop of water, it forms a food vacuole in the paramecium. Gradually the food is digested in these vacuoles, and in time some of it is made into new protoplasm by assimilation. Some of the food is oxidized and gives energy. Of course, oxygen keeps diffusing into the cell, and carbon dioxide diffuses out. Paramecium breathes in the simplest possible way; diffusion takes place through the surface of the whole body.

5.5 Vorticella is one of the most interesting of the protozoa. On the rim of its open mouth is a row of cilia. Vorticella is anchored by a stalk. *Hugh Spencer*

CHAPTER FIVE — A MILLION KINDS OF ANIMALS

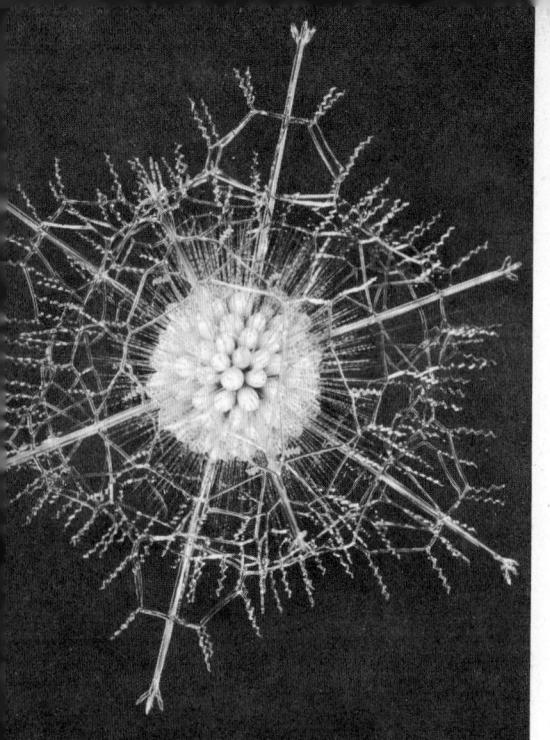

5.6 Skeleton of a Radiolarian. These and other protozoan skeletons make up much of the material on the ocean bottom. *American Museum of Natural History*

The contractile vacuole at each end fills up with excess water, now and again, and bursts, emptying the water outside the cell. Then new ones form.

The paramecium shown in Figure 5.4, like some others, has two nuclei, a large one and a small one. Both nuclei divide when the animal divides in half during reproduction.

You have already met the clumsy, slow-moving ameba. Figure 5.5 shows you a beautiful protozoan in the shape of a bell which waves gracefully on the end of its stalk. And look at the complex protozoan with a shell described in Figure 5.6. There is infinite variety. You have met only a very few of the 15,000 or more different kinds of protozoa, the first animals.

SIMPLE MANY-CELLED ANIMALS
Phylum 2 — Porifera
Phylum 3 — Coelenterates

The sponge animals. When we wanted to study simple plants, we went to a pond or creek. To study simple animals, we shall again go to the water — this time to the ocean, although some of the animals, such as the sponge animals, live in fresh water, too. Be sure to take some containers for holding salt water and some of the smaller specimens you may find. We shall explore the pools of water that are left in the rocks as the tide goes out. And we can walk along the beach where seaweeds are caught between the tides. Here we shall find a great variety of animals. Let's begin with a study of the very simple ones.

It is generally believed that the first animals to appear on the earth lived in the sea. They were very, very simple animals. Here they have lived ever since, although, throughout the ages, more and more different kinds of animals appeared; in general more complicated kinds of animals appeared. Look closely at the rocks covered with water. On some of them you may see a yellowish or grayish growth which feels soft when you touch it. This is a mass of small sponge animals growing very close together. These animals are less than one-eighth inch high, but some sponge animals grow much larger. Each animal is a small sac attached at its bottom and open at the top. The walls of the sac have tiny holes. Water is sucked in through these holes by means of cilia inside. With the water come floating particles of plants and animals. These are kept as food and the water leaves through the open top. This sponge does not look much like an animal to you, but it lives like an animal, in that it eats other living

5.7 Sea anemones of different kinds. The taller ones may be several inches high. The anemones in front show which important structures? *Nature Magazine*

things; it cannot make its own food. Some species live in salt, others in fresh water. They belong to the lowest group (or phylum) of many-celled animals. The phylum is **Porifera** (Poh-rif′e-ra), which means "animals riddled with holes." See table on page 135.

More complex animals. In a pool with the sponges you may see some larger, brightly colored animals called **sea anemones** (a-nem′o-nees) or "flowers of the sea." They are shown in Figure 5.7. When you see the beautiful pink and bluish green or orange anemones, you would not guess that these are animals. They belong to Phylum 3, **Coelenterates** (see-len′ter-ates). See table on page 135. The body is a sac, but more complicated than the sac of the sponges. It has an opening or mouth on top, leading into a large cavity. There are no holes or pores in the walls. Around the mouth are long, waving parts called **tentacles** (ten′te-kls). These have special cells that can shoot out stinging threads. When a tiny fish or some smaller animal is stung and then caught in the tentacles, it is pushed into the cavity and digested there. Life is hard for the smaller animals swimming or drifting in the shallow water where anemones grow fastened to the rocks. As the tide goes out and the water gets low the anemone pulls in its tentacles and forms a solid little mound.

Related to the anemones are animals that swim freely about in the ocean. These are the jellyfishes. They live usually in deeper water and you are not likely to see one unless it has been

CHAPTER FIVE — A MILLION KINDS OF ANIMALS

down from the middle. Around the edge of the bowl are long tentacles. If, in bathing, you ever met a school of jellyfish, you learned that the tentacles can sting. The stinging cells paralyze smaller animals on which the jellyfish preys. Jellyfish push themselves through the water by contractions of the body which squeeze water out of the "bowl," a type of jet propulsion.

If you have ever explored along the shore of southern oceans you have seen rock called coral: this is a kind of limestone made by the coral animals. There are thousands of different kinds of coral animals. They all grow in colonies and each tiny animal of the colony forms a shell of lime about itself. But in other ways the animal is much like the anemone. See Figure 5.10. When the animal

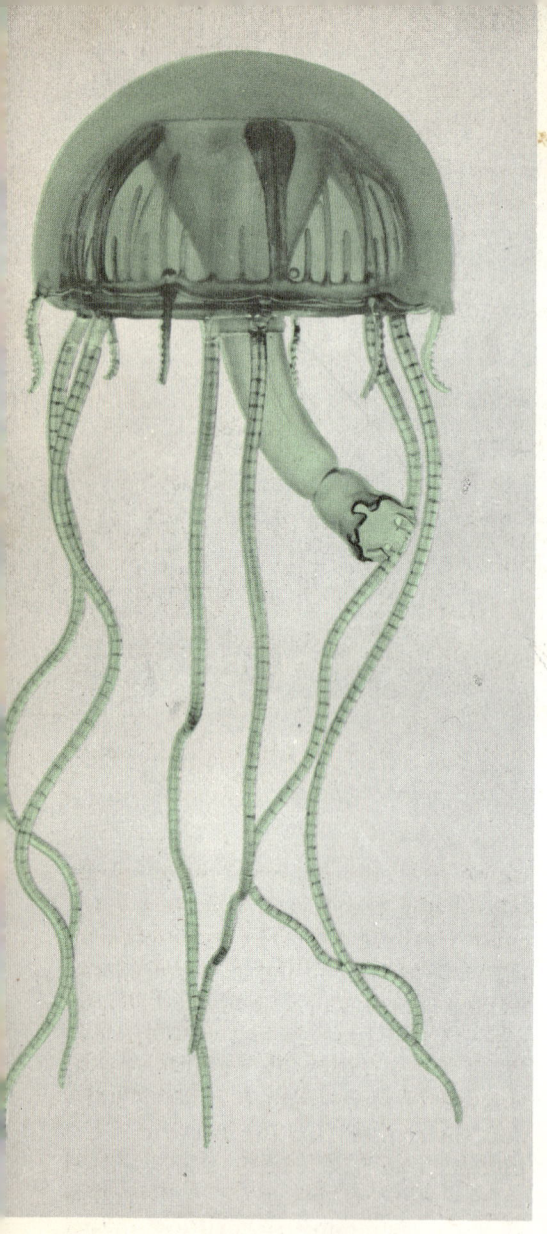

5.8 This jellyfish has a long tube through which it eats. With its tentacles it catches and paralyzes its prey. *American Museum of Natural History*

washed up on the shore; here it dries up quickly in the sun. Its body is made up of a jellylike substance; of course, it is not a fish. In shape it is like a bowl turned upside down; its mouth hangs

5.9 Hydra is a fresh-water relative of the corals. This is a photograph of a glass model. *American Museum of Natural History*

5.10 Organ-pipe coral. The tiny animal within each tube can extend brightly colored tentacles. What is the tube made of? *American Museum of Natural History*

dies and decays the shell is left behind. Each new generation of coral animals builds its shells on the shells of its parents. This has been going on for ages, so that whole islands, like the Bermudas, have been formed in tropical waters by countless billions of the tiny coral animals.

There are a few fresh-water relatives. One of these is the tiny HYDRA (Fig. 5.9) which you can study in the laboratory. See the Appendix for more details.

WORMS OF DIFFERENT KINDS

PHYLUM 4 — PLATYHELMINTHS

PHYLUM 5 — NEMATHELMINTHS

PHYLUM 6 — ANNELIDS

Animals that can glide — flatworms. Turn up some stones or shells under water near the shore or look in the cracks in the rocks. You may see a yellowish **flatworm.** It looks like a leaf about one inch long but it glides smoothly along. Figure 5.11 shows you another flatworm, PLANARIA, made famous by biologists because it has been used so much in experiments. *Planaria's* home is fresh water, and it is easy to raise in an aquarium. Perhaps you, too, could do some experiments with it. Consult your teacher about buying and raising Planaria.

Later you will read of tapeworms and liver flukes which live as parasites in man and other animals. They, too, are flatworms or members of the phylum **Platyhelminths** (pla-tee-hel'minths).

Worms like white threads — roundworms. When the tide is low, if you pick up a stone you may find a half-

CHAPTER FIVE — A MILLION KINDS OF ANIMALS

inch white thread actively coiling itself up and uncoiling. This is a common roundworm. It, too, has a front end with a definite head; it has organs used for digesting food, and various other organs. The pond water you brought in to make a hay infusion may well contain small roundworms, too. But the important roundworms are those that live as parasites in animals. There are many kinds, the most dangerous being the hookworm and trichina. You will learn more about these when you study diseases. All these roundworms, sometimes called threadworms, belong to the phylum **Nemathelminths** (nem-a-thel'minths). There are many kinds of roundworms living in salt and fresh water. Some other kinds live in damp soil.

Worms with rings. Lastly you will find worms whose body is made up of rings or **segments**. They are very common in all the oceans and they live at all depths. Many kinds are small but one common kind is a foot long, and one kind has been described that reaches a length of six feet. Some eat plant food; some are scavengers and help clean up the ocean floor; some eat other animals and still others are earth swallowers like the earthworm (Fig. 5.12).

You all know the earthworm that lives in your lawns and vegetable gardens. You have seen robins and other birds pull them out of the ground. The earthworm burrows and eats its way through the ground, swallowing soil with its decaying plant materials. The parts of soil that can't be digested are left behind in little ropes called castings. These hold together until they are dry. Earthworms breathe the air which is mixed with the soil. They don't have lungs; they breathe right through their moist, slimy skin. But when it rains hard and the soil becomes soaked with water the worms have to come up for air. As earthworms eat their way through the soil, they get it well mixed. The biologist Charles Darwin watched earthworms closely as he worked in his garden in southern England. He figured that there must be more than 50,000 earthworms in each acre of his ground. In burrowing, he said they constantly bring fresh soil to the top, passing ten tons of soil through their bodies in each acre every year. In this way they bring soil from the bottom to the top and keep it thoroughly stirred up. They slowly and silently do the work of a strong farm hand with a hoe.

5.11 Planaria, enlarged six or seven times. It has a front (anterior) end and a hind (posterior) end. Note the eyes and eating tube.

Earthworms have a food canal with complex organs that digest food. They have blood, too, and nerves. They

5.12 An earthworm burrowing in the soil. It looks shiny because its skin is moist. *Schneider and Schwartz*

5.13 This shows the rough, upper surface of a common starfish. Can you see the eyespot? The five arms are firm, but they bend.

have other organs somewhat like those of higher animals. These segmented worms belong to the sixth phylum, **Annelids** (ann'el-ids). If you want to study earthworms in detail turn to the Appendix.

The mighty ocean. In our trip to the ocean we have so far met animals so different that they are placed in six different groups or phyla. Swimming, floating, gliding, crawling, or attached to the ocean floor or rocks or wharves, these thousands of kinds of simple animals live together. We sometimes forget that oceans cover a greater surface than the land. And animals can live at all depths in bright light and in the dark; some are found more than 19,000 feet down. There are many more animals and plants in the oceans than on land. The smaller kinds of plants and animals exist in the greatest numbers; many are eaten by the larger animals and these are eaten by the still larger ones. Thus there are chains of living things in the ocean, as on land. At the beginning of every chain in the ocean we find green plants, algae. At the end is some large animal, usually a large fish, which may then be eaten by us.

ANIMALS WITH SPINY SKINS

PHYLUM 7 — ECHINODERMS

Starfishes and their relatives. You can find starfish on the rocks at the edge of the water when the tide is low. Of course, they are not fish; they have no bones. They have a horny, rough covering. True fish, like all other

5.14 The sea urchin has a beautifully marked shell beneath these spines. *American Museum of Natural History*

5.15 The zebra snail, like all snails, creeps on its one foot. Snails are mollusks. Can you name some other mollusks? *Davis*

animals with a backbone, have a front and a hind end; when cut down the middle they have a right and a left side which are similar. We say they have **bilateral symmetry.** Starfishes and their relatives have **radial symmetry,** like a wheel, or star, as Figure 5.13 shows.

Some kinds are brown, with a bright yellow eyespot, some purplish, some bright red. The eyespot is not an eye; it is a sieve that strains the water entering the body. This water then flows through water vessels running all through the body. Look at the lower side of the starfish, at the rows of tube feet on each arm or spoke of the wheel. Each tube foot has a suction cup at its end. Water in the water vessels fills the tube feet and pushes them out. By pushing out and pulling in the many tube feet in succession the starfish moves along slowly and smoothly. The tube feet help in breathing too. When the starfish folds itself over an oyster it injects a substance which paralyzes the oyster and makes it open up. (It was long thought that the starfish opened the oyster by pulling at the shell, tiring the oyster's muscle.) Then it turns its stomach inside out, pushes it into the opening between the shells, and slowly digests and then absorbs the oyster. You can see the damage starfish might do in oyster beds. People sometimes try to kill a starfish by tearing it apart. But what happens? Each part **regenerates,** or grows back, the portion it has lost. You end up with two instead of one! Earthworms regenerate too, when cut. The front end grows into a whole worm.

Figure 5.14 shows you a starfish relative with a beautifully marked shell under the spines. It is like a prickly, slowly moving pincushion, also built on the plan of a wheel, with its mouth on the bottom. The sand dollar, about the size of a silver dollar somewhat thickened in the middle, is another relative with a beautifully marked shell. These animals, and many, many other kinds belong to the phylum **Echinoderms** (eh-kine'o-derms). Echinoderms have radial symmetry and a spiny covering. They all live in salt water and eat small animals and dead and decaying particles of living things. See the table, pages 133–136.

UNIT TWO — THE MANY KINDS OF PLANTS AND ANIMALS

5.16 The clam has a double shell and a hatchet foot. The clam at the right is using the foot to plow through the sand. *Nate and Pat Bartlett*

INVERTEBRATES WITH SHELLS

PHYLUM 8 — MOLLUSKS

Soft bodies with hard shells. You all know clams and oysters and snails; or at least you know their shells if you don't know much about the animal inside. They are **mollusks.** There are 80,000 different kinds with shells and most of these live in water. Some, like the snail (Fig. 5.15), have a single shell; some, like oysters and clams (Fig. 5.16), have a hinged shell; and a few have just a tiny shell inside the body. The slug shown in Figure 5.17 and the octopus (Fig. 5.18) have no shell at all after they grow up. All mollusks have a soft body and some kind of foot. Snails and slugs creep on their strong, muscular foot. Clams use their hatchet foot like a plow for moving through the mud or sand. Oysters and mussels don't have much of a foot; they spend their lives attached to rocks or other shells. The octopus uses its foot, which is in the form of tentacles, for seizing large prey. The octopus has an unpleasant trick of shooting out a dark liquid like ink behind which it hides. Then with its sharp beak and tentacles, it tears its prey to pieces. Some of its relatives, known as squids, grow to a size of more than fifty feet.

CHAPTER FIVE — A MILLION KINDS OF ANIMALS

5.17 Although the slug is a mollusk, belonging to the same group as the snail, it has no shell. This one has just laid its eggs on a leaf. *Mary C. Dickerson*

5.18 The grown-up octopus has no shell. Its eight waving feet or tentacles have sucking cups. It can get a good hold with these.

Oysters, clams and mussels are vegetable feeders, turning algae into animal proteins. Thus they are a valuable source of food for us. Oysters have long been raised in oyster beds and harvested with great profit along the eastern coast. They need little care other than being supplied with empty shells to which they attach themselves. But they do require clean water. Oysters do not grow well in water polluted (made unclean) by sewage or garbage. Also oysters do not thrive in muddy water, which deposits soil washed from farm land on the oyster beds. Both sewage and soil affect the algae the oysters feed upon. Throughout the oceans, as on land, organisms are closely tied up with one another and are affected by changes in their environment.

Oysters are now raised in large numbers in Japan to supply cultured pearls. An easy way has been found of introducing a tiny foreign body into the oyster without injury to the oyster. This object stimulates the secretion of the characteristic shiny substance which we know as the pearl.

Some mollusks compete with us for food. The slug, a vegetable feeder with a good appetite, is a serious pest in vegetable and flower gardens. And another mollusk that has caused even more serious losses is the shipworm. This mollusk bores into timbers under water, in time destroying wooden wharves.

INVERTEBRATES WITH JOINTED LEGS

Phylum 9 — Arthropods

Let's meet some arthropods. Figure 5.19 shows you examples of five groups of **Arthropods** (are'throw-pods). You know the insects well; perhaps you feel you know them too well. You know the spiders and you have all eaten or seen lobsters, crabs, or crayfish, called **crustaceans** (cruss-tay'shyns). The **centipedes** (sen'ti-pedes), or hundred-leggers, and the **millipedes,** or thousand-leggers, are small and inconspicuous; you may never have noticed them. The arthropods, invertebrates with jointed legs, are animals without bones but with a firm outer covering. In fact, the covering is so hard that it is often spoken of as an outer skeleton.

The **insects** make up an enormous group. Wherever you may live — east, west, south, north, in crowded cities or lonely deserts — you see insects of one kind or another. They live in or on the ground, in the air, in water. More than 700,000 different kinds have been named. And this is probably only about one fifth of the number of kinds! Not a day passes that somewhere a new kind of insect isn't discovered, more likely several in a day. Many scientists, called **entomologists** (en-to-mol'o-jists), devote their lives to the study of insects. You may someday want to be an entomologist yourself; good entomologists are very much needed.

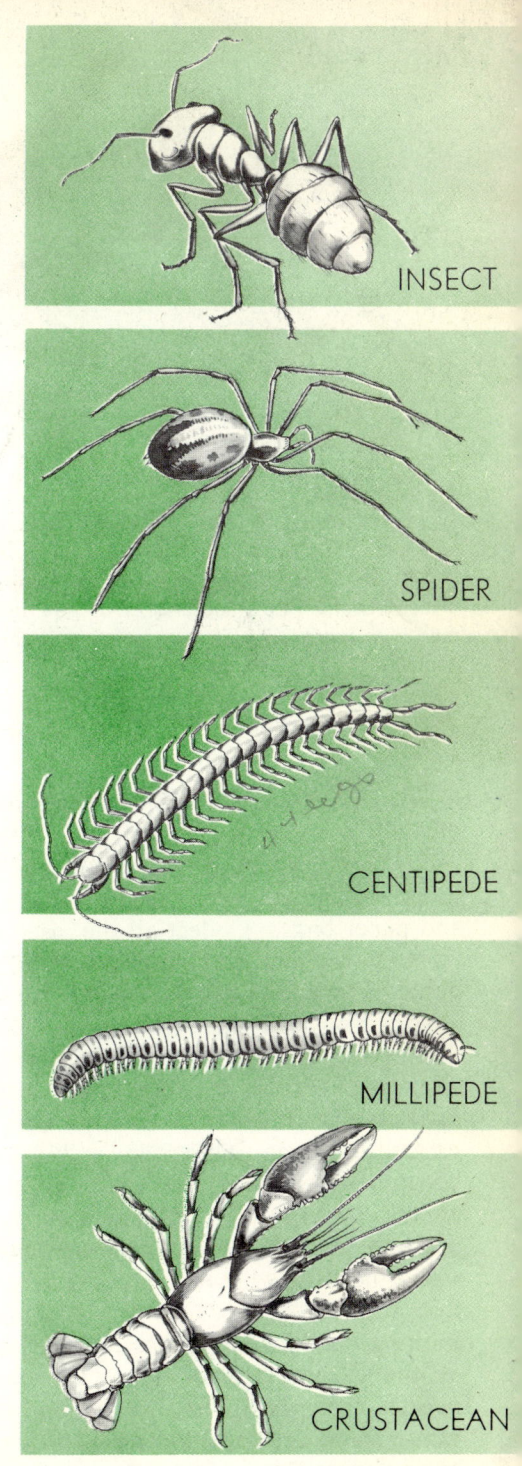

INSECT

SPIDER

CENTIPEDE

MILLIPEDE

CRUSTACEAN

5.19 Examples of the five large groups of arthropods.

CHAPTER FIVE — A MILLION KINDS OF ANIMALS

5.20 This grasshopper, from an entomologist's collection, is pinned. Do you see the pin? How many segments do you see in the abdomen? Note the three pairs of legs, the hind ones for jumping. One of the large compound eyes is shown. *Ewing Galloway*

What is an insect? Go out-of-doors if you can and study insects, even to a vacant lot if you live in a city. Take a collecting net, and small bottles, and paper bags. Collect all the insects you can find but don't forget to bring home food for those you bring back alive. You will have to know what they eat. And the plants you bring must be kept fresh. Use glass jars or aquaria. Probably you will want to collect some insects in a killing bottle, which your teacher will help you make. Perhaps you will also want to make a display of insects, showing where they live, what they eat, and other things about them. You may be able to bring back insects belonging to each of the groups described in the next pages: butterflies, flies, grasshoppers, beetles, and ants. But how will you know for certain whether they are insects?

You must see six jointed legs and three distinct body parts with a firm covering. The body parts are a head with feelers, called **antennae** (an-ten'nee); a middle region, the **thorax** with three pairs of legs and perhaps wings; and an **abdomen** (ab-doh'men). The abdomen never has legs. It has distinct rings or segments. Most insects have two pairs of wings; some have only one pair, and others have no wings at all. We call the wings, legs, and feelers **appendages** (ap-pend'a-jes). The grasshopper in Figure 5.20 shows all these parts clearly. Figure 5.20 also shows the grasshopper's sense organs: large compound eyes consisting of many six-sided lenses. Very small simple eyes are in front of the compound eyes. And there are eardrums on the thorax hidden by the wings. In some insects antennae are used for hearing as well as for smell and touch.

5.21 Three stages in the life history of the milkweed butterfly. Which stage is not shown? The pupa stage or chrysalis is shown in the insert. How does it compare with the larva? How can the adult fit into such a small chrysalis?

You have heard flies and bees buzz. That's the wings beating furiously, more than 300 times a second. They fly fast. Grasshoppers keep up with a slowly moving automobile, but "darning needles" break the speed laws of some states, at sixty miles an hour. Insects, however, can't keep up high speeds for long without stopping.

The life story of insects. The life story of insects is worth knowing. Let's trace it in the common monarch, or milkweed, butterfly shown in Figure 5.21. A butterfly goes through remarkable changes in its life. The female monarch lays large numbers of eggs on the lower side of a milkweed leaf. Each egg hatches into a striped green caterpillar. This is the second or **larva** stage. The beautiful, striped caterpillar has no distinct thorax and abdomen, but it has a head with strong jaws that can chew milkweed leaves. It crawls slowly on its stubby legs, and eats and eats. In time it draws itself together and forms a hard coat around

CHAPTER FIVE — A MILLION KINDS OF ANIMALS

5.22 Silkworm moth. Adult (top), empty cocoons (center), larva (bottom). The adults lay eggs which hatch into larvae. Each larva spins a cocoon of 2400 to 3600 feet of silk fiber. Do you know what the larvae eat and how silk thread is made from the cocoons? *American Museum of Natural History*

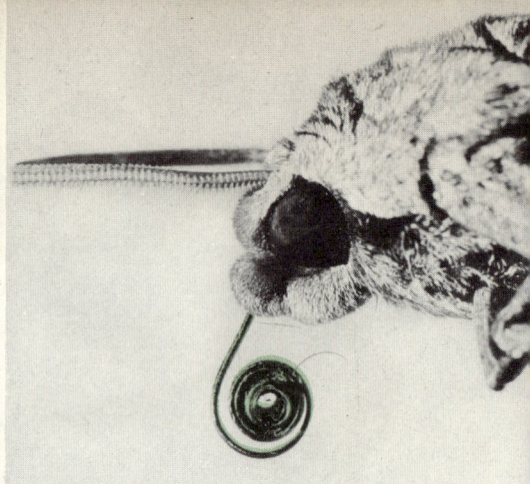

5.23 Coiled sucking tube of a moth. *General Biological Supply*

its soft body. This is the third or **pupa** stage. It is then called a **chrysalis** (kris′a-liss). Now the insect cannot eat. It seems to be resting, but many changes go on inside. In less than two weeks the chrysalis breaks open and a sad-looking, full-sized butterfly with crumpled wings crawls out. It opens out its wings slowly. When they are dry, it flies off as the **adult** butterfly.

All butterflies and moths go through four stages much like this. But in moths the caterpillar spins a house or **cocoon** (kuh-coon′) around itself. This is its pupa stage. Figure 5.22 shows a larva, empty cocoons, and the adult of the silkworm moth. All moths and butterflies have a **complete metamorphosis** (met-e-more′foe-sis). This long word means change in form. Ants, bees, wasps, flies, mosquitoes, beetles, and many other insects go through a complete metamorphosis, with four stages in their life history.

Some insects, the grasshopper, for example, have no resting stage. They have only the egg, the **nymph,** which is much like the parent, and the adult. Many nymphs live in the water until they are adults, as in the case of dragonflies, stone flies, and many others. This type of life history is called an **incomplete metamorphosis.**

Moths and butterflies. Moths and butterflies (a group of insects called LEPIDOPTERA) have large wings covered with microscopic scales. The scales

96   UNIT TWO — THE MANY KINDS OF PLANTS AND ANIMALS

5.24 The Luna moth. The Luna is a little larger than this picture and is pale green, except for the spots. Few moths are brightly colored. *Bureau of Entomology*

are often brightly colored and in gay patterns. Have you ever handled one of these insects? You will know from the "powder" left in your hand how easily the scales come off. Butterflies and moths suck **nectar** (a sugary liquid) from flowers. Their mouth parts form a tube, sometimes several inches long. Figure 5.23 shows you how it is kept coiled up like a watch spring when not in use.

The adult butterfly which sucks nectar may be of some help to us. But in the caterpillar, or larva, stage many butterflies and moths may do much harm by eating leaves and destroying crops and shade trees.

Many people are afraid of moths which fly at night; yet they admire butterflies. Their fear is unreasonable since moths are almost like butterflies, and all of them are harmless. Figure 5.24 shows you the beautiful blue-green Luna moth. Moths have a heavier and a "hairier" body than butterflies and their antennae are feathery; the butterfly's feelers are smooth and sometimes knobbed at the end. But in other respects moths and butterflies are similar.

Flies. This group includes thousands of different kinds of flies. It includes the mosquitoes and the gnats, or midges — insects that are a nuisance to us and to many other animals. Some flies also damage crops. The Hessian fly, for example, in its larva

CHAPTER FIVE — A MILLION KINDS OF ANIMALS

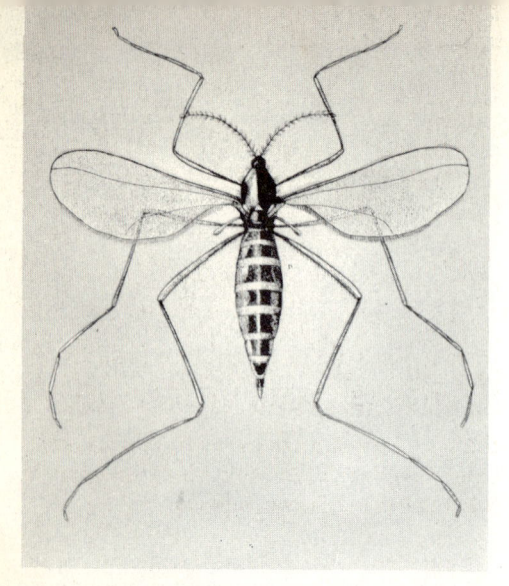

5.25 Find the stumps, or halters, that take the place of the second pair of wings in this Hessian fly. *U.S. Bureau of Entomology*

5.26 Note the shovellike tongue of the housefly. How is it used? Note also the hairy body and legs. These flies travel between filth and our food.

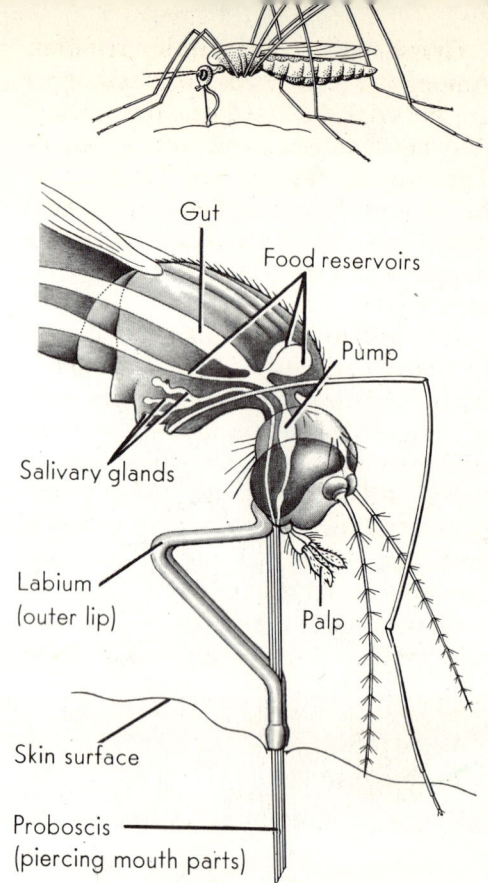

5.27 In the mosquito the piercing mouth parts form a tube through which blood is pumped up. When not in use, this pump is kept in a sheath which is really the outer lip.

stage damages wheat by sucking juices from the stem. Flies have only one pair of wings; stumps take the place of the second pair, as Figure 5.25 shows. They all have very complicated mouth parts, but those are not the same in all flies. Have you ever watched a housefly feed? It makes its food liquid first and then laps it up. Look at Figure 5.26. Then, in Figure 5.27, see how the mosquito feeds.

All flies have four stages in their life history. The housefly lays its eggs in kitchen garbage, manure or other filth. They hatch into white wormlike larvae called **maggots.** The maggot forms a case around itself and turns into the pupa or resting stage. From it comes the adult fly. All this can take place in about twelve days. As in all insects, the adult never grows. The tiny flies you see so often are probably the common fruit flies; they never become houseflies.

98 UNIT TWO — THE MANY KINDS OF PLANTS AND ANIMALS

Grasshoppers and their relatives.
Among the relatives of the grasshopper are the crickets, katydids, cockroaches, praying mantises, and many others. The praying mantis, see Figure 5.28, has powerful front legs and strong jaws which can cut off the head of a grasshopper with great ease. It would never attack you.

It is best to have living grasshoppers to study. You would look for them in fields. All these insects have two pairs of wings. While the insect is at rest, stiff forewings cover the wings used in flying. All of them have chewing mouth parts; and most of them have powerful hind legs, which they use for jumping. See the Appendix, page 563.

Grasshoppers are also called locusts, especially in Europe and Asia. The locusts of Biblical times were probably grasshoppers. Then, as now, they did great damage. In our western states,

5.28 A praying mantis finishing her egg case. How does it resemble the grasshopper? It is a relative. *Selena Johnson*

5.29 Inspecting the damage done. A few hours earlier this was a field of corn! Note that all the broad leaves and even parts of the ears have been eaten by grasshoppers. This photograph was made in Kansas in 1955. *United Press*

CHAPTER FIVE — A MILLION KINDS OF ANIMALS

5.30 The Colorado potato beetle does much damage in its larva and adult stages by eating the leaves. How do you know it is a beetle? *U.S. Department of Agriculture*

and in other parts of the world, every few years they suddenly increase into armies of such vast numbers that when they move into an area, within a few hours they completely strip fields of wheat or corn. See Figure 5.29.

Beetles. You will know a beetle by its hard wing covers, which cover the top of the abdomen. They fit so closely that you can scarcely see the seam down the middle of the back. If you have ever seen a field of potatoes, you must know the Colorado potato beetle shown in Figure 5.30. Then there is the firefly whose light goes on and off like a flashlight, about once every second. The light is on the lower side of the abdomen. The larva, called a glowworm, is found on the ground in the grass. If you can fill a tumbler half full of glowworms, you will have enough light to read by. You will hear later about the ladybird beetle which is so useful in fighting harmful insects. Or you may have heard of the carrion and burying beetles which are scavengers. They may bury animals as large as a rat. Beetles have many interesting habits; you would enjoy reading about them. In fact, you would enjoy reading about all kinds of insects. *The Fabulous Insects* is a collection of short insect stories.

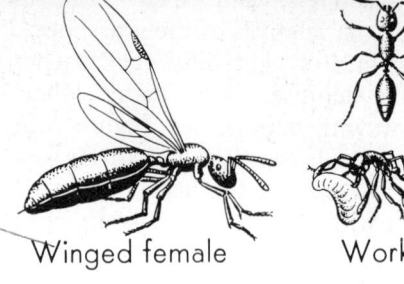

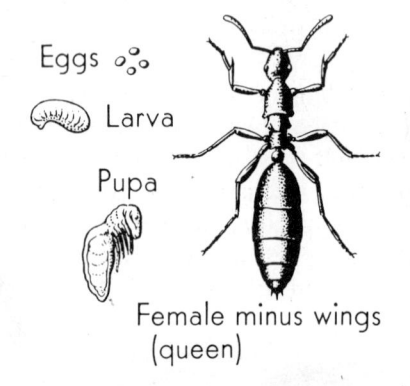

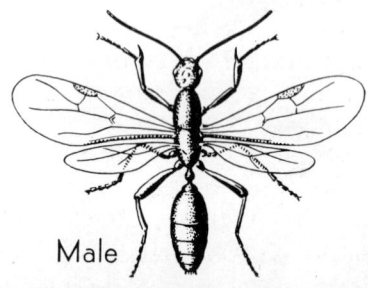

5.31 The life history of the little black ant. Start on top. How many kinds of adults are there? How does the worker differ from the others?

100   UNIT TWO — THE MANY KINDS OF PLANTS AND ANIMALS

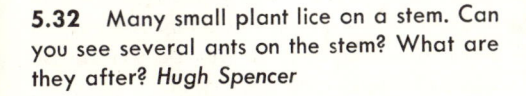

5.32 Many small plant lice on a stem. Can you see several ants on the stem? What are they after? *Hugh Spencer*

5.33 An ant tending a mealy bug. Mealy bugs are relatives of the aphids. They also make honeydew. *American Can Co.*

The social insects. We can't begin to learn about all the many kinds of insects — they are divided into some 26 large groups. But you will want to take a look at the insects that live in communities: ants, some bees, wasps, and termites. The work each insect does is of advantage to the whole community; these are, therefore, called the social insects.

Have you ever picked up a rock and seen hundreds of ants, running back and forth, some carrying large white bundles? You have disturbed an ant nest; and the bundles are the pupae which are being carried to some safe hiding place. Or at the edge of the woods you may have seen a large mound of earth with ants scurrying about. This anthill is a big "town" with thousands of inhabitants. There are tunnels underground connecting the many chambers in which the young are housed and fed. Everything is done by the many thousands of worker ants. They are small ants without wings. Look at Figure 5.31. The nest contains one big female ant which can fly when young. She is the queen. After she mates she loses her wings and settles down to lay eggs. In some nests there are several queens. There are also a few male ants with wings; they seem to do no work at all. The workers have many jobs; they gather food for the larvae and the queen; they keep moving larvae and pupae about from room to room depending, no doubt, on temperature and moisture conditions. Among some kinds of ants there are special soldiers with large biting jaws. They may even raid the nests of other ants. Among other kinds of ants the workers make gardens. They plant molds here. Then they gather plant lice (called aphids) which feed on the molds. The plant lice produce a sweet liquid (honeydew) which they give up when they are stroked. We do much the same when we raise and milk cows! See Figures 5.32 and 5.33.

CHAPTER FIVE — A MILLION KINDS OF ANIMALS

Honeybees. Would you like to rent bees? Perhaps you wouldn't but the owner of a large orchard or of a seed farm rents bees if he can afford it. It pays, for then his plants will be cross pollinated by the bees. More and better fruit and seed result. See Figure 5.35. When you study flower reproduction you will see how important bees are for cross pollination, or the carrying of pollen from flower to flower, and how this helps reproduction. In fact some beekeepers move their bees from place to place as flowers come to bloom in one section or another. Beekeeping, when done on a large scale like this, is a profitable business. The owner is paid for the use of his bees and he can sell the honey they make.

There may be 35,000 bees in a hive, and most of them are workers. The worker bees make the honey from nectar they collect from flowers. They secrete wax, make it into the honeycomb, and fill the cells with honey. They collect pollen and make it into food called beebread. This is fed to special larvae — those that develop into queens. As among ants, only the queen lays the eggs; the males (drones) do no work. See Figure 5.36. Workers live only several weeks or at most several months. But it takes an egg only three weeks to grow into an adult, so new bees are coming along all the time. In the spring or summer a large mass of bees and the old queen often leave the hive to start a new colony, as shown in Figure 5.34. The beekeeper must be ready to receive this swarm in a new hive.

Termites. Termites live in large communities, too. They are sometimes incorrectly called "white ants." Most kinds live in the tropics but some live even in our northern states. Termites burrow and build their nests in wood.

5.34 A swarm of bees that have left the old home. *U.S. Bureau of Entomology*

5.35 (Above) In gathering nectar, the bee becomes covered with pollen. This is accidentally carried to other flowers. *Dept. of Agriculture*

5.36 (Below) From left to right these are worker, drone (male), and queen (female) bees. How can you tell one from the others? *Root*

TABLE 6
INSECTS

They help us by:	They harm us by:
Pollinating flowers — bees, some flies, butterflies, moths	Destroying stored grains — weevils
Killing harmful insects — ladybug beetle, ichneumon fly	Destroying growing crops — Hessian fly, cutworm, potato beetle, etc., scale moth, corn borer
Making honey and wax — honeybees	Destroying fruit and seeds — codling moth destroys apple; cotton boll weevil
Making silk — silkworms	Destroying wood in buildings — termites, carpenter ants
Making shellac and dyes — lac insect and cochineal insect	Destroying trees — gypsy and tussock moths, engraver beetles, tent caterpillars
Aiding decay — maggots of many flies, carrion beetle	Destroying fabrics (clothing and carpets) — clothes moth, buffalo bug
	Carrying disease germs — mosquitoes, flies, fleas
	Living as parasites on animals — lice, fleas, ticks, larvae of botflies

CHAPTER FIVE — A MILLION KINDS OF ANIMALS

5.37 A beam of wood almost completely destroyed by termites. What can be done to prevent damage to wood by termites? *Science Service*

5.39 Tarantulas are large hairy spiders. How would you know that this is a spider?

5.38 The black widow spider is about one-half inch long. The lower side of the abdomen with its distinct red hourglass marking is shown in the upper right. Compare the male, shown at the lower right, with the female. This is one of the very few poisonous spiders in the United States. *U.S. Department of Agriculture*

To keep frame houses from being wrecked where there are termites around, one can soak the timbers that touch the ground in creosote. Or better still, one can use concrete for foundations and lower floors. Termites (Fig. 5.37) must have at least a portion of their nest in moist soil.

Other arthropods — the spiders. Look again at Figure 5.19 and compare an insect with a spider. They are both arthropods; both have a firm outer covering and jointed legs. But as Figure 5.38 shows, spiders have four pairs of legs and only two body parts; the head and thorax are joined together. They never have wings, nor antennae, nor compound eyes.

House spiders do not bite; and garden spiders, which very rarely bite, cause no more than a slight irritation. The black widow spider is about the only really poisonous spider in the United States. The tarantulas of the

UNIT TWO — THE MANY KINDS OF PLANTS AND ANIMALS

Red fox cubs about three months old. In five months they will be independent and may live to reach an age of twelve years. *H. H. Harrison*

The rough nest of the robin is sometimes built in a sheltered place. *A. Cruickshank*

Barn swallows build their nests of mud with a lining of grass or feathers. *A. Cruickshank*

(Right) The mourning dove builds a crude stick platform low in trees. *Shostal*

(Below) The common tern sometimes nests in a hollow on the beach. *A. Cruickshank*

One kind of caterpillar is said to eat 86,000 times its hatching weight in the first 56 days. *Muriel V. Williams*

Praying mantis is about two inches long. *Shostal*

Houseflies are close to the average size for the entire animal kingdom, from tiny one-celled species to huge whales. *Muriel V. Williams*

Tiger swallowtail on a rhododendron blossom. *H. H. Harrison*

The forms, patterns, and colors of sea animals are varied. Most of these are mollusks, but notice the starfish in the lower right. *A. Devany*

5.40 An orb web spun by a garden spider. Can you see the spider? The web entangles insects which are quickly pounced on by the spider. *Hugh Davis*

5.41 The scorpion has its sting at the tip of its abdomen, which can be waved over its head. The claws are harmless. Note how it carries its young on its back.

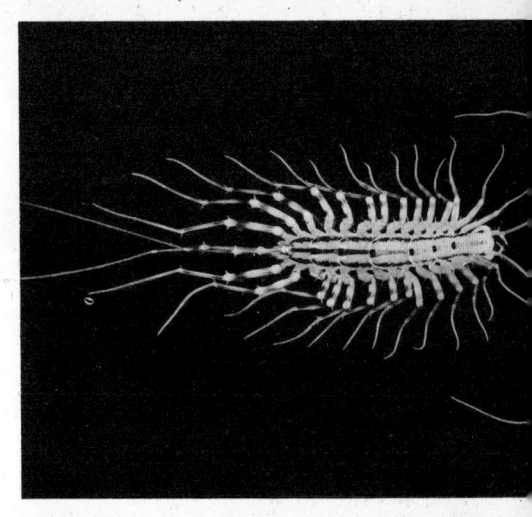

5.42 The harmless house centipede is less than an inch in length. How do you know that it is not a millipede?

Southwest give painful, though not dangerous bites. See Figure 5.39.

Most spiders can give off a special liquid from the abdomen that hardens in the air into a silk thread. The webs may be used as homes or as a means of catching prey. Each species has its own characteristic web (Fig. 5.40) and many webs are complicated structures woven according to a definite pattern. The house spider spins a tangled mass of threads in some quiet corner; this is a cobweb. The trapdoor spider digs a hole in the ground and covers it with a door opening outward on a hinge.

You must know the "daddy-longlegs," or "harvestman," with its long spindling legs; it belongs to the spider group. So do the ticks, small spiderlike forms that often carry diseases. And so does the scorpion shown in Figure 5.41. They look fierce but scorpions in our country don't do much harm.

Centipedes and millipedes. Centipedes don't really have a hundred legs; they have one pair to each ring or segment. See Figure 5.42. But they move so fast they give the impression of having many more legs. Except for the house centipede they are likely to be found under bark or in rotten logs, where they feed on smaller animals, like insects and spiders. The larger centipedes of the South and the tropics can give a painful bite. The millipedes, with their two legs to each segment, are slow moving. They live concealed in damp places and most of them are scavengers, part of the cleanup department of the earth.

CHAPTER FIVE — A MILLION KINDS OF ANIMALS

5.43 Lobster catching a crab. Both are crustaceans. How can you distinguish lobsters from crabs? *American Museum of Natural History*

Crustaceans. You know lobsters and crabs that live in the ocean. If you have explored rocky pools at the shore you have seen barnacles. Perhaps you have found crayfish in fresh-water streams. Perhaps you have eaten shrimp. All of these water forms and a few land-living animals belong to the large group of crustaceans. What is a crustacean? That is hard to answer briefly. Any animal that seems to be an arthropod and does not fit into any of the other four groups is a crustacean. Within this group are found the largest of the arthropods. Examine Figures 5.43 and 5.44.

Lobsters aren't red until they are boiled. Crabs and lobsters are much the color of the seaweeds among which they live. They have powerful pincers or claws, and legs that can be used for walking or swimming. Crabs walk sideways, instead of head first. Both crabs and lobsters have eyes on long stalks and in many other ways they are interesting animals.

5.44 Rock barnacles are crustaceans. They spend most of their lives attached to rocks or wharves or ship bottoms.

UNIT TWO — THE MANY KINDS OF PLANTS AND ANIMALS

5.45 Examples of each of the five chief classes of vertebrates.

ANIMALS WITH BACKBONES
Subphylum Vertebrates

Vertebrates. You already know much about the **Vertebrates,** the animals with a backbone. These are the fish, amphibia (frogs, toads, salamanders), reptiles (snakes, lizards, alligators), birds, and mammals. You are a mammal. Look at Figure 5.45 above. Zoologists include two other small groups with these five groups of vertebrates and make Phylum 10 of them all. They call this phylum **Chordates** (core'-dates). But outside a college laboratory we don't meet any members of these two small groups. We meet only those chordates that are vertebrates. The vertebrates are the animals that have a true backbone or **spinal column** and a boxlike skull, or **cranium.** The brain is inside the cranium. Let's start with the simplest vertebrates, the fishes.

FISHES AND THEIR RELATIVES

Vast numbers of fish. You have read that there is about three times as much sea as land, and the oceans are deep. Fish live in all of them, in tropical waters and in arctic seas. It is hard for us to imagine how vast the fish population is. Every year we kill about eleven billion herring. Two hundred billion more, perhaps, are eaten by larger fish. But the herring is one of about 12,000 different kinds of fishes. And do you know the number of people living on this earth? Fewer than three billion human beings!

You can see that fish in such vast numbers must be tremendously important to us. The value of fish as a source

5.46 Which characteristics of fishes does this trout have? Where are the gills? How many fins has the trout?

CHAPTER FIVE — A MILLION KINDS OF ANIMALS 107

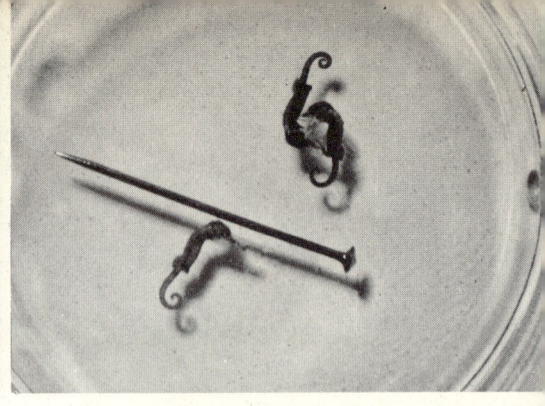

5.47 Fish swim by moving the muscular tail from side to side. Some fish have large flat tails as in the picture above left. The sea horse (babies above and adult below) has a long narrow tail which it can use in swimming or in holding fast to objects in the water. *New York Zoological Society and Wide World Photo.*

of food runs into several hundred millions of dollars every year. Fish oils supply much needed vitamins A and D. Other valuable by-products include fertilizer, glue, and fish meal.

Learning about fish. Perhaps near your home or school you can catch several kinds of fish in streams or ponds. Or if you live in a large city you can perhaps visit a large aquarium and see many different kinds. In any case you will want to read about the many interesting fish — the flatfish, like the flounder with its two eyes on the same side of its head; the "flying" fish; the large tuna fish, weighing a ton; the tiny tropical fish, the guppies, that bear their young alive.

What is a fish anyway? Fishes are backboned animals with a covering of slimy scales. They live in water and breathe the oxygen dissolved in water. For this they use special breathing organs, called gills. See Figures 5.46 and 5.47. No matter where you live you can obtain fish and see these parts: the bright red gills under the gill covers; the strong tail, used for swimming; the fins, used mostly for balancing; and the scales.

108   UNIT TWO — THE MANY KINDS OF PLANTS AND ANIMALS

5.48 Sharks have no true scales, no true bones, and they lack gill covers. Note the mouth. Can you see two shark suckers (true fish) attached to the lower side? They are not parasites. They are merely stealing a ride. Shark suckers eat scraps of food left over from the shark's meal. *New York Zoological Society*

Close relatives. Sharks and dogfish are related to fish but are not true fish. Their skeletons are not made of bone, but of cartilage. See Figure 5.48. And there are also the closely related lungfishes found in Australia, Africa, and South America. They breathe by means of gills when they are in water but use their lungs when the water dries up.

Fish migration. Some fish, like birds, migrate thousands of miles. Eels are particularly interesting. In the autumn, eels, both in our country and in Europe, are found swimming down fresh-water streams into the Atlantic Ocean. They swim to a region east of the Bermuda Islands. Here they lay their eggs in deep waters. Then the parents die. After about a year the young eels begin their long journey to homes they have never seen along a route they have never traveled. They return to the rivers from which their parents came.

Salmon live in the ocean as adults. But when **spawning** (egg-laying) time comes they swim up streams to shallow water. Here the eggs are laid. Among some kinds of salmon, the parents then die. In time the young fish swim back to the sea. When they grow up, they come back to the same stream to lay their eggs. When we build dams in these streams, "fish ladders," runways with steps, are built along the banks so that the salmon can get to the higher level by easy stages. Since salmon are a valuable source of food, strict laws have been passed for their conservation. Fish ladders are required by law, and the numbers of parent fish that may be caught on their way to the spawning grounds is restricted.

Much has been learned about fish migration by the Federal Bureau of Fisheries. Fish are tagged; a record of the kind of fish and place of tagging is made. Then when fishermen catch tagged fish they return the tags to Washington, along with information as to where and when the fish were caught.

CHAPTER FIVE — A MILLION KINDS OF ANIMALS

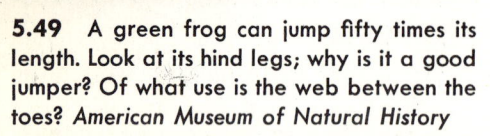

5.49 A green frog can jump fifty times its length. Look at its hind legs; why is it a good jumper? Of what use is the web between the toes? *American Museum of Natural History*

5.50 The American toad cannot jump as far as the frog. Why not? Compare its covering with that of the frog. *Schneider and Schwartz*

FROGS AND OTHER AMPHIBIA

Frogs and toads. Look for frogs along the edge of a pond or creek or just below the surface of the shallow water, with only their eyes and nose showing. A frog's skin is soft and moist, covered with slimy mucus. Have you ever tried to hold on to one? Figure 5.49 shows the shiny skin; it shows, too, why frogs are hard to catch.

Now toads are, in general, slow moving and heavy compared to frogs. See Figure 5.50. They live away from water after they are full grown; they return to the water only in the spring to lay their eggs. Their skin is soft but dry. Some people think they can get warts from handling toads; this has never been found to be true. Toads don't harm us in any way; in fact, they are of great help in our gardens; they eat many of the insects which would otherwise destroy plants. Frogs, too, are great insect eaters. They catch insects on their long slimy tongue. This is flipped out of the mouth and pulled back so fast you can scarcely see what is going on.

What are amphibia? Of course, amphibia are vertebrates; like fish they are cold-blooded. That means they have about the same temperature as their **environment** (surroundings). All amphibia breathe by means of lungs; they can stay under water for only a short time. They all have a soft, naked skin. Those with moist skins must stay where it is moist, or they will dry out and die. They remain near water when not actually in the water. Amphibia get their name from the fact that they live a "double life." All but a very few live first as **tadpoles** or "pollywogs" in water. Figure 5.51 shows some tadpoles. During most of this time they swim about, and they breathe by means of gills. Gradually the gills disappear and lungs form.

5.51 Tadpoles of the green frog feeding on water plants. In how many ways do tadpoles differ from adult frogs? How are they similar? *Hugh Spencer*

Legs develop at this time, too. Then the animal can live on land.

Some kinds of amphibia look quite different from frogs and toads; they have long slender bodies with tails. Many of these look much like lizards but their skin is soft and moist. These are salamanders. If you live in the eastern part of the United States you may have found under rotting logs or damp leaves the red-backed salamander, and the little salamander (or newt) which in one stage is bright red with dark spots. In the West you could find the brown tree salamander or the gay-colored painted salamander. Salamanders are timid, harmless creatures; their feet have no claws and their jaws are weak. They, too, live on insects. And they, like all the other amphibia, are eaten by snakes and birds. You will find a little fieldbook called *Reptiles and Amphibians* of great help to you.

REPTILES — VERTEBRATES WITH SCALY SKINS

Importance of reptiles. Reptiles are the snakes, the turtles, the lizards of warm, dry climates, and the alligators and crocodiles that live in southern inland waters. In this country the snakes, turtles, and lizards, with few exceptions, are harmless to us. In general they don't bite, and yet, for some reason, many people have an unreasonable fear of them, a dislike, a feeling that they should be killed. This is unfortunate, for most kinds of reptiles are not only harmless but are useful to us. Snakes are of great help in keeping down rats and mice around the farm. Lizards eat insects, many of which are harmful. Water snakes and some turtles eat amphibia and some fish, but many of these aren't the fish we depend on for food. (Some kinds of turtles also catch birds.)

What have these animals in common that makes them all reptiles? They have a scaly covering, but the scales are dry — quite different from the fish's scales. You must at some time have felt leather made of lizard's skin. Now look at Figures 5.52, 5.53, and 5.54. They all have lungs; when they live in water, they must come up for air. Most kinds of reptiles like sun and heat. Being cold-blooded, they take on the temperature of their surroundings.

CHAPTER FIVE — A MILLION KINDS OF ANIMALS

5.52 This harmless garter snake is one of our commonest snakes. It sometimes bites when handled roughly, but its bite is harmless unless infection is allowed to set in. By means of their swiftly moving little tongues, snakes learn of their surroundings. Unlike most other snakes, the garter snake bears its young alive. *U.S. Bureau of Biological Survey*

5.54 The snapping turtle is found in ponds or rivers. Notice the deep notches on its dull brownish shell. This is one of the very few turtles that bite. Don't handle them; they have strong jaws. *American Museum of Natural History*

5.53 This swift is a typical lizard, harmless, fast-moving, and timid. Notice the claws on its feet. Why is it called a reptile?

Peculiarities of snakes. Have you ever wondered how a snake moves without legs? The x-ray photograph in Figure 5.55 gives you part of the answer. Look at all the ribs. Each pair is connected by muscles to the scales. By movements of the ribs, the scales are hooked onto the uneven surface of the ground, one after the other. Thus the snake wriggles on its scales.

Snakes that live in colder regions are active during only a short season. As fall comes on they go into a state of hibernation (high-bur-nay'shun) — winter sleep — underground. Respiration almost stops. There are other interesting facts about snakes. Look

112   UNIT TWO — THE MANY KINDS OF PLANTS AND ANIMALS

5.55 This x-ray photograph of a snake shows the long backbone and the many ribs which help in locomotion. *General Electric X-ray Corp.*

5.56 A hognose snake losing its old skin. Why must it shed its skin so often? *American Museum of Natural History*

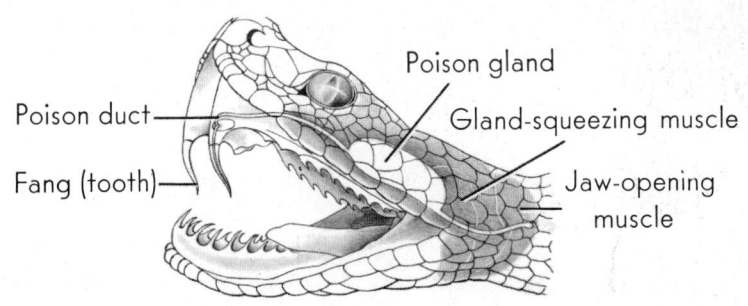

5.57 The head of a rattlesnake ready to strike. The mouth can be opened even wider than shown here; the jaws become unhinged in back and pull apart. Do you see the poison gland and the small duct which leads into the fang?

at Figure 5.56 to see how they wriggle out of a skin that has become too tight. The scaly skin does not grow. It splits open and a new and bigger one has formed underneath. Now look at Figure 5.57 to see the mouth. It is formed in such a way that it can be opened to take in an animal wider than the head of the snake. Frogs and much, much larger animals are eaten and swallowed whole.

Poisonous snakes. We have only a few kinds of poisonous snakes in the United States — rattlesnakes, coral snakes, the water moccasin, and the copperhead. All but the water moccasin are timid; they attack only when disturbed. And, except for the coral snake, you can recognize all our poisonous snakes by the triangular head. The water moccasin or "cottonmouth" lives mostly in the southeastern states in swamps, but it has spread somewhat to drier regions westward and north. Coral snakes live in the South, both east and west. Copperheads are found only in the East. But rattlesnakes live in most parts of the country. In spite of this few people are bitten by them because they usually give fair warning with their rattles before they strike. The amount of poison injected depends largely on the size of the snake.

In tropical countries snakes are a real danger. In India alone they kill about 20,000 people every year. One of the most deadly snakes in India is the cobra. There are also pythons which coil themselves around their victims and crush them to death.

CHAPTER FIVE — A MILLION KINDS OF ANIMALS

Carolina Wren

Cliff Swallow

Chickadee

Sierra Junco

Hummingbird

5.58 These birds are called perching birds. What does each bird eat? How can you recognize each? What materials can birds use for building their nests? Carolina Wren, *Hugh Davis;* Sierra Junco, *Nature Magazine;* Chickadee, Nests of the Cliff Swallow, and Hummingbird, *American Museum of Natural History*

UNIT TWO — THE MANY KINDS OF PLANTS AND ANIMALS

BIRDS — VERTEBRATES WITH FEATHERS

You can spend a lifetime studying birds. Many people do; they are called **ornithologists** (or-ni-thol′o-jists). Once you learn to recognize some birds by their call notes or songs or by their appearance, you will want to learn more. Which of the birds shown in the pictures do you know? A pair of binoculars, a notebook and a good bird guide are necessary. You will have to make an early start, for birds are early risers; it is then they are most active. First look for the size. Is it like an English sparrow in size (about 6 inches)? Or like a robin (about 10 inches)? Or like a crow (about 20 inches)? Then notice its shape. Is it slender? What is the length and shape of the tail? Does it have a crest or topknot on its head? Is the bill short and strong or long and slender? Do you see patches of color, particularly on its head, its throat, its breast, its wings? And lastly how does it act? Does it flick its tail as it perches? Does it dart out after insects? Does it feed on the ground? Does it climb up the tree or run down the trunk? Does it flit from branch to branch?

You may know best the starlings and the pigeons of our crowded cities, the robins, bluebirds, and song sparrows of our suburbs. But even if you are a city dweller, go out in the spring to become acquainted with birds. They are a very important part of our world, and they are fun to study.

How birds are important to us. A few birds, such as some hawks and other birds of prey, may occasionally kill chickens; some songbirds eat our best strawberries and cherries; and ducks and loons eat some of the fisherman's trout; but, in general, birds are useful to us. Even the birds of prey eat rabbits, field mice, other small mammals, and certain kinds of insects which destroy our crops. The smaller songbirds, too, help us keep down insect pests, and other kinds eat the seeds of weeds. The vultures and some of their relatives are scavengers; they feed on the dead and decaying flesh of animals. A world without birds would be a very different world.

5.59 The bill usually tells you something about the bird's food. For what kind of food is each best fitted?

CHAPTER FIVE — A MILLION KINDS OF ANIMALS

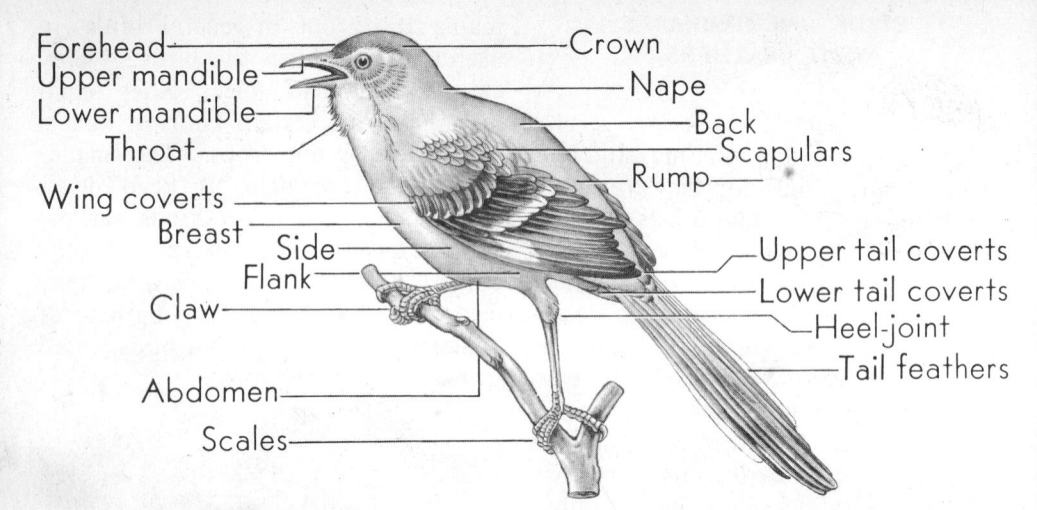

5.60 This mockingbird is labeled to show names of parts. Such names are used in describing birds. Can you use the terms to describe a robin?

The characteristics of birds. Birds have feathers on their bodies. Their legs are usually covered with scales. They have beaks, without teeth. Besides the pair of legs they have a pair of wings. They are warm-blooded, with a temperature up to 112° F. Some of their bones are hollow. Figure 5.60 is a drawing of a mockingbird, showing the names of various parts.

Bird migration. The golden plover flies over land and water in one stretch from Canada to South America without resting. It takes two days and nights! The arctic tern (a bird like a gull) nests and rears its young in the far north. Several months later it flies to the antarctic — 11,000 miles each way! How can birds travel so far without food or rest? How can some return in some cases to the very nest where they were hatched? Why do they migrate anyway? We have no definite answers to these questions yet, although various theories have been offered. But we do know that birds generally migrate in the spring and fall. Many of the songbirds spend the summer in the north and the winter in the south. Some, on the other hand, winter over in the northern states and fly to the arctic in the spring. Look closely at Figure 5.61. Could you make a bird calendar like the one below?

A BIRD CALENDAR FOR BOSTON, MASSACHUSETTS

Bird	JAN.	FEB.	MAR.	APR.	MAY	JUN.	JUL.	AUG.	SEPT.	OCT.	NOV.	DEC.
Baltimore oriole												
Bluebird												
Blue jay												
Junco												
Red-breasted nuthatch												

1. REDSTART
2. 60 SPECIES
3. SCARLET TANAGER
4. GOLDEN PLOVER
5. WESTERN TANAGER
6. PACIFIC COAST BIRDS

5.61 Spring migration routes of some common birds. The routes in this drawing are numbered: **1**, redstart; **2**, sixty species; **3**, scarlet tanager; **4**, golden plover; **5**, western tanager; **6**, Pacific Coast birds. Some of these birds follow almost the same routes south in the fall. Which of these birds travel the longest distance? Some of the 60 species which follow route 2 are the bobolink, chuck-will's-widow, the gray-cheeked thrush, the bank swallow, the blackpoll warbler, and the nighthawk. The picture above the map is of Canada geese taken during migration. You will find it interesting to find out the migration routes of the Canada goose in North America. *Ewing Galloway*

CHAPTER FIVE — A MILLION KINDS OF ANIMALS

MAMMALS — VERTEBRATES WITH HAIR OR FUR

What are mammals? You may have thought that mammals were the vertebrates that bear their young alive. But that is not accurate. Figures 5.62 and 5.63 show simple mammals, living in Australia, that lay eggs! And you know, too, that some fish and some reptiles also bear their young alive. Then how can a mammal be described? First, mammals feed their young on milk made in special mammary or milk glands. Second, they have hair or fur on their bodies. It may be only a very little hair, as in the elephant, walrus, and whale. But there is always some.

About 4000 different kinds of mammals are known: some live in the oceans (whales and porpoises); some live in the sea and on land (seals and sea lions); some spend much time in fresh-water lakes and streams (beaver, muskrat, and otter); some live largely underground (moles and shrews); a few live high up in trees (monkeys and sloths); but most live on the ground. No matter where they live, all mammals have lungs. Whales and porpoises can stay under water a long time, but once in so often they must come up to breathe.

Mammals, of course, are of great use to us. Think of the beef, veal, lamb, and pork we eat. Whales, too, are now used as food, and the blubber (fat) is made into oil. In many other parts of the world other mammals are used as food. Think, too, that their skins are made into leather and used as fur and that parts of the body make gelatin, glue, and other products. Some mammals dig among the roots of plants and keep down insect pests. In fact, as you learn more about the world of living things, you will realize more and more that the many different kinds of

5.62 The spiny anteater of Australia and on the right a model of the egg it has laid. Besides the spines it has true hairs like all mammals, and it feeds its young on milk. *American Museum of Natural History*

organisms depend one on the other. Have you ever seen a house made of cards, and seen what happens when just one card is slipped out from below? Much the same would occur if any one group of organisms should disappear.

How mammals can be grouped. If you have ever been to a zoo or a museum which has collections of mammals, you may have noticed that they are arranged in groups. Those that are most like each other are put together. They are grouped according to various characteristics but often according to the kind of teeth they have and how they feed. Let's have a quick look at some of these different groups. Pages 120 and 121 show us some examples of each of five groups.

Mammals with pouches — Marsupials. Australia has many kinds of pouched mammals, or **marsupials,** (mar-soup′i-als). Probably you know the kangaroo best. After the egg layers, they are the simplest mammals. The young are only partly developed when they are born, and they are carried in a pouch

5.63 The duckbill of Australia, another egg-layer. It, too, feeds its young on milk, and it is covered with fur. But look at its webbed feet and its bill. These are not ordinary characteristics of mammals. *American Museum of Natural History*

for a long time. The only pouched mammal found outside of Australia is the opossum shown on page 120. Note its tail. The Virginia opossum is the one that acts as though it was dead when discovered; it "plays 'possum." (This, by the way, is what the hognosed snake does, too.)

Mammals that gnaw — Rodents. No matter where you live, whether in the hot desert or near the arctic snow, you know **rodents.** There are very many kinds — rabbits, rats, mice, squirrels, prairie dogs, marmots, beavers, woodchucks, and many others. The two pairs of front teeth (**incisors**) are large and strong; they keep growing out as they wear down from constant use. Look at the squirrel and prairie dog.

Mammals with grinding teeth. Most of the animals in this large group have hooves, either a single or a double hoof. Some lack a hoof. A hoof is an enlarged and thickened toenail. All of them have grinding teeth in the back of the mouth, used for chewing grass and leaves, and small teeth in front, used for cropping. Some of them, like cows, sheep, deer, and others, chew their cud. As the animal grazes the grass is immediately swallowed. It remains in a special, large pouch of the stomach until the animal settles down to rest. It is then brought up and thoroughly chewed. Find the two cud-chewers on page 120.

Mammals that eat meat — Carnivores. Not only cats and dogs, but bears, wolves, foxes, skunks, weasels, and many others — **carnivores** — (Figure 5.64) have long eyeteeth used for tearing flesh. The claws may be strong and blunt or sharp and curved as with cats. Bears relish berries and small insects as well as smaller carnivores. The skunk and the raccoon may be frequent visitors to your garbage pail, but they eat insects, too; skunks dig in the soil for these. The fox may occasionally steal a chicken, but it is helpful to us by eating many field mice; so, too, the weasel, which eats mice and rabbits.

CHAPTER FIVE — A MILLION KINDS OF ANIMALS

Kangaroo

Opossum

Camel

Mountain sheep

Squirrel

Prairie dog

Bobcat

Sea lion

Monkey

Gorilla

5.64 The kangaroo, opossum, camel, mountain sheep, squirrel, prairie dog, bobcat, sea lion, monkey, and gorilla are all mammals. Why are they called mammals? Which animals are enough alike to be put together into subgroups?

CHAPTER FIVE — A MILLION KINDS OF ANIMALS

5.65 You have read about five important groups. But there are many other mammals that fit into other groups. There are, for instance, the flying mammals like this brown bat. Notice its long finger bones and how they help to stretch out the membrane used in flying. Bats are great insect eaters; they help to keep down insect pests. Most bats live in colonies in caves, hollow trees, or buildings. *American Museum of Natural History*

Primates. The mammals that we like to think of as the highest group (it includes ourselves) are the **Primates** (pry-may′tees). Here belong the **lemurs** (lee′-moors), small relatives of monkeys that walk on all fours and jump from tree to tree. In this group are the monkeys with long tails; the great apes, such as the chimpanzees; the gorillas; and the orangutans. Of course, zoologists classify man as a primate. In general the primates are certainly the highest group as far as brain development goes. They are also superior in the structure of their hands and feet. They all have five fingers and toes. The fingers (and sometimes the toes) are so placed that the hand (and sometimes the foot) can be used for grasping. But, of course, some other kinds of mammals are far superior to us in some ways. Some can see more acutely; some can smell more acutely; some have keener hearing; some can run faster; some can swim better; some are much stronger. However, in brain development and ability to think none of the other mammals is the equal of man.

Animals in review. Many pages back you started a study of the many animals of the earth. You saw only a very few of the almost one million different kinds. If you were to examine each living species for only one minute and if you were to keep at it day and night, it would take you almost two years to review the **Animal Kingdom.** You started with the single-celled animals. With the help of a microscope, a whole new world opened itself out to you — the world of **protozoa.** Then you saw **coelenterates,** whose beautiful colors and unusual shapes often remind one of flowers; the saclike **sponges;** the **worms** of different kinds, a few living on land, most in water, and some as parasites in other animals; the spiny **echinoderms;** the shelled **mollusks.** It took a long time to get acquainted with the **insects** and the other less familiar **arthropods.** So far you had met only **invertebrates;** except for the insects, these were largely water-living forms. And then you met the more familiar **vertebrates** — **fishes, amphibia, reptiles, birds** and **mammals.**

UNIT TWO — THE MANY KINDS OF PLANTS AND ANIMALS

USEFUL WORDS IN BIOLOGY

zoology	regeneration	termite
paramecium	mollusk	chordate
cilia	crustacean	vertebrate
protozoa	arthropod	cranium
coelenterates	centipede	migration
porifera	millipede	spawning
tentacle	entomology	amphibia
hydra	antenna	environment
planaria	thorax	tadpole
platyhelminths	abdomen	reptile
nemathelminths	appendage	ornithology
annelids	chrysalis	marsupial
echinoderms	larva	carnivore
symmetry	pupa	primate
bilateral	metamorphosis	mammal
radial	nectar	

TEST YOURSELF

1. Which of the following statements are true of protozoa? Copy those, and only those, into your notebook. (a) More than 10,000 different kinds of protozoa are known. (b) One large animal phylum consists of protozoa alone. (c) All protozoa are single-celled. (d) Most kinds live in fresh water. (e) Some kinds are parasites. (f) When protozoa die their protoplasm hardens and forms rock. (g) They are too small to have a nucleus. (h) Some kinds have shells which eventually form rock. (i) Paramecium is an example of a protozoan. (j) Paramecium is large enough to be seen with the naked eye.

2. Explain how paramecium carries on each of its life functions.

3. (a) Where do the animals of the Phylum Porifera live? (b) What do the porifera look like? (c) How do the porifera eat?

4. Name three kinds of animals that belong to the coelenterates, and explain how these animals live and feed.

5. (a) Name one kind of platyhelminth, or flatworm, that you can raise in your aquarium. (b) Name two kinds that live as parasites.

6. How will you recognize a roundworm, or threadworm, and where may you find them?

7. Which two roundworms cause serious diseases in man?

8. Explain how earthworms (segmented worms) are of importance to us.

9. Unlike the animals you have studied up to this point, earthworms have a number of organs similar to yours. Which organs like yours do they possess?

10. (a) What does the starfish (an echinoderm) look and feel like? (b) How does it move and eat?

11. About mollusks: (a) What are their characteristics? (b) Name the mollusks you have seen or read about. (c) Explain how mollusks are harmful and beneficial.

12. (a) Name five groups of arthropods. (b) To which group does each of the following belong: honeybee, crab, ant, crayfish?

13. What are the distinguishing characteristics of insects?

14. (a) Describe the life history of an insect with complete metamorphosis, naming the insect. (b) Do the same for an insect with incomplete metamorphosis.

15. In a table give the characteristics of moths and butterflies, grasshoppers and their relatives, beetles, bees, wasps, and ants.

16. Many insects are helpful to us; many are harmful. Tell the ways in which they may be helpful and harmful, giving an example in each case.

17. You can easily distinguish an insect from a spider. By what characteristics?

18. (a) How do centipedes and millipedes differ in appearance? (b) What does each feed on?

19. The vertebrates are a subphylum of the Phylum Chordates. What are the five large groups into which the vertebrates are divided?

20. Fish are interesting for their variety, their large numbers, their structure, their importance to us, and their migration. Tell what you know on each of these subjects.

21. Name some of the interesting close relatives of fish.

22. What characteristics must an animal have to be classified among the amphibia?

23. Describe the life history of an amphibian.
24. How do salamanders resemble and differ from lizards?
25. (a) What do amphibia eat? (b) What animals eat them?
26. (a) What are the characteristics of reptiles? (b) Into what four groups are they divided?
27. Tell what you know about (a) the structure and locomotion of snakes; (b) their feeding habits; (c) their hibernation; (d) their danger to us.
28. How do you distinguish birds from other vertebrates?
29. If you were an ornithologist, which characteristics would you look for in trying to identify a bird?
30. Tell several startling facts about bird migration.
31. Which two characteristics distinguish mammals from other vertebrates?
32. State all the ways you can think of in which we make use of mammals.
33. Starting with the most primitive mammals, name five large and easily recognized groups.

DO IT YOURSELF

1. **Field studies.** You will never know much about animals unless you get out-of-doors in all seasons and at all hours, with your eyes and ears open and your mouth closed. Go alone or in small groups. Observing is a skill; it will take you time to learn it. Observe closely as many kinds of animals as you can discover. Keep records. Observe how they act; note their habitats; try to discover what they eat and what enemies they have. Note the tracks they make. Do they live singly, in pairs, or in small or large groups?

2. **A home or school museum or zoo.** A corner in your room at home or in school can be made into a worthwhile museum, and the museum may well include living specimens, too. Look up *How to Make a Home Nature Museum* by Vinson Brown, Little, Brown, 1954. You will find an excellent bibliography in this book, too.

3. **Finding invertebrates of various phyla.** Search in small, shaded pools (especially salt-water pools) for small sponges growing on sticks or stones. Hydra can often be obtained on plants in fresh-water ponds; or get some from a biological supply house. When put into an aquarium they will probably attach themselves to the glass sides, where you can easily study them. Planaria, too, can often be found in fresh-water ponds, or they, too, can be bought. In vinegar that has been standing for some time you sometimes find vinegar eels, examples of threadworms. All of you can find earthworms if you dig for them, or on the soil surface after a rain. Unless you live near the shore you will not be able to find an echinoderm. But mollusks are easy to find: snails in the woods, slugs near gardens and fields, snails and "shellfish" in salt water, fresh-water clams in ponds. If you can't find crayfish in streams or crabs at the shore, you can raise the tiny daphnia or the brine shrimp. (You will find directions for raising the last two in *The American Biology Teacher*, December, 1954, in an article, "Antidote for Formalin.") The General Biological Supply House, 761 East 69 Place, Chicago, Ill. can also supply you with instructions. Insects are easy to obtain, and so are spiders.

4. **Keeping microscopic pets.** Boil a small handful of hay and two or three wheat seeds in a pint of water. After several days add a little pond water. Allow this hay infusion to stand at room temperature for about ten days. Then, under the microscope, examine water taken from different levels to become acquainted with your different kinds of pets. You will probably have some paramecia, some very much smaller protozoa, perhaps some rotifers, and other forms. Try to identify the protozoa with the help of a college textbook such as *Protozoology* by Richard R. Kudo, Thomas, 1946, or *How to Know the Protozoa* by T. L. Jahn, Brown, 1950, which has a pictured key.

5. **Studying paramecium.** If you have a good culture of paramecia, put two or three drops of water taken from near the surface on a slide with some shreds of lens paper. (This holds the paramecia in one spot so you can observe them better.) Don't allow the slide to dry up. Examine with the low power of the microscope. Observe their locomotion. As they roll

over notice the depression on one side. Do they always roll the same way, clockwise or counterclockwise? Look for the contractile vacuole at each end, forming, bursting, and forming anew. Look for a paramecium which is dividing. Does it divide lengthwise or crosswise? Place some grains of powdered carmine on the slide. Look for red "food vacuoles" after a little while; the carmine is taken in but can never be used as food. Although you can't see cilia you do see that the surface of the paramecium is blurred, due to the lashing of the cilia. To see the nuclei you need a stained specimen.

(A good solution for getting paramecia to multiply rapidly is this: Add a pinch of very hard-cooked egg yolk and a pinch of powdered Brewers' yeast to a small jar of the following solution, which may be made in large amounts and kept: 12 grams sodium chloride; 0.3 gram potassium chloride; .4 gram calcium chloride; .2 gram sodium bicarbonate in a liter, or 1000 cc., of distilled water. But use only 1 cc. of this solution to 100 cc. of distilled water.)

6. Looking for parasitic roundworms in plants. Read "Plant Parasitic Nematodes" by Robert C. Goss, *The American Biology Teacher*, December, 1954, and then try to find some of these worms in the roots of plants in your garden.

7. How grasshoppers live. Provide a large terrarium with plenty of growing plants. Have plenty of sod and keep the plants moist. Learn how grasshoppers use their legs for jumping and climbing. Watch them eat; it's fascinating.

8. Earthworm experiments. Put some earthworms into a large terrarium containing plenty of sod. Cut an earthworm through the middle and see whether either part regenerates its lost half. You might also watch their reaction to mechanical objects, to light, and to sound. Watch the worm eat and crawl.

9. A mural of invertebrates. On a large roll of wrapping paper show one or more representatives of each of the invertebrate phyla.

10. Study of a living fish. Study a goldfish in an aquarium. How does it use its fins, its tail? Watch its gill covers and see the bright red gills beneath them. How often does it move its gill covers? Is there any relation between the opening of its mouth and the moving of the gill covers? Do the two gill covers move together? How are the scales arranged? Is there any part of the body not covered with scales? Feed the fish and watch it eat. Does it seem to hear a loud noise or notice a very bright light? Describe your experiments.

11. Learning about different kinds of fish. Even in a large city you can learn about fish by visiting a fish market, preferably on a Thursday or Friday. Study the many mollusks and arthropods, too.

12. Amphibia and reptiles. Go out-of-doors to study amphibia and reptiles. Take full notes on their habitats and their habits. This is a long-time project. Use one of the many fieldbooks for identification.

13. Bird study. Contact the National Audubon Society, 1120 Fifth Ave., New York City, or your state Audubon Society to learn how they can help you in the study of birds, and what help, if any, you can give them. Set yourself a goal to learn to recognize ten more birds by sight and by call. Recordings of bird songs can be obtained from Cornell University Records, 124 Roberts Place, Ithaca, New York.

14. Breeding mammals and pigeons. This is a good project for city dwellers. Look through the publications of the Department of Agriculture to read up about breeding pigeons. The biological supply houses will give you information on raising white mice, rats, hamsters. Later in your work you will want to use rats or hamsters for nutrition experiments and other experiments.

ADVENTURES IN READING

Besides the books referred to above, you will certainly want to consult and read parts of the following.

1. *The Fabulous Insects* edited by Charles Neider, Harper, 1954 (you won't lay it down); *Near Horizons* by Edwin W. Teale, Dodd, Mead, 1942 (a chapter called "Insect Mystery Stories"); *Curious Creatures* by Erna Pinner, Jonathan Cape, London, 1951 (invertebrates

CHAPTER FIVE — A MILLION KINDS OF ANIMALS

and vertebrates, all interesting); *Burglar in the Treetops* by George Heinold, Holt, 1952 (enables you to become acquainted with many of our common wild animals); *Our Desert Neighbors* by Edmund C. Jaeger, Stanford University, 1950 (scientific and interesting sketches of desert animals); *Animal Tales* by Ivan Sanderson, Knopf, 1946 (takes you from the forests of Guinea to the Arctic, and from the Tibetan Alps to the depths of the ocean); *The World Beneath the Sea* by Otis Barton, Crowell, 1953 (full of adventures and anecdotes about animals—land animals, too); *Between the Tides* by Philip Street, Philosophical Library, 1953 (for those interested in seashore life).

2. *The Life of the Spider* by John Crompton, Houghton Mifflin, 1951. Full of interesting information.

3. *The Book of Naturalists* by William Beebe, Knopf, 1944. Much of interest in this book but particularly "The Odyssey of the Eel" by Rachel L. Carson.

4. *The Ways of Fishes* by Leonard P. Schultz, Van Nostrand, 1948.

5. "The World We Live In" by Lincoln Barnett, a series of beautifully illustrated articles in *Life*, December 8, 1952; February 9, April 13, June 8, September 7, October 19, November 30, 1953; April 5, June 7, September 20, November 8, December 20, 1954.

6. *Parade of the Animal Kingdom* by R. W. and V. Z. Hegner, Macmillan, 1947. A reference book which is very complete.

7. *Big Fleas Have Little Fleas* by R. W. Hegner. Unfortunately out of print. If you can find a copy you will enjoy the cartoons and the very entertaining text on protozoa.

8. *Animals without Backbones* by Ralph Buchsbaum, University of Chicago, 1948.

9. "Collecting Insects" in *Life*, June 16, 1952. Very helpful.

10. *Field Guide Series* edited by Roger Tory Peterson, sponsored by National Wildlife Federation, Washington 12, D.C. includes "Birds," "Western Birds," "Butterflies," "Mammals," "Shells of Atlantic and Pacific Coasts."

11. *Field Books* published by Putnam's, including *Beginner's Guide to Fresh Water Life*, 1950, *Beginner's Guide to Seashore Life*, 1949, by Leon A. Hausman, and other fieldbooks on insects and on various other kinds of animals. *Field Book of Insects* contains valuable instructions for collecting.

12. *Turtox Service Leaflet No. 1*, General Biological Supply Co., Chicago 37, Illinois. Good instructions for collecting insects.

13. *A Guide to the Study of Fresh-Water Biology*, 4th Ed., by James and Paul R. Needham, Comstock, 1938.

14. *Handbook of Frogs and Toads* by Albert H. and Anna A. Wright, Comstock, 1942; *Handbook of Lizards* by Hobart M. Smith, Comstock, 1946; *Handbook of Salamanders* by S. C. Bishop, Comstock, 1943; *Handbook of Turtles* by Archie Carr, Comstock, 1952. All these are authoritative works.

Chapter 6

Classifying plants and animals

Sorting is necessary. You have just read about a very few of the many kinds of plants and animals on our earth. As you read you noticed that it was helpful to sort them, first into Plant and Animal Kingdoms, and then into subdivisions, and perhaps into further subdivisions. With so many thousands of forms it is hopeless to keep track of them without sorting. Can you imagine the job people had keeping track of living things before anyone had thought up a good way of sorting, or **classifying,** them? Aristotle, the great Greek philosopher and scientist classified animals more than 2300 years ago, about 350 B.C. He made an excellent beginning. St. Augustine later divided all plants and animals into three groups; those that are useful to us, those that are harmful to us, and those that are of no importance to us. You can imagine how many mistakes were made! Other people worked on the problem throughout the centuries. Finally, a little more than 200 years ago, a Swedish biologist, **Carolus Linnaeus** (Lin-nee'us) (1707–1778) thought up a simple, practical scheme. We use his scheme today, with many improvements.

Sorting coins or stamps. If you understand how stamp or coin collections are arranged you will have no trouble in understanding the classification of living things. Look at Figure 6.1. You separate the stamps or coins according to a *characteristic* that is easy to recognize. For example, you divide your coins into three main groups according to country; you make a pile of English, and French, and United States coins. Now what do you do

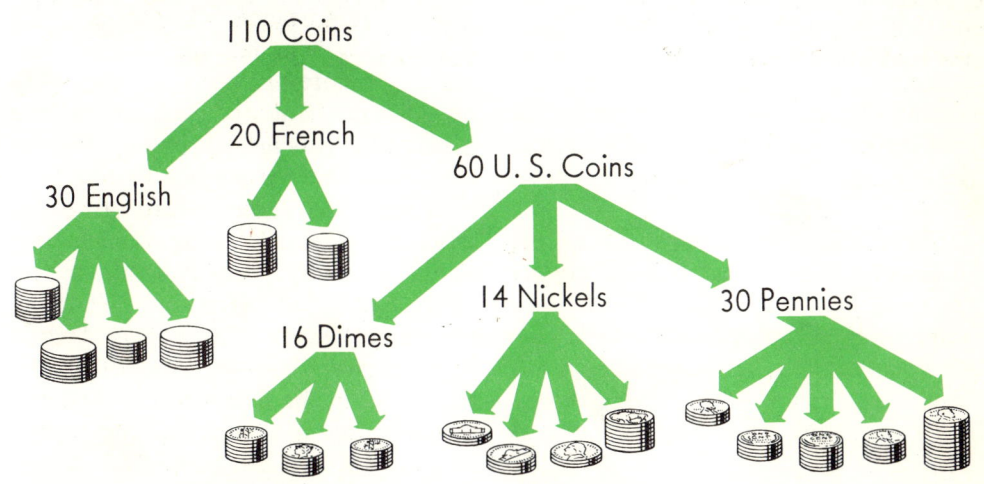

6.1 Let's see how U.S. coins are subdivided. First the large pile is divided according to value into dimes, nickels, and pennies. Then these are subdivided according to the year in which they were coined. What does this do to the size of each pile? Does it increase or decrease the number of characteristics they have in common?

CHAPTER SIX — CLASSIFYING PLANTS AND ANIMALS 127

with your large pile of United States coins? You divide them into groups, of course. This time you subdivide according to a different characteristic, their value. So you get three smaller piles, one of dimes, one of nickels, and one of pennies. When you look at the coins closely, you discover that each pile can be subdivided into groups again according to the year in which the coins were made at the mint. According to this characteristic the pennies fall into five groups.

There are important facts to be learned from this diagram. First, when you begin to classify, you make a few large groups; that is, each group you make has a large number of specimens (coins). As you use further characteristics to make subdivisions each group is made into several groups. In other words, you get more groups but each group has fewer specimens.

A second important fact is this: When you first divide into groups and the group has many specimens in it, these specimens have few characteristics in common. The pile of United States coins is large — 60 coins. They have a few characteristics in common, among them the characteristic of having been made in the United States. But the smaller the subdivision (the fewer the specimens), the more characteristics the specimens have in common.

Classifying living things. It's easy to classify coins. First of all there are relatively few kinds; and secondly, one good look at them usually tells you all you need to know for classifying them. This is not true of living things. But the scheme we use is the same as with coins.

We start with two kingdoms, the Plant and Animal Kingdoms. We divide the plants and the animals according to certain characteristics, into a few main groups; we call these main groups **phyla**. Then we divide each phylum, according to a different characteristic, into subdivisions called **classes**; the classes are divided into **orders**, the orders are divided further into **families**; the families into **genera** (jen′e-ra); the genera into one or several different kinds of living things, called **species** (spee′shees). For example, the vertebrates (really a subphylum, instead of a phylum) are divided into 5 classes, one of which is the mammals. The class mammals is divided into many orders; one of these is the CARNIVORA. The order Carnivora is divided into families; these in turn are divided into different genera. One of these is the cat **genus** (jee′nus, singular of genera), another one is the dog genus. The cat genus is composed of several species; among them are the house-cat species, the leopard species, and the puma species as shown in Figure 6.2.

Linnaeus named animals and plants. Linnaeus did something else of the greatest importance. He thought up a simple way of naming animals and plants. Before Linnaeus' day there was no scientific name for each animal and plant; scientists just wrote long descriptions, anywhere from one to five lines long, and used these instead of names. Other people used common names just as we do today. But common names often lead to confusion. For example, the name "gopher" in western United States is given to several kinds of ground squirrels; in the Southwest a gopher is a snake; and in the far South a gopher is a tortoise. When people talk about gophers, therefore, we may not know what animal they are talking about. What is needed is a name that is short and that at the same time tells us some-

6.2 The Persian cat, the leopard, and the puma are placed in the same genus because of their similarity. However, they differ from each other. For this reason each is placed in a different species. *National Zoological Park*

6.3 The coyote (on the left) and the dog are different and belong to different species. But they are so much alike that they are put into one genus, Canis. *N.Y. Zoological Society and United States Bureau of Animal Industry*

thing about the animal or plant. How could such a name be found? Linnaeus had the answer. And in making up such a short name he used Latin instead of his own Swedish language, which so few people know. Let us see how his system works.

Take another look at Figure 6.2. Cats, leopards, and pumas are plainly much alike. And they all look much like lions and tigers. Therefore, they can all be put together into a grouping called a genus. But they are different from each other, too. Each different kind of animal within a genus was called a species by Linnaeus. Thus there would be a cat species, a leopard species and a lion species within the one genus. This particular genus he named *Felis* (a Latin word meaning cat).

Then each kind of animal was given as its first name the genus name and as its second name a species name. The cat is *Felis domestica;* the lion is *Felis leo,* the cougar is *Felis cougar.* Notice that the genus name is written with a capital letter.

Now look at Figure 6.3. Coyotes and dogs are put together into a second genus. Linnaeus called this genus *Canis.* The scientific name for the dog then became *Canis familiaris.* Can you see what a clever scheme this is? If you read about an animal called *Canis dingo,* you would not have to look at Figure 6.4 to know in a general way how this animal looks.

CHAPTER SIX — CLASSIFYING PLANTS AND ANIMALS   **129**

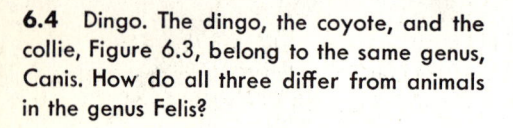

6.4 Dingo. The dingo, the coyote, and the collie, Figure 6.3, belong to the same genus, Canis. How do all three differ from animals in the genus Felis?

6.5 Red fox. The red fox belongs to the genus *Vulpes*. Looking at it, *you* might put it into the genus Canis. Scientists see important differences. *Hugh Davis*

Linnaeus named all the kinds of animals he knew in this way. As time went on, whenever new living things were discovered, they could usually be fitted in with those they resembled most closely; then they were named.

The classification and naming of plants. You read that plants are classified and named by the same system as animals. All maples, for example, belong to the genus *Acer* (ay'sir). One species, from which we get maple sugar, is *Acer saccarum*. The red maple is *Acer rubrum*. The big-leaved maple of the West is *Acer macrophyllum*. Oaks belong to the genus *Quercus* (kwir'cuss). *Quercus virginiana* is the live oak of the southeastern states. *Quercus alba* is the white oak of the northeastern and central states. *Quercus chrysolepis* is the western canyon oak.

Sometimes there are slight but regular differences between members of a species, so that we further subdivide species into **varieties**. There are two varieties of red maple. Each is given a different third name added to *Acer rubrum*. Animal species may be divided into varieties, too, and given a third name.

From species up to phylum — A summary. We saw how similar species are put into one genus. In the same way similar genera are put into one family. For example, look at Figure 6.5. The red fox belongs to the genus *Vulpes*. This genus looks much like the genus *Canis*, doesn't it? These two genera are thus put into one family (Canidae). Going one step further you notice that all the members of the cat tribe (family Felidae) look something like the dog tribe; their teeth, for instance, are much alike. Certainly they look much more like the dog tribe than they look like cows or sheep. Therefore the family which includes dogs and the family which includes the cats are put into one order, the Carnivora. Now the mountain sheep shown in Figure 6.6 belongs in an order (Ungulata) with animals more or less like itself. The animals in this order are clearly not

6.6 Bighorn mountain sheep. Do they belong to the order Carnivora? Why do they fit into the class Mammalia? *American Museum of Natural History*

Carnivora. They resemble the Carnivora in that they have hair or fur and in that they feed their young on milk. So both orders are put into one class, Mammalia (mammals). Study the chart below and then look at Figure 6.7.

From species up to kingdom.

Similar **species** go into a larger grouping, the **genus**

Similar **genera** go into a larger grouping, the **family**

Similar **families** go into a larger grouping, the **order**

Similar **orders** go into a larger grouping, the **class**

Similar **classes** go into a larger grouping, the **phylum**

Similar **phyla** go into a larger grouping, the **kingdom**

CHAPTER SIX — CLASSIFYING PLANTS AND ANIMALS

ANIMAL KINGDOM

There are many other phyla

Phylum CHORDATA
Subphylum VERTEBRATA

The other classes include birds, reptiles, amphibia, and fishes

Class MAMMALIA

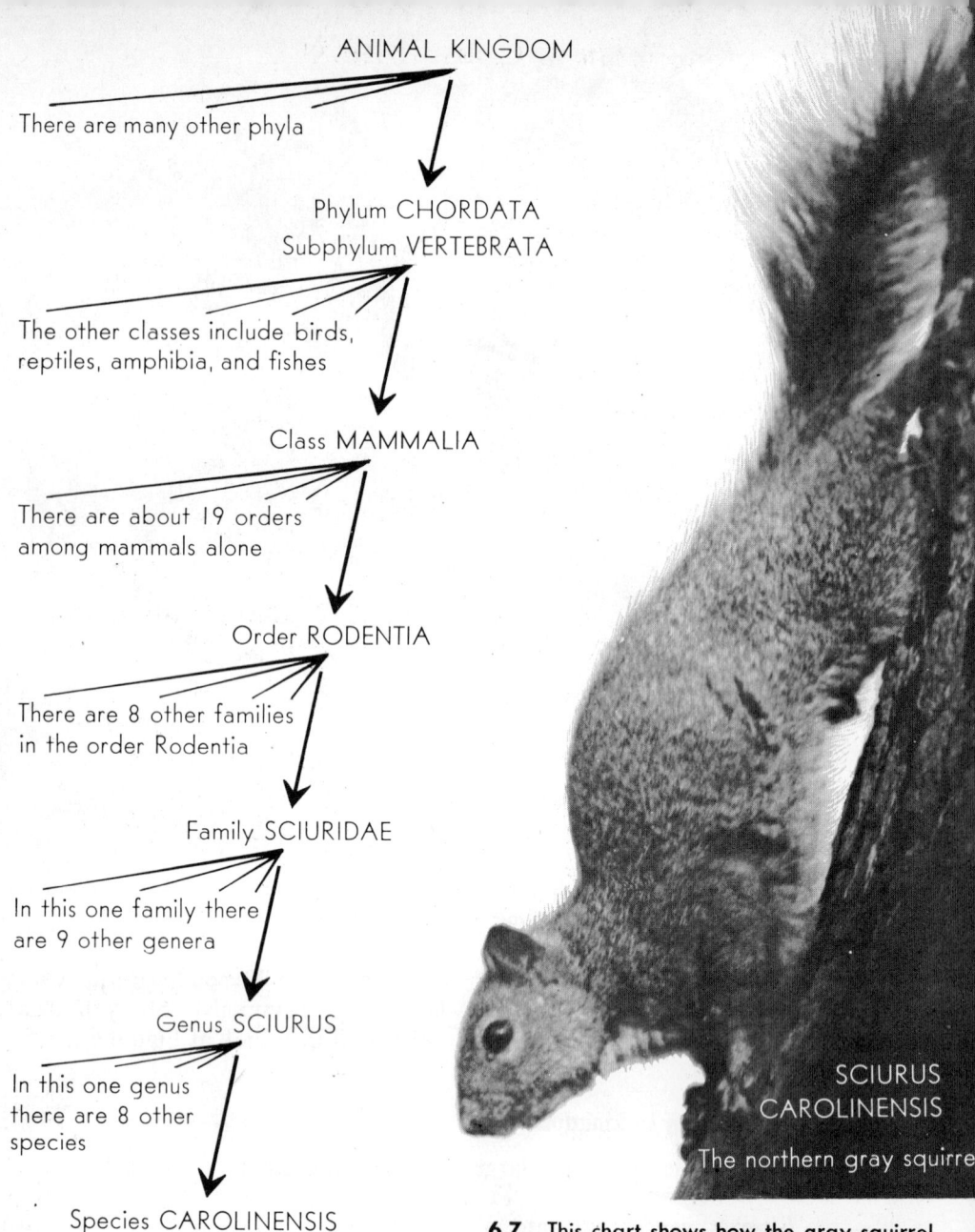

There are about 19 orders among mammals alone

Order RODENTIA

There are 8 other families in the order Rodentia

Family SCIURIDAE

In this one family there are 9 other genera

Genus SCIURUS

In this one genus there are 8 other species

Species CAROLINENSIS

SCIURUS CAROLINENSIS
The northern gray squirrel

6.7 This chart shows how the gray squirrel fits into the animal kingdom. The first subdivision is the phylum. Which subdivisions follow in turn? A chart that shows how one animal is classified is simple; but, if you were to make a chart to include the classification of all animals, you would need a sheet of paper at least as large as your room. It would take you many years to do the job. *Pinney from Monkmeyer*

ANIMAL CLASSIFICATION

PHYLUM I. Protozoans (*Protozoa*)
Single-celled. Live in fresh or salt water or where it is moist. Some parasitic on other animals, causing disease. Some form shells and build limestone rock. (All other phyla are many-celled.)

PHYLUM II. Sponge animals (*Porifera*)
Baglike with many small openings through the sides. Attached. Some form colonies. Mostly salt water forms. Sponges.

PHYLUM III. Coelenterates (*Coelenterata*)
Baglike with one opening. Tentacles and stinging cells. Some free-swimming, some attached, some forming colonies. Jellyfish, sea anemone, coral, Hydra.

PHYLUM IV. Flatworms (*Platyhelminthes*)
Planaria lives in streams. Many parasitic on other animals, causing disease. Tapeworm, liver fluke.

PHYLUM V. Roundworms (*Nemathelminthes*)
Cylindrical body without segments. Many very small. Some live in water. Some parasitic on other animals. Hookworm, trichina worm.

PHYLUM VI. Segmented worms (*Annelida*)
Long, cylindrical body with segments or rings. Living on land or in water. Thin, moist skin; most without legs. Earthworm, clam worm, leech.

PHYLUM VII. Echinoderms (*Echinodermata*)
Radial symmetry, usually with five divisions. A spiny skin. Live only in salt water. Starfish, sea urchin, brittle star, sea cucumber, crinoids.

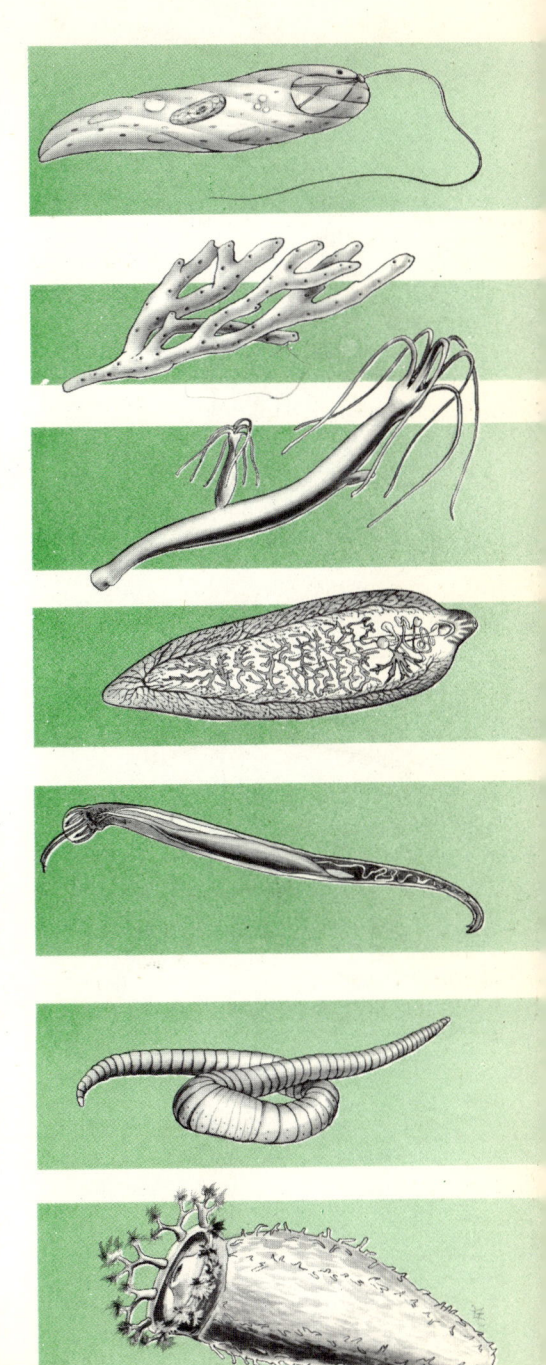

CHAPTER SIX — CLASSIFYING PLANTS AND ANIMALS

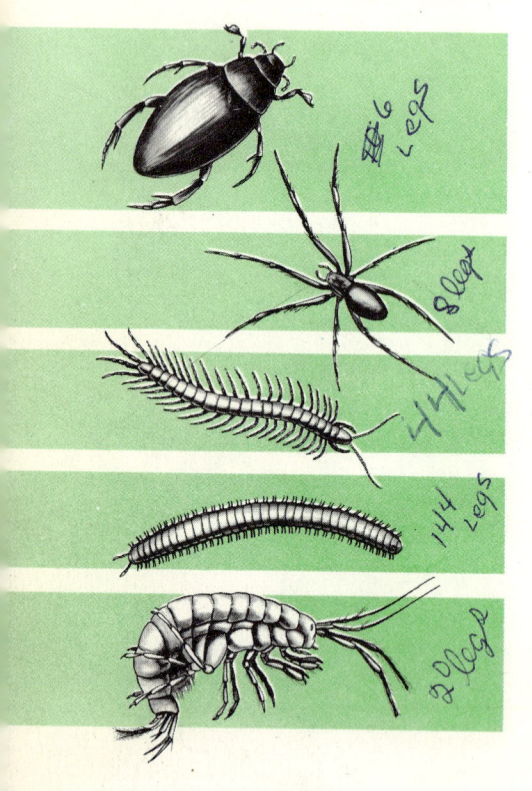

PHYLUM VIII. Mollusks (*Mollusca*)
Soft-bodied invertebrates with a shell. In some the shell is internal and reduced in size. Live in fresh or salt water or on land. Snail, oyster, slug, clam, octopus.

PHYLUM IX. Arthropods (*Arthropoda*)
A hard outside covering. Segmented body and jointed legs.

CLASS 1. INSECTS (*Insecta*): Head, thorax, and abdomen with three pairs of legs on thorax. Complete or incomplete metamorphosis in their development. May live on land or in water. Grasshopper, butterfly, beetle, bee, fly, mosquito, moth.

CLASS 2. SPIDERS (*Arachnoidea*): Two body parts and four pairs of legs. Spider, scorpion.

CLASS 3. CENTIPEDES (*Chilopoda*): Segmented body. Each segment has one pair of legs. House centipede.

CLASS 4. MILLIPEDES (*Diplopoda*): Segmented body. Each segment has two pairs of legs.

CLASS 5. CRUSTACEANS (*Crustacea*): Five or more pairs of legs. Two pairs of antennae. Live in salt water, fresh water, or in damp earth. Lobster, crab, barnacle.

PHYLUM X. Chordates (*Chordata*)
The name is from the word "cord" and refers not to the spinal cord but to the notochord which is present in adults of some subphyla and which develops into the backbone of the vertebrates. Most zoologists recognize three small subphyla other than the vertebrates.

Subphylum. Vertebrates (*Vertebrata*): With a backbone made up of segments called vertebrae.

CLASS 1. FISH (*Pisces*): Scaly, moist skin. Live in water. Breathe by means of gills. (The sharks and some other fishlike animals have skeletons of cartilage and are put into a separate class.)

CLASS 2. AMPHIBIANS (*Amphibia*): Thin, moist skin. Most live first in water, breathing by gills, then lose the gills, develop lungs, and live on land.

CLASS 3. REPTILES (*Reptilia*): Dry, scaly skin. Breathe by means of lungs.

CLASS 4. BIRDS (*Aves*): Feathers.

CLASS 5. MAMMALS (*Mammalia*): Hair covering. Feed young on milk from mammary glands.

PLANT CLASSIFICATION

THIS SIMPLIFIED TABLE WILL HELP YOU TO REVIEW THE PLANT KINGDOM.

PHYLUM I. Thallophytes (*Thallophyta*)
The simplest plants; no flowers, seeds, roots, stems, or leaves.
Subphylum I. Algae: Thallophytes with green coloring matter. With few exceptions, aquatic. Green, brown, and red seaweeds, diatoms.
Subphylum II. Fungi: Thallophytes lacking green coloring matter. Mushrooms, molds, yeasts, and bacteria.

PHYLUM II. Bryophytes (*Bryophyta*)
Plants without flowers or fruits. Green. Mostly with simple stems and rootlike and leaflike parts. Small and inconspicuous.

CLASS 1. LIVERWORTS (*Hepaticae*): With a somewhat branched, ribbonlike structure flat on the ground, with simple rootlike parts; or with stems and rootlike and leaflike parts.

CLASS 2. MOSSES (*Musci*): Erect or horizontal. More complex in structure, with stems and leaflike and rootlike parts.

PHYLUM III. Pteridophytes (*Pteridophyta*) Plants without flowers and seeds. Green. True leaves, roots, and stems with conducting tissue much like that in higher plants.

CLASS 1. FERNS (*Filicinae*): In temperate zones, mostly small with horizontal stems (a few tree ferns in tropics). Spores borne on leaves or modified leaves.

CLASS 2. HORSETAILS (*Equisetinae*): Few species. Jointed stems with leaves reduced to scales. Spores in conelike structures. Stems harsh to touch.

CLASS 3. CLUB MOSSES (*Lycopodinae*): Few species. Creeping herbs with erect stems. Most species bear spores in conelike structures.

PHYLUM IV. Spermatophytes (*Spermatophyta*)
Plants with flowers and seeds. Practically all are green. Vary in size from less than an inch to more than 400 feet. Complex structure.

Subphylum I. Gymnosperms (*Gymnospermae*): Woody perennial plants with naked seeds mostly borne on surface of cone scales. Leaves mostly needlelike or scalelike and evergreen. Includes the conifers, ginkgoes, and cycads.

Subphylum II. Angiosperms (*Angiospermae*): Woody and herbaceous perennial, biennial, and annual plants with seeds developing within a fruit. Leaves mostly broad and not evergreen.

CLASS 1. MONOCOTYLEDONS: Usually parallel veined leaves. Flower parts in three's. Single cotyledon in seed.

CLASS 2. DICOTYLEDONS: Netted veined leaves. Flower parts mostly in two's, four's, or five's. Two cotyledons in seed.

USEFUL WORDS IN BIOLOGY

classification	order	species
phylum	family	variety
class	genus (genera)	kingdom

TEST YOURSELF

1. Tell of some of the various attempts made throughout the centuries to classify living things.
2. In all classifying, what is true of the relation between the number of kinds in a group and the number of characteristics the specimens have in common?
3. Starting with the kingdom, name in order the biological divisions and subdivisions or groupings down to the smallest.
4. Give the scientific names of the cat and the dog, stating how Linnaeus arrived at these names.
5. (a) What are the names of the red maple and the large-leaved western maple? (b) What do these names show about the relationship of these trees?

DO IT YOURSELF

1. **Learning to use a key.** Go out-of-doors to study trees, flowering plants, seaweeds, or any form of plant or animal life and try using an identification key such as is given in a fieldbook. The man who made the key did the hard part of the work; your job is easy, although it takes close observation on your part.

2. **Classifying library cards.** Perhaps your class subscribes to *Science News Letter*, *Nature Magazine* (The American Nature Association, 1214 16th St., Washington 6, D.C.), *Natural History* (American Museum of Natural History, New York 24, N.Y.), *Cornell Rural School Leaflets* (Cornell University, Ithaca, N.Y.), or to magazines or leaflets. If so this would be a good time to make a card for every article of interest to your work and to classify these cards.

ADVENTURES IN READING

"Long Live Linnaeus" by Donald C. Peattie should interest you. It is in *Reader's Digest*, June 1952.

Unit Three

Plants — the world's food makers

CHAPTER 7

Leaves

CHAPTER 8

Roots and stems

Our planet has fifty-five million square miles of land; and most of it, even much of the so-called desert, is green with plant life. In these plants are chloroplasts, the tiny active green bodies which make it possible for you and me to live. Most of this green mantle that covers the earth consists of plants with roots, stems, and leaves. These are the plants that supply us with many useful products, but most of all with food. Unless our livelihood depends on crops, most of us pass a field of alfalfa or corn (opposite) or wheat without giving it another thought. Many of us take plants for granted. Because plants are fixed in the ground we sometimes forget that they are alive, just as you and I are alive. And they are active, too; but their activity is hidden within the cells. In fact, much of the plant itself is hidden. Would you believe that in a field of grain one small plant standing about two feet high may have 380 miles of roots underground? It's only about 730 miles driving distance from Philadelphia to Chicago, a distance that takes hours to travel by car!

And when we see a forest on the distant hills we are likely to forget that what is going on in those trees is of great importance to us. The wood they are making may become lumber for houses, ball bats, newspapers. Their leaves and smaller twigs fall and form a sort of sponge that helps prevent floods. Plants play such an important part in our lives that it will pay us to know more about them. Let's take a close look at their roots, and stems, and leaves.

Chapter 7

Leaves

An interesting experiment. Plants don't eat. Yet they live and grow. Their cells contain the same kinds of food substances as our cells — starches, sugars, proteins, and fats. How do they get there? Do these substances come from the soil?

More than three hundred years ago Jan van Helmont, a Flemish physician, asked himself these questions. To answer them he performed this simple experiment. He filled a large tub with soil which he had weighed very carefully. Then he planted a willow twig in it. He watered the plant regularly, and he kept this up for five years. By this time the twig had become a small tree with many roots and branches and leaves. Van Helmont then removed the tree carefully, making sure that no soil remained clinging to its roots. He weighed the tree and again weighed the soil. The tree weighed 160 pounds; but the soil weighed only two ounces less than when he started the experiment! What conclusions would you draw from this experiment? The only possible conclusion is this: if only two ounces came from the soil, all the rest of the materials that made the small tree — almost 160 pounds — came from the air or from the water or from the two together. Evidently plants can do extraordinary things. We had better examine them more closely.

Leaves. Let's start with the leaves of the common flowering plants. There is tremendous variety in size and shape. The cone-bearing trees, such as the pines, spruces, and hemlocks have needlelike leaves. Some kinds of cactuses have little or nothing by way of leaves. See Figure 7.1. But plants without leaves are the exceptions.

Leaves grow to an enormous size; think of the palm trees. And a fern that grows in the Everglades of Florida has a frond (leaf) that is longer than most automobiles — 20 feet. One species of pine has needles 12 inches long.

Most leaves have two distinct parts: a stemlike part called the **petiole** (pet′ee-ohl) and a flat, wider part, the **blade**. See Figure 7.2. Think how many different kinds of leaves you have seen. The blade may be almost any shape, and it may be smooth or hairy, paper-thin or thick, and leathery or fleshy. It may have parallel veining (in monocots) or net veining (in dicots). Do you remember seeing this on page 74? But in one way nearly all leaves are alike. They are green. They contain chlorophyll. Even the leaves of the purple beech and of the red coleus growing on your window sill at home or at school contain chlorophyll. The chlorophyll is merely hidden by other coloring matter.

Looking inside a leaf. A thick, fleshy leaf such as the sedum leaf is good for study. You can cut it crosswise and then, with the aid of a knife, pull off some of the "skin," or **epidermis** (ep-i-der′mis). It is colorless, thin, and transparent; that is, you can see through it. The epidermis is found on both the upper and lower sides of the leaf. Feel the green tissues between the two layers of epidermis. They feel soft and moist.

7.1 A prickly pear cactus. The flattened green stem bears only clusters of spines. Turn back to this picture after you have finished this chapter and explain how a cactus gets its food.

7.2 The water lily leaf has a large blade that floats on the water. You can't see the petiole in this picture. It is attached to a stem at the bottom of the pond. *N.Y. Botanical Garden*

Now if you can examine a cross section of a leaf under the microscope you will see two kinds of cells between the layers of epidermis. Under the upper epidermis are long narrow cells, standing up in a straight row; these are called **palisade** cells. They are bright green. If you look at a thin slice under the microscope, you can see many oval green bodies. These are **chloroplasts;** they contain the chlorophyll. Beneath the palisade cells are more loosely packed cells, called spongy cells. These are irregular in shape, and they have large air spaces between them. They, too, have chloroplasts, but fewer of them. Figure 7.3 shows you all this and shows you a section through a small vein.

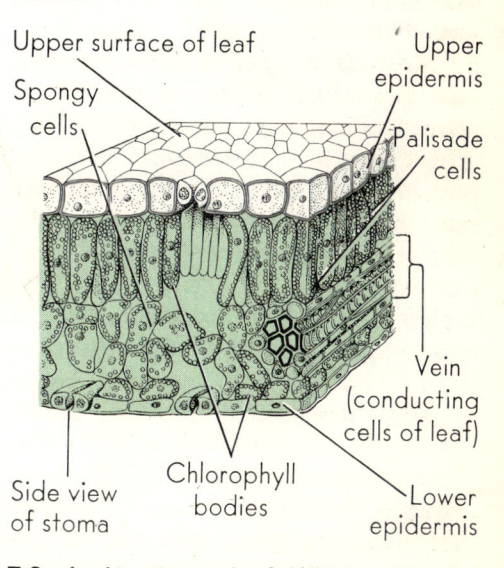

7.3 Looking into a leaf. Which two layers lie between upper and lower epidermis? What is in the spaces between cells?

CHAPTER SEVEN — LEAVES

Epidermis. The epidermis is a single layer of cells closely fitted together, as Figure 7.3 shows. You can see that most of these cells have no chloroplasts. But here and there among the epidermal cells are pairs of smaller green cells. They show up better when you look down on a piece of epidermis spread out flat, as you see it in Figure 7.4. Here you can see that each of these cells is curved like a slender kidney bean. The two cells lie in such a way that an opening is left between them. This opening is called a **stoma** (stoh'ma). Each stoma connects an air space within the leaf with the air outside. The upper epidermis of most plants has few or no **stomata** (stoh'ma-ta, plural of stoma).

The two cells enclosing the stoma are called **guard cells,** because they regulate the size of the opening. In most plants, during the daytime, each guard cell becomes more bent, taking the shape of a half doughnut. In this way the opening is made larger. At night the guard cells straighten out, making the stoma smaller; but the opening is never shut completely.

Most leaves have an enormous number of stomata. A medium-sized cabbage leaf may have about 11,000,000 of them, and a sunflower leaf may have up to 13,000,000. Most stomata are, as you just read, on the lower side of the leaf. But in leaves that float on the water they are mostly on the upper side. As you read further, you will see how important stomata are to the plant.

More about chloroplasts. Chloroplasts are found in all parts of the plant that are green, not only in the leaves. In the flowering plants chloroplasts are tiny, round or oval bodies. But do you remember that in the alga called Spirogyra the chloroplast is a wide spiral band running from one end of the cell to the other? Large, star-shaped chloroplasts are found in certain other algae. But no matter what its shape, the chloroplast is always a living body containing chlorophyll.

Chlorophyll has never been made in the laboratory; the only way you can get it is to dissolve it out of the chloroplasts by means of alcohol. There are two green pigments made of carbon, hydrogen, oxygen, nitrogen, and magnesium. Chloroplasts also contain yellow pigments; one of these is **carotene,** a substance very important to you in your food. But the yellow substances are ordinarily hidden by the green pigments. They show up only when there is little or no chlorophyll, as in apricots and peaches after they ripen.

Ordinarily, green pigments form in a plant only in the presence of light; this is not true of the yellow pigments. Have you ever noticed the pale sprouts on potatoes kept in a dark place? On the other hand, strong light makes chlorophyll disappear, too. The only reason leaves in strong sunlight are so

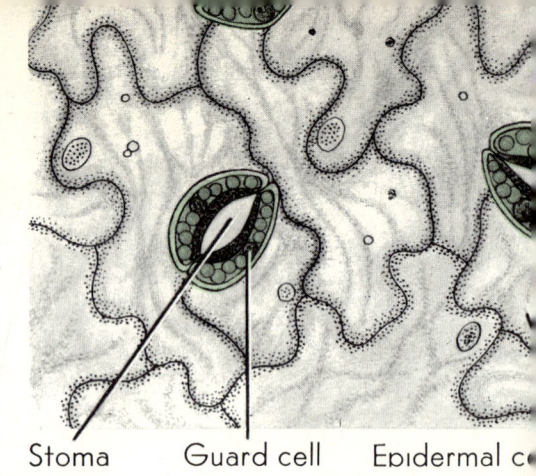

7.4 A tiny piece of lower epidermis. How many stomata do you see? Are they open or closed? What are the cells on each side of a stoma called?

| FRESH SPECIMEN | AFTER BOILING IN ALCOHOL | AFTER TREATMENT WITH IODINE |

7.5 Perhaps you will try this experiment in your own classroom. Recall that iodine turns starch blue. Study the drawings above. Note that the leaf tested is only partly green. What important fact does this experiment tell you about photosynthesis?

---

green is that their active cells are constantly forming new chlorophyll which takes the place of the chlorophyll that is disappearing. In the fall, when the temperature is lower and the days shorter, leaves form green pigments more slowly. It is then that the yellow coloring, which has been hidden by the green, shows up, giving the brilliant yellow tints to some autumn foliage. A red pigment appears in some kinds of plants at this time.

Manufacture of carbohydrates. All through the spring, summer, and autumn every green part of the plant works during the daylight hours. Their chloroplasts are making carbohydrates. The brighter the day, the more active are the chloroplasts, for light is needed for this manufacture called **photosynthesis** (foh-toh-sin'theh-sis). The chloroplasts are combining two simple compounds: water (H_2O), which entered the plant through the roots, and carbon dioxide (CO_2), which came in from the air through the stomata. How do the chloroplasts do it? We don't know. Chemists have tried to imitate the process but they have not fully succeeded. But they have got this far. They have made chloroplasts do the whole job of carbohydrate manufacture after they were removed from the cell, proving that it is the chloroplast that does the job. And they do know that there are several steps in the manufacture before the simple sugar, **glucose** ($C_6H_{12}O_6$), is produced.

In most plants much of this sugar is soon changed to starch, $(C_6H_{10}O_5)_n$, while in some, like sugar beets, sugar cane, and sugar maple, the glucose is changed to the kind of sugar you use on the table (**sucrose**), $C_{12}H_{22}O_{11}$. Look at its formula; this is called a double sugar. Van Helmont was right, wasn't he? Air — at least part of it — and water helped very much to make the 160-pound tree.

CHAPTER SEVEN — LEAVES

Cane

Beet

Maple

Double sugars ($C_{12}H_{22}O_{11}$)

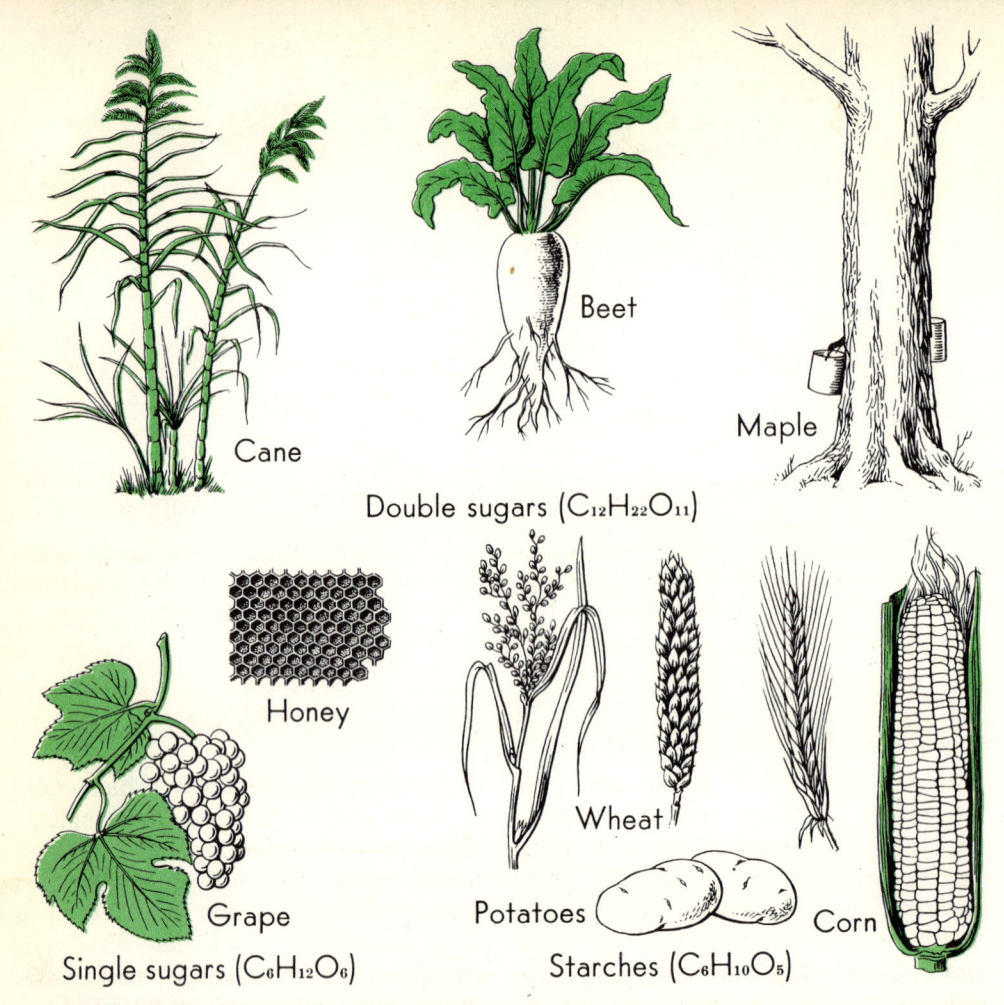

Honey

Grape

Wheat

Potatoes

Corn

Single sugars ($C_6H_{12}O_6$)

Starches ($C_6H_{10}O_5$)

7.6 Did you think that sugars and starches are made in factories? All of them are made in plants. All we do is take them out of the plant, refine them, and pack them. Some plants store more carbohydrates than others. Which of these plants supply starches? Which supply sugars? Where does the honey come from?

A busy factory. In a factory, electrical energy is often changed into mechanical energy; sometimes it is chemical energy that is changed. You hear engines humming and roaring. Much work is being done. In the living leaf you can't hear machines humming, and your eye can't follow the process. Yet simple compounds are being **synthesized** (put together), and energy changes are taking place. The leaves of a medium-sized apple tree make about 44 pounds of carbohydrates per year. See Figure 7.6.

Light (**radiant**) energy is absorbed by the chlorophyll. Somehow light energy is changed into chemical energy; this remains locked up in the carbohydrates. All day long while the sun is shining on the green parts of the plant, the chloroplasts, especially those in the palisade cells of the leaves, absorb

UNIT THREE — PLANTS — THE WORLD'S FOOD MAKERS

7.7 Miles of green plants with their chloroplasts working actively. What are the results of their work? How does the work of the chloroplasts benefit the plants? How does it change the atmosphere around them? *H. Armstrong Roberts*

the light energy. Even on gray days they absorb some energy and make carbohydrates slowly. At night they stop. Sometimes people make the chloroplasts work overtime by exposing the leaves to artificial light after dark.

Here is a much simplified account of sugar-making in chloroplasts. Six molecules of carbon dioxide are united with six molecules of water. The products are a molecule of sugar (glucose) and six molecules of oxygen. The light energy used becomes chemical energy in the sugar. A chemist might write all this in chemical shorthand as shown below.

Notice that in this factory as in most factories, there is a by-product. But this by-product is something that is very precious to us — it is the oxygen, which is then given off to the surrounding air. See Figure 7.8, page 146.

$$6CO_2 + 6H_2O + \text{light energy} \longrightarrow C_6H_{12}O_6 + 6O_2$$

CONTAINS CHEMICAL ENERGY

CHAPTER SEVEN — LEAVES

7.8 The plants in the above experiment are Elodea, a water plant. Bubbles of oxygen (mostly) rise from the plants in the jar on the left. Explain why.

Protein manufacture. Now let's find out what happened to the two ounces of soil that van Helmont lost during the five years he carried on his experiment. These two ounces of soil entered through the roots, a very little at a time. Part of the two ounces combined with sugar to make proteins. You will remember that the protein molecules are very large and that they contain more elements than sugar. Besides carbon, hydrogen, and oxygen, all proteins contain nitrogen. In addition, some contain some phosphorus, some iron, some magnesium, some iodine, some calcium. Some proteins contain several of these. Except for the carbon, hydrogen, and oxygen, all the elements enter in the form of mineral compounds through the roots. Even the nitrogen is in the form of a simple compound when it enters. The large amounts of nitrogen gas in the air can't be used by the plant.

The protoplasm of many cells throughout the plant combines the mineral compounds with the sugar; chlorophyll plays no part in this. The energy stored in the sugar then goes into the protein. Simple compounds containing nitrogen are made first, then larger and larger nitrogen compounds. Out of these the protoplasm makes substances called **amino acids.** The amino acids are then built into proteins. That is why amino acids are sometimes spoken of as the "building stones" out of which proteins are made. Perhaps you already know that your body can make use of the proteins in food only after it has broken them down again into amino acids.

Figure 7.9 shows you a small plant with some of the many elements and compounds surrounding it both in the air and in the soil. Remember that a plant uses simple compounds, and never elements, for its food manufacture.

The manufacture of proteins is a very complicated process; it can take place in any part of the plant. And it goes on in almost all plants — in algae and fungi as well as in higher green plants. Yet, animal cells, as far as we know, never make proteins from sugar and simple mineral compounds. That means that animals depend on plants for both their carbohydrates and their proteins.

You saw how very important soil rich in mineral compounds is to the plant. You see now how important the soil is to us. We and the other animals depend on plants to supply us with proteins and, of course, with carbohydrates too. Some of us sit quietly by when water or wind carries away the top layers of soil containing these precious mineral compounds. But if water or wind or any other agent swept food from our pantries or from the grocer's shelves into the ocean, we'd be really upset, wouldn't we?

Fat manufacture. Plants change some of the sugar they manufacture into fats. Whatever energy is stored in the sugar is then transferred to the fat. This change can take place in any part of the plant. Fats, you will remember, also contain carbon, hydrogen, and oxygen, but a smaller percentage of oxygen. In some kinds of plants much fat is made and stored, often in fruits or seeds. Nuts of all kinds are seeds rich in fat. Thousands of tons of fat from coconuts are used for food and cosmetics. Thousands of carloads of fat from cotton seeds and soybeans are used for food and in making paints. And you know of the many uses of olive oil.

Respiration in leaves. In making fats and proteins, the protoplasm needs energy. This energy comes from the oxidation of sugar, which is constantly going on in all living cells of the plant. Energy is needed, too, for changing some of the food manufactured by the plant into its own protoplasm. This process is sometimes called **assimilation.** As more protoplasm is made, the plant

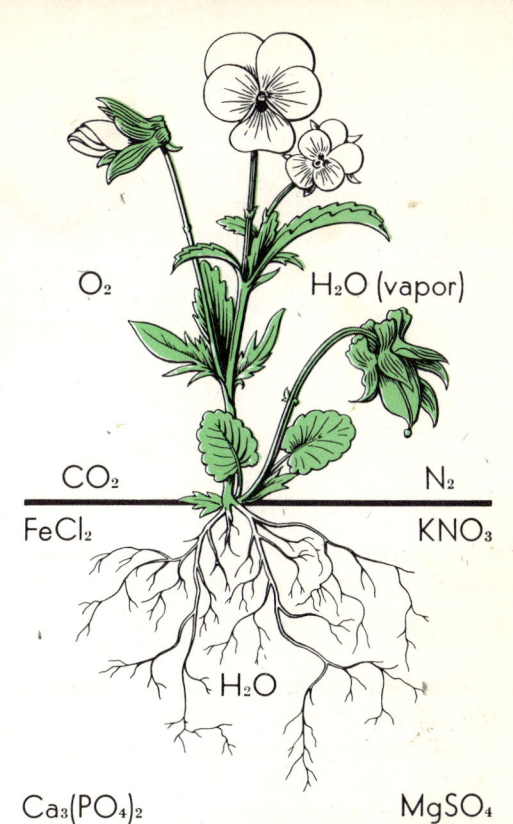

7.9 Plants make proteins out of carbohydrates and simple compounds from the soil. Which compound could supply the nitrogen needed? Which other elements could be supplied by the compounds in the soil?

can make more cells and grow. Some of the energy released in oxidation is lost from the cells as heat. Not much, to be sure, but a little. In other words, there is constant energy release in the cells of the plant from the oxidation of sugar. Botanists call the oxidation in the cells of a plant **respiration.** It goes on as long as the cells are living.

While the green parts of a plant are making carbohydrates in the daytime, they are constantly releasing oxygen. Some of this oxygen stays right in the plant and unites with the sugar in respiration. But in bright sunlight so much oxygen is produced that it cannot all be used up. Much of it then diffuses out through the stomata. At night, however, after photosynthesis stops, the concentration of oxygen inside gradually becomes less than outside; then oxygen diffuses from the surrounding air through the stomata to the cells in which respiration is taking place.

Now carbon dioxide is formed when sugar is oxidized. All the carbon dioxide that comes from the respiration in the cells in the daytime will be quickly used up by the chloroplasts which are manufacturing carbohydrates. At night carbohydrate-making stops. Carbon dioxide is no longer being used then by the chloroplasts, and it diffuses out through the stomata. Note this: Though respiration goes on all the time, it is only at night that oxygen enters the plant and carbon dioxide goes out.

What have you learned? Chloroplasts in higher plants are found mostly in the leaves. The chloroplasts with their chlorophyll are necessary for the first step in all food manufacture — making of carbohydrates. Some of the carbohydrates are made into fats and proteins in any part of the plant. In this way the plant gets its food; then it makes protoplasm and grows.

In the meantime respiration is going on in all the cells: the oxidation of food and release of energy. This is a process of breaking down food compounds; it is exactly the opposite of photosynthesis, in which food compounds are built up. The table below should make this clear.

But green plants do far more than make their own food. They make the food used by the whole world of animals and, indirectly, the food of all fungi and nongreen plants which live as parasites or saprophytes. Green plants keep storing energy; animals and colorless plants use up the stored energy in growing and keeping alive.

We are so completely dependent on plants and the animals which eat plants that adequate space must be conserved for them and the soil must not be allowed to lose its fertility. The number of plants we need for food is growing ever larger.

And besides making foods that contain energy, green plants keep putting oxygen into the air. Thus animals and colorless plants depend on green plants for food and for the continued supply of oxygen.

TABLE 7

	PHOTOSYNTHESIS (building up of foods)	RESPIRATION (breaking down of foods)
Energy Changes	Light energy changed to chemical energy of sugar	Chemical energy of food changed to other kinds of energy
Materials Used	Carbon dioxide and water	Food and oxygen
Materials Produced	Sugar and oxygen	Carbon dioxide and water
When Occurring	Only in light	At all times
Where Occurring	Only in green cells	In all living cells

USEFUL WORDS IN BIOLOGY

petiole
blade
palisade cells
stoma
  (stomata)
guard cells
photosynthesis
carotene
glucose
spongy tissue
radiant
  energy
respiration
sucrose
amino acids

TEST YOURSELF

1. What important conclusions did van Helmont draw from his experiment?
2. Describe fully and locate each of these tissues in the blade of a leaf: epidermis, palisade cells, and spongy cells. Of what use is each kind of cell?
3. Explain how guard cells change their shape; what effect does this have on the size of the opening between them?
4. Of what is chlorophyll composed? What effect do shorter autumn days have on the formation of chlorophyll? Why do some leaves turn yellow in the fall?
5. In the manufacture of carbohydrates: (a) what compounds are combined? (b) what compound is formed before starch? (c) what energy changes take place? (d) which structure in the cell is directly concerned in the process?
6. In the manufacture of proteins: (a) what six important elements do plants get only from the soil? (b) with what does the plant combine those elements? (c) what are amino acids?
7. Which of these statements is true of protein manufacture from sugar and mineral compounds? "It goes on in algae and fungi as well as in higher plants." "It can take place in any living part of the plant." "It does not take place in animals." "Sunlight is as necessary for protein manufacture as for photosynthesis." Write the true statements in your notes under protein manufacture.
8. (a) Define respiration in a plant. Then tell: (b) when and (c) where it takes place in a plant, (d) what energy changes occur, and (e) what chemical changes occur.

DO IT YOURSELF

1. **Microscopic study of a leaf.** Use a thick leaf such as a sedum leaf. With a knife peel off a small piece of leaf epidermis, mount it on a slide in water, and look for stomata under low and high power. Try both upper and lower epidermis. Do you notice a difference? Then cut a thin cross section and examine that under the microscope, or use a prepared, stained leaf section. You should see upper and lower epidermis (with stomata in cross section), and palisade and spongy cells containing chloroplasts. Make and label a diagram and take notes on what you see.

2. **Is light necessary for the making of carbohydrates?** Use a geranium, green coleus, or some other plant that has been kept in the dark for a couple of days. Cover the top and bottom of one leaf with aluminum foil, or anything else that will shut out all light. Place the plant in bright light, giving it plenty of water. After two or three hours remove the covered leaf and an uncovered leaf to discover whether they differ with regard to starch content. Do you remember how to test for the presence of starch? But in order to be able to see the bluish-black color, your leaves must have the chlorophyll removed before you apply the starch test. This can be done by boiling the leaves in water and then soaking them in hot alcohol until the leaf shows no more green. It would be good for several groups of students to do this same experiment. Why?

3. **Is chlorophyll necessary for the making of carbohydrates?** Have you a plant such as a geranium or tradescantia at home or in school that has leaves that are partly green and partly white? Place the plant in strong sunlight and then test one leaf as described above. Be sure to make a sketch of the leaf showing the green and white areas before you remove the chlorophyll. Draw and color the leaf after you have tested it for starch.

4. **Is carbon dioxide necessary for making carbohydrates?** This is an interesting experi-

ment for you to plan and perform. Hints: (1) How can you give a growing plant air without carbon dioxide? (2) Do you know of anything that absorbs carbon dioxide? (3) What will be your control? (4) How will you be sure that plants are free from starch when you begin? Do you remember all the steps in the procedure for testing leaves for starch? Write fully what you did, your observations, and your conclusions.

5. Variety in leaves. Perhaps you have already started a collection of leaves. If not, you may wish to start a collection now. Look closely at the shape of the blade, its margin, its texture, and its veining. Examine the petiole, too. You may want to make a separate collection of leaves used as food by us. To preserve them, leaves must be thoroughly dried while being pressed between layers of newspaper or blotting paper. They can then be fastened to heavy paper sheets and labeled.

ADVENTURES IN READING

1. *Food and Life*, 1939 Yearbook of the United States Department of Agriculture. Contains much useful information.
2. *Plant Growth* by Lawson Edwin Yocum, Ronald, 1945. Gives a short and simple account of plant growth.
3. *Botany* by Robbins and Weier, Wiley, 1950. Is a good reference book, not too difficult. It will be useful for the next chapter, too.
4. "Photosynthesis" by E. I. Rabinowitch, *Scientific American*, August 1948. Is not easy, but exciting.
5. Recent issues of *Science News Letter* should keep you informed of the many experiments being carried on in the hope of understanding and duplicating the activities of chloroplasts.

Chapter 8

Roots and stems

The plant as a whole. Imagine for a moment that we were fixed in the ground and buried to our knees. A man from Mars would get a very wrong impression of us. But that is the way we see most plants. Beneath the ground are the long or widely branching roots so necessary for anchoring the plant and bringing in water and minerals. See Figure 8.1. When these substances reach the leaves, you know what happens: sugars are made first, and then other foods are made from sugars or from sugar and minerals. You already know something of what goes on in leaves. Let's now look at stems and roots.

Woody stems. When you were little, did you have a swing hung from a branch of a tree? You got taller and so did the tree, but the swing did not get higher from the ground. Clotheslines and wire fences are sometimes fastened by bolts or staples to trees. They, too, always remain the same distance from the ground. Why? In time the bolts disappear; they are buried in the wood, and after a few years the fence wire runs right through the tree. You have guessed, if you did not know already, that tree trunks get taller by adding to their tips; in fact all stems grow longer only by growing at their tips. And they get bigger and bigger around by adding layers near the outside of the stem.

The outside of woody stems. There is much to be seen on the outside of a twig (small branch) of a woody stem.

8.1 You can use the yardstick to tell how far this main root extends underground. How high is the stem? A plant like this is well anchored. Some plants, however, have much shorter roots. *Illinois Agricultural Experiment Station*

CHAPTER EIGHT — ROOTS AND STEMS

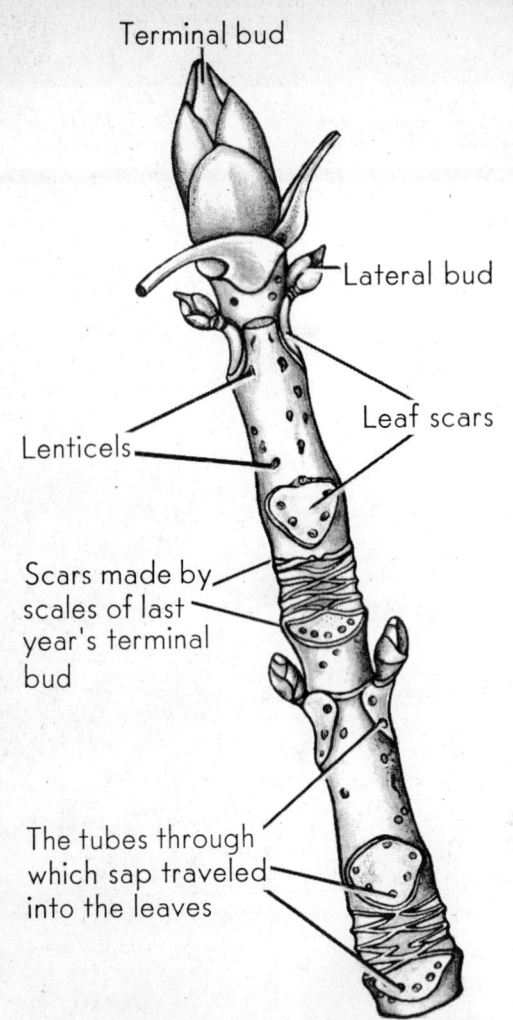

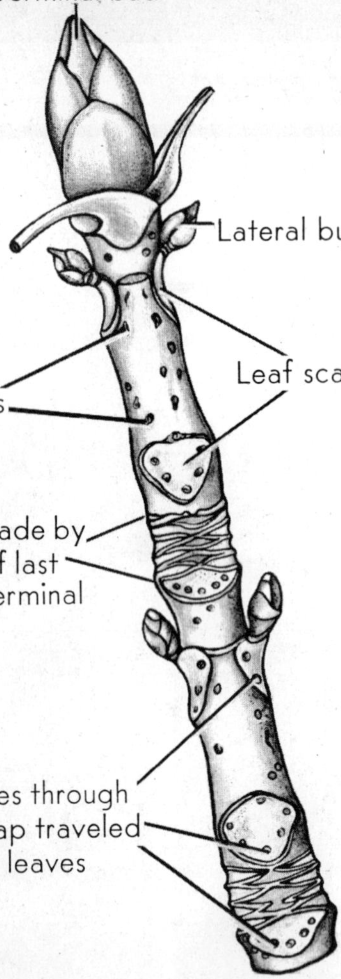
Terminal bud
Lateral bud
Leaf scars
Lenticels
Scars made by scales of last year's terminal bud
The tubes through which sap traveled into the leaves

8.2 End of horse chestnut twig, about natural size. How much did this stem increase in length last year? How can you tell? How many large lateral buds are shown? Where do lateral buds form with relation to the leaves? As the leaves fall off, the petiole leaves a scar. What is the shape of the scar in the horse chestnut?

If you live where there are distinct seasons, examine a twig which has lost its leaves. The horse chestnut twig shown in Figure 8.2 is a good one to study. At the end of the twig you will find a thickened part called a **terminal bud.** Along the sides you will find **lateral buds.** These buds grew there during the summer. If you were to take buds apart carefully, you would find that they were covered with thick scales. Underneath the scales you would find a stem tip with tiny leaf parts. Some buds contain both leaf and flower parts.

The buds are **dormant** (not growing) all winter. But when warm weather comes (or the rainy season in some places), the leaf, stem, and flower parts in the bud again begin to grow. The scales are pushed aside and fall off. The stem tips grow longer and the leaf and flower parts grow larger. Each summer new terminal and lateral buds are formed and become dormant. Each spring they begin again to grow. But each year when growth starts again only some of the lateral buds open up. Many still remain dormant and in time are lost. Since a lateral bud forms just above every single leaf, just think how the trees would look if all of these buds grew into branches! The terminal bud produces special substances (hormones) which travel down and prevent many of the buds from growing. In this way the well-formed, much-branched tree develops. See Figure 8.3.

Take another look at the horse chestnut twig and find shield-shaped scars where the leaves were attached. Note that each lateral bud is just above one of these scars. The part of the stem where a leaf is attached is a **node.** The space between two nodes is an **internode.** In woody stems, internodes grow in length only during their first year. The stem gets longer only by the addition of new parts in the terminal bud. That's why the swing didn't get higher.

Now look again at the twig. Do you see little round or oval spots on the bark? These are openings called **lenticels** (lent′i-cells). Air and moisture

8.3 Elm trees on the village green, Rowley, Massachusetts. *Dave Lawlor*

can pass through the lenticels of bark just as through the stomata of leaves.

The inside of woody stems. You can quite easily peel the **bark** off the twig of a tree. Underneath it the stem is white and hard. This part is the **wood**. Botanists call it **xylem** (zy′lem). If you cut the end of the twig cleanly you will find some soft tissue at the center. This is the **pith**. Not all plant stems have all these parts, but all woody plants have bark, xylem, and pith. Water and some minerals move from roots to leaves in the xylem. The xylem is strong and gives stiffness to the tree. It's the xylem we use for lumber.

CHAPTER EIGHT — ROOTS AND STEMS 153

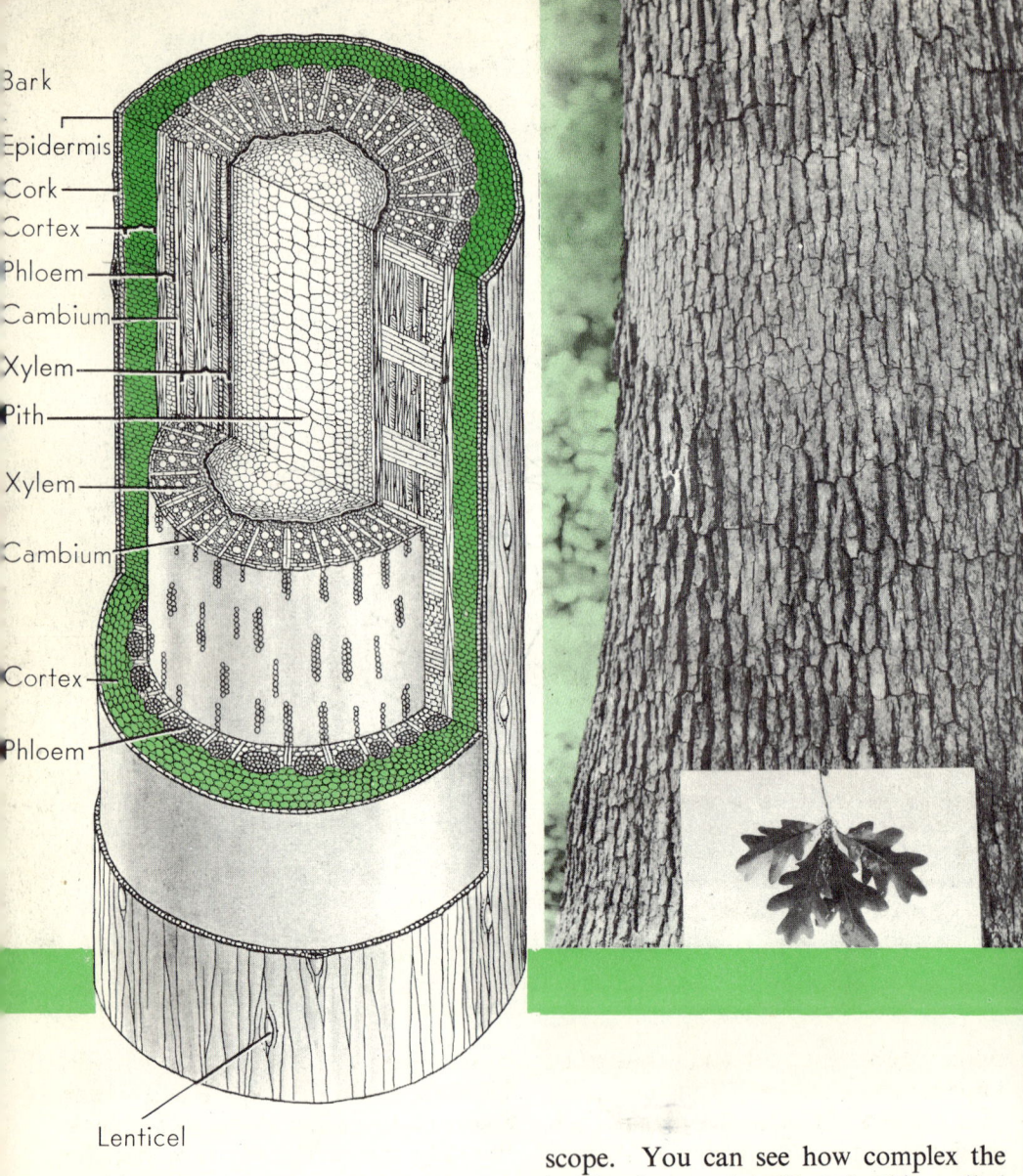

Bark
Epidermis
Cork
Cortex
Phloem
Cambium
Xylem
Pith
Xylem
Cambium
Cortex
Phloem
Lenticel

8.4 This diagram of a one-year-old stem shows a number of tissues besides xylem, cambium, and pith. Can you name the other tissues after reading the text?

Figure 8.4 shows a one-year-old stem cut both crosswise and lengthwise, as it would look if magnified by a microscope. You can see how complex the inside of a stem is! Find the thin-walled pith cells at the center. Find the xylem and the bark. Between the xylem and the bark is a thin layer of small thin-walled cells. This is the **cambium**.

Bark. Now look at the diagram more closely. You will see that the bark is made up of several kinds of

154 UNIT THREE — PLANTS — THE WORLD'S FOOD MAKERS

8.5 These old trunks of an oak (left) and shagbark hickory (above) have thick bark with deep cracks. In winter you can learn to tell many trees by their bark. Contrast the bark of these trees with the smooth, paper-like bark of the white birch (right). *U.S. Forest Service and H. Armstrong Roberts*

tissue: on the outside, **epidermis**; underneath that, **cork**, boxlike cells; then thin-walled cells, the cortex and finally a layer of **phloem** (flow'em). The phloem, then, lies close to the xylem. Only a thin layer of cambium separates the two. The phloem also conducts substances, mostly down. So it and the xylem make up the conducting or **vascular** tissues of the plant.

The epidermis of most woody plants lasts for only a year or two. But the cork remains and on most trees gets much thicker as the plant grows older. New layers are added on the inside. The cork of the cork oak that grows in Spain may get to be several inches thick. We strip the cork from these trees for use in making bottle stoppers and floor coverings. The cork and certain other bark tissues of old redwood trees may be as much as a foot thick. As the bark of most trees gets thicker it splits and cracks in patterns. Many trees can be recognized by their bark pattern and color. In some trees the bark cracks only on the oldest part of the tree. See Figure 8.5.

CHAPTER EIGHT — ROOTS AND STEMS

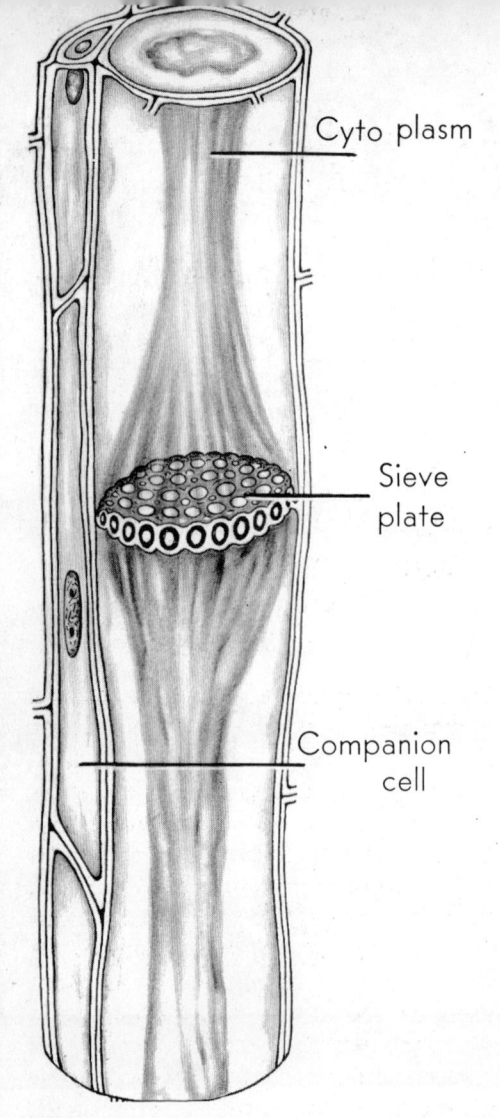

8.6 Note the holes in the sieve plate which lies between the upper and lower cell. Sieve tubes carry manufactured food through plants.

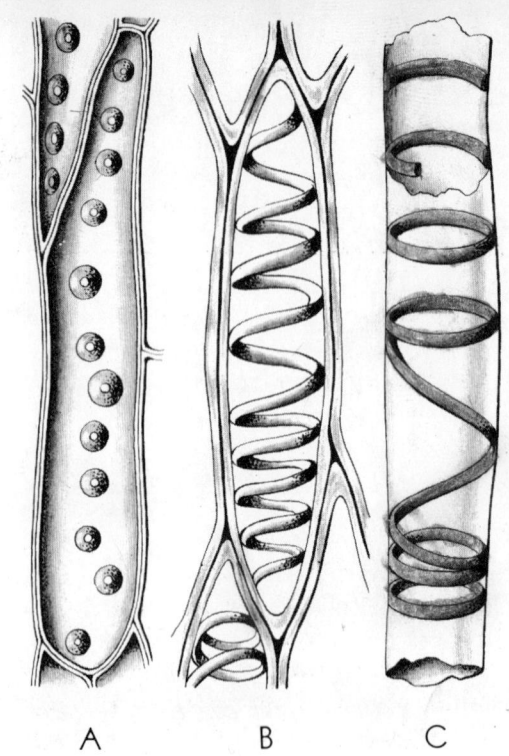

Labels: Cyto plasm, Sieve plate, Companion cell

8.7 There is variety in water-conducting tubes. **A** and **B** are found in conifers (they are called tracheids); **C** is a tube found in flowering plants. The walls are thickened in different ways.

The phloem tissue contains several kinds of cells. As you read, it conducts substances down the stem. Note the **sieve tubes,** Figure 8.6. These sieve tubes carry sugars and other foods made in the leaves to the growing parts of the stem and the roots. The end walls of these cells, as you can see, are like a sieve, and the protoplasm of the cells extends through the holes. Just exactly how the sieve tubes carry food is not known, but you can readily see why a tree soon dies if a ring of bark with its sieve tubes is removed all the way around the trunk. All the cells in the roots and the stem below the ring are starved. New phloem cells are formed from time to time by division of the cambium cells. In some woody plants the cambium forms new phloem cells regularly every year.

Xylem. Look again at the xylem of Figure 8.4. Note first the large, round or nearly round openings. These are

8.8 Cross section of a 30-year-old part of a tree. How can its age be told? Notice that some annual rings are thicker than others. Why might this be? This picture shows the dark center portion called heartwood and the outer portion called sapwood. Which is the older?

the ends of **tubes** in which water moves from the root to the leaf. These tubes, or ducts, grow from large, thick-walled cells piled one on top of another. The walls at the ends of the cells disappear, and the protoplasm dies and is absorbed by surrounding cells. See Figure 8.7. Thus a strong duct is formed; in some trees it may be several feet long. These ducts are directly connected with others above and below by having holes form in the walls at their ends. Because of this, long continuous passageways run through the xylem. And among the conducting tubes are cells with thickened walls which add strength to the stem.

Notice the other kinds of tissues arranged like the spokes of a wheel that extend from the pith through the xylem into the bark. These are the **rays** which conduct food and water across the stem in both directions. Often the ray cells are packed with food materials.

Annual rings. In Figure 8.8 you can see that the xylem is in layers, one layer wrapped around the other. Each year when new growth starts, cambium cells divide and form a layer of new xylem cells outside the layers already there. Of course, when you look at the cut end of a stem these layers show as rings. So we speak of **annual rings** forming in the xylem, one ring each year. Look at Figure 8.8. Normally, then, we can tell the age of many kinds of trees by counting the number of rings. But, of course, we must count them in the oldest part of the trunk, the part just above the ground. All gymnosperms and woody dicots grow in diameter this way, year by year. And now do you understand why a nail driven into a tree trunk is finally buried in the wood?

In most trees water moves only in the new annual ring. After one or two years the tubes become filled with materials. Other cells in the xylem remain alive usually for several years but finally all of them, even the cells in the rays, die and become darker in color. The older, dark colored rings are called **heartwood,** and the newer, light colored rings are called **sapwood.** Figure 8.8 shows this. Heartwood is

8.9 This giant redwood was already an old tree when Columbus discovered America. How do we know this is true? U.S. Department of *Interior*

usually more durable and stronger than sapwood, and is therefore more desirable for lumber. Sometimes, through injury, decay organisms such as fungi get into the heartwood of a tree and destroy it, leaving the sapwood intact. Now you know why such hollow trees can remain alive indefinitely unless a strong wind blows them down. The California redwood above can go on growing in spite of the road running through it. You can now explain why this is so.

Roots. Roots of woody plants are very much like stems. They are covered with bark and they have xylem inside. Cambium cells between bark and phloem make new phloem and xylem each year. The roots of most plants, however, do not have a center of pith. Figure 8.10 shows you the tissues you find in a root. The vascular tissues, that is the xylem and phloem of the root, connect directly with the xylem and phloem of the stem. They extend from the tip of the finest

158   UNIT THREE — PLANTS — THE WORLD'S FOOD MAKERS

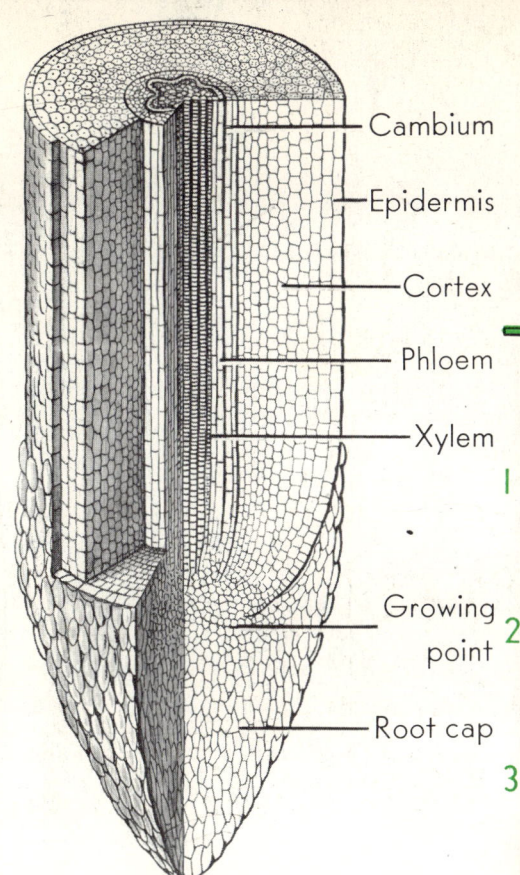

8.10 The tip of a young root. Which of the tissues found in a young stem do you find in this root? What is at the very tip of the root?

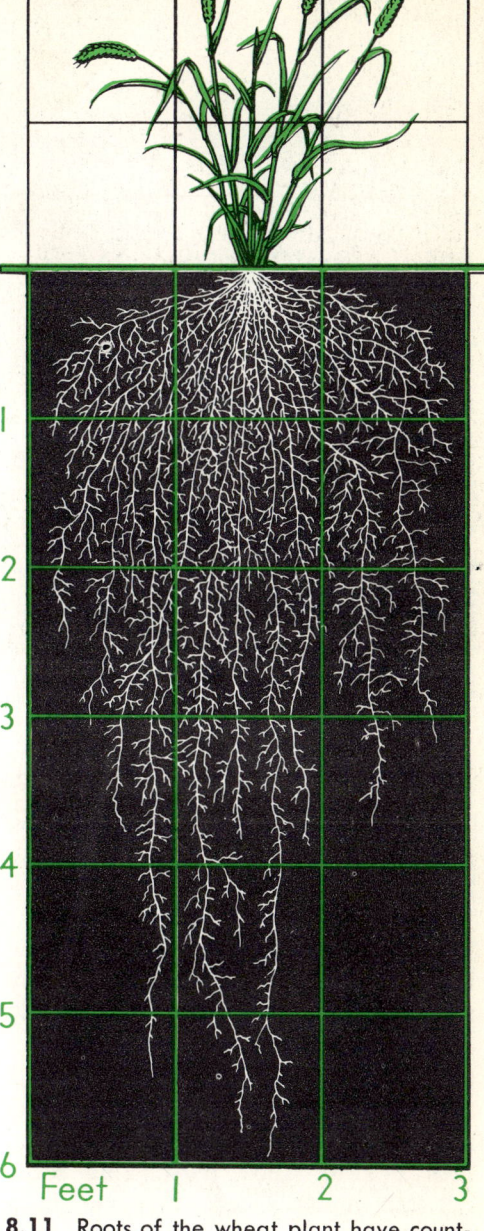

8.11 Roots of the wheat plant have countless branches. How far down and how far out do they extend?

roots, through the trunk of the tree, into the finest twigs and into the leaves. The veins of a leaf are really small bundles of xylem and phloem connected directly to these tissues in the stem. Thus materials in a plant can move in a direct line from the root tips to the leaves, or from leaves to root tips.

Roots do not form buds as stems do. They do, however, form branches, as you know if you have ever pulled up a plant. You discovered then how firmly roots anchor the plant to the soil. But they do something else just as useful. Roots that spread far hold the soil in place. When water rushes

CHAPTER EIGHT — ROOTS AND STEMS

159

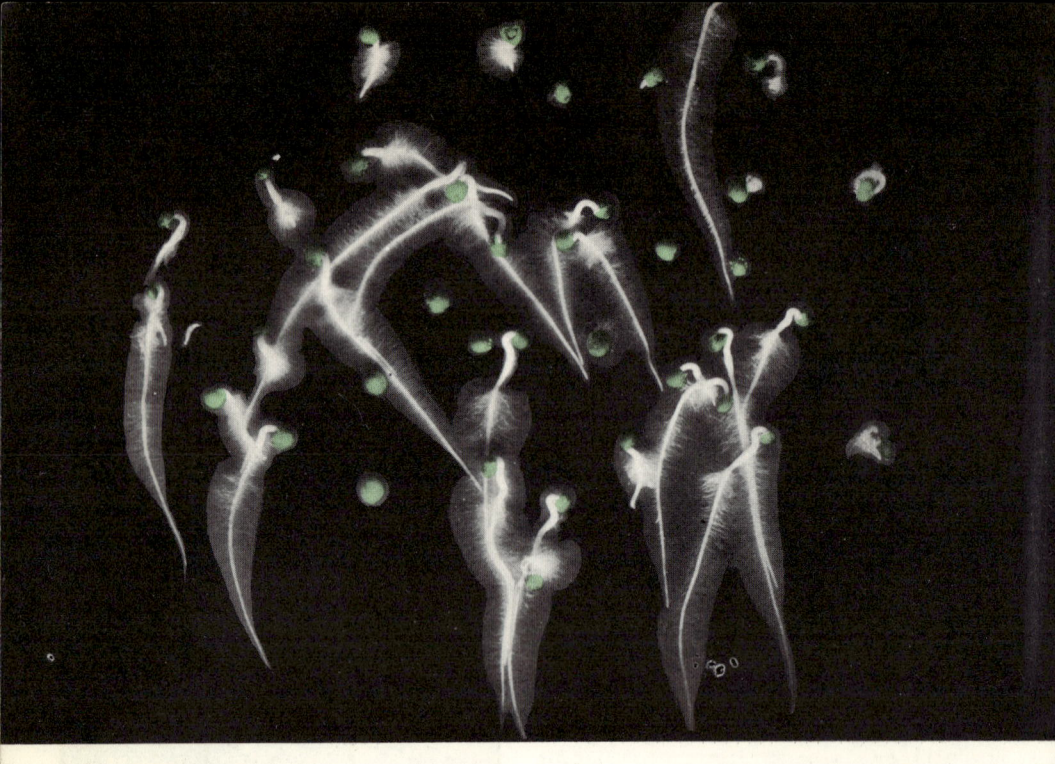

8.12 Sprouting seeds. Each one has a young root with root hairs. Where on each root are the shortest root hairs? Why do you find the shortest hairs here? *Blakiston*

down hillsides or strong winds blow, such roots are of great help to the farmer; they help save his soil.

Root tips. Like stems, roots grow in length only at their tips. It is only at or very near the tips of roots that cells are active. It is here that water and minerals enter. The older roots are covered with bark so thick that it is almost waterproof. You can easily get root tips to study by placing seeds between moist sheets of paper in a covered dish. Radish, bean, or corn seeds will do very well. See that the paper is kept moist at all times. In a few days the seeds will sprout as shown in Figure 8.12. At the very end of the root is a structure called a **root cap**, which you can see only if you have a microscope. It shows in Figure 8.10.

The cells of the root cap get rubbed away as the root pushes through the soil, but new cells form continuously. The root cap protects the young cells behind it from injury. Near the end of the root you will see a white, fuzzy growth. If you look at this part of the root with a magnifying glass or microscope, you will find that the fuzz is really made up of slender white hairs. These are **root hairs.** The root grows in length only between the cap and the first root hairs. Growth of the root in length, therefore, does not disturb the position of the root hairs in the soil. Figure 8.13 is a drawing of three root hairs growing among soil particles. You can see that each hair is really an extension of an epidermal cell. The walls of these cells are very thin, and see how closely they lie in

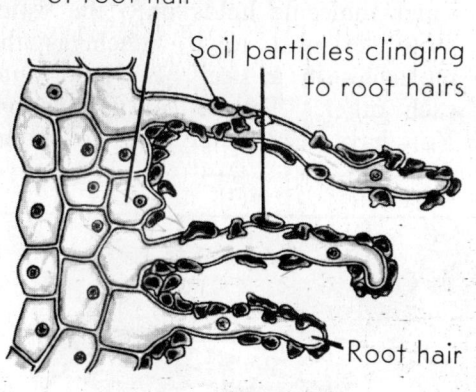

8.13 Three root hairs magnified. Each hair is a single cell.

contact with the particles of soil, and with the water in the ground. Even though root hairs are found only on the youngest tips of roots every plant has vast numbers of them. One rye plant may have as many as 14 billion root hairs with an estimated length of 6000 miles of root hairs.

How water and minerals enter roots. How do the water and the minerals get into the root hairs? You know that certain substances can diffuse through cell walls and cell membranes. You have learned also that plant cells have large vacuoles filled with cell sap. Cell sap is water containing both minerals and food substances. Now the water in the soil has minerals dissolved in it. These minerals diffuse into the cells when their concentration is greater outside than inside the cell; and normally it *is* greater outside than in. Water, too, diffuses into the cell whenever its concentration outside the cell is greater than its concentration inside. This is what normally happens to well-watered soil. But in fertilizing lawns and gardens, it is easy to put on so much fertilizer that the concentration of water becomes less outside than inside the root cells. You know what happens then. Water diffuses out of the cells, and the plant dies of drought, even though there may be lots of water around its roots. Most land plants cannot live in land flooded with sea water for this reason.

Water and minerals from root to leaf. In the daytime, in warm, sunny weather, a wet bathing suit dries quickly. The water in it evaporates. Water evaporates from plant leaves, too, in such weather. Evaporation from leaves is called **transpiration.** In any living plant the water tubes are filled with water at all times, from the tips of the roots to the veins in the leaves. Transpiration takes water out of the leaf cells, lowering the concentration of water in the cells. Water then diffuses into the cells from xylem in the veins. The veins are kept full by diffusion of water from the soil into the roots. While transpiration takes place in the leaves there is a continuous stream of water upward through the roots and stem with its branches. A good-sized birch tree may transpire as much as 350 quarts of water on a hot, dry day. A single corn plant may lose three or four quarts of water daily. If the plant is to live, all that is lost must come in through the roots.

You can now explain why plants must be handled carefully when they are transplanted. Parts of the roots, especially the root hairs, are destroyed in digging the plant. If all the leaves are left, transpiration continues at the same rate as before, but water can't get into an injured root system at that rate. Do you see why gardeners usually "cut back" the top of a plant when they transplant it? This slows down transpiration.

Biologists have long tried to explain the rise of water through the xylem tubes from roots to leaves, a distance of three hundred feet or more in some trees. It was formerly believed that capillarity played a part but now the rise is explained differently. It is believed that transpiration actually *pulls* water up through the xylem. Each water molecule holds onto the water molecules next to it, much as the molecules in a steel wire hold onto each other. This is called **cohesion.** You have seen water cling to water.

8.14 The sugar beet has a fleshy taproot which anchors the plant and stores much food. What else helps to hold this plant to the ground?

UNIT THREE — PLANTS — THE WORLD'S FOOD MAKERS

A drop of water will hang on the end of your finger. Try it. Enclosed in the narrow tubes of the xylem, water molecules cohere strongly enough to pull each other to the top of a tall tree.

But there is another force that at certain times and in certain plants causes water to rise. When the stem of quite a few kinds of plants is cut off near the ground, water flows out of the top of the cut stem above the roots. The plant is said to **bleed;** the water must have been pushed out by the roots. This is called **root pressure.** The flow of maple sap when the tree is "tapped" in spring is caused by root pressure. When transpiration stops or almost stops during rainy or foggy weather, root pressure of some plants forces water out through pores at the ends of the leaf veins. Much of the "dew" on grass on a springtime morning came out of the plant in this way. Just how a root can force water up through a stem is not surely known, nor is it known why only some plants have root pressure. Perhaps you will be the biologist who finds out.

It should now be clear to you how water enters, moves through, and goes out from a woody plant. Most of the minerals move to the stem and leaves in the stream of water passing through the xylem. Some rise in the phloem, however.

Variations in roots and stems. Some plants have one main root, called a **taproot.** These are usually hard to pull up, and trees with taproots like the oak are the least likely to blow over in a storm. Some herbs like beets and carrots have fleshy taproots which store much food. See Figure 8.14. In plants like the sweet potato, which has no taproot, other roots become thickened.

Stems, too, show variations. Some are very short. The dandelion and the carrot have stems so short that the leaves seem to grow from the root. Some stems grow horizontally on the surface of the ground; others grow horizontally just under the surface. The stems of a number of grasses and of ferns are like this. Some stems are thickened and hold much food. The white, or Irish, potato is a thickened underground stem which holds much starch. We think of the potato as a stem because it has buds (called eyes) like any true stem; and below the buds are scales, which sometimes are like tiny leaves. You have seen these buds sprout into stems and leaves along toward spring. See Figure 8.15.

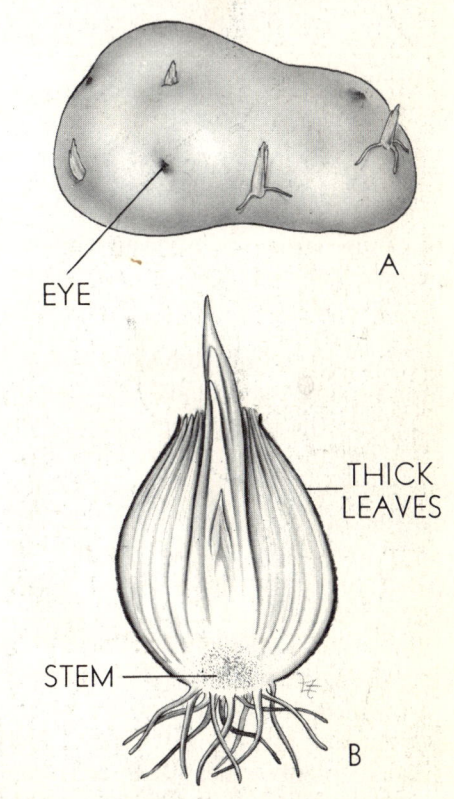

8.15 Two kinds of underground stems: **A,** potato, a tuber; **B,** onion, a bulb (note that much of this bulb is composed of thick leaves). Only a small part is stem.

CHAPTER EIGHT — ROOTS AND STEMS

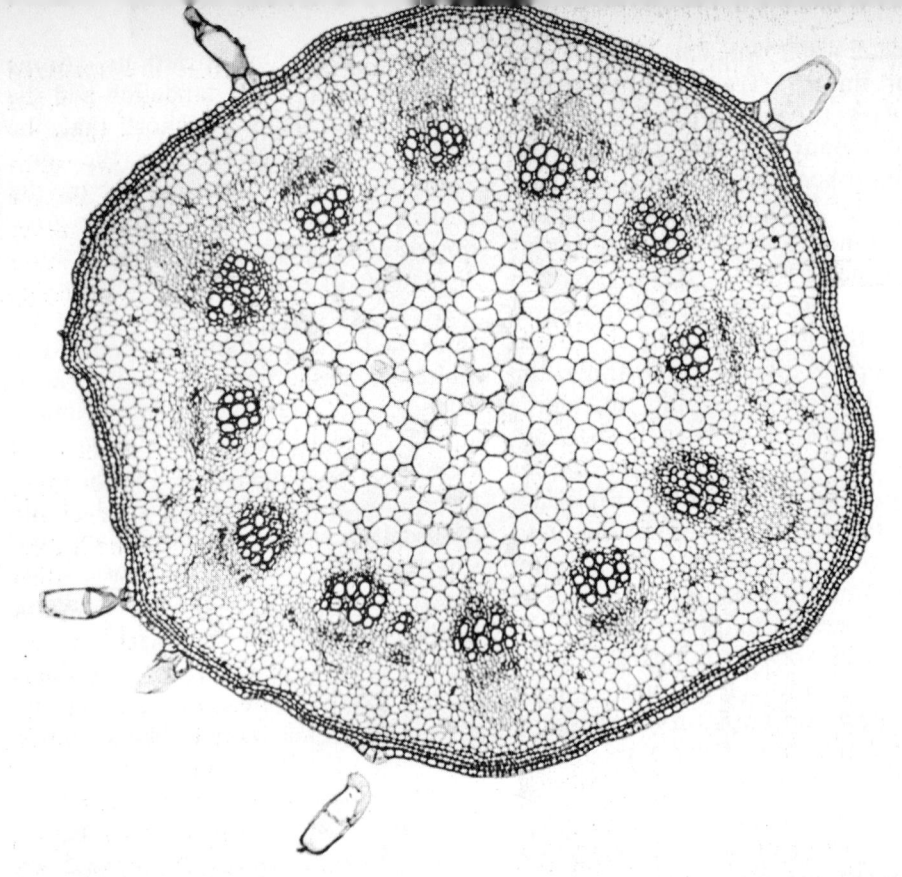

8.16 Cross section of a young sunflower stem. Note that the vascular bundles are arranged in a circle around the pith. *Modified from Textbook of Botany, Harper and Brothers*

Differences in branching of stems are especially striking. Some, like the pine and spruce, have only one main stem. As these trees get older, the lower branches keep right on growing longer. This makes the tree look like a cone with its point up. Some, like the elm, have a branched main stem. These often have the shape of an umbrella.

Stems show great variation in their internal structure, too. The stems of herbs, especially when they are young, have mostly thin-walled cells. They stand erect only when their cells contain all the water they can hold (when the cells are **turgid**). That is why herbs wilt if they lose water faster than they take it in. Dicot herbs contain little xylem and phloem; they have mostly pith and cortex. The xylem, cambium, and phloem are found in small **vascular bundles,** which lie in a circle around the pith. See Figure 8.16. Each bundle has its xylem part toward the pith and the phloem toward the outside of the stem. During growth, the cambium makes more xylem and more phloem, thus increasing the diameter of the stem. In some plants a cambium layer forms between the bundles and makes complete rings of xylem and phloem, as in trees.

Monocot stems, like those of corn, wheat, bamboo, and palm, have separate vascular bundles, too. See Figure 8.17. But these bundles have no

UNIT THREE — PLANTS — THE WORLD'S FOOD MAKERS

cambium. The bundles are scattered through the pith in corn and palms but are found near the outside of the stem in wheat and bamboo. Mature stems of wheat and bamboo are hollow because the pith cells are torn to pieces as the stem grows in diameter. Palm stems grow very little in diameter as the tree grows older.

What have you learned? Roots and stems of woody plants have conducting, or vascular, tissues which connect the lower parts of the plant with the leaves. Xylem consists of long, thick-walled tubes, or ducts, made of many cells from which the end walls disappear. Water and minerals travel through the ducts from roots to the leaves. Among the ducts lie thick-walled fibers which give strength to root and stem.

Phloem, which lies outside the xylem, has sieve tubes through which manufactured foods, principally, move down and up. Cambium cells lie between xylem and phloem. These form new xylem and phloem each growing season; and this accounts for the growth in thickness of the stem and root. The growth of xylem shows as annual rings in stems, telling us the age of the stem.

Both root and stem, when young, have epidermis on the outside. This is later replaced by bark, which consists of layers of cork (dead cells), thin-walled cortex cells, and phloem.

On examining the outside of a stem you find terminal and lateral buds. After being dormant for awhile the terminal buds of a woody stem grow, accounting for the increase in length of the stem. Some of the lateral buds form branches; some remain dormant for many years. Roots do not form buds, but they, too, form many branches, and they, too, grow longer

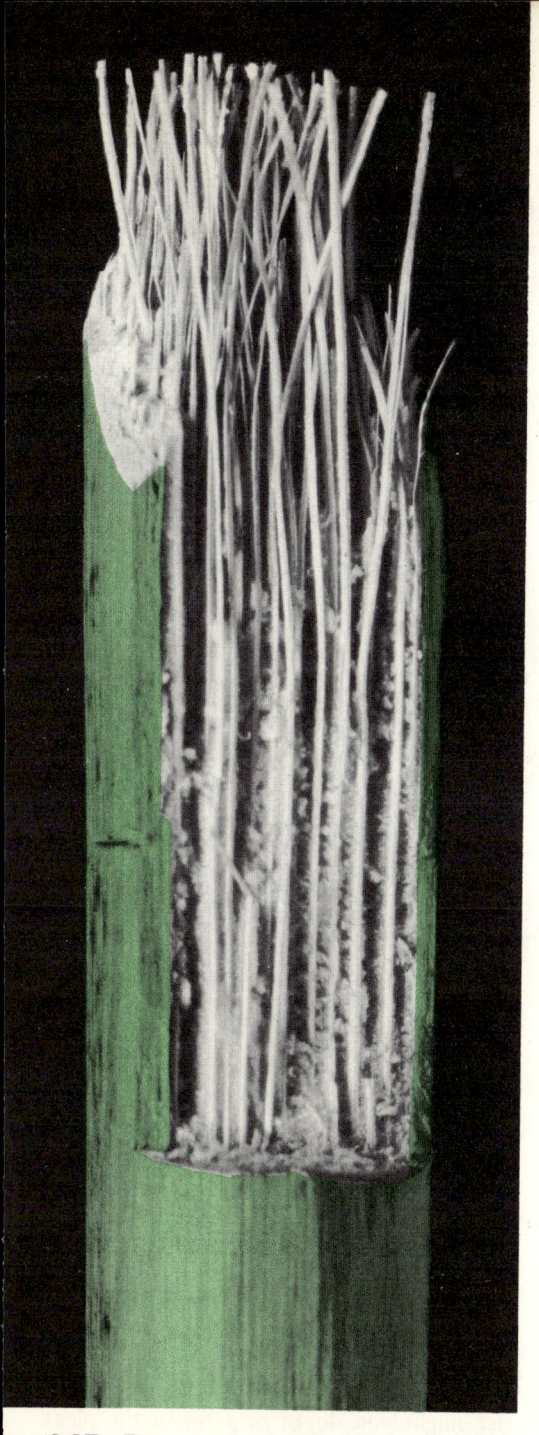

8.17 The vascular bundles in a corn stem. Corn is a monocot. How do these vascular bundles compare in position with the vascular bundles in a young dicot stem? Where is the pith? *Blakiston*

only at the tip. Near the tip of every root of most plants are tiny root hairs. A root hair is an extension of a single epidermal cell; it is, therefore, well fitted for absorbing water and minerals from the soil. Can you explain how each substance diffuses into the root hair cell?

From the root hairs the water travels into the ducts which extend to the veins of the leaves. As water is transpired from the leaves, this continuous stream of water through the ducts of root, stem, and leaves is pulled upward; the molecules of water cling together by cohesion. At certain times water is pushed up through the stem by root pressure.

Roots and stems, of course, are not all alike. Can you explain how monocot stems and stems of herbs differ from woody stems? Can you explain why the Irish potato and the tulip bulb are considered stems? Can you explain and describe the fleshy taproot of the carrot plant and the root of the sweet potato plant?

The roots and stems of woody plants seem dead to us. Large parts consist of dead cells, it is true; the living, active cells are concentrated in small regions. Some of these are the many growing tips, the cambium region, and the delicate root hair cells. But much happens in these living cells. Can you now explain what goes on in roots and stems and how they are fitted for helping the leaves in the manufacture of foods?

USEFUL WORDS IN BIOLOGY

terminal bud | cambium | heartwood
lateral bud | cork | sapwood
dormant | cortex | root cap
node | vascular tissues | root hair
internode | vascular bundles | transpiration
lenticel | ducts | turgid
xylem | sieve tubes | cohesion
phloem | annual rings

TEST YOURSELF

1. Tell the following about buds on a woody plant: (a) their position, (b) their covering and contents, (c) their dormancy, (d) how they determine the shape of the plant.
2. Arrange the following in tabular form. Beginning on the outside, name in order the tissues found in a woody stem, and next to each tissue write what it does for the plant.
3. Explain how the trunk of a tree grows in diameter.
4. (a) Draw a root hair cell and label the parts. (b) Show by means of labeled arrows what normally enters the root hair.
5. How much water may be transpired by a medium-sized birch tree in a day?
6. What are the two forces that move water from the roots to the leaves of a tree?

PROBLEMS TO THINK ABOUT

1. By studying a cross section of an old tree, one can tell that the year 1750 in the region where the tree grew was a particularly dry year and that the year 1820 was a wet one. How?
2. After watering a wilted house plant what else might you do to help revive the plant quickly?
3. Explain why transpiration may increase when water is added to the soil, and under what conditions adding water to the soil would decrease transpiration.

UNIT THREE — PLANTS — THE WORLD'S FOOD MAKERS

DO IT YOURSELF

1. How does the lack of certain minerals affect the plant? Plant about 30 soaked pea seeds in clean sand or Vermiculite, moistened with distilled water or rain water. When the seedlings are about three inches high, put several of them into each of the following solutions, with only the roots under water. Observe them closely for about a month and take notes every four days. Observe all parts of the plant. Is there a difference in the rate of growth?

Solution 1. Well water or tap water.
Solution 2. (common minerals present)

water (distilled or rain water)	1 liter
calcium nitrate	1 gram
magnesium sulfate	0.25 gram
monosodium acid phosphate	0.25 gram
potassium chloride	0.10 gram
ferric chloride	2 drops

Solution 3. (no nitrogen) Use calcium sulfate instead of calcium nitrate.
Solution 4. (no magnesium) Use calcium sulfate instead of magnesium sulfate.
Solution 5. (no calcium) Use sodium nitrate instead of calcium nitrate.
Solution 6. (no iron) Omit the ferric chloride.

2. The size of the root system. How do the roots of a young bean plant compare in extent with the parts above ground? Carefully uproot a young bean plant about five inches tall that has been raised in sawdust. Wash the root system clean. Measure the lengths of all the stems and all the roots and compare the total length of roots and stems. Make a diagram to show how they compare.

3. Study of root hairs. Sprout about six mustard or radish seeds on moist blotting paper in a small covered bowl. (Peas or corn may be used but they grow more slowly.) Do not permit the blotting paper to dry. Examine the roots every day with a magnifying glass. *Do not touch them.* When do the root hairs appear? Where do they grow? Take notes. If you have a microscope you might try to mount some root hairs in water and study them under low power. Record your observations.

4. Root structure in a taproot. Use young carrots with leaves attached. The stem is the very top of the carrot, to which the leaves are fastened. Cut off the tip of the carrots and place them in a tumbler containing red ink and water. After the plants have been in bright light for a few hours, cut cross sections of a carrot at various levels; cut a longitudinal section. Can you explain what you see? Draw and label: epidermis, cortex, vascular tissue or ducts, cells storing starch. How can you discover which cells store starch?

5. How much water is lost by a potted house plant? Use a geranium or some other plant which has one main stem. Water the plant well. Enclose the pot and the soil in a rubber sheet or aluminum foil so that water can be lost only through the leaves and stem. Weigh the plant carefully and place it in the sun. Weigh it again after two hours, three hours, and if possible just before dark. Keep notes. Try to calculate the amount of water lost per square inch of leaf surface.

6. Getting plants to root. Read "Construction and Use of a Rooting Box" by Thomas Coy in *The American Biology Teacher*, May 1954. Use this method to raise some shrubs to plant at your home or school.

ADVENTURES IN READING

1. *Plants* by Herbert S. Zim, Harcourt, Brace, 1947. Contains suggestions for root and stem experiments.
2. "The Rise of Water in Plants" by Victor A. Greulach, *Scientific American*, October 1952. Throws some light on a question which has been bothering botanists for many years.
3. *Circle of the Seasons* by Edwin Way Teale, Dodd, Mead, 1953. In the chapter "November" you can read how leaves are cut off in the autumn.
4. For reference use *Botany* by Robbins and Weier, Wiley, 1950, recommended in Chapter 7.

Unit Four

How our bodies work

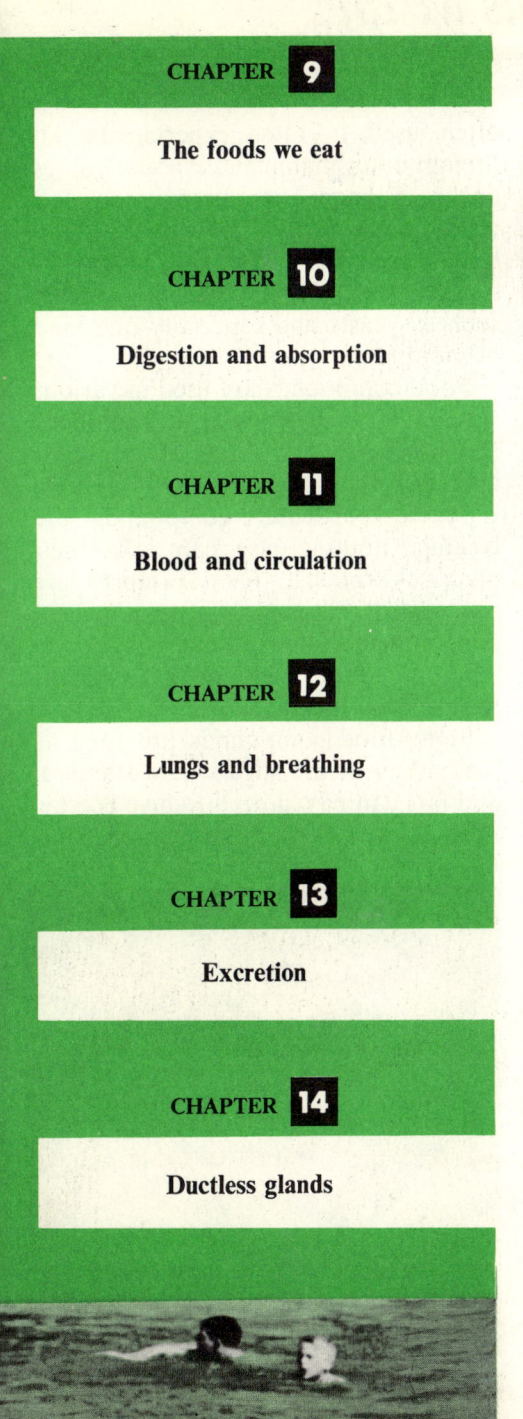

CHAPTER 9

The foods we eat

CHAPTER 10

Digestion and absorption

CHAPTER 11

Blood and circulation

CHAPTER 12

Lungs and breathing

CHAPTER 13

Excretion

CHAPTER 14

Ductless glands

A great teacher and writer of biology who lived in England at the close of the last century once wrote: "Suppose it were perfectly certain that the life and fortune of every one of us would, one day or other, depend upon his winning or losing a game at chess. Don't you think we should all consider it a primary duty to learn at least the names and the moves of the pieces?"

Of course, Thomas Henry Huxley, who wrote that, meant this: How many of us have learned the names and the moves of the pieces in our bodies which enable us to win in the game of life and death? You look with surprise at those of your friends who do not know the scores of the major baseball games from day to day. Do you look with surprise at those who do not know the names and the exact position of the organs in their own bodies?

Do you know how your blood is circulating even as you read these words? Do you know the needs of all of your billions of cells? Do you know how foods are changed into simpler substances that can be made into the protoplasm that is you — your brain, your muscles, your bones? And do you know of the substances in your blood (hormones) that regulate many of the activities in your body, keeping you normal in size and weight and in brain development?

In short, what makes these young people perform as they do? How much do you really know of this machine that is you — a machine more intricate than the greatest calculating machines, a machine more efficient in its use of fuel than any machine designed by man? Turn the page to begin this fascinating story.

Chapter 9

The foods we eat

The source of our foods. We eat bread, beefsteak, potatoes, beans, and hundreds of other foods. Where do they all come from originally? Directly or indirectly, they come from green plants. You have read that green plants provide all the food that we and all other animals eat. You read that the green plants manufacture sugars (photosynthesis), that the sugars may be changed to starches or to fats, and that the sugars may combine with some of the minerals, making proteins.

The make-up of our foods. Lamb has a different make-up from beef and a different taste; beans differ from peas. Yet in all our many hundreds of foods we get the same few kinds of compounds over and over again. We get proteins, sugars, starches, fats, minerals, water, and, last but not least, vitamins. These food compounds are called "nutrients" in some books. It is these compounds that are needed by our bodies.

In the many kinds of animals and plants there are hundreds of different kinds of proteins, fats, sugars, and starches. And in each food we eat there are different combinations of these various food compounds. Naturally, then, no two kinds of foods taste the same or are the same.

How we use each food substance. No one yet knows exactly how each food substance is used; experiments to find out more about this are being performed all over the world. The laboratory white rat is the animal most often used in these experiments, although other mammals, especially dogs and pigs, have often been used. Recently much has been learned about how a cell uses food substances by studying simple microscopic plants, such as yeasts and especially one kind of mold (*Neurospora*).

Food compounds are used in various ways in our bodies. Special compounds are necessary for some of our cells and for special purposes in all our cells. If these particular compounds are lacking, nothing else can take their place. Proteins, for example, are needed for the making of protoplasm; and minerals help build up bones. And, of course, you know that vitamins have special uses.

Some food compounds are used as fuel. Any of the sugars, and starches, and fats can be oxidized to give energy. And by being slightly changed, they

9.1 What was the original source of the egg eaten by the skunk and the milk lapped

UNIT FOUR — HOW OUR BODIES WORK

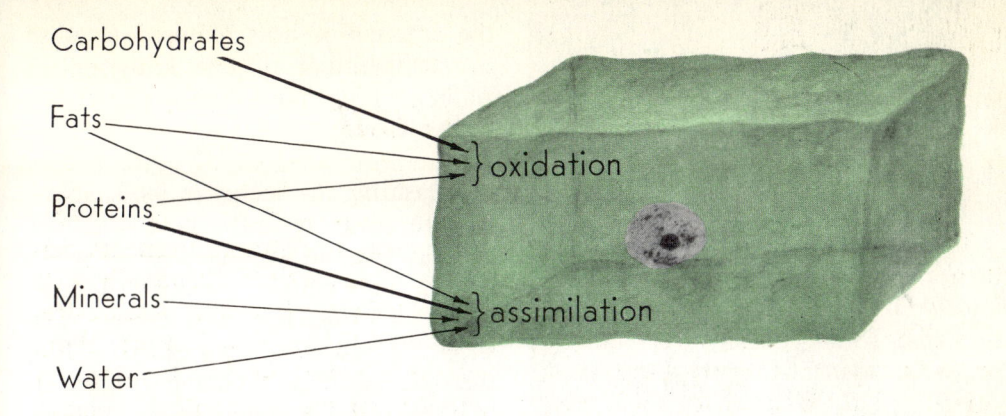

Carbohydrates
Fats
Proteins
} oxidation
Minerals
Water
} assimilation

9.2 How some food compounds are used by a living cell. In what two principal ways are food compounds used? Which compounds are used in each process? Why are two arrows drawn as darker lines? Why is it important to know how foods are used?

can be stored and used later. If one kind is lacking, no harm is done; some of the others can be used in their place. Proteins can be oxidized, too, to give energy. It makes no difference which kind of protein; one kind will do as well as any other kind for oxidation. But, in general, the body does not waste its proteins for oxidation.

Energy in the body. You know that the carbohydrates, fats, and proteins contain chemical energy. When they are oxidized their chemical energy is changed to heat energy and other kinds of energy. Heat energy given off by oxidation keeps the temperature high enough for your cells to carry on their many activities. Since energy is so important to us, we should know just how much energy we can expect to get from each bit of food we eat. The chemical energy of food can be measured as heat energy. Let us see how that can be done.

Measuring heat energy. Measuring heat energy is not the same thing as reading temperature on a thermometer. But to measure heat energy, we must have a unit for measuring. If you want to know how much taller you

up by the cat? What is the source of all the food eaten by animals? Which food substances do all contain? *Johnson, Schneider and Schwartz, Gehr*

CHAPTER NINE — THE FOODS WE EAT

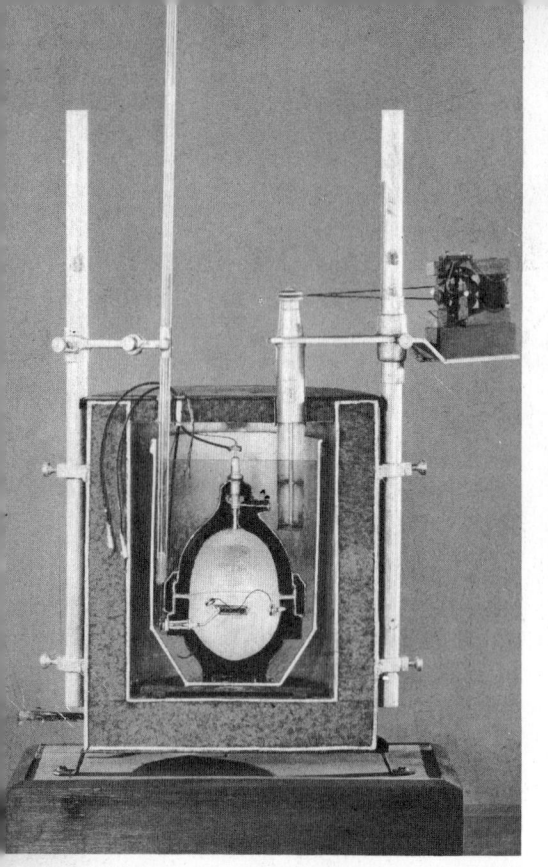

9.3 Cross section of a calorimeter. Where is the food burned? Of what use is the thermometer? The water is stirred by the electric motor. Why is the outside wall of the calorimeter so thick? *American Museum of Natural History*

are than I, you use the foot and inch as your units of measurement. If you want to know how much more you weigh than I, you use the pound as the unit. These units were agreed upon a long time ago. And you are so accustomed to measuring in feet and pounds that you have a good idea of how long a foot is and how heavy a pound is. Now the unit for measuring heat energy is the **Calorie,** with a capital C. You have heard the word many times, of course. A Calorie is the amount of heat required to raise the temperature of one kilogram of water (a little more than a quart) one degree Centigrade.

Measuring the energy in food. Now we are ready to learn how scientists can say that an average slice of white bread, for example, contains 70 Calories. This is how it is done. The slice of bread is weighed exactly. It is then placed inside a chamber in which it is burned. Around the chamber is water in a jacket. Can you see the jacket in Figure 9.3? The outside of the jacket is insulated with asbestos or some other material that prevents the escape of heat. All the heat given off by burning goes into the water. Of course, the amount of water used must be measured. And its temperature at the start must be known. Then by seeing how much the temperature of the water rises you can know how many Calories of heat were given off by the burning bread. This apparatus is a **calorimeter** (cal′o-rim′e-ter). By consulting the table on page 186, you can see how much some common foods vary in the amount of energy we might get from them.

Measuring our energy output. Sometimes your physician is interested in finding out how much energy your body gives off. He could put you into a large-sized calorimeter built for people, but instead, he measures the amount of carbon dioxide you give off or the amount of oxygen you take in. (See Fig. 9.4.) Then knowing your exact size and weight, he can calculate how much heat energy your body gives off. He calculates your heat production when your body is at complete rest, as complete as it can ever be while your heart beats, your chest goes through breathing motions, and your other

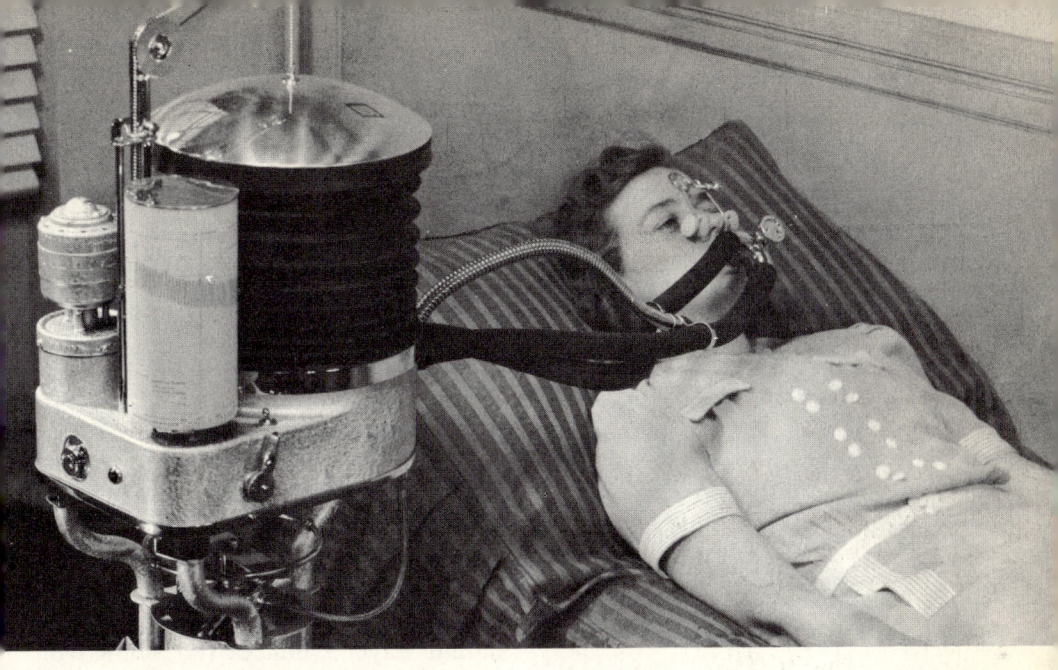

9.4 A basal metabolism test. The apparatus measures the amount of oxygen used by the girl while at rest. How does the physician use such data? *Sanborn Company*

internal organs are at work. You are allowed no food for several hours before the test is made; your digestive organs will, therefore, be almost at rest. In this way the physician gets what is called your **basal metabolism** (met-tab′o-lism), or your metabolism while you are resting. Metabolism means all the chemical changes going on in the body. The more work you do, the more chemical changes are going on, and the higher will be your metabolism rate.

The basal metabolism is highest in young babies and grows less throughout life. In men it is generally somewhat higher than in women. But even normal individuals show great differences in basal metabolism rates.

Your Calorie needs. Look at the table which gives your average daily Calorie needs. Of course, these are very rough estimates, for the number of Calories you need per day depends not only on your age and your sex but also on your size and your weight and how you spend your day — how active you are. You will be interested in the table which shows how many Calories are used in a variety of occupations. This table can be used to calculate your actual Calorie needs if you multiply the figures, given in decimals, by your body weight. For example, if you weigh 120 pounds, in sitting quietly for an hour, you will need 120 × 0.2 or 24 Calories. But the

TABLE 8
AVERAGE DAILY CALORIE NEED

Age	Boys	Girls
12	2300–3000	2100–3000
13	2500–3500	2300–3400
14	2600–3800	2400–3000
15	2700–4000	2400–2800
16	2700–4000	2250–2800
17	2800–4000	2250–2800

CHAPTER NINE — THE FOODS WE EAT

TABLE 9
CALORIES USED IN VARIOUS ACTIVITIES

Activities	Calories per pound per hour
Sitting quietly	0.2
Standing relaxed	0.2
Walking (*3 miles per hour*)	0.9
Walking (*4 miles per hour*)	1.5
Running	3.3
Swimming (*2 miles per hour*)	3.6
Bicycling (*racing*)	3.4
Bicycling (*moderate speed*)	1.1
Playing ping-pong	2.0
Fencing	3.3
Carpentry (*heavy*)	1.0
Dancing (*waltz*)	1.4
Dishwashing	0.5
Violin-playing	0.3
Typewriting rapidly	0.5
Writing	0.2

figures you obtain in this way are *over and above* your basal metabolism needs. Those can be easily calculated by using this little table.

TABLE 10
BASAL METABOLISM

Calories per pound per day		
Age	Boys	Girls
13	18	14
14	19	17
15	16	11
16	15	10
17	14	10

However, once you have figured out your average Calorie needs, and once you know, in a general way, which foods give many and which foods give few Calories you can probably afford to forget about Calories. Of course, if you are much overweight or underweight you will, in any case, seek the advice of a physician. And don't be misled by all you hear and read about Calories in advertisements of foods and drinks. Some young people nowadays are so anxious to keep their weight down that they get too few Calories. On the other hand, middle aged or older people must be careful not to get too many Calories. They should know that it takes only 4000 extra Calories a day to produce a pound of fat!

More about proteins. In planning food for a family there is much more to be thought of than Calories. There is a great deal we should know about proteins. Your proteins should provide about 25% of the Calories you eat in a day. About 30% of your Calories comes from fats, and the rest from carbohydrates. The average person should have 3 ounces (80 grams) of protein a day. The table on page 186 shows you what percentage of each food is protein, fat, and carbohydrate. You already know that you must have some protein in your diet; you need it for building tissues.

Another important thing to remember about proteins is that there are so many different kinds of proteins. Some are more useful to us than others. In general, proteins in animal foods are more like the proteins in our own cells; therefore, they are more useful to us than plant proteins. You read earlier that plants build up (synthesize) proteins. During this building up they make compounds called amino acids. These they put together in various proportions to build a protein molecule. And a huge and complicated molecule it is! There are some 25 of these building blocks, or amino acids, known to chemists. Some of the amino acids that you need for building your cells occur in plants in such small amounts that you need large quantities of that plant food to give you enough of the particular amino acid. Wheat, for example, with its many proteins, has only one protein which has the right building blocks and which can take the place of an animal protein. Legumes (beans and peas and so on) have various useful amino acids. This is particularly true of soybeans and peanuts.

More about fats and carbohydrates. As you know, these are the energy foods. Fats give twice as much energy, pound for pound, as carbohydrates and proteins. However, don't count on getting too much of your energy from the fats you eat. They are harder for your digestive organs to deal with than the other food substances. Also if energy is needed immediately there is no food as satisfactory as sugar. You may know that lumps of sugar and bars of chocolate are often given to football players just before a game. The fats and carbohydrates that you don't oxidize are changed to a great extent, into body fat. This is stored under the skin, in the muscles, and next to internal organs.

Some fat tissue is useful to keep us warm. And when a person is unable to eat because of lack of food, or because of illness, this fat tissue can be oxidized, providing energy. But remember what you read about too much fat, especially as you grow older. It has been said, "The thin rats bury the fat ones."

Don't jump to the conclusion, however, that every fat person is a big eater. He may actually eat less than another person who stays thin. His body deals with the food differently. But this much is clear: he is eating more than *his* body needs.

Water in the diet. Under normal conditions, without exercise, you need about two quarts of water daily. Most of this comes from the water and beverages you drink; some is contained in the solids you eat. Water is used in making protoplasm; it helps in diffusion by dissolving many substances; in the blood it helps to carry substances from one part of the body to another; and it has many other uses.

Minerals. We need very small amounts of the minerals but they are just as important to us as the foods made by plants. Of course, we get most of our minerals from plants; they absorb them from the soil. Minerals are of many kinds, and they have many uses in the body. You may know that calcium and phosphorus compounds are needed for making bones and teeth and that iron compounds are needed for making red blood cells. But to enable the red blood cells to use the iron, a very tiny amount of copper is also needed. Sodium, potassium, and calcium compounds affect the heartbeat. Magnesium, calcium, and chlorides help indirectly in digestion. So does zinc; and it helps in respiration too. Iodine is used by the thyroid gland. Fluorine helps prevent tooth decay; and many communities add it to the water.

In an ordinary diet, if your vegetable food is cooked in such a way that minerals are not lost, or if some vegetable food is eaten raw, you get enough of most of the minerals. But you should make sure that your foods give you enough calcium, iron, and iodine. In many parts of the world, we can't depend on vegetables for iodine. It can then be obtained from salt-water fish and other sea food or from iodized salt.

In experiments to discover the use of minerals, rats have been much used. See Figures 9.5 and 9.6. They have also been used in many experiments

9.5 Experiments teach much about diet. If the rats are of the same age and sex, what might have caused the differences in weight and appearance? *General Baking Co.*

which have taught us about still other important food substances, the vitamins.

Two mysterious diseases. In former days sailors on long voyages almost always fell ill. Their muscles ached, blood flowed from their noses if they were very ill; they became weaker and weaker and often died. They suffered from **scurvy**. Their food consisted of salted meat and dry crackers. Were they poisoned by this? Or was it the long exposure to sea air which made them ill? About the year 1600 an English ship's doctor tried giving lime juice to sailors, together with the salted meat and dry crackers they usually got. These men did not get scurvy. As a result of this experiment a law was later passed in England: A large

9.6 These rats of the same sex were born in the same litter. At 22 weeks of age, one weighed $2\frac{1}{3}$ times as much as the other. Their diet differed in only one respect. The large rat received more calcium. What conclusions can you draw? *U.S. Department of Agriculture*

UNIT FOUR — HOW OUR BODIES WORK

supply of lemons or limes must be taken on all long voyages. This is how English sailors got the name "limeys."

Somewhat later, attention was called to a disease in the Japanese navy. The sailors were eating almost nothing but rice, polished rice, such as we usually eat. The men on long voyages soon suffered from numbness and then paralysis. They grew very weak, and eventually some died. This was not scurvy. It was a disease which had long been known in the east among people who were too poor to eat anything but rice. The disease was called **beriberi** (ber'ree-ber'ree). So the government tried the experiment of giving their men other foods in addition to the rice. This worked; outbreaks of beriberi became less frequent. The government officials were satisfied; but scientists were not satisfied — their curiosity had been aroused. Why should a diet of polished rice make men ill?

A mystery is cleared up. Some years after the new diet had been ordered for the navy, Dr. Christian Eijkman (Ike-man), a Dutch scientist living in the East Indies, became interested. Hundreds of people suffering from beriberi came to the hospital daily. They must be helped; the cause of beriberi must be found. Now Eijkman had noticed that when chickens ate nothing but polished rice, they showed much the same symptoms as his patients. They developed a disease called polyneuritis (polly-new-rye'tis). Figure 9.7 shows a chicken sick with polyneuritis. Eijkman began to wonder: Are the "polishings," or coatings, which are removed from rice when it goes through the mill of any importance? He decided to try out his hypothesis (guess) by using chickens in a carefully controlled experiment.

9.7 This chicken has polyneuritis, a disease like beriberi in man. How can it be cured? *Illinois Agricultural Experiment Station*

He began by feeding a large number of chickens a diet consisting only of polished rice. As he expected, they soon developed polyneuritis. Then he divided his sick chickens into two groups; one group was given more polished rice; the other group was given polished rice with the polishings added to it. Within a few hours this group showed improvement; soon they recovered completely. Those in the other group died. After repeating his experiment, Eijkman concluded that the coating of the grain of rice contains something that is needed by chickens. He then ordered his patients to eat these coatings or polishings, and they, too, recovered from beriberi.

When other scientists read of these experiments they began to study the chemical make-up of these polishings. Finally, in 1911 Casimir Funk, a Polish

CHAPTER NINE — THE FOODS WE EAT

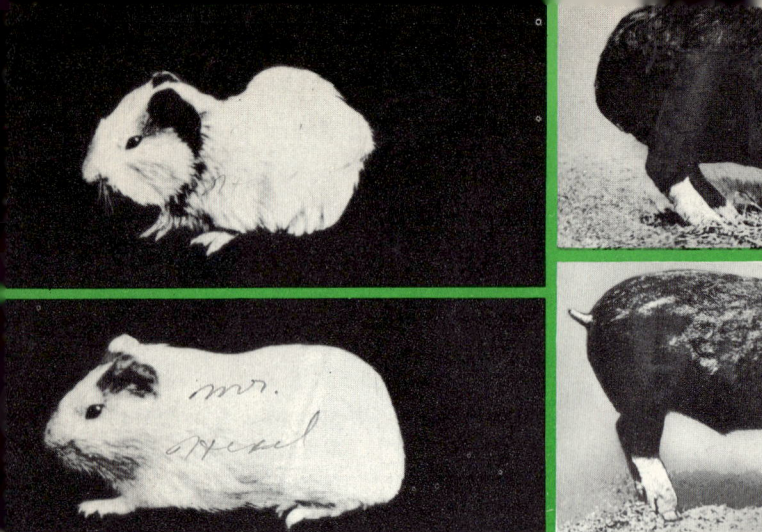

9.8 The smaller guinea pig has scurvy. What must have been lacking in its diet? What kinds of food would supply the lack? *U.S. Department of Agriculture*

9.9 Above is a pig suffering from rickets. Below is the same pig after small daily doses of cod liver oil. What did the oil supply? *Wisconsin Agricultural Experiment Station*

biologist, extracted the important substance. He called it a "vitamine." Later this word was changed to **vitamin** and the substance was called vitamin B. More recently it has been renamed **thiamin,** a part of vitamin B complex.

Another vitamin is discovered. In the meantime other scientists were on the track of another vitamin. In feeding experiments with rats they gave the rats measured amounts of pure carbohydrates, proteins, fats, minerals, and water — just what they thought would make the best diet for the rats. To their surprise, in each experiment the rats developed an eye disease; then they sickened, and finally died. In their next experiment, as the eye disease appeared, they divided the rats into two groups. Those in the first group were given small amounts of raw milk in addition to their regular food. Almost at once these rats regained their health and as long as they continued to get the raw milk they remained normal. The rats in the second group, in the control group, remained on the original diet. They received no milk, and they soon died. It was concluded that the raw milk contained something else besides the regular food compounds and that this "something" is necessary for health and life; and evidently only very small amounts of it are needed. It was called **vitamin A.**

Beriberi, scurvy, and the eye disease caused by lack of vitamin A are called **deficiency** diseases — diseases that are caused by a lack of some substance in the diet which is necessary to life. But these are not the only deficiency diseases known.

Further discoveries. Other controlled animal experiments were now performed. Guinea pigs were given scurvy and were then cured by being given foods containing the necessary vitamin, which was called vitamin C. (Figure 9.8.)

Important discoveries followed one another in close succession. More than

178 UNIT FOUR — HOW OUR BODIES WORK

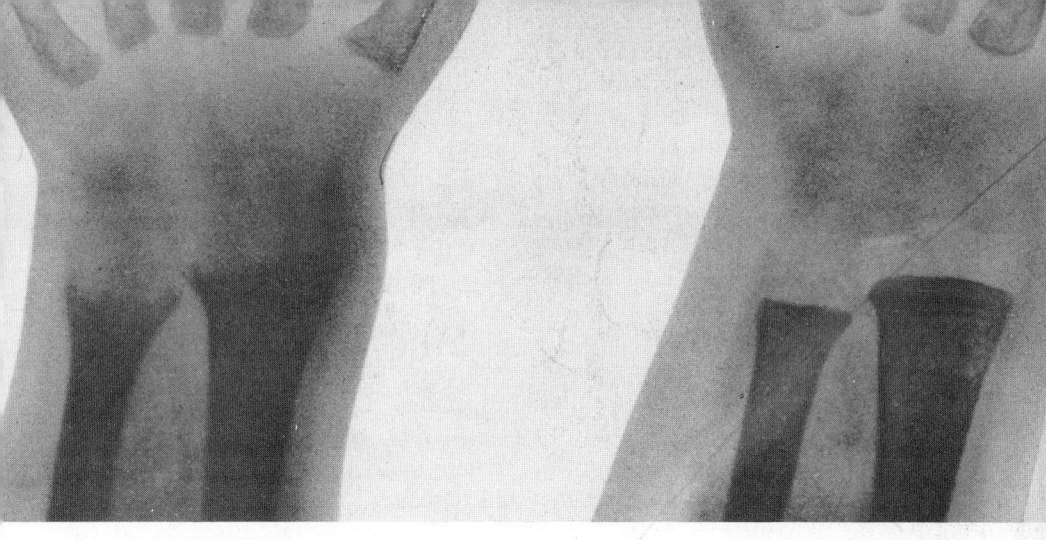

9.10 The x-ray to the left was taken on Feb. 3. This child had a bad case of rickets as shown by the fuzzy edge of the two bones in the arm. Treatment was begun. The second x-ray was taken June 25. What difference can you see in the ends of the arm bones? What treatment was probably given the child? *General Baking Co.*

a dozen vitamins are now known. No doubt others will be discovered. As each vitamin is discovered scientists try to learn four things about the vitamin: (1) what the vitamin does in the body; (2) its exact chemical composition so that they can make it in the laboratory; (3) whether the body can make the vitamin for itself, and if not, which foods are rich in it or contain it; (4) how quickly foods lose their vitamins when they grow old or when they are cooked.

Vitamin A. Vitamin A is one of the few vitamins we can make in our own bodies; other animals, too, make it and store it in the liver. Liver, therefore, is a food that is rich in vitamin A. Egg yolk, butter, and the fatty part of milk are also good sources of it.

The liver can make its own vitamin A only if it is supplied with **carotene** (care'o-teen). Carotene is a yellow substance found in carrots and other yellow vegetables and fruits. Green, leafy vegetables also contain it; its yellow color is here hidden by the green.

Vitamin A does not dissolve in water; thus none is lost if you cook vegetables in too much water. But extreme heating, especially in the presence of oxygen, destroys it. Don't overcook your vegetables and, if possible, use a pressure cooker which keeps out air.

You would think that all of us could easily get enough vitamin A; but somehow a good many people have a slight deficiency of vitamin A. Your body uses it for making **visual purple** in the eyes, a substance you need for seeing in the dark. Lack of vitamin A makes the tear glands dry up with great damage to the eyes.

Vitamin D. Have you heard of babies or young children having rickets? Their bones and teeth remain soft; their legs may not support them properly. Figure 9.9 shows you how rickets affects a young pig. Calcium and phosphorus compounds cannot be built into the bone tissue without the help of vitamin D. And milk, which contains the minerals, has practically no vitamin D. That is why babies and young animals are given cod-liver oil or halibut-liver oil; these contain large amounts of vitamin D. Until this was discovered you can imagine there were many children with rickets.

Look closely at Figure 9.10. Natural foods contain almost no vitamin D. But the cereals, yeasts, and other plants contain a substance closely related to vitamin D (it is called ergosterol). It can easily be turned into vitamin D. All that is needed is to expose the grains or even the bread to ultraviolet light. Exposing a substance to ultraviolet light is called **irradiation** (ir-ray-dee-ay'shun).

Many animal tissues contain **cholesterol** (ko-les'te-role), a substance related to vitamin D. This also can be irradiated and turned into vitamin D. Milk contains cholesterol, and both fresh and evaporated milk are often irradiated to add vitamin D. Instead of irradiating milk, fish-liver oils or yeast can be irradiated and fed to cows. The cows will then give milk richer in vitamin D.

We, like many other animals, have a substance in our bodies that can be changed into vitamin D. It is in the skin; and the sunshine, which contains ultraviolet light, can bring about the change. That is why vitamin D is sometimes called the "sunshine vitamin." But if we live in smoky cities or in parts of the world which have long winters, we can't count on getting much vitamin D that way. Another trouble is that window glass, except very special glass made of quartz, keeps out the ultraviolet light.

Vitamin C. Vitamin C is now generally known as **ascorbic acid,** which means the substance which keeps you from getting scurvy. The vitamin, besides its other uses, seems in some way to be connected with the making of connective tissues in the blood vessels. When your tissues bruise easily, you may have a mild deficiency of ascorbic acid. No doubt you know that citrus fruits, that is, lemons, grapefruit, oranges, and limes, contain much ascorbic acid. Tomatoes, both canned and raw, are just about as good for you. And so are many green vegetables, especially spinach, broccoli, parsley, and green peppers, and cabbage, too, when eaten raw. Ascorbic acid is the most easily lost of all the vitamins in cooking because it dissolves so easily in water. For this reason, keep the water in which vegetables have been cooked. High temperatures destroy it, too, especially in the presence of oxygen. And if soda is added in cooking to keep the vegetables looking green, even more of the vitamin is lost. An acid, however, helps to preserve the vitamin. Tomatoes, therefore, being acid, can be boiled without danger of destroying the vitamin. In canning, heat is applied while the tomatoes are in sealed cans; little of the ascorbic acid is destroyed. That is why canned tomatoes make a good substitute for raw citrus fruits.

You can see that to get a good natural supply of ascorbic acid you must eat many vegetables regularly. You cannot make this vitamin in your own body, and animal foods have practically none.

The vitamin B complex. One of the most important vitamins in this group is **thiamin,** once called vitamin B_1. As more and more vitamins are being discovered, each one is given a name instead of a letter. This is the vitamin that is thrown away with the "polishings" of rice. It seems that all plants can make it but no animals. The

9.11 The rat above was fed a diet lacking niacin. It is shown below after six weeks of a diet rich in niacin. Explain why it is necessary to use large numbers of animals when experiments of this kind are conducted. *U.S. Department of Agriculture*

yeast plant makes a great deal of it. Wheat, like the other grains, has a good supply too, but it is lost when the grain is made into flour. Have you ever seen the words "vitamin enriched" on the wrappings of white bread? Like most other vitamins this one can be made at small expense in the laboratory. It can easily be put back into the flour by the baker. Dried beans, peas, soybeans, and peanuts are also fairly well supplied with it. Although we won't get beriberi, some of us may well be a little short of thiamin. This shows itself in fatigue and a poor appetite, later in loss of weight and irritability.

To this day hundreds of millions of undernourished people in Asia lack thiamin. Their diet is still mostly rice; they cannot afford to raise other foods. Dr. Robert R. Williams, who first isolated and made thiamin, believes that at a cost of 35 cents a year per capita (35 cents spent on each individual) these people might get sufficient thiamin to keep them from showing symptoms of the lack of this vitamin.

Niacin (ny′e-sin) is in the B complex group. This was once called the rich man's vitamin because it is found in the largest amounts in the more expensive foods, such as meat, fish, and eggs. Milk contains a substance that can be changed into niacin in our bodies. Like thiamin, it is found also in yeast and in those parts of grains lost in milling. You can get skin and nerve disorders from a deficiency of niacin.

CHAPTER NINE — THE FOODS WE EAT

But most of us don't suffer from a deficiency of it. Until this vitamin was discovered there were frequent outbreaks of a disease known as pellagra. It was thought for a while that this must be a contagious disease, since almost all members of certain communities showed the symptoms of pellagra. But then it was discovered that these were always communities in which the members were poorly fed, because of either poverty or ignorance. Scientists then suspected a vitamin lack.

Riboflavin (rye-bo-flay'vin) is another vitamin found with thiamin and niacin in whole grains. Milk has it too. Have you noticed how many of the vitamins are found in milk? Riboflavin is stored, also, in the kidney and liver of animals, and in eggs, and fish. Its lack causes various eye, mouth, and skin symptoms.

Biotin is also in the B complex group. Too little biotin may give you an inflammation of the skin. Again milk, and liver and kidneys have a good supply; and so has molasses. And there is **folic acid** in the B complex group; it is found in green leaves. That's easy to remember; folic comes from the same word as foliage. This vitamin is now used for treating certain kinds of anemias (shortage of red blood cells). So is another B complex vitamin, B_{12}. This by no means finishes the list of B complex vitamins. But it is good to remember that if we are getting enough thiamin, niacin, and riboflavin in our diets, we are sure to get enough also of the others of the B complex group.

Other vitamins. There is a whole group of "E" vitamins found in a large variety of foods. No doubt they are important to us; but it is not known just what they do for us. When hens lack vitamin E, their eggs do not hatch. Rats seem to need it, too, for reproduction.

There is also a group of "K" vitamins. Normally we can make vitamin K in our own bodies. It is found, too, in egg yolk, liver, green vegetables, and tomatoes. It helps in the coagulation of blood.

Saving vitamins. You already know that some vitamins are destroyed when exposed to the oxygen of the air; the warmer it is, the faster they go. So your first rule is refrigeration! Your second rule is: Don't let vegetables stand around after they are peeled and cut up; that exposes more surface to oxygen. Third: If possible, cook in closed pots to keep out as much air as possible. And start cooking your vegetables in boiling water; this has lost its air and thus the dissolved oxygen.

Most vitamins are soluble in water. Therefore, don't overcook vegetables and cook in as little water as possible; don't pour vitamins and minerals down the drain.

Vitamin pills. Most of the vitamins are now made in the laboratory and can be bought in capsules or pills at the drugstore. Normally, you will not have to depend on them. If you eat a varied diet which contains fresh vegetables and some raw vegetables, you are likely to get all the vitamins you need. It is better to depend on natural foods, for in this way you may be getting other vitamins which have not yet been discovered but which may be of great importance.

A greater interest in diet. You have heard and read about conservation, haven't you? The papers are full of it.

EAT THE BASIC SEVEN EVERY DAY

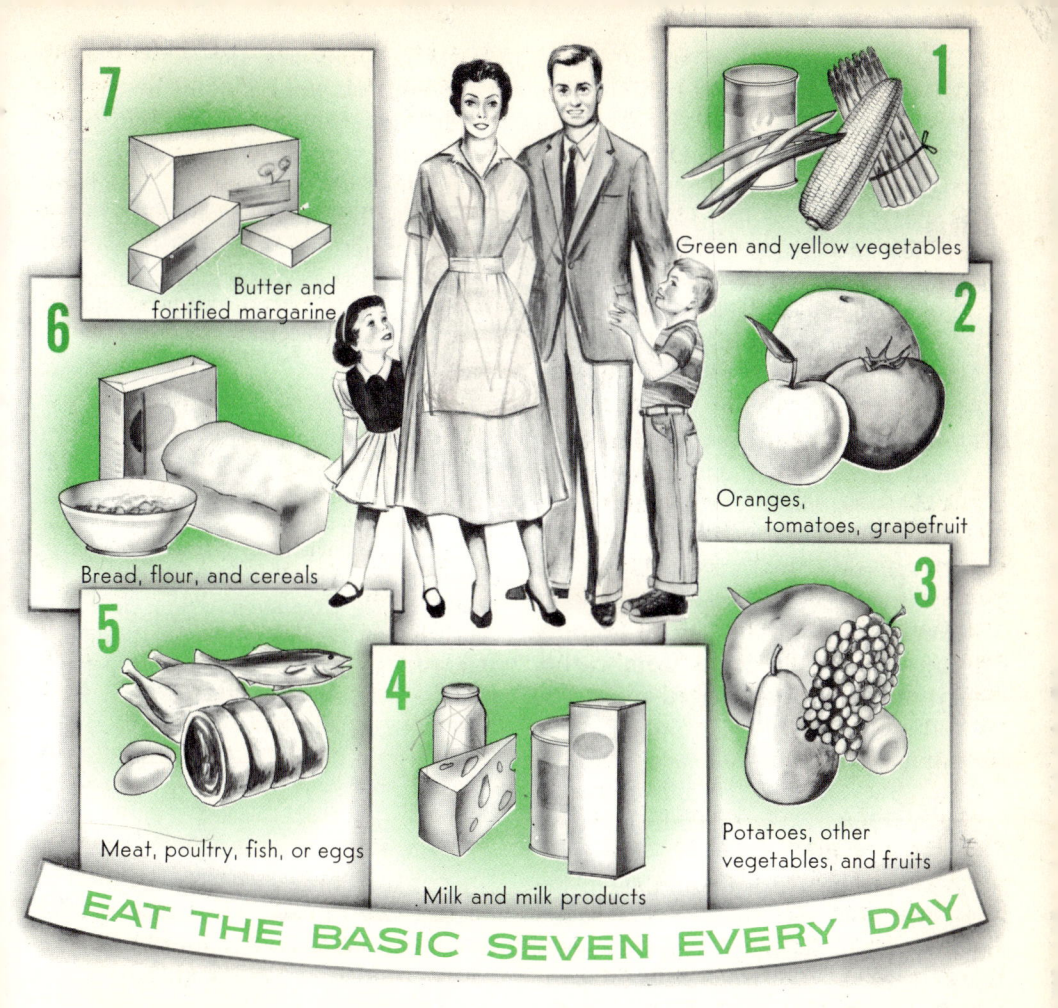

1. Green and yellow vegetables
2. Oranges, tomatoes, grapefruit
3. Potatoes, other vegetables, and fruits
4. Milk and milk products
5. Meat, poultry, fish, or eggs
6. Bread, flour, and cereals
7. Butter and fortified margarine

9.12 The Basic Seven. Everyone should eat a generous serving from each group every day. Can you explain, in the case of each group, why these foods are included among the Basic Seven? Does your daily diet include foods from each group?

And with this interest has come a greater interest in diets. All over the world populations are increasing rapidly; food production does not increase at the same rate. Productive farm land is decreasing. We must learn how to produce greater quantities of nutritious food on fewer acres by better farming methods and conservation practices. We must all make the best use of the foods we have. We can all save much food through a wise choice and use of food. For this we should all have at least a rough idea of the composition of foods (table on page 186), and we should know how to get our supply of vitamins regularly with our meals. Using the Basic Seven, Figure 9.12, will help you.

What have you learned?

1) About Calories: A Calorie is the amount of heat required to raise the temperature of a little more than a quart of water one degree Centigrade; at 14 years the average daily

CHAPTER NINE — THE FOODS WE EAT

Calorie need for boys is about 2600–3800; for girls, 2400–3000. Do you remember how the energy in food is measured? Do you remember how your basal metabolism is measured?

2) About proteins: Proteins contain amino acids which are rebuilt into your own protoplasm; plant proteins, in general, not as useful as animal proteins because they have too little of certain amino acids; you should have about 3 ounces of good proteins per day (about 25% of Calories you eat should come from proteins); can also be oxidized.

3) About carbohydrates: Used for release of energy; sugar gives energy very rapidly; about 45% of Calories you eat should come from carbohydrates; can be changed and stored as body fat.

4) About fats: Used as carbohydrates are, but they release more energy; about 30% of your Calorie intake should be fat.

5) About water: Used in making protoplasm and to dissolve and carry substances; about 2 quarts needed per day.

6) About minerals: Must not be wasted in cooking vegetables; calcium and phosphorus needed for bones and teeth; iron (and copper) needed for red blood cells; many others needed in small amounts.

7) About vitamins: The deficiency diseases you read about are **beriberi** (lack of thiamin in B complex, in coatings of seeds); **scurvy** (lack of ascorbic acid, in citrus fruits); **rickets** (lack of vitamin D, the "sunshine" vitamin. Do you remember about irradiation?); **pellagra** (lack of niacin, mostly in animal foods); **eye disease** (lack of vitamin A, in yellow vegetables and many others). You should know which foods are the very best for giving you your supply of each of the following vitamins, and which conditions most readily destroy each vitamin: thiamin, niacin, riboflavin, biotin, folic acid, vitamin B_{12} (all in B complex), and vitamins A, C, D. The facts are clearly stated under the name of each vitamin in the preceding paragraphs.

USEFUL WORDS IN BIOLOGY

calorie	deficiency disease	riboflavin
calorimeter	visual purple	biotin
basal metabolism	irradiation	rickets
	cholesterol	pellagra
amino acids	vitamin	B complex
scurvy	ascorbic acid	
beriberi	thiamin	
	niacin	

TEST YOURSELF

1. What are the units of measure for temperature and for heat? How much heat does a Calorie represent?
2. Explain, as though to a friend, why a strictly vegetarian diet (no animal foods) is not as good as a mixed diet.
3. Arrange all the food compounds, including vitamins, under these headings: made by plants; not manufactured by plants but obtained from them; obtained from animals; obtained mostly from neither plant nor animal.
4. What is the principal use to the body of each of the following: iodine, iron, phosphorus, calcium, protein, carbohydrates, fats?
5. Which vitamin do you associate with each of the following conditions: night blindness, beriberi, scurvy, rickets, pellagra, profuse bleeding?
6. What are six rules to be followed in storing, serving, and cooking foods in order to preserve the maximum amount of vitamins and minerals?

7. Which three foods will you be sure to include in your diet to give you enough of vitamin A, of vitamin C, of thiamin, of niacin, of riboflavin, of biotin? Keep in mind that we all want variety in our foods.

8. How can bread and milk be treated at small expense to give us more vitamins?

DO IT YOURSELF

1. **Vitamin experiments.** If you can keep white rats or hamsters in school or at home you can do your own experiments on the effect of the lack of vitamin A and other vitamins. You must be sure to get full directions for keeping laboratory animals before you begin to experiment. You can get directions for keeping animals as well as suggestions for experimental diets by writing to the General Biological Supply Co., 761 East 69 Place, Chicago, Ill., by consulting back numbers of *The American Biology Teacher*, or ordering the pamphlet *Adventures in Biology*, from the New York Association of Biology Teachers, Board of Education, Brooklyn 2, New York.

2. **Planning meals for yourself for three days.** By consulting the food table on page 186 and your own Calorie needs according to tables on pages 173 and 174, plan meals for yourself for a three day period. Your calculations should include snacks. Keep the following in mind: variety, source and amount of proteins, proportion of protein to fats and carbohydrates, number of calories per portion, supply of minerals and vitamins, etc. Be prepared to defend everything on your list. Each meal need not be perfectly balanced, but within a period of twenty-four hours you should have a balanced diet. This can be submitted to the class for criticism.

3. **Making charts.** With a little research, ingenuity, and some neat handwork, you or a committee could make some useful and decorative charts to be used in the biology classroom, in the cafeteria or corridors of your school, or in your own kitchen. For example, you could show the composition of some common foods; you could give suggestions for good and inexpensive lunches; you could list DONT'S in cooking.

4. **Discovering "fads" in diet.** By talking to your friends, see whether you can learn of any food fads among them. These can be discussed in class and the truth may be arrived at by research. This research may consist of further reading, consulting some good authority by letter, and possibly by long-range animal experimentation.

ADVENTURES IN READING

1. *Food for Life* edited by Ralph W. Gerard, University of Chicago Press, 1952. Furnished free to teachers by the Continental Baking Co., Inc., New York 20. You will find much useful information in the text, tables, and diagrams.

2. *Vitamins in Nutrition and Health* by Audrey Z. Baker, DeGraff, 1954. A small book with full tables, good for reference. Readable.

3. *Magic in a Bottle* by Milton Silverman, Macmillan, 1948. Contains a chapter called "Food Against Death," which tells about the discovery of vitamins.

4. *Eating for Health* by Pearl Lewis, Macmillan, 1948. Is a simple introduction to foods, including sample diets.

CHAPTER NINE — THE FOODS WE EAT

TABLE 11   **COMPOSITION**

Food	Measure	Calories	Protein (%)	Fat (%)	Carbohydrate (%)
Cereals					
(1) Bread, white, enriched	1 slice, average	65	8	2	52
(2) Bread, whole wheat, 60%	1 slice, average	72	9	3	46
(3) Cornmeal, bolted yellow	⅔ cup, cooked	106	8	1	78
(4) Oats, rolled	⅔ cup, cooked	119	14	7	68
(5) Rice, white	¾ cup, cooked	105	7	0.3	79
(6) Spaghetti, tomato sauce	1 serving	271	3	5	17
Dairy products					
(7) Butter	1 pat, average	73	0.6	81	0.4
(8) Cheese, American Cheddar	1 ounce, average	112	24	32	2
(9) Ice cream, plain	⅙ quart	210	4	12	21
(10) Milk, whole	6 ounces, med. glass	123	3	3	4
(11) Eggs, raw, whole	1 medium, average	79	13	12	0.8
(12) Margarine, fortified	1 tablespoon	95	0.6	81	0.4
Fruits and Nuts					
(13) Apple, fresh	1 large, 3" diam.	97	0.3	0.4	15
(14) Banana, fresh	1 medium	99	1.0	0.2	23
(15) Grapefruit, fresh	½ small	44	0.5	0.2	10
(16) Grapes, American	1 bunch, 22–24 aver.	78	1.0	1.0	15
(17) Orange, whole	1 medium	76	0.9	0.2	11
(18) Prunes, dried	4–5 medium	149	2.0	0.6	71
(19) Peanuts, roasted	16–17 nuts	89	26.0	44.0	23
Meats and Fish					
(20) Bacon, medium, cooked	1 5-inch strip, crisp	31	14	27	2
(21) Beef, round, fried	1 slice, 3" × 2" × ½"	233	23	16	
(22) Chicken, roasted	3 slices, 3½" × 2½" × ¼"	193	28	9	
(23) Lamb chop, shoulder	1 chop, 4" × 3½" × ½"	245	17	22	
(24) Liver, beef, fried	1 slice, 2¾" × 2" × 3/16"	82	25	8	8
(25) Frankfurter, boiled	1, 5½" long, ¾" diam.	121	15	14	3
(26) Codfish cake	1 cake, 2½" diameter	122	11	11	16
(27) Salmon, canned	½ cup, scant	102	21	10	
Vegetables					
(28) Beans, navy, pea bean, kidney, pinto	½ cup, cooked	105	22	2	62
(29) Beans, snap	½ cup, cooked	42	2	0.2	8
(30) Cabbage, fresh, head	¼–⅓ cup, shredded	15	1	0.2	5
(31) Carrots, raw	1 large, ¾ cup, cubes	45	1	0.3	9
(32) Cauliflower, raw	4 rounded tablespoons	22	2	0.1	4
(33) Lettuce, head	1 large leaf	2	1		3
(34) Onions, mature, raw	1 large or 2–3 small	49	1	0.2	10
(35) Peas, fresh, raw	¾ cup shelled	101	7	0.4	18
(36) Potatoes, white, cooked	1 medium in skin	129	2	0.1	19
(37) Potatoes, sweet, baked	1 large	213	2	0.7	28
(38) Spinach, fresh	⅔ cup, cooked	25	2	0.3	3
(39) Tomatoes, canned	½ cup	21	1	0.2	4

Figures are given in round numbers. The daily diet for growing boys and girls should include besides proteins, fats, and carbohydrates, the follow-

UNIT FOUR — HOW OUR BODIES WORK

OF FOODS *

	Ca (mg)	P (mg)	Fe (mg)	Vitamin A I.U.	Thiamin (mcg)	Riboflavin (mcg)	Niacin (mg)	Ascorbic Acid (mg)	Vitamin D I.U.
(1)	14	25	.5		60	37	0.6		
(2)	14	42	.6		84	49	0.9		
(3)	3	42	.3	90	45	18	0.3		
(4)	16	110	1.6		165	42	0.3		
(5)	3	28	.2		15	9	0.4		
(6)	23	80	1.0	1336	125	76	1.6	19	
(7)	2	2		330		1			4
(8)	247	173	0.2	493	11	142			
(9)	132	104	0.1	540	40	190	0.1		
(10)	212	167	0.1	288	72	306	0.2	2	4
(11)	27	105	1.4	570	60	170			45
(12)	trace	2		258–429					
(13)	9	15	.5	135	60	30	0.3	8	
(14)	8	28	.6	430	90	60	0.6	10	
(15)	17	18	.3		40	20	0.2	40	
(16)	17	21	.6	80	50	30	0.4	4	
(17)	50	35	.6	285	120	45	0.3	74	
(18)	27	43	1.9	945	50	80	0.8	1	
(19)	11	59	.3		45	24	2.4		
(20)	2	16	.1		60	10	0.3		
(21)	13	250	3.5		122	153	5.3		
(22)	22	305	2.7		92	214	10.2		
(23)	9	168	2.3		153	196	4.4		
(24)	6	187	6.1	9600	115	1190	6.8	?	23
(25)	5	98	1.4		111	135	1.2		
(26)	11	71	.8	130	44	49	0.7	?	5
(27)	98	173	.8	48	18	108	3.9		275
(28)	44	139	3.1		180	72	0.6		
(29)	65	44	1.1	630	80	100	0.6	19	
(30)	23	16	.3	40	35	30	0.1	26	
(31)	39	37	.8	12000	70	60	0.5	6	
(32)	15	50	.8	63	70	77	0.4	48	
(33)	2	3		54	6	7		1	
(34)	32	44	.5	50	30	20	0.1	9	
(35)	22	122	1.9	680	360	180	2.1	26	
(36)	17	84	1.1	30	168	55	1.6	17	
(37)	51	83	1.2	8287	143	89	1.1	28	
(38)		55	3.0	9420	120	240	0.7	59	
(39)	11	27	.6	1050	50	30	0.7	16	

ing substances represented in the above units: *calcium, 1300; iron, 15; vitamin A, 5000; thiamin, 1400; riboflavin, 2000; niacin, 14; ascorbic acid, 85.*

* Adapted from *Food Values of Portions Commonly Used* by Bowes, A. de P. and Church, C. F.

CHAPTER NINE — THE FOODS WE EAT

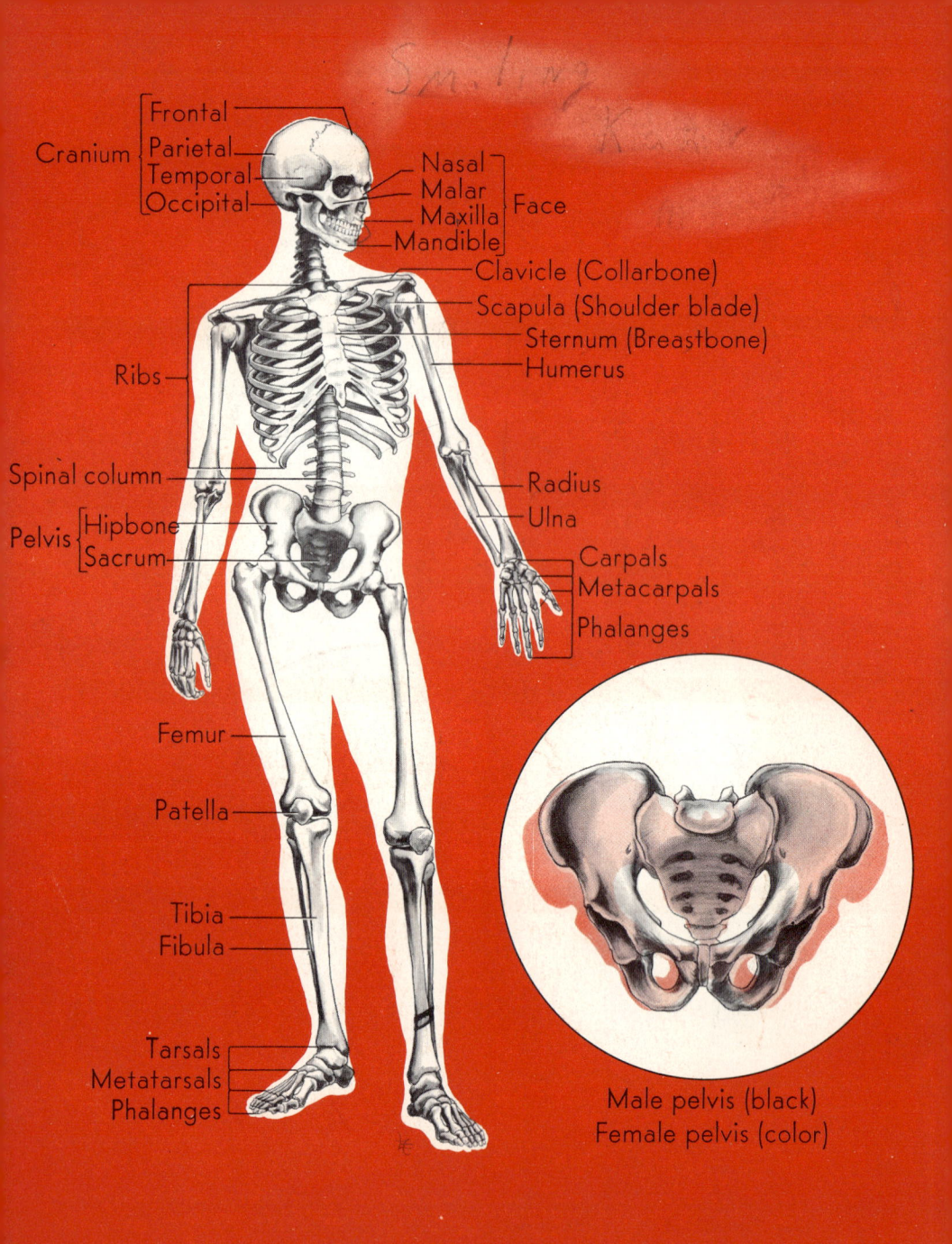

The skeletal system of man

Male pelvis (black)
Female pelvis (color)

188 UNIT FOUR — HOW OUR BODIES WORK

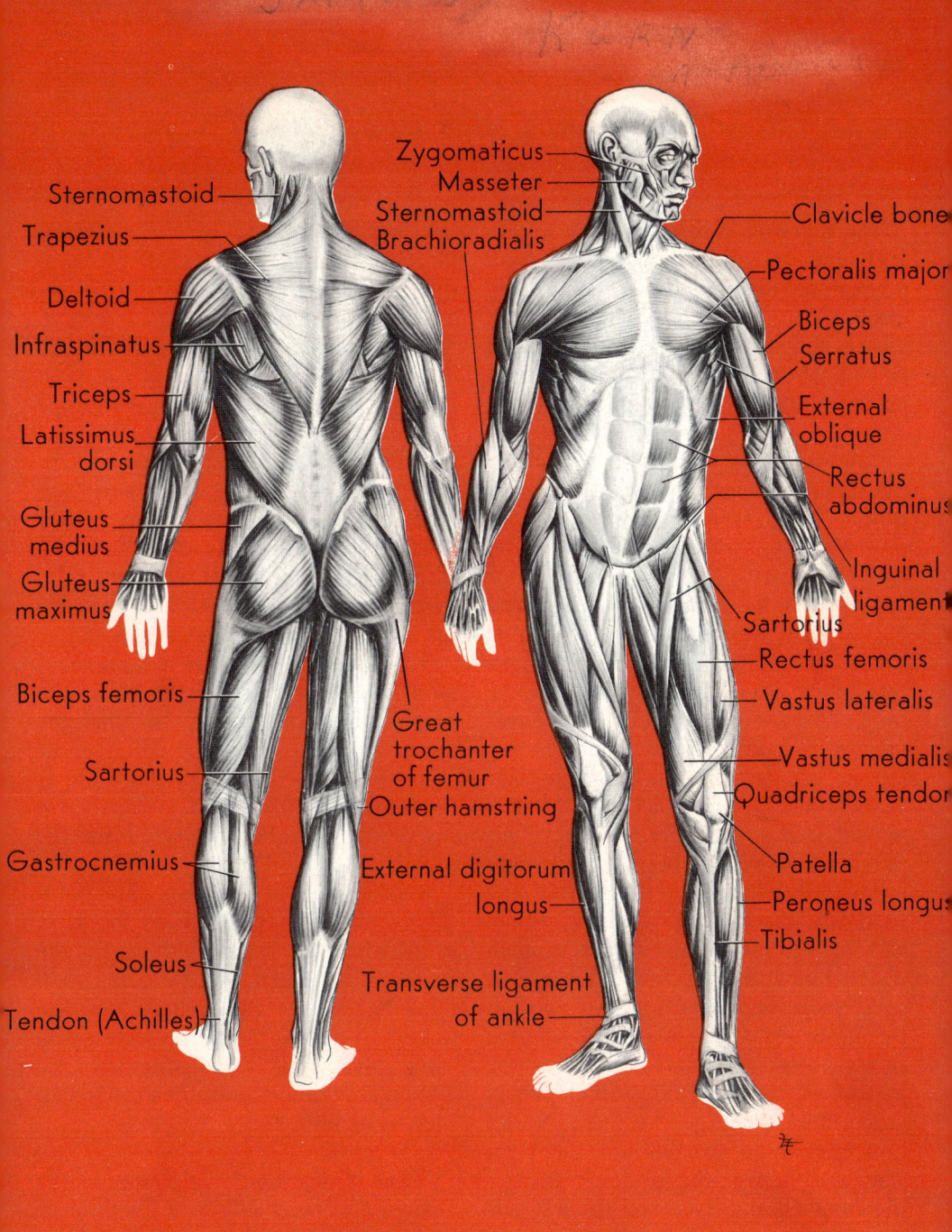

The muscular system of man

CHAPTER NINE — THE FOODS WE EAT   189

Chapter 10

Digestion and absorption

The digestive tube. Look at Figure 10.1 and trace the passage of food through the digestive tube or **alimentary canal.** Your alimentary canal is about 25 feet long. Most of it, of course, is in your abdominal cavity. When food leaves your throat it enters a long straight food pipe, the **esophagus** (ee-sof´a-gus); from there it goes into the **stomach.** Here it remains for some time. The last of it does not leave until two to four hours after eating. But food doesn't lie quietly in your stomach; it is steadily squeezed and moved around until it is a pulpy mass. Then the stomach begins to push this pulpy mass, bit by bit, into the long, narrow, coiled tube, the **small intestine.** Look at its coils — twenty feet of tubing. It, too, has muscular walls. As they contract, the food is moved along, but very slowly. This part of the journey takes about eight hours. By that time the last of the food has reached the large intestine. The large intestine, or **colon,** is a much wider but much shorter tube. The small intestine opens into the colon at the lower right side of the abdominal cavity. Here, by the way, lies the **appendix,** a small fingerlike pocket attached to the large intestine. Notice how the colon extends up the right side and across the abdomen under the stomach and liver; on the left side it turns down again. It ends in the **rectum.** The rectum opens to the exterior by an opening known as the **anus** (ay´nuss). It took you a few minutes to trace these parts of the digestive tube. For a meal to travel the length of this tube takes twelve hours or more. But much happens to the food as it travels.

What happens to food? Food in the digestive tube is not yet really in your body at all. It is merely in a tube that runs through your body. Yet the billions of cells making up your body need food all the time to carry on oxidation and other activities. How does the food reach them? Of course, through the blood. How, then, does food get from the digestive tube into the blood? That's a long story.

The walls of the tube are made of many layers of cells. Blood vessels lie among these cells. By the time the meal you ate reaches the colon, most of it has diffused through the walls of the tube into the blood stream. We say the food has been **absorbed** into the blood.

But most of the food you eat cannot diffuse through cell walls in the form in which it is eaten. Many of the sugars, all the starches, fats, and proteins have large molecules; they are unable to diffuse through a membrane. They must first be **digested** in the alimentary canal, and then only can they be absorbed into the blood.

What is digestion? Digestion is the changing of food substances with large molecules into substances that have much smaller molecules. In digestion, large molecules are chemically changed into molecules small enough to diffuse through cell membranes and also small enough to be used in making more

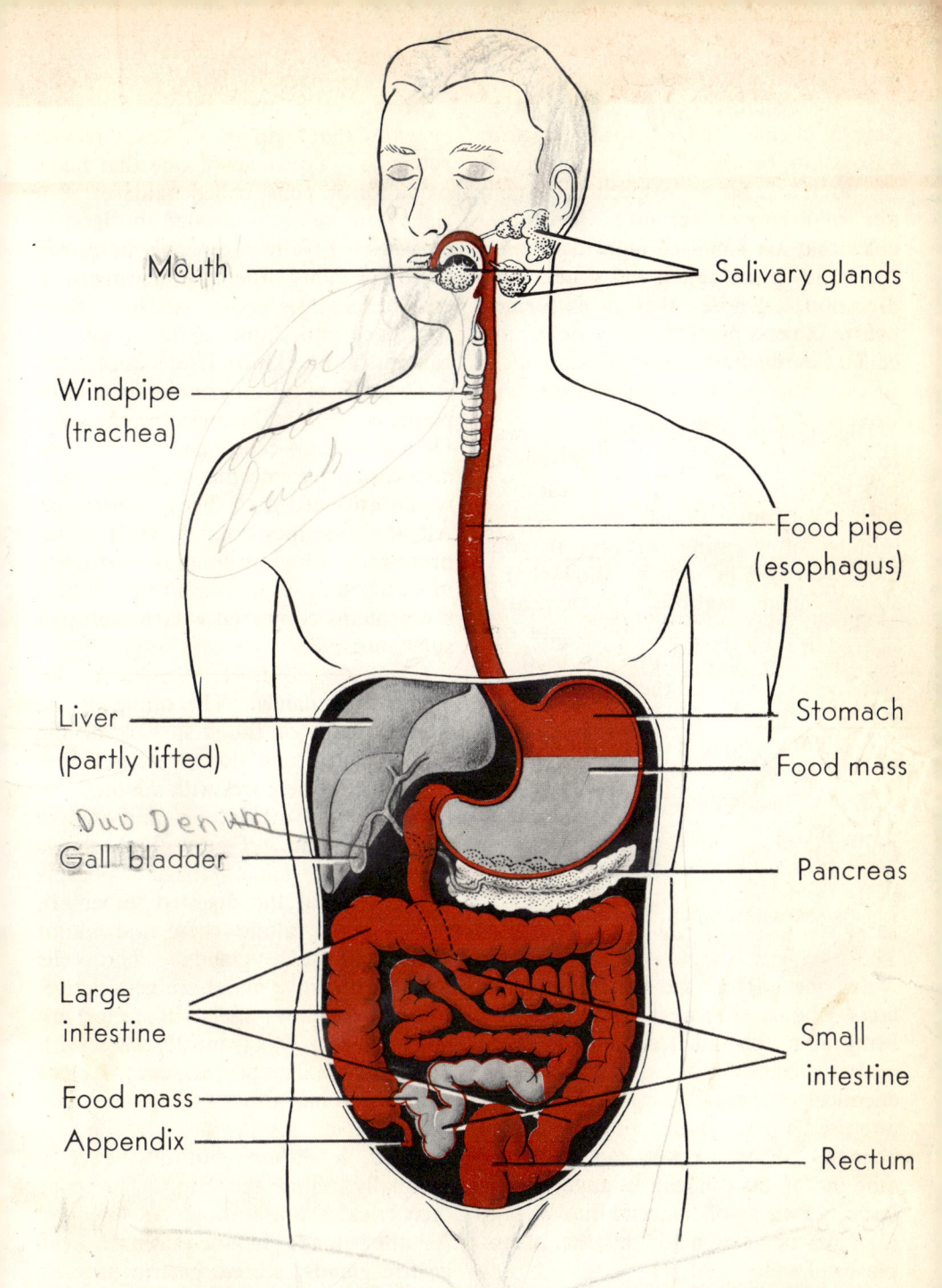

10.1 Man's digestive system. The organs are not drawn in correct proportion or in exact position. Food masses are indicated in the stomach and at the lower end of the small intestine. How long does it take food to travel the full length of the alimentary canal? What digestive organs are shown that are not part of the canal?

CHAPTER TEN — DIGESTION AND ABSORPTION

protoplasm. This chemical breakdown of large molecules into small ones does not, in general, occur in one step. Several chemical changes take place in succession before the large molecules of starch and fat and especially protein are small enough for use. The molecules that are small enough to be used by the body are called **end products** of digestion. Those that are formed before the end products are reached are called **intermediate products.**

Digestion in a test tube. One way to show digestion in a test tube is to put some boiled starch in a test tube with a very little saliva. After several minutes of warming the tube in your hand you will be able to show that a simple sugar, **maltose,** has appeared in the test tube. Can you figure out all the tests that must be used as controls to prove that the saliva changed starch to sugar?

We know what it is in saliva that makes this chemical change go on. It is a substance called **ptyalin** (tie'a-lin). Although there is only the smallest trace of ptyalin in saliva, that is all that is needed. Ptyalin is an **enzyme.** Let us see what enzymes are.

Enzymes. Here are three important facts about enzymes. (1) Enzymes bring about chemical changes in some other substance or speed up such chemical changes. (2) The enzyme is not used up while bringing about the change. That is why a very tiny amount of ptyalin can change a very large amount of starch into sugar. (3) Enzymes are made by the protoplasm of cells.

Chemists know of many chemical substances that have the first two characteristics of enzymes. Such substances are called **catalysts** (cat'a-lists).

Enzymes are special catalysts; they are always made by living protoplasm.

Living cells make many kinds of enzymes that help in all kinds of cell activities. You read of one that helps oxidation in cells, called oxidase. But right now we are interested in **digestive enzymes.** Ptyalin is one of these, but there are many others. Each digestive enzyme changes some particular food substance into simpler compounds. It can act on one kind of substance only.

The cells of all other animals, and of plants as well, make digestive enzymes. Even the single-celled animals such as ameba and paramecium make enzymes which are needed to digest their food. All the enzymes known so far are proteins. Some are simple proteins made up only of amino acids. Others are proteins combined with nonprotein substances.

Digestive glands. The lining of the stomach and of the first part of the small intestine is dotted with pores. You can see the pores with a hand lens. Each pore opens into a microscopic **digestive gland.** Figure 10.2 shows some of these glands — bags or pockets in the wall of the digestive tube. In the stomach alone there are about 35,000,000 such glands. The cells lining a digestive gland are very active. Their protoplasm makes (secretes) **digestive juice.** This is mostly water with one, or sometimes several, enzymes and perhaps some other substances dissolved in it. As the digestive juice is secreted, it diffuses out of the cells, gradually filling the bag. The juice then trickles out through an opening. As the glands in the stomach, the **gastric glands,** secrete gastric juice, it trickles into the cavity of the stomach. The juice from the **intestinal glands** goes into the small intestine. And each juice has its special enzyme or enzymes.

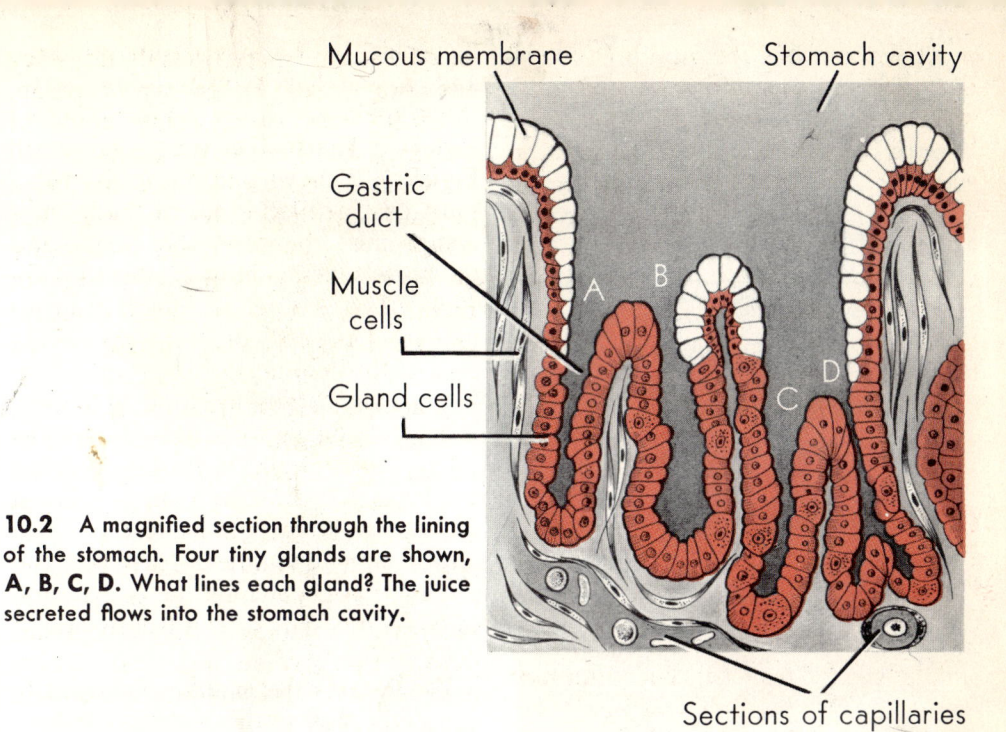

10.2 A magnified section through the lining of the stomach. Four tiny glands are shown, **A, B, C, D.** What lines each gland? The juice secreted flows into the stomach cavity.

All living protoplasm has the power of secretion. But when a group of cells secretes some substance in large amounts we call this group of cells a **gland.** Some glands secrete sweat, some tears, some digestive juices. Not all glands are digestive glands.

Sometimes secreting cells are found in one large mass, forming a big gland organ. The microscopic bags are clustered together, and a small tube or duct carries off the juice they make. There are many of these clusters, each with its small duct, emptying into one large duct. They are like a bunch of grapes attached to the main stem. The **salivary** (sal'i-very) **glands** are gland organs of this kind. The main duct from each salivary gland opens into the mouth. Look at Figure 10.1 to see the three pairs of salivary glands. And find also the pancreas and the liver. Each of these is a large gland organ with a duct which leads the secretions into the alimentary canal.

The mouth. Let's see in more detail what happens to food as it goes through the alimentary canal. Begin by exploring the inside of your mouth with your finger. Can you feel how smooth the lining is? This is the **mucous** (mew'kus) **membrane,** a delicate lining membrane. The same kind of membrane lines the whole alimentary canal. Along its whole length its cells secrete a slimy, thickish substance called **mucus.** Mucus keeps the membrane smooth and helps the easy passage of food.

Now provide yourself with a mirror and some food. Notice how the tongue keeps pushing the food between the teeth; then by curling backward it helps in swallowing. Besides this, of course, it has special cells called taste buds.

The teeth. You probably know the four kinds of teeth. In each quarter up front you have two incisors and one canine, all used for biting off food. Then come the grinding teeth — two

CHAPTER TEN — DIGESTION AND ABSORPTION

Toothless (Anteater)

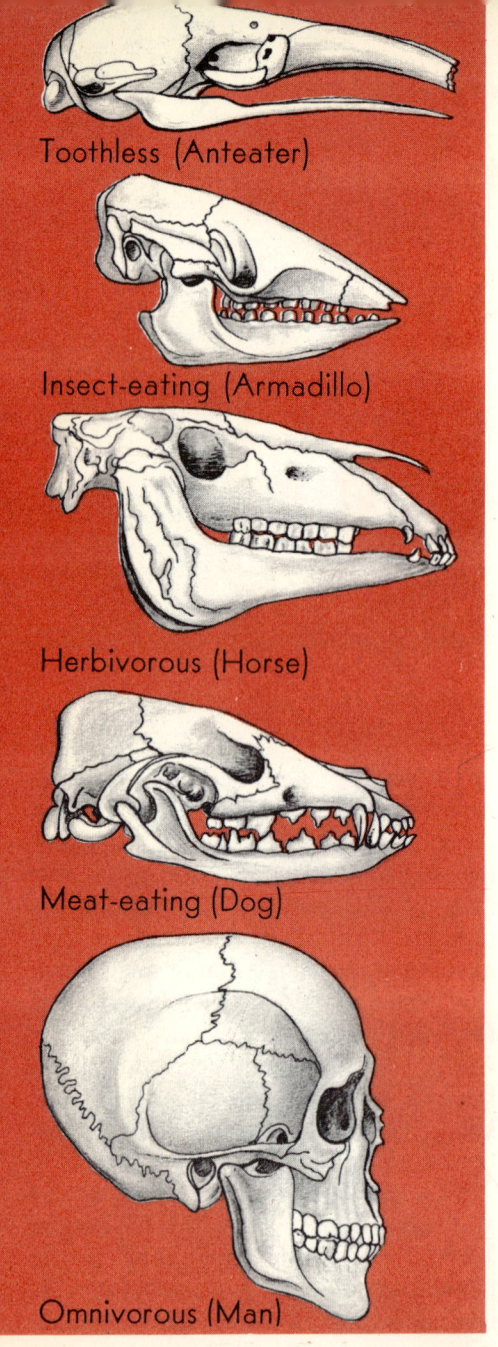

Insect-eating (Armadillo)

Herbivorous (Horse)

Meat-eating (Dog)

Omnivorous (Man)

10.3 The armadillo eats insects larger than ants; they need to be chewed. Which teeth are the best developed in the dog? How do its bicuspids and molars compare with ours? Now look at the horse. What are its incisors good for? What are its molars good for?

bicuspids, with a surface for grinding, and if you have your wisdom teeth, three molars, with a larger grinding surface. That makes thirty-two in all. Figure 10.3 shows that our teeth, which must deal with all kinds of food, are a compromise between the dog's and the horse's teeth. Now examine Figure 10.4. The enamel is lifeless mineral matter deposited or built by living cells in the dentine.

Chewing breaks up food and gives it a good chance to be mixed with the saliva, which begins to flow freely when we begin to eat. Even the smell and thought of food will make the saliva flow in larger quantities. Have you seen a hungry dog watching the preparation of its food? Why does it lick its lips?

Food leaves the mouth. Fortunately you don't have to think about swallowing every time your food starts down the food pipe. You swallow automatically. But you can also make up your mind to swallow or not to swallow. But once you have swallowed and food has entered the upper part of your food pipe, you have no more control over it. In the throat are voluntary (striated) muscles. You can control these as you wish. In the food pipe and along the rest of the digestive tube the muscles are involuntary (smooth). They are not under conscious control.

The involuntary muscle fibers which make up the walls of the food pipe lie in rings. One ring contracts after another; with each contraction food is pushed farther down. If you have ever watched a worm crawling you will know how a wave of contraction runs along its whole body. This slow but steady wave of muscular contraction is called **peristalsis** (perr-i-stall'sis). In the food pipe when food is caught in this wave, it is forced onward toward the stomach.

10.4 Longitudinal section of an incisor. All our teeth have the same three regions. What are they? (shown on the right) What material covers the exposed part of the tooth? With what is this substance replaced in the root? What is under the outside of the tooth? What lies in the very center?

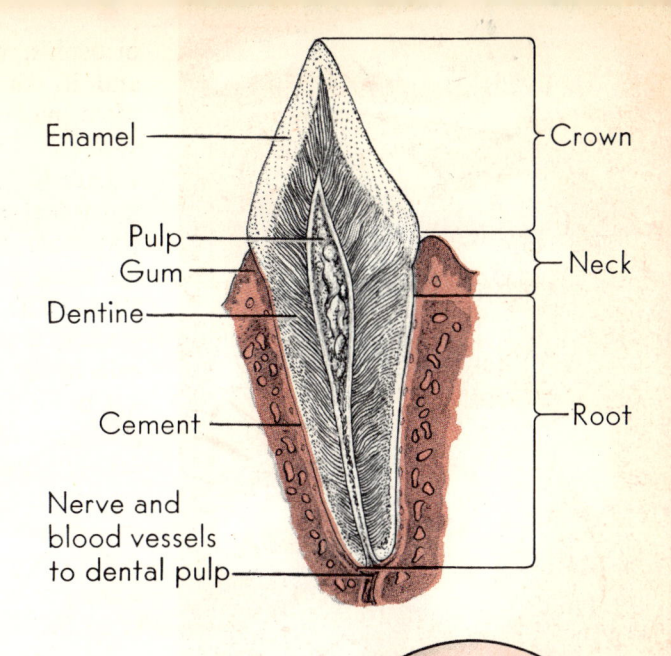

Enamel — Crown
Pulp
Gum — Neck
Dentine
Cement — Root
Nerve and blood vessels to dental pulp

10.5 Part of the food pipe (esophagus). Note that the muscles are involuntary (smooth). You cannot stop movement of food down the food pipe after you have swallowed it.

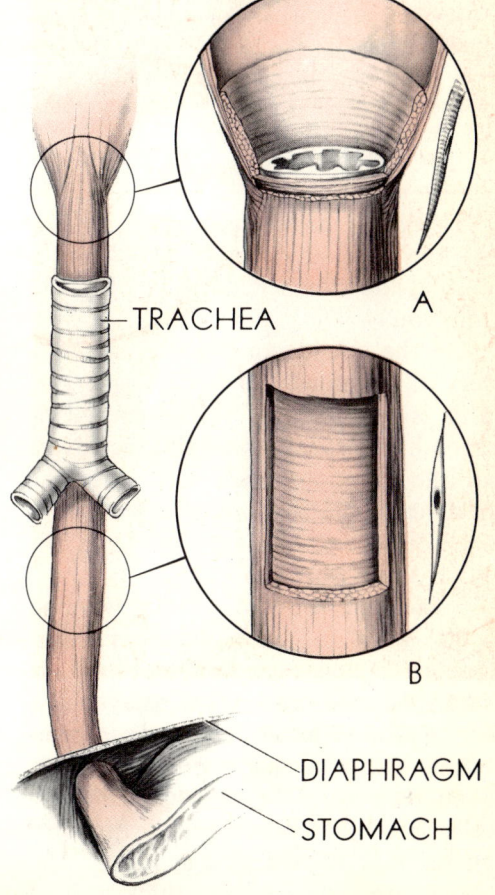

TRACHEA
A
B
DIAPHRAGM
STOMACH

CHAPTER TEN — DIGESTION AND ABSORPTION

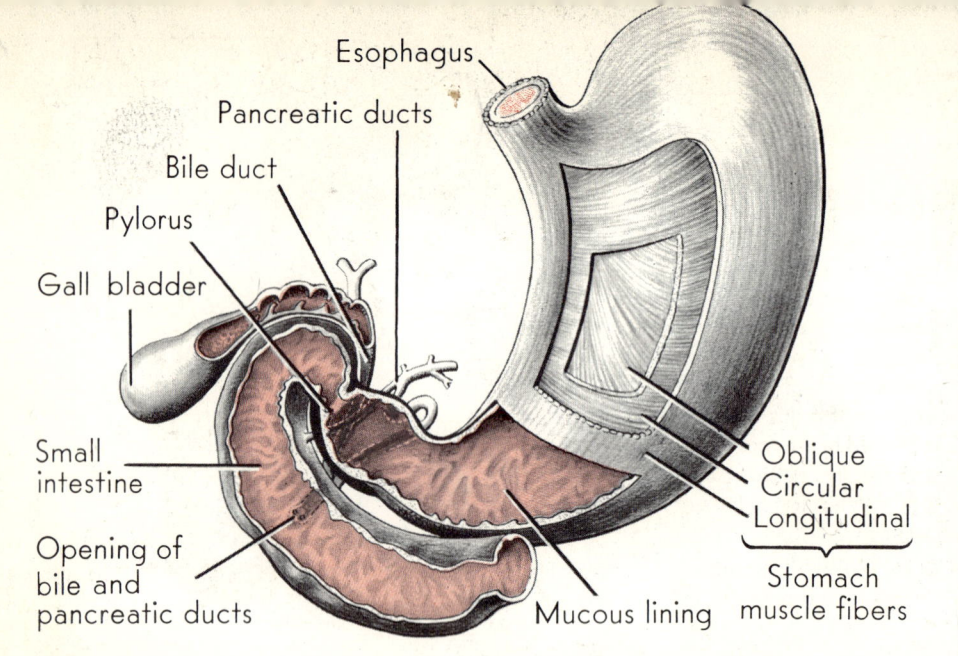

10.6 The stomach and the upper end of the small intestine. In the stomach note the mucous lining and the three layers of muscle. Notice, too, how the stomach narrows where it joins the intestine. What name is given to this passageway? When you know more about the small intestine, you will want to consult this diagram again.

Tissues of the stomach. Before tracing the food any further, let's take a look at the stomach. Figure 10.6 will help you.

On the outside of the stomach is a very thin **serous** (see′russ) **membrane**. This is one form of **epithelium**. This smooth, moist serous membrane covers all the internal organs and lines the body cavity. As the organs slide over each other or against the inside of the cavity there is little friction.

Under the serous membrane we find three layers of involuntary muscles. One runs lengthwise, one around the stomach, and the third diagonally. Lining the stomach is mucous membrane, also a form of epithelial tissue. Scattered among the mucous membrane cells are the microscopic digestive glands that secrete gastric juice. The glands are sunk into the thick wall of the stomach. Naturally blood vessels and nerves run through and between all these many kinds of tissues.

Stomach movements. Even if you chew your food well, much of it is still in large pieces when it arrives in the stomach. After that for two to four hours the food is moved back and forth and around. These churning movements break up the pieces of food still further and mix them thoroughly with the gastric juice.

While all this is going on, the rings of muscle at each end of the stomach are more or less contracted. Only liquids can pass through the ring into the small intestine; they begin to pass through as soon as they arrive in the stomach. But after a couple of hours, the ring of muscle (pyloric sphincter) between the stomach and intestine

UNIT FOUR — HOW OUR BODIES WORK

10.7 A painting showing Dr. Beaumont examining Alexis St. Martin. The doctor is seated directly next to St. Martin whose family is shown on the left.

relaxes somewhat. Peristalsis goes on in the stomach as well as churning movements. Thus the softened and well-broken-down portions of food are pushed through the opening. But only a little is allowed through at a time. The ring of muscle contracts again and shuts the opening. After a while it opens once more. After several hours the last of the meal will have been delivered to the small intestine in small batches.

A look into the stomach. If you could look at the inside of your stomach with a magnifying glass at the moment the food arrives there, you would see **gastric juice** trickling out of the microscopic glands in the wall. And if you are enjoying the sight, and smell, and taste of your food, you would see the juices flowing even faster.

In the early part of the last century, William Beaumont, one of our first American surgeons, was fortunate enough to see all this happening in a human stomach. At an army post in Michigan a trapper, Alexis St. Martin, was shot through the stomach. There was a large hole, large enough to put a fist into, right through the wall of his stomach between the ribs. St. Martin recovered but the hole remained until his death at the age of eighty-three. Beaumont could look into St. Martin's stomach; he could pour water through

CHAPTER TEN — DIGESTION AND ABSORPTION

197

the opening or introduce food; he sometimes suspended food in the stomach for a certain length of time and then pulled it out; he siphoned out digested foods; he measured the contents of the stomach and tested the gastric juice chemically.

St. Martin continued to make his living by chopping trees; in the meantime Beaumont learned a great deal about the work of the stomach.

Gastric juice. Gastric juice is mostly water, a little hydrochloric (high-dro-klor′ic) acid, and several enzymes. One of the enzymes is **pepsin.** Pepsin breaks down the very large protein molecules into somewhat smaller molecules (called peptones). These are some of the intermediate products of protein digestion. Their molecules are not small enough to be used by the body. A second enzyme, **rennin,** curdles milk and helps in its later digestion. There are still other enzymes of no great interest to us. The hydrochloric acid, however, is of interest. Hydrochloric acid is not an enzyme. But without it pepsin does not digest protein. Hydrochloric acid also reacts with a number of insoluble minerals, such as calcium phosphate, producing soluble minerals.

These are then able to diffuse through cell membranes. You can easily make some artificial gastric juice in the laboratory and try out its effects on proteins and minerals. Find out whether it digests starch.

All this time you may have been asking yourself why gastric juice doesn't digest the walls of the stomach, since protoplasm is largely proteins. The coating of mucus gives some protection to the cells. But no altogether satisfactory answer to this interesting question can be given here.

Juices in the small intestine. Take a look at Figure 10.1 and find again the two large gland organs, the pancreas and the liver. Though food never enters them, they are a very important part of the digestive system. They have small ducts which carry their secretions into the upper part of the small intestine. To be exact, the secretion from the liver, called the **bile,** reaches the small intestine indirectly. It goes first to a storage sac, the **gall bladder.** From the gall bladder the bile is fed, when needed, into the small intestine.

Tiny intestinal glands are sunk in the walls of the small intestine. They

TABLE 12

THE WORK OF THE DIGESTIVE JUICES

Juices	Enzymes	Insoluble food products	Intermediate products	End products ready for use
Saliva	Ptyalin acts on Starch		Double sugar	
Gastric	Pepsin acts on Protein (Rennin curdles milk) HCl (not an enzyme) acts on Minerals		Peptones	Soluble minerals
Pancreatic	Trypsin acts on Proteins Amylase acts on Starch Lipase acts on Fats		Peptones Double sugar	Fatty acids and glycerin
Intestinal	Erepsin acts on Sugar-splitting enzymes act on Lipase acts on Fats		Peptones Double sugars	Amino acids Simple sugars like glucose Fatty acids and glycerin

make intestinal juice. Thus three different juices meet the food in the upper part of the small intestine, the intestinal juice, the very important pancreatic juice, and the bile. These juices become thoroughly mixed with the food. All kinds of chemical changes begin to take place in the food. In the meantime everything in the small intestine is being pushed along slowly by peristalsis.

Food in the small intestine. Let us take stock of what changes have occurred by the time food reaches the small intestine. A good many of the minerals have been made soluble by hydrochloric acid in the stomach. A very little starch has been changed by saliva into a double sugar ($C_{12}H_{22}O_{11}$). These double sugars are intermediate products of digestion. They will be further changed into simple sugars like glucose. Most of the starch has not even been touched. Some of the proteins have been changed into intermediate products. Little is ready for absorption except minerals. You can see that much is still to be done. All the rest of digestion takes place in the small intestine.

A close look at Table 12 shows you three interesting things. First, how large a share of the work of digestion is done by pancreatic and intestinal juices. Second, that the bile from the liver is not a digestive juice; it has no enzymes; it helps only indirectly in digestion. And third, that intestinal juice is important for finishing up the jobs begun and left undone by the other juices. Look carefully at the table and you will see that intestinal juice acts mostly on intermediate products.

Functions of bile. Fat is turned to oil by the heat of the stomach. Before oil can be digested it must first be divided into smaller droplets, just as other foods must be chewed into small pieces before digestive juice can accomplish much. If you shake some oil in a test tube with some bile salts or a ground-up chicken liver, the oil turns into a milky-looking liquid which is called an **emulsion** (ee-mul'shun). What has happened? Your shaking separates the oil into small droplets. Then the bile forms a thin coating around each droplet, keeping the droplets from running together. When the large mass of oil is broken up this way into an emulsion, enzymes can begin the work of splitting up the fat molecules. Another use that bile has is to make active the fat-splitting enzyme in pancreatic juice.

Absorption. You have been reading about the digestion of food. Now you are ready to find out how the digested foods get into the blood — **absorption.** Absorption is more than simple diffusion through a lifeless membrane. The cells that do the absorbing take an active part in the process. We know this because they use more oxygen and give off more carbon dioxide while they are absorbing.

You can guess that most of the absorption must take place after the food mass is well along in the small intestine. The minerals are about the only things that are ready for absorption in the stomach or in the upper part of the small intestine. Just look again at the table on page 198, and notice how the end products (small molecules) begin to appear only in the small intestine. The small intestine is particularly well adapted (fitted) for absorption. Inside, the small intestine is moist and pink, like the lining of your cheeks. But instead of being smooth it is wrinkled into deep folds; these folds may be $\frac{1}{3}$ inch deep. Then

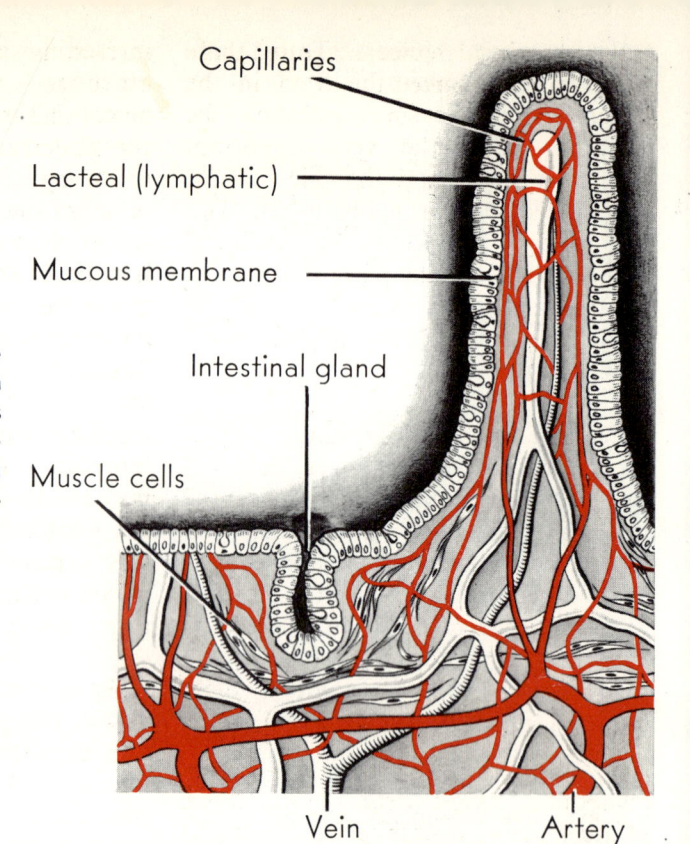

10.8 One of the villi of the small intestine cut through lengthwise. How many kinds of tubes does the villus contain? Can you see the opening of one intestinal gland alongside the villus?

if you used a magnifying glass, you would see that the surface of the folds looks like plush or velvet. The folds are covered with microscopic projections, millions of them. The little hairs are called **villi** (vill′eye), plural of **villus.** They sway back and forth, now lengthening, now shortening. If you rubbed your hand over them, you would feel that they are soft. You can see one magnified in Figure 10.8. The wrinkles in the lining increase the absorbing surface by a great deal, and the millions of villi increase it still more. The greater the surface, the more can be absorbed.

Figure 10.8 shows you other adaptations for absorption. A villus is covered with a very thin membrane, only one layer thick. And inside, blood vessels lie very close to the membrane. Digested foods don't have far to travel to get into the blood. In the center of the villus is a tube called a **lacteal** (lak′tee-al). The digested fats enter this instead of going into blood vessels. Eventually, lacteals connect with blood vessels.

The large intestine. There is no more digestion in the large intestine and no more absorption, except the absorption of water — large amounts of it. Normally, most of the food has been digested, except the thick cellulose walls of plant cells and some other substances; we have no enzymes to digest these — cattle, of course, do. These cellulose walls make up what is known as roughage. Roughage is useful in stimulating the walls of the intestines to contract; it helps peristalsis and keeps the food moving along. After much of the water has been absorbed these undigested substances are **eliminated**.

The liver. Besides its gland cells, which secrete bile, the liver has other cells that store carbohydrates in the form of **glycogen** (glye′ko-jen). Glycogen is an insoluble carbohydrate which can be changed back to a simple sugar.

But the liver does something more. When you eat proteins you break them down into end products called amino acids. Some of the amino acids, especially some of those that come from the digestion of plant proteins, can't be used for building your own particular kind of protoplasm. But they are not wasted. They are carried to the liver and there are changed into two substances, one useful to the body, the other useless. The useful product is glucose, the useless one is a nitrogen compound called **urea**. The waste product, urea, is carried by the blood to the kidneys, where it is excreted.

Why glands start working. Secretion of digestive juices must be well timed or food will be wasted. You read that the sight and smell or even the thought of food sends messages along the nerves to the salivary glands and the gastric glands and that they, then, begin to secrete actively. Also the food touching the mucous lining stirs up the glands. But how about the digestive juices that are needed several hours after you have enjoyed your meal? Or how about those juices that come from organs like the pancreas and liver, which are never touched by food? They need to be stirred up, too. How is this done?

The answer was found by two English scientists, Bayliss and Starling, some fifty years ago. They performed a most interesting and important experiment on dogs. Believing that there was something in the blood that stimulated the pancreas to secrete, they did the following: They joined a large blood vessel of one dog to a large blood vessel of a second dog. Thus the blood of each dog flowed through the body of the other. But this was the only connection between the dogs. Then one animal was fed and the other was left unfed. After some time the digested food arrived in the small intestine. And what do you think happened? There was a flow of pancreatic juice in both dogs! The experiment was repeated and similar ones were performed always with the same results. The only logical conclusion was that the pancreas was stimulated by some substance carried by the blood. That is why the pancreas in the second dog began to secrete. What this substance was and where it came from they did not know at that time. But they called it **secretin** (see-cree′tin).

Now we know that secretin is made by the mucous membrane of the small intestine. When the first food from the stomach arrives in the small intestine, it stimulates the mucous membrane to make secretin. The secretin diffuses into the blood, circulates, and in a short time reaches the pancreas. Here the message "Secrete" is delivered.

Secretin is one of the many "chemical messengers" in the body. Such substances that are carried in the blood and act as chemical messengers are called **hormones**. There is probably another hormone that stimulates the liver; and perhaps there is one for the gastric glands, too.

Slowing up of glands. Dr. Walter B. Cannon of Harvard University discovered that digestive glands can be slowed up as well as stimulated. He

CHAPTER TEN — DIGESTION AND ABSORPTION

performed many experiments in which he angered or frightened or in some other way excited a cat. In every case, the flow of gastric juice almost stopped. He has written a fascinating account of his experiments in his book, *The Wisdom of the Body*. But whether or not you will get this book and read it, you have learned an important lesson in hygiene. Don't excite yourself by getting angry or thinking of unpleasant things while you eat.

What have you learned? You have learned by now that the digestive system is an intricate and wonderful system. Did you notice how nicely the parts of the system normally work together? Did you notice that each step depends on preceding steps and that the enzymes work at the right times and places? It is not surprising, in a complicated system, that things go wrong once in a while.

You should have, too, a pretty clear picture of the digestive system, the alimentary canal and the large glands connected with it, as shown in Figure 10.1. You should know what is meant by digestion and absorption. And then you should know these facts:

(1) Each digestive juice contains one or more enzymes. Enzymes are catalysts made by living cells. Each food substance is acted on by a different enzyme or sometimes by several enzymes.
(2) Most food substances are such large molecules that digestion occurs in several steps.
(3) There are muscles in the walls of the digestive tube. In the stomach these muscles churn the food. In the rest of the tube there is a wavelike contraction of the rings of muscles. This is called peristalsis. The food is pushed along by peristalsis.
(4) Food remains in the small intestine about 8 hours. Most of the digestion and absorption go on here.
(5) The small intestine is fitted for absorption in several ways. Do you know what these adaptations are?
(6) The liver is important. The bile it makes turns oils into a digestible emulsion. And the liver turns unused amino acids into a useful sugar, and it stores sugar.
(7) Digestive glands are stimulated to secrete partly by the presence of food in the organ, which starts nerve messages, and partly by hormones.
(8) Your digestive glands can be kept from secreting by your emotions of fear, anger, or excitement of any kind.

USEFUL WORDS IN BIOLOGY

alimentary canal
esophagus
colon
digestion
end products
intermediate products
enzyme
catalyst
ptyalin
digestive gland
gastric gland
intestinal gland
salivary gland
peristalsis
serous membrane
pancreas
double sugar
simple sugar
pepsin
hydrochloric acid
pyloric sphincter
gall bladder
emulsion
absorption
villus
lacteal
glycogen
urea
secretin
hormone

TEST YOURSELF

1. "Food in the alimentary canal is not yet really in your body; it is merely in a tube that runs through your body." This makes necessary two processes. What are they?

2. Copy the following sentences and fill in the words that best complete the meaning: Ptyalin is an example of an ——, which acts on ——, changing it to ——. This process is called ——. *Do not write in this book.*

3. (a) State three important facts about enzymes. (b) Why cannot all catalysts be called enzymes?

4. Make a drawing of a simple digestive gland and label secreting cells and digestive juice.

5. Name the tissue (a) that covers each organ of the alimentary canal, (b) that lines each, and (c) that forms an important part of the wall between covering and lining.

6. Besides the salivary glands, what two other digestive gland organs do we have that lie outside the alimentary canal?

7. A look at the table on page 198 shows that with one exception the end products of digestion are formed in one organ of the alimentary canal. Which organ is that? What is the exception?

8. (a) Where in the body are fats changed into an emulsion? (b) How are they changed? (c) What is the advantage of having them changed?

9. Explain at least four ways in which the small intestine is adapted for absorption.

10. (a) Explain how digestive glands in the mouth and stomach are usually stimulated. (b) What might slow up their activity? (c) What does secretin do? (d) How was it discovered?

DO IT YOURSELF

1. A look at internal organs. If you dissect a freshly killed frog you can get a good idea of your digestive organs, and of your heart and lungs as well, even though the frog's organs differ from yours in some respects. Cut away the body wall from the ventral (lower) side of the frog, as follows. While the frog is lying on its dorsal side (back) grasp the loose body wall with a pair of forceps at the extreme lower part of the body. Make an incision and then cut out a complete rectangle from the whole lower part of the body. *Caution.* As you cut, hold your scissors horizontally and keep raising the body wall in front of the point of your scissors with your forceps. In this way you will not damage the organs below the body wall. In the region of the arms you will be obliged to cut through the bones that make the shoulder girdle.

During the breeding season the female frog has large masses of eggs. Remove these to see the other organs. In the region of the heart are the large, flat, dark-red lobes of the liver. Attached to the liver is the green gall bladder. On the frog's left side is the long, whitish, tubular stomach. Feel its firm, muscular walls. At its lower end it narrows to form the intestine. Trace the coils of the intestine. They are held in place by a very thin membrane, the *mesentery*. Do you see blood vessels in the mesentery leading to the wall of the intestine? The small intestine widens into the large intestine. In the region of the stomach, caught in the folds of the mesentery, is the long, narrow pancreas.

Other organs you will see are: the spleen, a dark-red ball; the lungs, two narrow, pointed, lavender organs lying against the back wall in the region of the heart; the kidneys, a pair of dark-red, rectangular organs close together against the back wall. In the male frog a pair of light-yellow, oval organs close to the kidneys are the male reproductive organs. Inflate the lungs by inserting a tube through the frog's mouth and blowing into it.

2. The need for controls in experiments. (a) What is the effect of saliva on starch? Make a starch paste by boiling a little starch in water. Add a small amount of saliva to a little starch paste in a test tube; shake it well for a minute or two; and then test some of it for sugar and some of it for starch. You cannot draw valid conclusions from your observations, however, since your experiment lacks controls. What controls are necessary? (b) What is the effect of gastric juice on hard-boiled white of egg (protein)? Artificial gastric juice can be made by adding to half a test tube of boiled water a few drops of dilute hydrochloric acid and a little powdered pepsin. Cut the white of egg into small pieces; measure the amount you put into a test tube; and add the gastric juice. Plug the test tube with cotton to exclude bacteria and prevent decay. What temperature would you recommend for the best results? Examine after 24 hours. What do you observe? What control is necessary? Write up the method, observation, and conclusion of these two experiments.

3. How does the presence of an acid affect the action of saliva? Add a small amount of saliva to some starch paste in a test tube. At once add some dilute hydrochloric acid and shake the mixture well. After some minutes test for sugar. May you draw conclusions from your results about the need for thorough chewing before swallowing food? Why or why not?

ADVENTURES IN READING

1. *The Machinery of the Body* by Anton J. Carlson and Victor Johnson, University of Chicago Press, 1953. A good reference book for answering many questions that arise.
2. *The Chemicals of Life* by Isaac Asimov, Abelard-Schulman, 1954. Goes into the subject of vitamins and enzymes in a more advanced way. Those of you who want to pursue this subject further will find the book helpful.
3. "Enzymes" by John E. Pfeiffer, *Scientific American*, December 1948 (in *Scientific American Reader*, 1953). A skilled writer on scientific subjects tells what has been discovered about enzymes. Not easy.

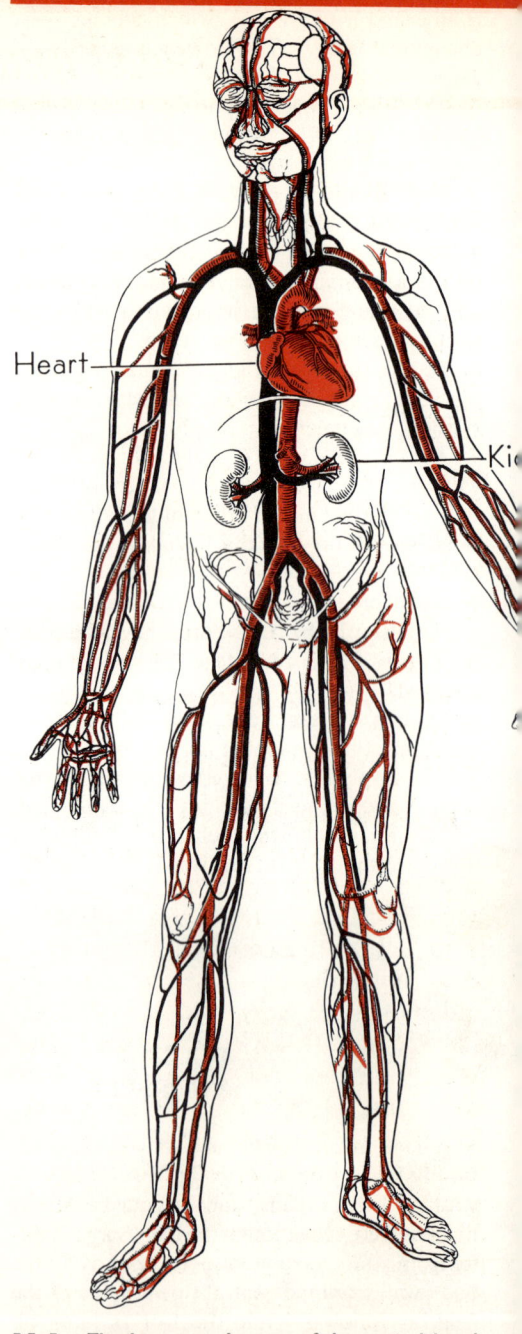

11.1 The heart and some of the main blood vessels. The arteries are red; the veins are black. The many, many smaller blood vessels, including the capillaries, and the lymphatic circulatory system are not shown.

UNIT FOUR — HOW OUR BODIES WORK

Chapter 11

Blood and circulation

Transportation. You have just read how food materials pass into the blood after they have been digested. Now let's learn about the **circulatory system,** which carries this blood to all the billions of cells in the body. You all know some of its organs; the **heart;** the **arteries,** which carry blood away from the heart; and the **veins,** which carry this blood back to the heart. You probably know less about the microscopic tubes connecting arteries and veins. These are **capillaries** (cap'ill-a-rees).

But blood is not the only liquid that circulates in the body. There is also a colorless liquid called **lymph.** Lymph surrounds the cells and flows through tubes known as **lymphatics.**

Blood vessels. Figure 11.1 shows you that the arteries and veins extend in every direction to every part of the body. But the picture cannot possibly show all the arteries and veins; it shows only the largest ones. Arteries and veins are very much branched, like a tree with all its branches. The finest branches run to and through every part of the body. They are so fine that they are only just visible to the naked eye. Blood moves from arteries into capillaries. But at their other ends capillaries join onto fine branches of a vein. See Figure 11.2. In this way blood gets into a vein. Then it can start back on its trip to the heart.

But while blood is in the capillaries important things happen. Capillaries have the very thinnest of walls. The wall consists of just a single layer of

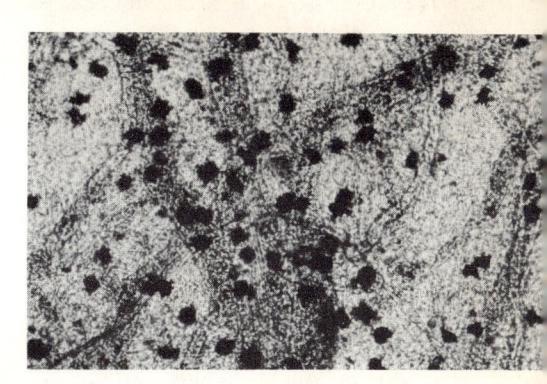

11.2 Part of the web of a frog's foot magnified 75 times. The dark spots are coloring matter in the skin. Can you see very faint narrow vessels? They are capillaries. What are the wider vessels? Every other part of the body, just like this web, has blood vessels running criss-cross through it. *Hugh Spencer*

cells. Diffusion goes on. There is a rapid exchange of substances between the blood and the body cells. And there are so many capillaries that every one of the billions of cells in the body has a capillary lying very near it. No matter where you prick yourself, you bleed, provided the pin goes through the outer layer of dead cells. And every internal organ has the same rich supply of capillaries.

What is blood? So much is known about blood that a whole book, and a very interesting one, has been written in answer to the question "What is blood?" The book is *The Story of Blood* by John H. Glynn. Only the simplest answer to the question can be given here. Fifty per cent of the blood is an almost colorless or straw-colored liquid called **plasma.** Plasma is something

CHAPTER ELEVEN — BLOOD AND CIRCULATION

Platelets

Red corpuscles

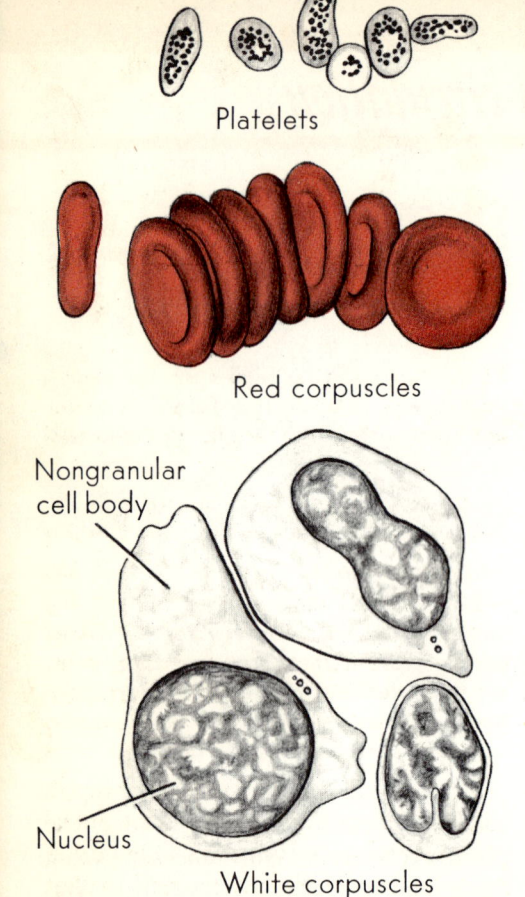

Nongranular cell body

Nucleus

White corpuscles

11.3 Three kinds of blood cells. How do these cells differ in size and shape? What part usually found in a cell is missing in the red corpuscles? In the platelets the nucleus is found in small pieces.

like very thin soup; it is mostly water. But in the water are dissolved the various digested food substances which were absorbed into the capillaries in the small intestine. These at some later time pass into the cells where they are used for oxidation and for building up new protoplasm.

But plasma contains much more than food used by cells. It carries the wastes produced by oxidation in the cells. And the plasma contains many kinds of proteins which have special uses in the body. Only in recent years have we learned about these proteins in the blood which are never used for building up new cells. Some of them for instance are **gamma globulins** (glob'-you-lins) which help protect you against some diseases. Another is **fibrinogen** (fye-brin'o-jen) which helps in clotting blood. Besides these substances, the plasma contains hormones, or chemical messengers, like secretin.

Plasma is constantly changing. In the capillaries among working muscle cells, the plasma picks up and becomes rich in waste substances; here, also, it loses foods and oxygen. In the villi, during absorption, the plasma becomes rich in digested food substances. If you have been eating hamburgers, there will be many amino acids in the plasma. Have you ever watched the loading and unloading of a baggage car at a railroad station? The car is full or nearly full of baggage at all times, but the baggage changes at every station; just so with the plasma. Only the blood does not come to a stop when it loads and unloads.

But blood is more than just plasma. The plasma carries three kinds of cells. They are shown in Figure 11.3. The cells make up about half the volume of the blood. That is why blood is thought of as a tissue.

Red blood cells. One drop of blood contains about 5,000,000 red blood cells. If your red blood cells were laid out flat next to each other they would cover an area as large as a baseball diamond. A red blood cell is like a disk squeezed in the middle. It has no nucleus. Its protoplasm contains a special protein known as **hemoglobin** (he'mo-globe'in). This is rich in iron. Hemoglobin unites very easily with oxygen but releases the oxygen just as easily. This is what makes red blood cells so useful. They pick up oxygen in the lungs and lose it to all cells. In uniting, hemoglobin forms a redder compound (oxyhemoglobin).

Red blood cells are made from cells in the red marrow of the bones. Before they are carried off in the plasma they lose their nuclei. No cell can live very long without a nucleus; a red blood cell lives about three months. Normally, red cells are dying off in your body at the rate of about 10,000 every second. If they are being destroyed at a still faster rate, or if they are not being made fast enough, or if you lose a large amount of blood, you may have too few red cells. Sometimes, too, you may have enough cells, but they contain too little hemoglobin, perhaps because there is too little iron in your diet. In all these cases the condition is called **anemia** (an-ee′me-a).

You have an organ behind the stomach called the **spleen**. It's about the size of your fist. Among other things the spleen is a reservoir of blood, and it is a storage place of red blood cells, especially. Some of the old red blood cells are destroyed in the spleen. Whenever you exercise, the spleen contracts harder than usual. In this way many of its stored red cells are put into the blood. And when people live at high altitudes where oxygen is scarcer, the spleen also contracts more vigorously. In both these cases the body is taking care of its own needs, providing oxygen carriers.

White corpuscles. We have several kinds of white corpuscles, or **leucocytes** (lew′ko-sites). The commonest kind were discovered near the end of the last century by the great Russian biologist Eli Metchnikoff (1845–1916). He called them **phagocytes** (fag′o-sites), which means devouring cells. White

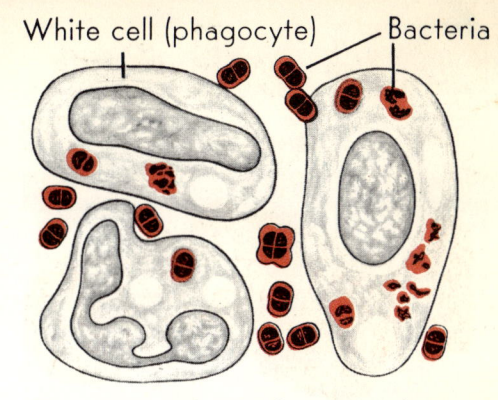

11.4 Three white cells (phagocytes) engulfing bacteria. In how many of the cells do you see bacteria being broken up and digested?

corpuscles can crawl about as an ameba does; they can even push their false feet out between the cells of the capillary wall, thus moving out of the capillary into the spaces among tissue cells. Here they are very useful to us, serving as a sanitation department. They engulf and digest bacteria or other unwanted particles.

When bacteria enter the body through some break in the skin, millions of the phagocytes and some of the other kinds of white cells are carried to that region and leave the capillaries. The phagocytes get busy eating. But sometimes the bacteria kill the white cells. The dead cells pile up as **pus**. The whole region becomes red, swollen, and hot to the touch because so much blood is present.

Some kinds of white corpuscles are made in the red marrow of the bones, just as the red corpuscles are. Other kinds are made in the lymph glands, about which you will read later.

Blood platelets and clotting. You saw the platelets in Figure 11.3. They are of great importance to us, since it is they that start the process of blood clotting. You know, probably, that some people are "bleeders"; their

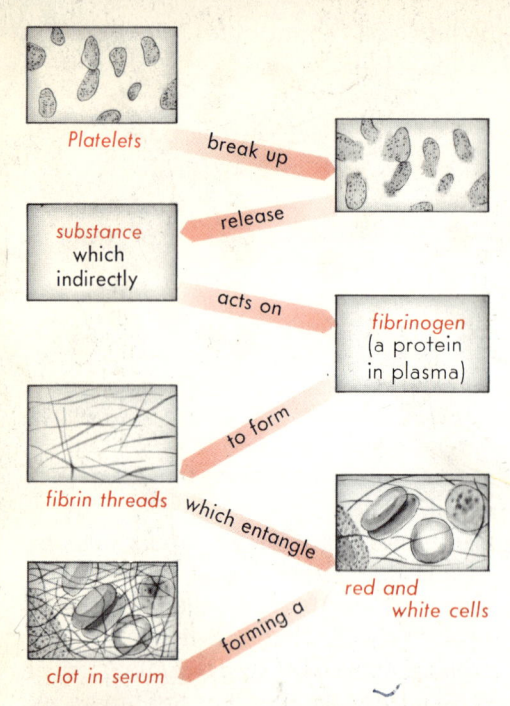

Platelets → break up → **substance** which indirectly → release → acts on → **fibrinogen** (a protein in plasma) → to form → **fibrin threads** → which entangle → **red and white cells** → forming a → **clot in serum**

11.5 How blood is supposed to clot. Begin at the top. Platelets start the process. Of what is the clot composed? What surrounds the clot?

blood clots very, very slowly, or not at all. But in most of us bleeding from small wounds stops almost at once because a clot forms and plugs up the cut. Various things can be done to stop the flow of blood from large cuts. Before an operation vitamin K and calcium may be injected to help clotting. And a substance known as **adrenalin** is often used to help clot blood.

One very much simplified account of how blood clots is this: When a blood vessel is damaged the platelets break up. As platelets break up they release an enzyme. This enzyme, very indirectly, causes changes in one of the proteins in plasma, the one known as fibrinogen. The fibrinogen hardens, but only if calcium is present; it hardens into threads. These are known as **fibrin** (fye′brin) threads. They entangle the red and white cells, and this tangled mass is the clot. Figure 11.5 should help to make this clearer.

You can see some of these steps in clotting if you allow beef blood to stand in a jar. Soon fibrin threads begin to form across the jar; and then you will see a large clot forming in the center. This clot is lying in a yellow liquid called **serum**. The yellow liquid, of course, is not plasma. Plasma contains fibrinogen; and this liquid has lost its fibrinogen. This liquid can never clot, but plasma clots. Physicians therefore find serum much more useful than plasma.

The clotting of blood is of great help to us. But clotting also has its disadvantages. Occasionally a clot forms in a small blood vessel, somewhere inside the body. Perhaps a rough surface starts the breaking up of platelets. The clot is carried along in the blood stream. Then, by some bad luck it may catch in one of the very narrow arteries in the heart muscle. These fine branches that supply food and oxygen to the heart muscle are **coronary** (cor-e-ner′i) arteries. The clot blocks the tiny artery, and the blood supply to the heart muscle is partly shut off. That is serious. It is called a **coronary thrombosis**.

Transfusions and blood banks. Long ago people tried to transfer blood from one person to another. They even tried to transfer sheep's blood. This was always unsuccessful. But occasionally human blood was transferred without harm to the patient. Fifty or more years ago Karl Landsteiner, a great physiologist (a scientist who studies how the bodies of living things work), discovered why some blood transfusions caused trouble. Most of us have proteins in our serum called **agglutinins** (ag-glue′tin-ins). These may make red blood cells cling to each

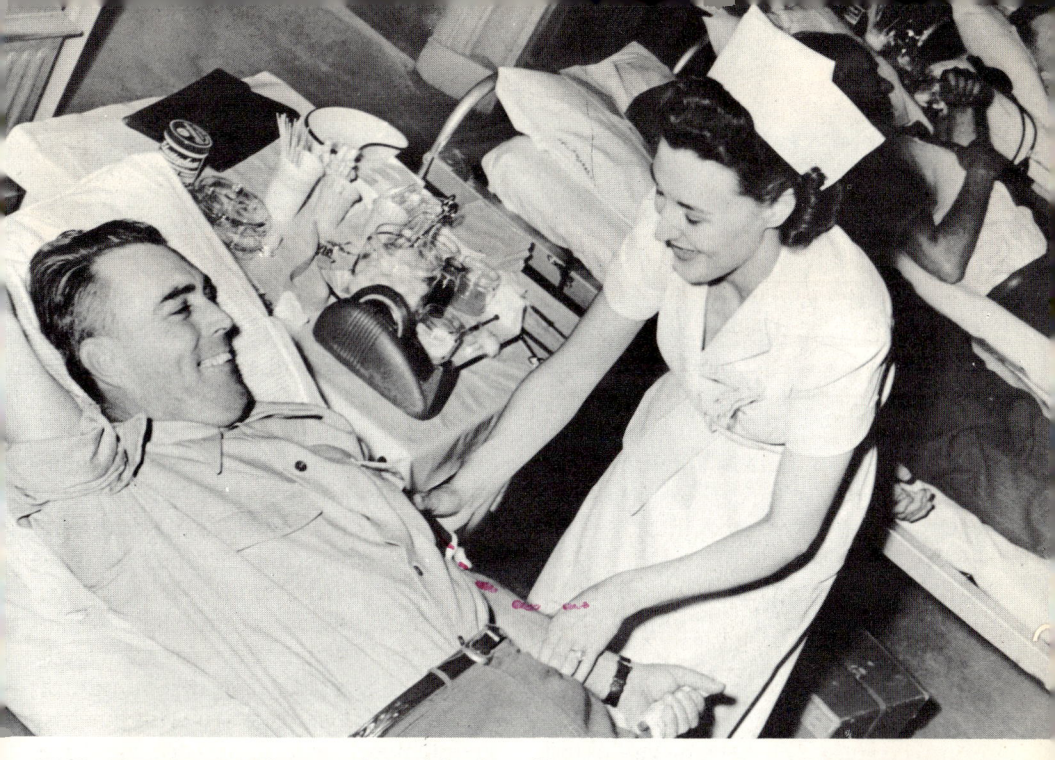

11.6 This photograph was taken while the man was donating blood for the third time at a Red Cross Center during World War II. How was the blood used? Under what conditions is there still a need for blood donations? *Keystone View*

other; they clump, or **agglutinate,** the cells. In many people the red cells have a particular protein called an **agglutinogen** (ag-glue-tin′oh-jen). It is this that reacts with the agglutinin and causes the clumping. Now Landsteiner discovered that people fall into one of four groups according to their agglutinins and agglutinogens. For convenience these groups are called A, B, O, AB. All races have these same four groups. Of course, we don't know to which group we belong until our blood is tested. Do *you* know what type of blood you have?

Suppose you belong to group A. That means that your red blood cells contain agglutinogen A and your serum contains anti-B agglutinins. Your serum certainly could not contain anti-A agglutinin, or your own blood cells would clump. A person in group B has in his cells agglutinogen B and in his serum, anti-A agglutinin. So if you put B blood into A, of course, there will be clumping of A's cells by B's serum, and also clumping of B's cells by A's serum. These clumps may block up some capillary and cause death.

But you read that there are four types of blood. A very few people have AB cells. Naturally the blood of these persons contains neither anti-A nor anti-B serum. And many of us (about 45%) have O blood. These people have no agglutinogens at all in their cells, but their serum contains both anti-A and anti-B agglutinins, as shown on page 210.

Of course it is safe to transfuse O blood into another O person. Their cells never clump. In fact, if possible,

CHAPTER ELEVEN — BLOOD AND CIRCULATION

TABLE 13
BLOOD TYPES

A type has A agglutinogens in cells	and anti-B serum
B type has B agglutinogens in cells	and anti-A serum
AB type has A and B agglutinogens in cells	and no agglutinins in serum
O type has no agglutinogens in cells	and both anti-A and anti-B serum

transfusions should always be made between people of the same type. But, in an emergency, O blood can also be transfused into an A person, although O has anti-A agglutinins in his serum. It is safe, for the amount of O's blood transfused into A, especially if not too much is given at one time, is small compared to the five or six quarts in A; O's serum will be pretty well diluted and it won't clump A's cells too much. And, of course, O's cells will not be clumped by A's serum because O's cells never clump. The same thing holds for transfusing O blood into a B or an AB person. For this reason the O person is sometimes spoken of as the "universal donor," but only in an emergency.

After the discovery of the four blood groups, transfusions became very common. But occasionally there are bad results even now for other reasons.

Recently two additional agglutinogens were found, M and N. A person may be either M, N, or MN. But since human blood contains no agglutinins against M, N, and MN, blood need not be matched with respect to them.

As transfusions became more and more common, especially among the wounded during the war, it was difficult to get a large enough supply of blood. Blood does not keep; the red blood cells die soon after blood leaves the body. But thanks to an important discovery made by a scientist in Argentina (Dr. Luis Agate), we can now keep blood for a long time. You know that blood is now collected in large amounts and is kept for a long time in **blood banks.**

The Rh factor. Besides the agglutinogens that may give trouble in transfusions, most people have another protein in the red cells that you have probably heard about. This protein is called the Rh factor (after the Rhesus monkey in which it was first discovered). About 85% of us have this substance; we are then said to be Rh positive. People who lack it are Rh negative. In certain cases when the parents differ with respect to this substance the unborn child may be harmed. This is how it works. If the father is Rh positive and the mother Rh negative, the child's blood may be affected before it is born. Its red cells may be destroyed. Sometimes it is necessary to give the infant a complete change of blood by transfusion as soon as it is born. The doctor can be ready for this. He knows it may be needed because he has tested the blood of the father and the mother. If the mother's blood is Rh positive and the father's Rh negative, the doctor knows there will be no trouble. Or if the parents' blood is of the same kind, no harm comes to the child. When you know more about reproduction and heredity this will be clearer to you.

Using separate parts of the blood. For a long time a **centrifuge** (sen'trifuge) has been used for separating the cells from the liquid part of the blood. The centrifuge spins the blood around in a tube so fast that the cells are pushed to the end of the tube while the liquid plasma remains at the top. Doctors can use plasma instead of whole blood for many purposes. The body usually has a large store of red cells in reserve, anyway. Plasma can be handled much more easily than whole blood. It can be dried and preserved. Soldiers can carry a small package of dried plasma, which can be made usable with distilled water.

Having learned how to separate plasma from red and white cells, scientists went one step further. They learned to separate out from the whole plasma the many proteins it contains. You may have read about blood **fractionation,** which made rapid strides during World War II. Professor Edwin Cohn of Harvard University was a leader in this work. Each special protein has a special use. You have read of a very few examples: fibrinogen, to help clot blood; gamma globulin, used against measles and polio; serum albumin, used for treating patients who suffer from shock. By separating these proteins, which have different uses, a given amount of blood can be made to go much farther. Also the separated proteins can be preserved much longer, and they occupy far less space.

The heart. Having learned a very little about the blood, let's take a look at the pump that moves the blood. This pump is the heart. It keeps the blood in constant motion and in rapid motion; a drop of blood may make

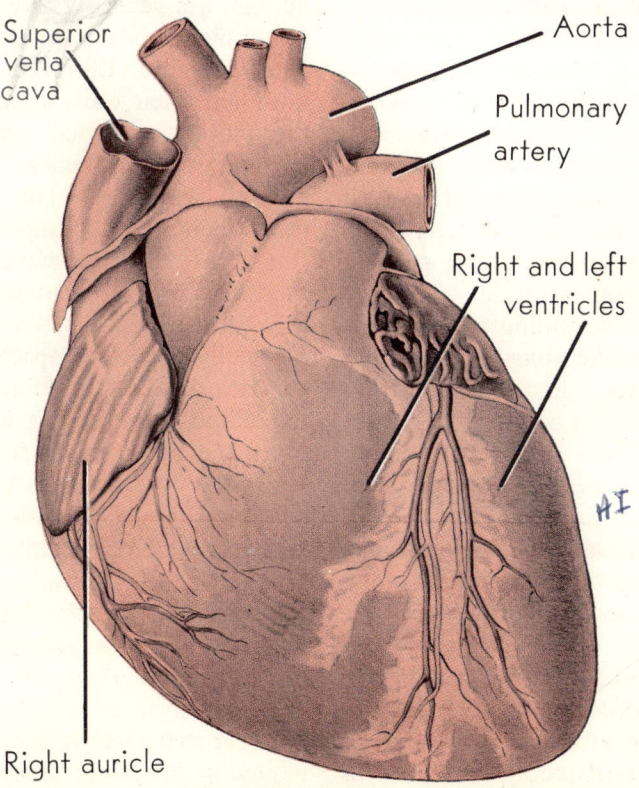

11.7 The human heart. This is the pump that keeps the blood in constant motion.

CHAPTER ELEVEN — BLOOD AND CIRCULATION

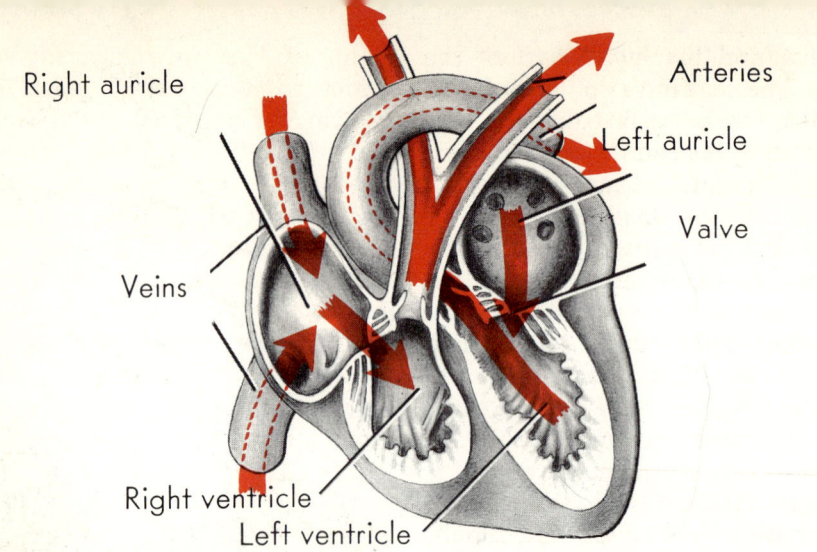

11.8 The heart cut open to show its four chambers and the principal blood vessels attached to it. The arrows trace the path of the blood through and from the heart.

the rounds of the body in less than half a minute. How is it done?

Blood is moved in the simplest way; it is pushed. If a liquid is put into a bag and the bag is squeezed, the liquid squirts out. If the bag is squeezed hard, the liquid will squirt out with great force. This is what happens every time the heart beats. The walls of the heart are made of powerful muscles. They contract, and squeeze on the blood that is inside. You can learn much by examining a beef heart which is much like yours, only larger. Examine the heart first from the outside, and then cut it open.

The heart has two small upper portions and the large lower portion that ends in a point. Look at Figure 11.7, which is a drawing of a human heart. Do you find the large blood vessels which are connected with the upper portions? When you cut the heart open, you can see that there are really four distinct chambers, two upper and two lower; and you see that at least one blood vessel opens into each of the chambers. The upper chambers are called **auricles** (or′i-kels). The blood vessels connected with the auricles are veins. These veins steadily pour blood into the auricles. Now look at Figure 11.8. When the auricles are filled, their walls contract and thus the blood is pushed gently into the two chambers just beneath them. These are the **ventricles.** The auricles have thin walls, containing little muscle. But the ventricles have very thick, muscular walls. That is what makes the ventricles look so much larger, especially the left ventricle. When the ventricle walls contract, they squirt the blood into the big arteries which carry the blood away from the heart. Ventricles contract with great force.

The right and left sides of the heart are completely separated from one another by a thick wall. Blood cannot pass directly from one side to the other; it is just as though there were two distinct hearts. As you read more about the circulation of the blood you will discover that there is a great advantage in having this complete separation of the blood in the right and left halves.

You can feel that your heart beats in a double beat. You now know why. First the two auricles contract; then the two ventricles contract. This occurs normally about 65–70 times per minute, somewhat faster when you are very young. If a frog's body is laid open to show the heart, you can see this double beat very clearly, though the frog happens to have only one ventricle instead of two. And you can see something else that is interesting. If a frog's head (with the brain) has been removed, the heart keeps on beating just the same. In this respect heart (cardiac) muscle is different from all other muscle tissue. It contracts rhythmically by itself. All other muscles need to be stimulated by nerves. Our hearts, too, are made of this special kind of muscle tissue.

William Harvey. You have probably known for a long time that the heart pumps blood and that this blood flows out through arteries and is returned to the heart by veins. But it took very many centuries to learn this. Men imagined all kinds of uses for the blood and the heart. This was before they knew that the body is made of living cells which need food and oxygen. For a long time people thought the heart was the seat of intelligence. The Greeks believed that the arteries carried air and the veins carried blood. But by the beginning of the 17th century, ideas like these had been largely given up. A little was known about the structure and the use of the heart, but very little. No one yet knew that the blood went all the way around the body in a complete circulation. Then came William Harvey (1578–1657), a brilliant English physician. He performed many accurate experiments, made careful dissections, and did some logical reasoning. He arrived at the idea of the circulation of the blood as we now understand it, and he published his ideas in a book. You may want to look into the book. It is called *The Motion of the Heart and Blood in Animals*.

Harvey showed first that the heart is muscular and serves as a pump. He discovered that the heart can hold two ounces of blood. It beats about 65 times a minute. Thus, he calculated, it drives ten pounds of blood out into the body in less than a minute. Evidently, the same blood is continually being pumped around again and again; this amount of blood could not possibly be made anew each minute. Therefore, he reasoned, the blood which leaves the heart must return to the heart. If the arteries carry it away from the heart, the veins must bring it back. Harvey did not see the microscopic capillaries

11.9 William Harvey, born about 400 years ago, discovered that blood circulates throughout the body. *Armed Forces Medical Library*

CHAPTER ELEVEN — BLOOD AND CIRCULATION

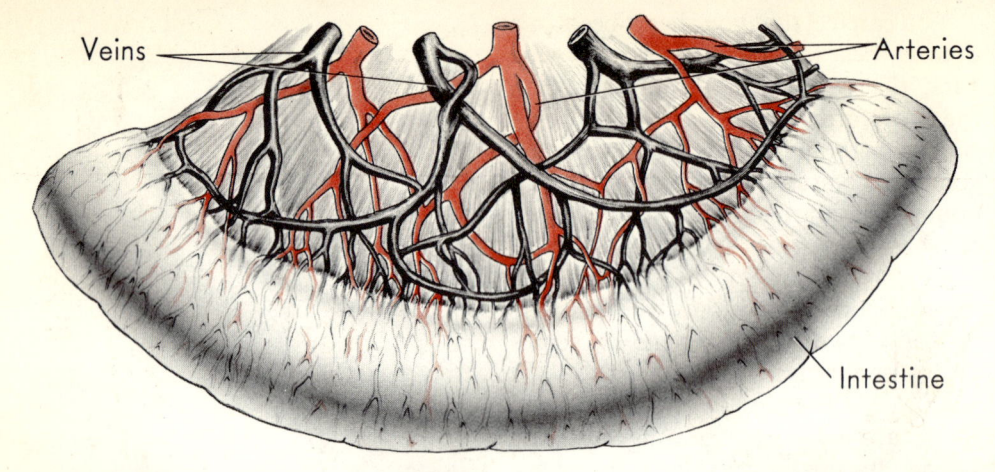

11.10 A piece of a cat's intestine showing branching arteries and veins. William Harvey saw small arteries and veins, but he could not see that they were connected. How are arteries and veins connected to each other? *Clay Adams* Co.

which we now know connect arteries and veins. But he did see what you can see in Figure 11.10. And he suspected that there must be still smaller blood vessels, too small for him to see.

Arteries help pump the blood. When a large artery is cut, you can see the blood coming out in spurts. But if a large vein is cut, the blood flows out smoothly. Do you know what first aid to use when an artery is cut? You can do various things. You can apply pressure at certain points where the artery lies near the surface, or you can apply a **tourniquet** (tour′ni-ket). It would be well if all of you were to join a first-aid class and learn how to stop bleeding.

Why does the blood in an artery move in spurts? To begin with, the heart sends the blood out in spurts. The walls of all arteries are elastic. As each rush of blood from the heart pushes on these elastic walls, the artery stretches and quickly comes back to normal, as any elastic substance does. In this way the blood which starts in spurts is pushed along in spurts by the elastic walls. You can feel the walls of a large artery stretching (beating) whenever you put your finger over an artery that lies near the surface. In most parts of the body the arteries are buried deep within the tissues; but in your temples, in your wrists, and in some other places they are close to the skin. Here you can feel them stretching with each squirt of blood. These are "pressure points." This stretching of the artery is called the **pulse.** Therefore, a pulse of 70 beats per minute means that your heart is beating 70 times a minute.

Walls of blood vessels. Even the tiniest arteries in all parts of the body have some of this elastic tissue. Inside the elastic tissue is a very smooth membrane (serous membrane). This is so smooth that there is little friction as the blood flows along. Outside of the elastic tissue are rings of involuntary muscle tissue and also some connective tissue, as Figure 11.11 shows. At certain times nerve messages reach the muscle cells of some particular

214   UNIT FOUR — HOW OUR BODIES WORK

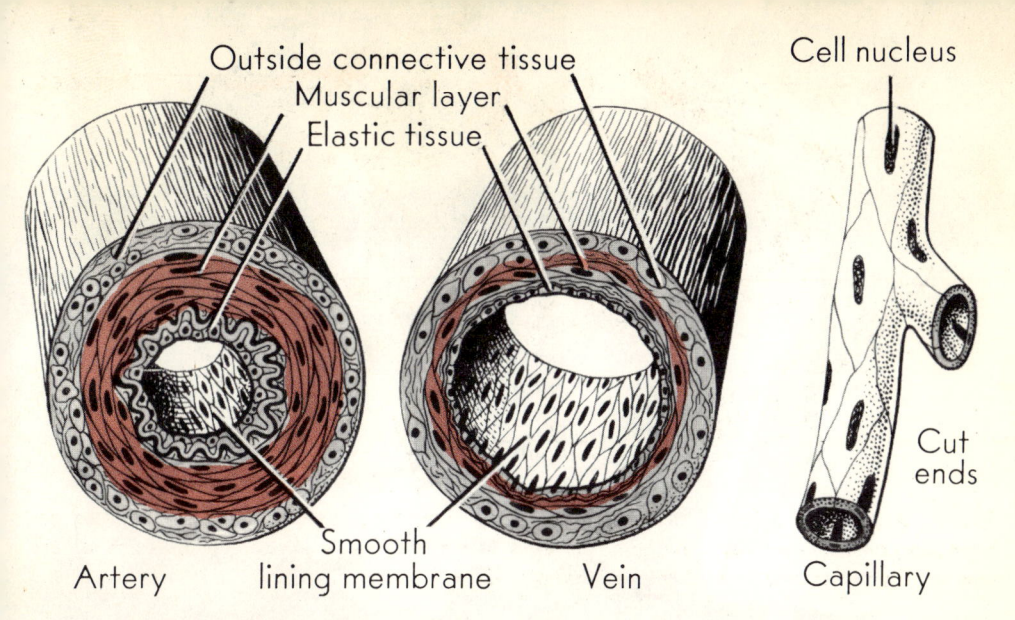

11.11 Looking at the inside first, which layers do you find in the walls of arteries and veins? Which vessels have thicker walls? How do capillaries differ from arteries and veins in structure? In which of these vessels does blood have highest pressure?

artery, and the muscle cells contract. This makes the artery into a narrower tube; in other words the artery can't carry as much blood at this time. On the other hand, when these muscles are completely relaxed, the artery is a far wider artery. What do you suppose is true of the artery leading to your face when you are blushing? What is probably true of the arteries leading to the small intestine when digestion and absorption are well started? Remember that these muscle fibers are of the involuntary kind; all these changes go on without your doing anything about it consciously.

The wall of a vein has the same layers: serous membrane, elastic tissue, muscle, and connective tissue. But there is far less elastic and muscle tissue. A vein is much less stiff. When not filled with blood, the walls collapse.

The walls of capillaries, as you can see, are quite different. They consist of nothing but the continuation of the smooth lining membrane found in arteries and veins. No muscles, no elastic tissue.

Blood pressure. Physicians measure blood pressure as shown in Figure 11.12. They use a device to press together the walls of a large artery thus stopping the flow of blood. A mercury gauge measures the pressure it takes to press the walls together. The pressure shown on the gauge is the normal pressure of the blood against the artery wall. Physicians really take two pressures, one at the time that the heart beats, the other while the heart is at rest.

Some people normally have a lower blood pressure than others. But there are many things that make your blood pressure higher or lower. For some reason, when you are angry or worried or even very happy — excited in any way — the walls of the tiniest arteries all over the body contract. Then, of course, as they get smaller, blood pres-

CHAPTER ELEVEN — BLOOD AND CIRCULATION

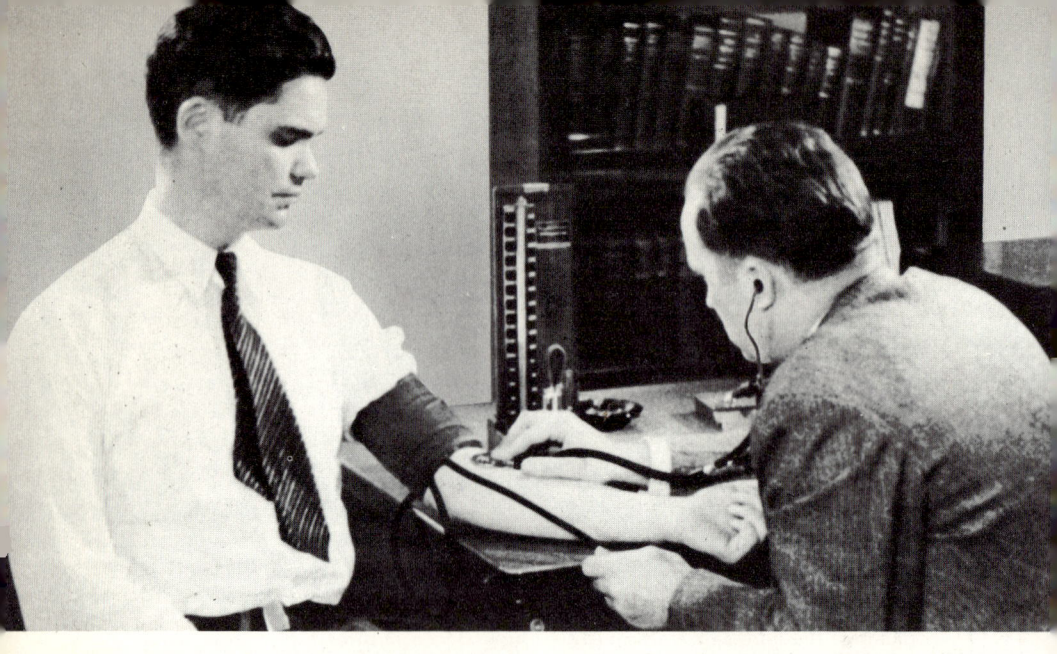

11.12 Taking blood pressure. What is the purpose of the tight dark bandage around the upper arm? Do you see the mercury gauge that measures the pressure? What emotional states may affect your blood pressure? *Encyclopaedia Britannica Films, Inc.*

sure goes up. Now if the worry or the nerve strain continues over a long time blood pressure may become steadily high. This continued high blood pressure is called **hypertension** (high-per-ten′shun). Hypertension overworks the heart.

Hardening of the arteries. Artery walls lose some of their elasticity with age. A substance formed in the body from eating animal fat (cholesterol) may have some connection with this; there is much that is not yet fully understood. The hardening of arteries (arteriosclerosis) sometimes is the cause of the breaking of the wall in smaller arteries. If this happens in the brain there is a **brain hemorrhage**. The escaped blood may damage some of the nerve cells. If the damaged cells control muscles, these muscles may be paralyzed. If the hardening is in the coronary arteries, the heart muscle may get too little blood. Sometimes, too, a clot, or thrombosis, forms or catches in these coronary arteries.

Fainting or "blackout." With sudden severe pain or for a variety of other reasons there is, sometimes, an insufficient supply of blood to the brain. The person "sees black," becomes unconscious, and loses control of his skeletal muscles. He faints, or "blacks out." Often he can avoid fainting by putting his head down between his knees.

An aviator may have a similar experience. When he makes a very fast and sharp turn or pulls out of a fast dive sharply, his blood is pushed away from the head. He blacks out for an instant, but recovers as soon as his brain is again supplied with blood.

Valves in the veins and heart. There is no pumping in the capillaries. Blood is pushed here by the force of the blood behind; it moves gently and fairly steadily into the veins. The flow of blood, all the way back to the heart through the veins, continues largely because of the pressure behind. But the flow through the veins is helped also by exercise. Every motion of the skeletal muscles squeezes the veins running through the muscle. As a vein is squeezed, the blood within is pushed toward the heart. It can't flow backward toward the capillaries, since there are pocket valves all along the inside of veins. Blood flowing toward the heart flattens these pocket valves, leaving a clear passageway. But if the blood reverses, it catches in the pockets and closes the passageway back to the capillaries. Figure 11.13 shows how these valves work.

There are valves in the heart, too. But they are different; they are tiny flaps of membrane attached to the walls between auricle and ventricle in both halves of the heart. They move back

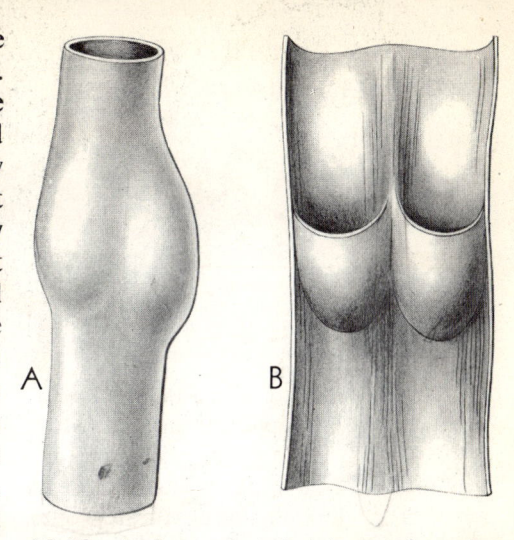

11.13 In **A** a vein is bulging at the point where a valve has stopped the backward flow of blood. **B** shows this vein cut open. Which way does blood in this vein travel, up or down?

and forth like swinging doors. Look at Figure 11.14A. Blood going from the auricle into the ventricle forces open the "doors." But when the ventricle contracts, as shown in B, the blood catches behind the doors and slams them shut. The only direction in which

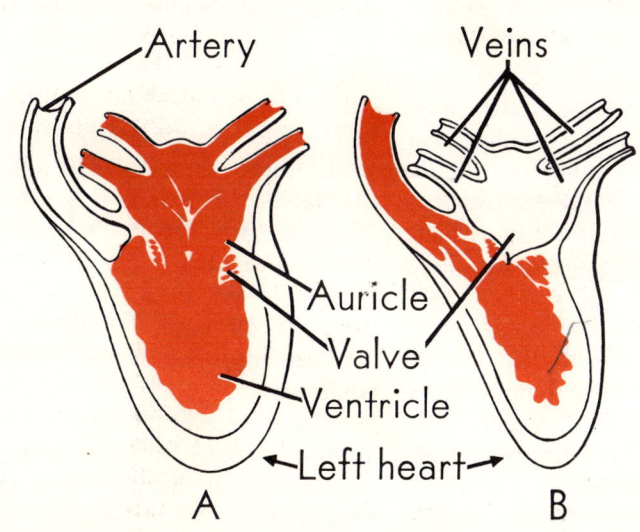

11.14 In **A** the valve between the left auricle and ventricle is open. In **B** the left ventricle has contracted. Why is blood not forced back into the left auricle? Where is it being forced? As the ventricle empties the auricle above it is filled again.

CHAPTER ELEVEN — BLOOD AND CIRCULATION

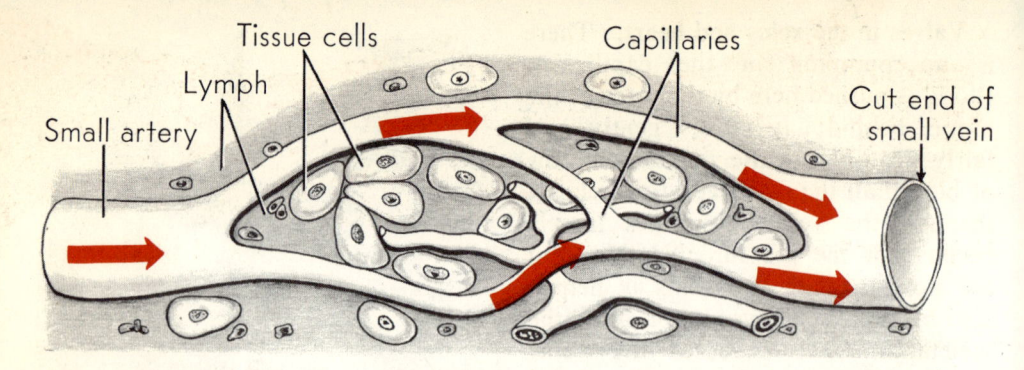

11.15 Body cells are surrounded by lymph. Find the tubes (lymphatics) through which lymph is returned to the blood. Are these small lymph tubes open or closed?

the blood can go then is into the **aorta** (ay-or'ta). Here in the aorta are some pocket valves which keep the blood from flowing back at the moment the left ventricle has emptied itself.

Surely you have heard of people who have leaking valves in the heart? With each beat of the heart a small amount of blood leaks back because the flaps of the valve don't quite meet. A heart with leaking valves is just like any other pump with leaking valves; it is less efficient.

Lymph. All tissue cells are surrounded by a liquid. This liquid is called **lymph.** You have seen this colorless lymph, no doubt, in a blister. Lymph is mostly plasma which has diffused from the capillaries. It is diluted, however, with water. And it contains white corpuscles, too, which have pushed their way through capillary walls.

Digested food, and the many other substances, diffuse from the blood in the capillaries into the lymph, then into cells. Cell wastes and secretions diffuse into lymph, then through capillary walls into the blood.

Lymphatics. At the very beginning of the chapter you read that there is a blood circulation and a lymph circulation. Lymph, after washing over tissue cells, is drained off by special thin-walled vessels called lymphatics. These tiny lymphatics lie among the cells in all parts of the body. They are open at their ends; thus they are quite different from blood vessels. See Figure 11.15. One good-sized lymphatic (the thoracic duct) is formed by the joining together of many small lymphatics coming together from all parts of the body. It connects with a large vein on the left side of the body under the collarbone. There is a similar, but smaller, one on the right side. Lymph enters the blood stream at these points.

Do you remember studying about villi in the small intestine? In every villus there is a lacteal among the capillaries. This lacteal is a lymphatic which absorbs fats. The lacteals join other lymphatics. Thus fats enter the blood stream in a very roundabout way. They enter where the lymph empties into the blood — under the collarbone.

Lymph is never pumped; it is pushed along very slowly indeed by the pressure of the liquid behind and by body movements. And, there are valves in the lymphatics like those in the veins; these keep the lymph from flowing backward.

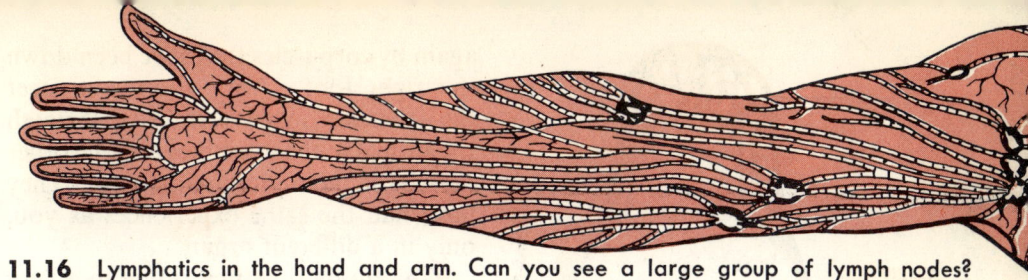

11.16 Lymphatics in the hand and arm. Can you see a large group of lymph nodes?

Lymph glands. Lymphatics have slight swellings in definite places as shown in Figure 11.16. These are **lymph glands,** or **lymph nodes.** They act as sieves, separating out the bacteria and other foreign bodies which were swept up by the lymph as it washed over the tissue cells. Lymph glands contain large numbers of white blood cells. These engulf and digest the bacteria. In fact, certain kinds of white blood cells are made in the glands. Other kinds are made in the spleen and are carried to the lymph glands. After an infection these glands may swell. Then you can feel them in the neck, in the crook of the elbow and knee, and in various other regions.

The course of the blood. Now imagine that you are small enough to seat yourself on one of the red corpuscles for a ride around the body. You will have to hold on tight, for part of the way you will be traveling very fast and your corpuscle will be pushed along in spurts. The whole journey will take less than one minute. Suppose you started from the left ventricle; you would be shot into the large artery known as the aorta. Soon you find that the aorta branches, one branch leading to the head, another to the arms. At this point you will part company with some of your friends who are riding on other corpuscles.

You continue, let us say, down the main artery toward the legs. But immediately you are saying good-bye to more of your friends, some of whom turn off to the stomach, some to the intestine, and some to other internal organs. The artery along which you are traveling has become a narrower tube and now branches, one branch leading down each leg. You happen to go into the left branch and soon you find yourself in the left foot, in a very small artery.

Suddenly things look different to you. The tube is extremely narrow; there is scarcely room enough for your corpuscle to get through. And you can look out through the walls! You are now in a capillary with very thin walls. You look down and you see that the corpuscle on which you are riding changes color. Oxygen has left the oxyhemoglobin and has diffused into the neighboring cells. The plasma in which your corpuscle is floating still looks the same, but it also is changing; food substances are diffusing out of the capillary, and the wastes of oxidation from neighboring cells are entering the capillary. But you never stop for any of these changes to take place. On you go, noticing soon that you are again in a slightly wider tube, and you cannot look out any more. You have left the capillary. You are in a vein. You are traveling along smoothly but you are going straight up hill. You soon notice that you are being joined

CHAPTER ELEVEN — BLOOD AND CIRCULATION

again by corpuscles that have been down the right foot. Very soon you meet the friends who have traveled through the stomach, the intestines and the other organs of the abdominal cavity. They have had the same experiences as you, only in a different organ.

You are by this time riding in a very wide vein. This wide vein (the **inferior vena cava**) connects with the right auricle and you soon find yourself dropped into the right auricle. Now examine Figure 11.17 to trace your course and that of some of your friends. This is a map; it does not pretend to show actual arteries and veins and capillaries; it only shows the **course** of the blood.

You are now back in the heart, but not where you started. You are on the right side; you started from the left. You are in the right auricle and here another reunion occurs. A large vein (**superior vena cava**) is bringing back your friends who have traveled to the head and arms. Your friends gather rather slowly, but suddenly you are all squeezed into the right ventricle. As this ventricle contracts, at once you are on your way again out of the heart once more. You go into an artery. This time it is a **pulmonary artery.** (It's an artery because it carries blood away from the heart.) Soon it branches and you will be pushed either right or left. Whichever way you go, the artery gets narrower and narrower. Soon you find yourself for a second time in an extremely narrow, transparent tube, a capillary. But this time you are in a capillary in the lung. You know that you must be in a lung, for as you look down you see your corpuscle becoming bright red once more. Oxygen is diffusing into your capillary and uniting with the hemoglobin in your corpuscle. In the meantime, though you can't see it happening, carbon dioxide diffuses

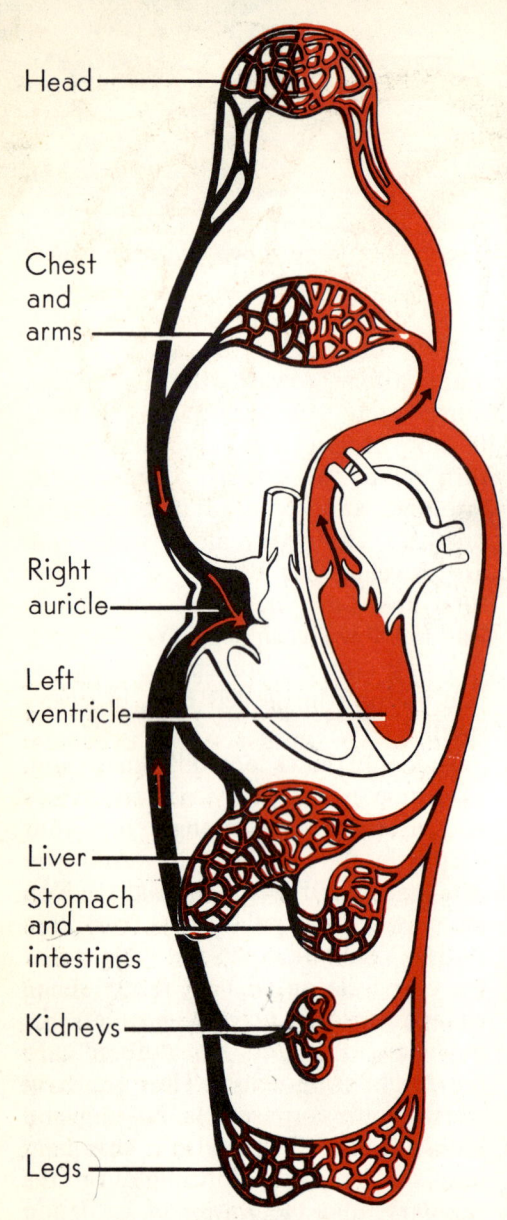

11.17 Diagram of circulation of blood from the left ventricle to right auricle. Blood goes from the left ventricle to the aorta. Some is carried to every part of the body, but only a few large organs are shown. Which are they? What kind of blood vessels are shown in red? What kind are shown in black? Does the blood in these contain much or little oxygen? This shows only part of the circulation. To see the other part, look at Figure 11.18.

UNIT FOUR — HOW OUR BODIES WORK

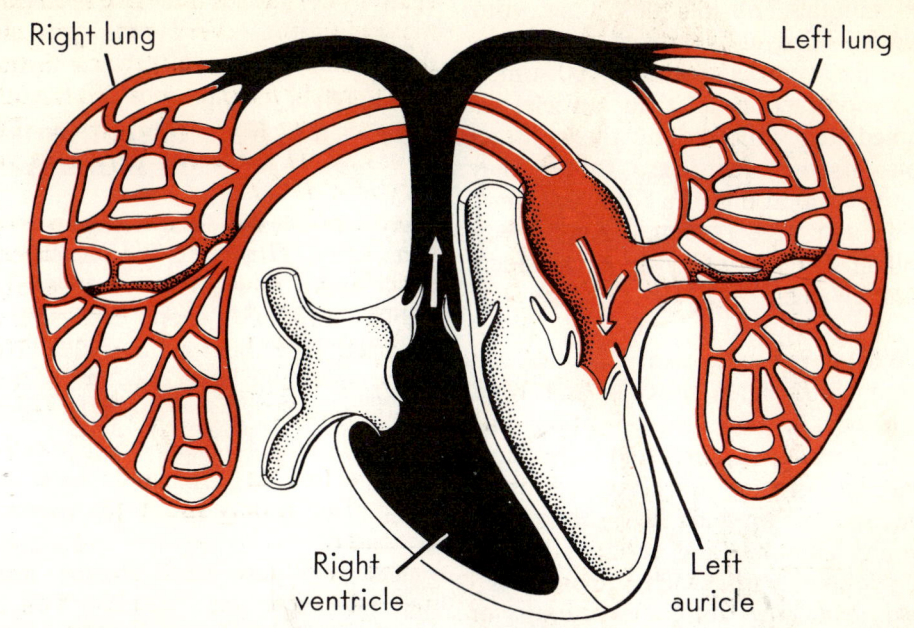

Figure labels: Right lung, Left lung, Right ventricle, Left auricle

11.18 Circulation of blood from right ventricle to left auricle. The right auricle is shown as though it were empty at this time. Actually, it is filling up with blood from the rest of the body. Notice how blood from the right ventricle goes only to the lungs. The black vessels are arteries. Does the blood in these arteries contain much or little oxygen? Are the red vessels veins or arteries? With which chamber do they connect? Does the blood in these vessels have much or little oxygen? Where does it get its oxygen?

out of the capillary into the lung. A little of it comes out of the corpuscle; most comes out of the plasma. It has been hidden there ever since you were riding among the working cells of the foot.

Now, riding on a bright red corpuscle, you gently go from a capillary into one of the small veins lying among the lung tissues. Then into larger and larger veins, and finally into one of two veins (**pulmonary veins**) which connect your lung with the heart. They run to the left auricle. Figure 11.18 will show you how you have been traveling.

Having gone through a second set of capillaries you are now at last on the left side of the heart. One contraction of the auricle sends you back to the starting point, the left ventricle. All of your friends have shared one experience with you; all of them have been through a lung capillary. The difference in their journey was this: instead of going through a capillary in the foot they went through a capillary in some other part of the body. But you have all been through two loops of blood vessels, and by doing this you have made one complete circuit of the blood circulatory system.

Those of your friends, however, who went through the stomach or intestines have much to tell you about. They took a side trip. They went through an extra set of capillaries in the liver before they went back into the vein (inferior vena cava) leading to the right auricle. They traveled in what is called the **portal circulation.** See Figure 11.17.

If studying this paragraph took you

CHAPTER ELEVEN — BLOOD AND CIRCULATION

ten minutes, during this time your auricles filled and emptied themselves into the ventricles about 700 times. The contraction of the auricles is immediately followed by the contraction of the ventricles, too. They pumped blood into the aorta 700 times while you were reading. And it was William Harvey who helped us understand all this!

What have you learned? You learned about three kinds of cells and what each does. You learned about the plasma which carries these cells; how food and wastes are dissolved in it, and special proteins like fibrinogen, gamma globulin, and serum albumin. (Do you know what each of these does?) You read how antibodies clump, or agglutinate, red blood cells in transfusions if the right types of blood are not mixed. You learned how, nowadays, instead of depending on blood banks, we often use dried plasma and how the plasma can now be separated into its different parts. And then you learned about lymph; how water and other substances from the plasma diffuse out of capillaries; how this liquid, together with white corpuscles which push through the wall, forms the lymph which bathes all the cells; and how the lymph is drained into special tubes, lymphatics, which return the lymph into the blood stream. There was much to learn, because the blood, this complex life-giving substance, is circulated to all parts of the body, reaching the trillions of cells of which your body is composed.

USEFUL WORDS IN BIOLOGY

artery
vein
capillary
plasma
red corpuscle
white
 corpuscle
phagocyte
leucocyte
platelet
fibrin
fibrinogen
gamma
 globulin
lymph gland
 (node)
hemoglobin
oxyhemoglobin
anemia
spleen
serum
transfusion
blood bank
fractionation
agglutinin
agglutinogen
ventricle
auricle
pulse
coronary
 artery
coronary
 thrombosis
hypertension
blood pressure
aorta
pulmonary
 circulation
portal
 circulation
lymph
lymphatic

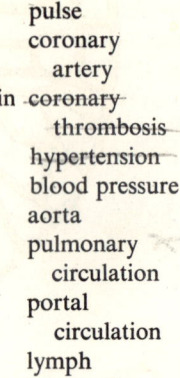

TEST YOURSELF

1. Describe the following as to position and function: the heart, arteries, veins, capillaries.
2. Which of the following sentences or phrases describe plasma? Copy into your notes all that do; omit those that do not. Carries food substances; carries wastes; is colorless; is a liquid; is constantly changing in composition while in the capillaries; is circulated through the body; is a part of the blood; carries three kinds of blood cells; comes to a stop when it reaches an artery.
3. In table form compare red and white blood corpuscles as to shape, size, number, chemical composition, where made, work done by each.
4. (a) Name the four blood types. (b) Explain why the blood used in a transfusion should be of the same type as the blood of the person receiving it. (c) Explain fully what happens if type A blood is given to a type B person.
5. Copy the following incomplete sentences and finish each by giving a full explanation: (a) Plasma is often as useful to doctors as whole blood because ———. (b) The advantage of depending on plasma instead of whole

blood is that ———. (c) One advantage of fractionation is that ———. *Do not write in this book*.

6. (a) Compare the structure of the walls of arteries, veins, capillaries. (b) Give the use of each tissue found in the artery wall.

7. (a) By what reasoning did Harvey arrive at the conclusion that blood circulates through heart, arteries, and veins? (b) What experimentation was necessary?

8. Explain how exercise and the presence of valves in the veins help circulation in the veins.

9. (a) Compare plasma and lymph as to where they are found, and their composition. (b) Where in the body are the lymphatics and the lymph glands?

10. Describe the complete circulation of the blood. Use drawings or words or both.

DO IT YOURSELF

1. To see circulating blood. With the low power of the microscope you can see circulating blood in the tail of a goldfish. Wrap wet absorbent cotton around the region of the gills. Tie the fish down (with a gauze bandage) in a Petri dish and cover its spread-out tail with a glass slide. Focus on the edges of the tail. Look for small branching arteries and the still narrower capillaries. Look for corpuscles in the vessels; evidently the walls of these small vessels are transparent. Does the blood ever stop for an instant? Does it reverse its direction? After about ten minutes put the goldfish back into the water.

2. Heart structure. You can learn a great deal about your own heart from a study of a fresh beef heart with blood vessels still attached. Find the small auricles, shaped like bent ears, at the broad end of the heart and the much larger ventricles; the left ventricle makes the point of the heart. Notice the smooth serous membrane that covers the heart. How do the muscular walls of the ventricles compare with the walls of the auricles? Feel them. Which chambers do the hardest pumping? Feel the walls of the blood vessels arising from the heart. How can you tell which are arteries and which are veins? Make a cut about three inches long in both ventricles. Look for flaps of tissue attached by fine cords hanging down into each ventricle; these are the valves between auricle and ventricle. Insert a glass rod into each blood vessel from the outside to see with which chamber it connects. Do you find fat tissue around the heart, especially between right and left ventricle?

3. Watching the heartbeat in the frog. The frog can no longer feel anything if you insert a dissecting needle at the base of its skull. Push the needle in far enough so that the brain will be separated from the "spinal cord." (This is called pithing.) The frog can then be laid on its back and opened up, exposing the heart. This will continue to beat for hours if the frog is kept in salt solution (see Chapter 3, "Do it yourself" No. 2). The frog's heart has two auricles but only one ventricle. The auricles look darker than the ventricle. Why? Watch the auricles contract. Do they contract separately or together? Which contracts more forcibly, auricles or ventricle? How long is the pause between heartbeats? Lower the temperature of the salt solution, but don't dilute it. Raise the temperature. Using a watch with a second hand make a note of the frequency of the heartbeat at each temperature.

4. Counting your pulse rate. Place the tips of two or three fingers (except the thumb) on the inner part of your wrist below the base of the thumb. Why can the pulse be felt easily here? Count the beats in one minute. Take your pulse after lying down for five minutes, while sitting quietly, after running swiftly for a short distance, after seeing some exciting game on television, and so on. Keep a record of the counts. Take your pulse rate while sitting. Compare with your classmates. What is the average rate for your group?

5. Writing of reports. Some interesting reports might be written on the following topics: what people of former ages thought about the blood and the heart; the life and work of William Harvey; blood transfusions, and recent discoveries about the blood. You will find *Biology and Its Makers* by Locy, Holt, 1915, helpful for historical reports. Recent issues of *Science News Letter*, newspapers and magazines will give you up-to-date information. If you have the use of a library ask the librarian

CHAPTER ELEVEN — BLOOD AND CIRCULATION

to show you how to use the *Readers' Guide to Periodical Literature*. You will want to consult it often. Of course, in writing the report you will put everything into your own words or your classmates will find your report dull.

ADVENTURES IN READING

1. In Chapters 3, 4, and 5 of *The Machinery of the Body* by A. J. Carlson and V. Johnson, University of Chicago Press, 1953, you will probably find answers to various questions which are still bothering you, but it won't be easy reading.
2. *The Human Body* by Logan Clendening, Knopf, 1945, is a more popular book but also reliable. Read Chapters 5 and 6.
3. "Blood" by Douglas M. Surgenor in *Scientific American*, February 1954. Contains much information but is difficult in some parts.
4. *Helping Your Heart* by Emanuel Goldberger, Longmans, Green, 1953. Gives practical information for the layman on circulatory diseases.

12.1 The summit of Mt. Everest. At 29,000 feet Tenzing with an oxygen tank and oxygen mask can still carry on. *United Press*

UNIT FOUR — HOW OUR BODIES WORK

Chapter 12

Lungs and breathing

The oxygen supply. Sir Edmund Hillary and Tenzing Norgay reached the top of Mt. Everest in 1953 after many other expeditions had failed. What led to their success? It was not merely their ability to scale rocks and avoid crevasses. Their success was due to their careful planning and their oxygen masks and oxygen tanks, which made it possible for them to get enough oxygen to supply their cells, particularly their brain and their muscle cells. You know that at a height far short of 29,000 feet, the air pressure is so low that it is hard to get enough oxygen to supply body needs.

Our lungs are well fitted for getting all the oxygen needed by our living cells, but only at altitudes where people normally live, at sea level and up to heights of five or six thousand feet. The lungs are made in such a way that they have an enormous amount of thin, moist membrane in contact with an

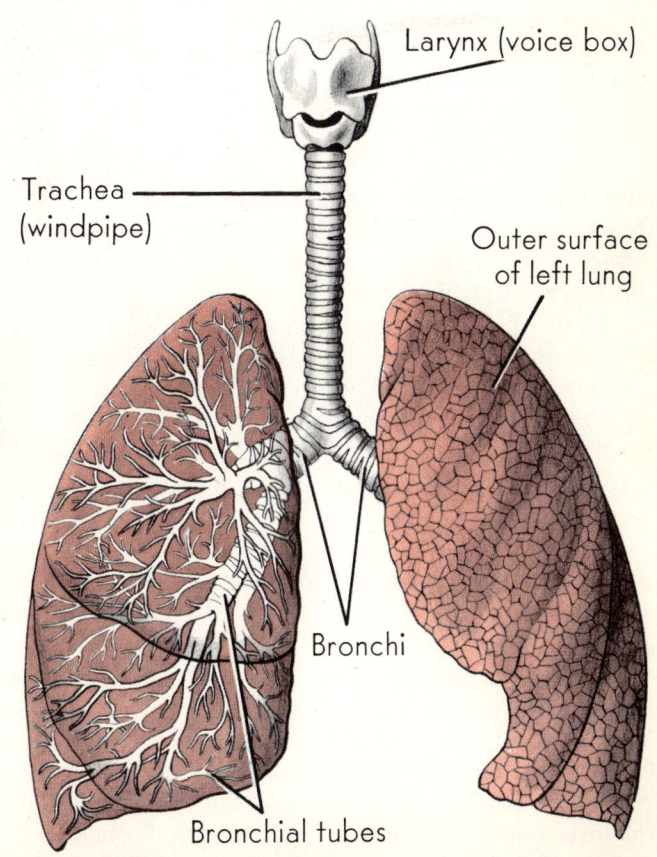

12.2 The right lung has been cut to show the larger bronchial tubes. See Figure 12.3 for the smallest bronchial tubes and the air sacs.

CHAPTER TWELVE — LUNGS AND BREATHING 225

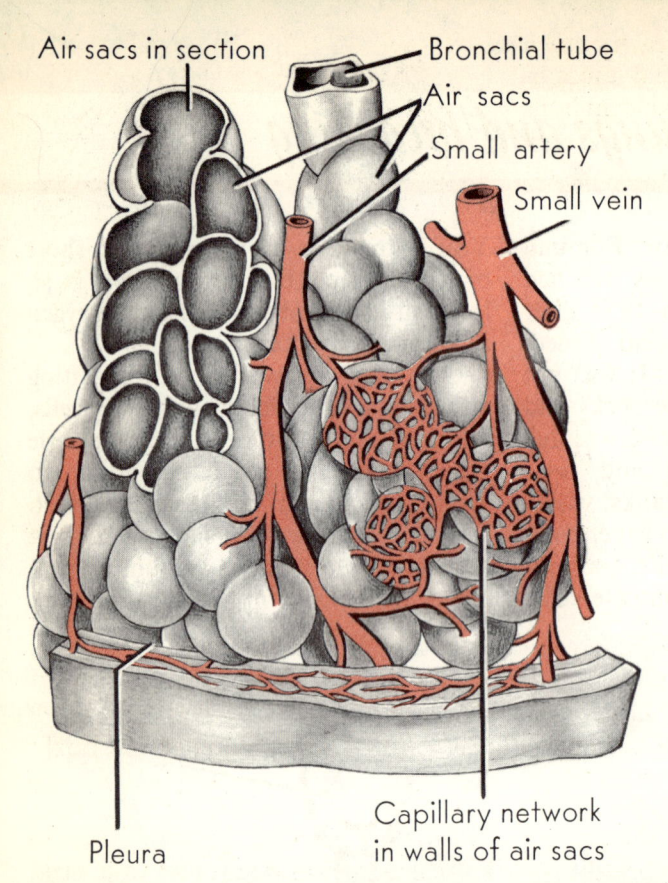

12.3 A piece of lung highly magnified. There are capillaries in the walls of all the air sacs. See right side of the picture.

Labels: Air sacs in section; Bronchial tube; Air sacs; Small artery; Small vein; Capillary network in walls of air sacs; Pleura

enormous amount of air. Normally, then, a constant exchange of gases occurs between the air and the blood. But to keep up this exchange, the chest cavity, in which the lungs lie, is equally well adapted. It can exhale, or push out, air at one moment and inhale a fresh supply of air at the next moment. First let's look at the lungs themselves; then let's investigate how the chest cavity works.

The lungs. Sometimes people think of the lungs as big balloons filled with air. They are not like this at all. You can see this if you examine an animal's lungs, which are much like ours. Your butcher can get them for you if you let him know a few days in advance. Ask for a sheep's or calf's lungs with the windpipe attached. The lungs are pinkish in color, and they feel soft. They are covered with a very smooth, moist membrane. This same membrane extends all the way around the inside of the chest cavity; it is called the **pleura** (ploo′ra). It is so smooth that when the lungs rub against the inside wall of the cavity there is practically no friction. Inflammation in this region is known as pleurisy.

If you cut into the lungs, you will see what is shown in Figure 12.2. The windpipe at its lower end divides into two large branches (**bronchi**— bron′keye). Each of these branches as it enters a lung divides like the trunk of a tree into smaller and smaller branches. These are the **bronchial tubes.** Of course, the picture shows only the coarser branches — the larger bronchial tubes; the fine ones are microscopic. At the tip of each branch of the microscopic bronchial tubes is an air sac. Each lung contains millions of air sacs. This is the real lung tissue. Figure 12.3 shows you some whole air sacs and some cut open.

The wall of an air sac is made of a single layer of flat cells (epithelium) and a thin layer of elastic tissue, and very good elastic tissue. It allows each air sac to expand enormously. Among the cells of the air sac is a network of capillaries. Gases can, thus, easily diffuse from the air sac into the blood and from the blood into the air sac. But you can see that the air sacs by themselves can do nothing about getting air into the lung or expelling it. The chest cavity does the work of inhaling and exhaling. When an iron lung is needed in polio cases it is not because the lungs are affected. It is because the chest cavity can no longer inhale and exhale.

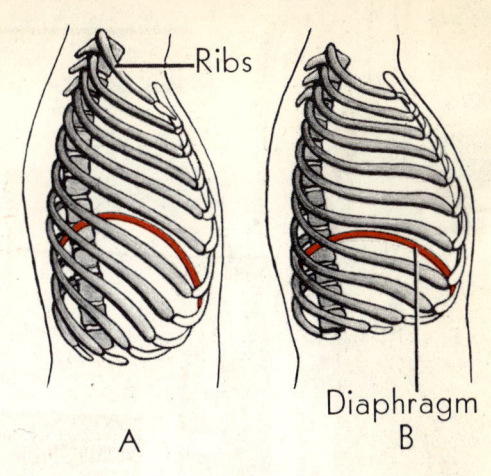

12.4 The chest cavity during breathing. Figure **B** shows the chest cavity being made larger from front to back. Muscles not shown here pull on the ribs and breastbone. Now look at the red line which represents the diaphragm at the bottom of the chest cavity. (Is the diaphragm in **A** or in **B** curved upward less?) Which chest cavity (the whole region above the red line) could hold more air, **A** or **B**?

The chest cavity. You breathe in (and out, of course) more than thirty pounds of air per day. Almost half as much air as is in the average living room circulates through your lungs in a day. With each breath you inhale and then exhale about a pint of air. That's a great deal of air for the chest to be circulating. Let's see what happens. Take a deep breath now — inhale. Can you feel muscles around your chest working as you inhale? There are muscles attached to your ribs and breastbone. As these contract the breastbone is pulled upward and forward. If you put your hand on your chest, you can feel this happening; you can even see it happening. Compare A and B in Figure 12.4 and you will see how the chest cavity grows larger from front to back as the chest muscles contract and as you inhale.

Hold a tape measure around your chest just below the armpits. Then take a deep breath. How many inches does your chest cavity expand?

But the chest cavity grows larger from top to bottom, too. A thick sheet of muscle, called the **diaphragm** (dye'a-fram), separates the chest cavity from the abdominal cavity. Of course, the food pipe and some of the main blood vessels run through it. But the diaphragm and the tubes are joined so closely that neither air nor liquid can slip between them. Look again at Figure 12.4A, which shows the diaphragm in its natural position when it is relaxed; it curves upward. But when you are inhaling, your muscular diaphragm contracts. Naturally, as it contracts it flattens out, making the chest cavity larger. (Look at B in Figure 12.4.)

CHAPTER TWELVE — LUNGS AND BREATHING

12.5 An "iron lung." This apparatus is used to produce breathing movements for paralyzed or weak patients. How does it work? *Children's Medical Center, Boston*

After you have inhaled and made the chest cavity larger, the chest muscles and diaphragm relax. Thus your chest cavity goes back to its smaller size. As it gets smaller air is forced out of the lungs. That is, you breathe out, or exhale.

Breathing goes on by itself whether you are awake or asleep. You may be wondering what starts the contraction of the chest muscles. There is a small region in the lower part of the brain in back (the **medulla oblongata**) which is the breathing center. Messages run from there to the chest muscles. When blood is carrying an extra large amount of carbon dioxide, the cells in this center are stimulated. Messages are sent out to the chest and diaphragm muscles. You breathe faster and deeper. The result is that you expel more air and with it more carbon dioxide. Then the concentration of carbon dioxide in the blood becomes normal and your breathing rate becomes regular. But concentration of carbon dioxide in the blood is not the only factor that affects the rate at which nerve messages leave the center. Sometimes the blood contains other materials which speed up or slow down the rate of breathing. And, of course, you can consciously regulate your breathing rate if you wish.

How air enters the lungs. You read how we make our chest cavity larger and smaller. But how does this affect the lungs? You will understand that if you do the following very simple experiment. Dip the open end of a medicine dropper into water while squeezing the bulb. As soon as you stop squeezing, water fills the dropper. What makes it come up? It is pushed up into the dropper by the force of the air pressure on the surface of the water outside the dropper. Since you do not see air pushing on the water you may think that the water is pulled up into the dropper or that there is a vacuum in the dropper which the water must fill.

This is incorrect. The water in this experiment lies between two air pressures: the normal air pressure outside, and the air pressure within the dropper. The pressure inside has decreased, since you have squeezed most of the air out of the dropper. Since the outside air pressure is much greater, it pushes on the water and pushes it into the dropper.

Just as water can be pushed by the pressure of air, so air itself can be pushed. As water is pushed into the medicine dropper so air is pushed into the lungs every time you make your chest cavity larger. While you are not breathing in or out, the pressure of air in the air sacs and the pressure outside are equal; air does not move in or out. But as soon as you increase the size of your chest cavity the pressure inside becomes less, and air is, therefore, pushed in.

Then you make the chest cavity smaller; the walls press on the air sacs, making them smaller. This raises the air pressure inside. As a result, air moves out; you have exhaled. Under normal conditions you inhale and exhale about 18 times a minute. But when you are running hard, your chest gets larger and smaller far more often than 18 times a minute; then you may "pant."

Exhaling never empties all the air sacs. Even hard and rapid breathing does not empty the air sacs that are farthest away from the windpipe. That does not matter, however. This air mixes slowly by diffusion with the fresh air you inhale.

The difference in general between ordinary fresh air and the air that leaves the lungs is shown in Figure 12.6. Note that the percentage of nitrogen is the same in the full air sac as in the emptied one. But differences appear in the percentage of oxygen, carbon dioxide, and water.

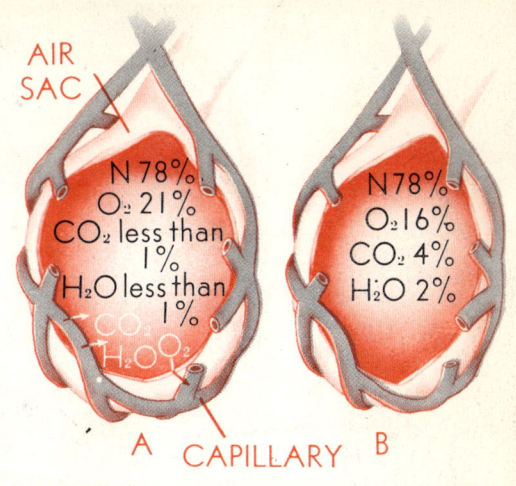

12.6 **A** is an air sac just filled with fresh air. **B** is an air sac being emptied. Note in **A** what percentage of each gas is found in fresh air. Now look at **B**. How have the percentages changed? What caused the percentages to change?

(A: AIR SAC — N 78%, O_2 21%, CO_2 less than 1%, H_2O less than 1%; B — CAPILLARY — N 78%, O_2 16%, CO_2 4%, H_2O 2%)

Air passages. From what you have read, you might think that the lungs connect directly with the outside air. But you know this is not the case. Air passes through the nose (sometimes the mouth), the throat, and down the windpipe (called the **trachea** — tray′kee-a) on its way into the lungs. Air, which often carries dust and bacteria, is constantly entering these passages; and in the passages are various cleaning and warming devices. As you read, see whether you can find such devices. Study Figure 12.7 and find the nose cavity, the adenoids, and tonsils. You can see that the adenoids, if they are oversized, might block up the nose cavity; then you must breathe through the mouth. You can also see why your throat hurts in swallowing food when the tonsils are inflamed and swollen. Now find the windpipe; it is much wider on top where the voice box (or **larynx** — lar′inks) is.

CHAPTER TWELVE — LUNGS AND BREATHING

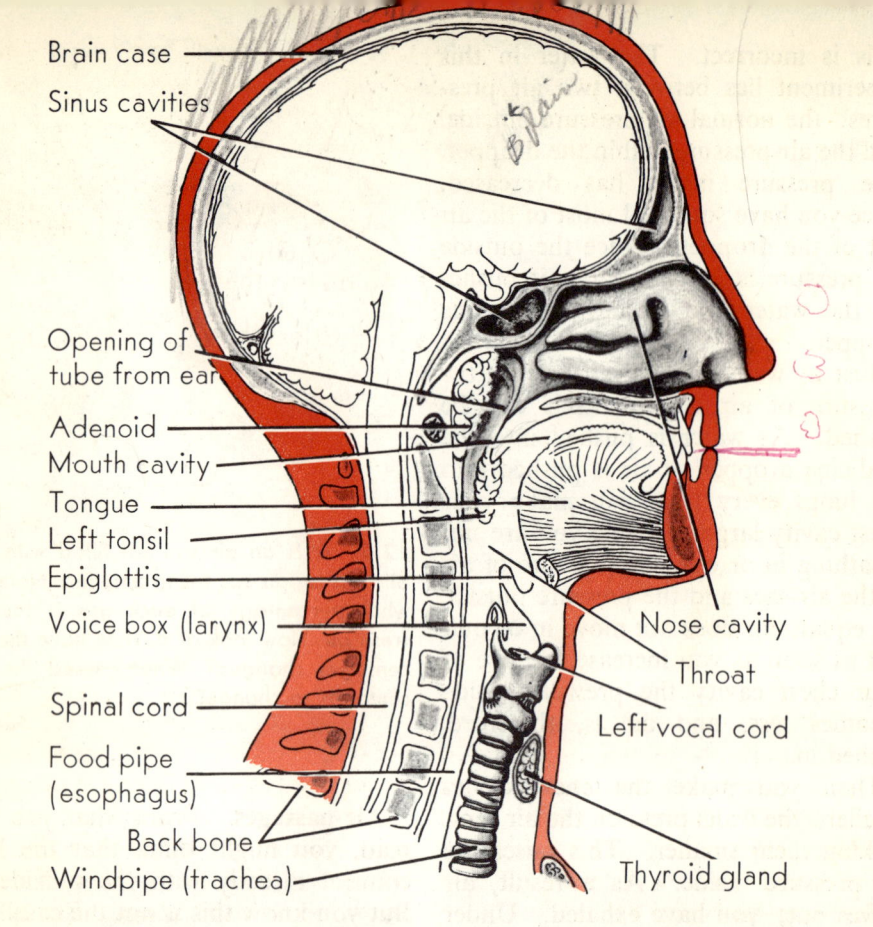

Labels on figure:
- Brain case
- Sinus cavities
- Opening of tube from ear
- Adenoid
- Mouth cavity
- Tongue
- Left tonsil
- Epiglottis
- Voice box (larynx)
- Spinal cord
- Food pipe (esophagus)
- Back bone
- Windpipe (trachea)
- Nose cavity
- Throat
- Left vocal cord
- Thyroid gland

12.7 Section through head and neck. Can you name in order all the passages through which air passes on its way to the lungs? Notice that when food leaves the throat, it must pass close to the top of the voice box. But the voice box has a trap door (the *epiglottis*) which closes down every time you swallow. If you try to talk while food is being swallowed, what is likely to happen? What harm could this do?

Your windpipe is about four inches long, but only about one-half inch across. It has hoops of cartilage in its wall; these make it stiff and keep it open at all times. But the hoops don't go all the way around in the back. Figure 12.7 shows you that the food pipe lies behind the windpipe; when you swallow large pieces of food they are able to get by since the back of the windpipe is soft and can push in. The windpipe is lined with epithelium. Some of these cells have cilia which lash upward, sweeping dust toward the throat. Others are goblet cells which secrete mucus. By coughing, you can expel this mucus together with any particles of dust caught in it. Goblet cells are shown in Figure 12.8.

Respiration and breathing. The words respiration and breathing are used by some people in ordinary speech as though they meant the same thing. The zoologist, however, makes a distinction between them. By breathing he means

230   UNIT FOUR — HOW OUR BODIES WORK

Ciliated epithelial cell

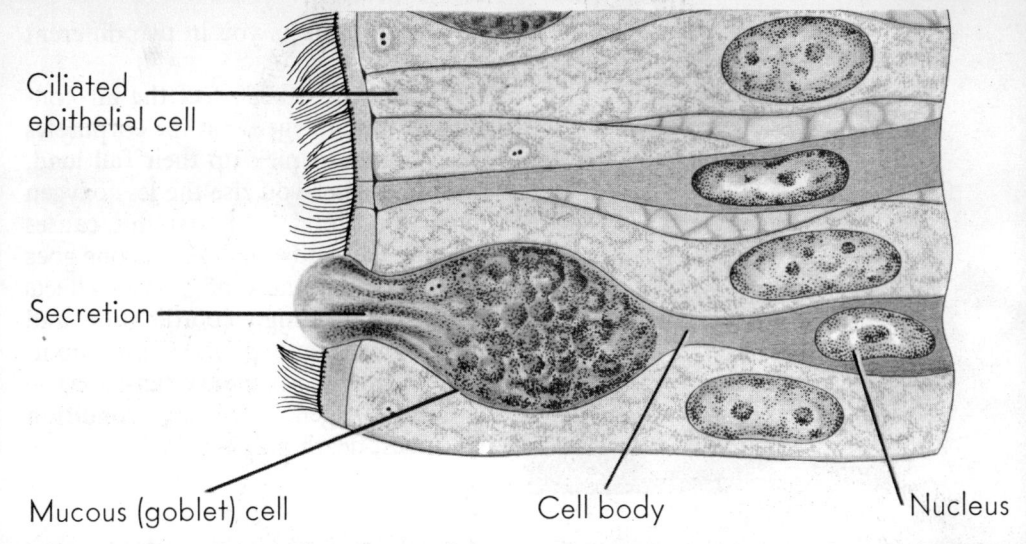

Secretion

Mucous (goblet) cell   Cell body   Nucleus

12.8 Mucous membrane lining the breathing passages. It contains two very different kinds of cells. How does each help in cleansing the air that enters?

inhaling and exhaling. Breathing is then followed by **cellular respiration**. This occurs in all the millions of cells. It includes these steps: oxygen diffuses into the cell; oxidation with release of energy, takes place in the cell; carbon dioxide and water are given off and diffuse into the blood stream.

Respiration, according to the zoologist, includes two processes: breathing and cellular respiration. Botanists use the word slightly differently. To them respiration means only cellular respiration, or the oxidation of food in the cells.

Artificial respiration. Cutting off the oxygen supply from the brain cells completely for as little as ten minutes spells death. But after the lungs are filled with water in drowning or after they are filled with some foreign gas the blood continues to deliver oxygen to the cells in small amounts for some time. As long as the heart muscle has enough oxygen to keep contracting a person has a chance to survive. For that reason in every accident in which breathing is stopped it is important to get fresh air into the air sacs as soon as possible. Artificial respiration should be begun at once. As oxygen is pumped back into the air sacs, the body cells gradually begin to work once more. In time the chest muscles will renew their contraction. But all this may take a long time. Artificial respiration must be continued sometimes for several hours, until the person again begins natural breathing, or until a physician declares the case hopeless. You will probably want to practice the back-pressure arm-lift method of artificial respiration. See Figure 12.9 on the next page for directions.

Altitude troubles. Not only mountain climbers but fliers, too, may be affected by decreased air pressure. Air pressure at sea level is 15 pounds to the square inch. Naturally the higher you go, the less is the air pressure. Up to 5000 or 6000 feet you usually don't feel the difference, but once you get above about 10,000 feet the lower

CHAPTER TWELVE — LUNGS AND BREATHING

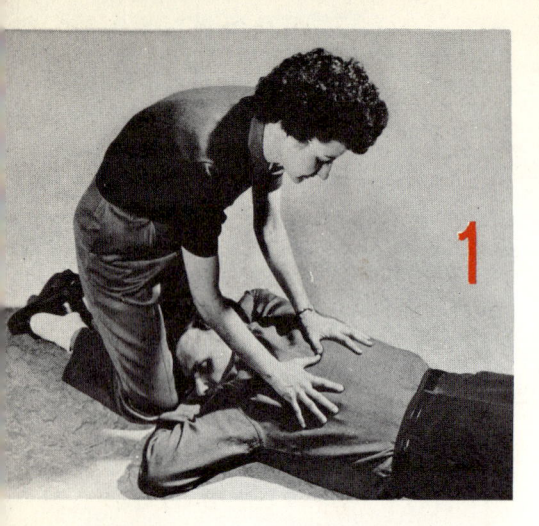

air pressure affects you in two different ways.

First, above 10,000 feet the air contains so little oxygen that the corpuscles are not able to pick up their full load. And the higher you rise the less oxygen enters the blood. At first this causes a feeling of well-being. But as one goes still higher, the lack of oxygen affects vision and hearing; coordination and judgment become poor. This condition is known as **anoxia** (an-ox'ia) — without oxygen. If this condition continues, death may result.

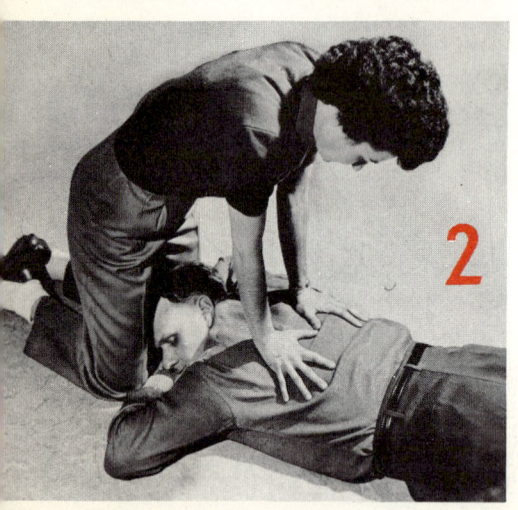

12.9 The Back Pressure-Arm Lift method of artificial respiration, also called the Holger Neilsen Push-Pull method. If you learn how to give artificial respiration, you may be able to save someone's life.

1. Place the victim on his stomach with his arms folded under his head and his cheek resting on folded hands. (See 1.)

2. Kneel at the victim's head looking toward his feet. Place your hands, fingers spread, on his back so that the thumbs are just touching. The base, or heel, of the hands should be slightly below an imaginary line running between the subject's armpits. (See 1.)

3. Keeping the elbows straight, rock slowly forward until your arms are approximately vertical to the floor. Pressure should be gradually increased as you rock forward. The amount of pressure should be adjusted to the size of the victim. (See 2.)

4. Slide your hands out to the subject's arms just above his elbows and rock backward slowly. As you rock backward, raise his arms until resistance and tension are felt at his shoulders. Drop the arms to complete the full cycle. The cycle should be repeated at the rate of 12 times per minute with equal time given to the compression (rocking forward) and the expansion (rocking backward) phases. Do not stop until the subject starts to breathe on his own or until a physician pronounces him dead. (See 3.)

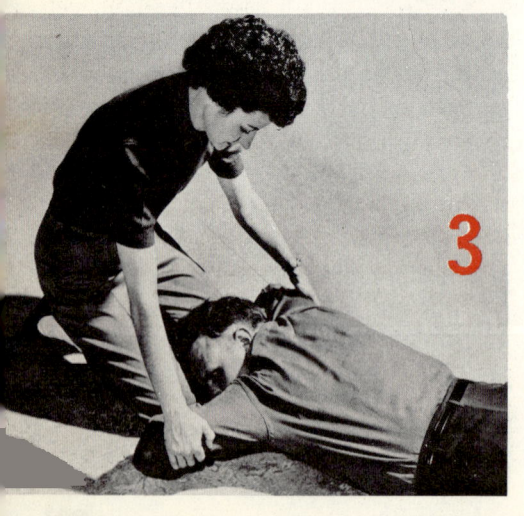

Secondly, lower air pressure means less nitrogen. Normally there is much nitrogen in the blood and body fluids. Not that it is of any use to us; it is there only because nitrogen forms about 78% of the air and it enters the blood by diffusion. When a flier ascends rapidly, the air pressure, and therefore the nitrogen pressure, becomes lower. The nitrogen forms bubbles in the body fluid for the same reason that bubbles form in a bottle of soda water when the pressure is lowered by removing the cap. The condition that results when nitrogen bubbles out in the blood stream is called the "**bends.**" Small blood vessels are blocked by the gas bubbles; the pain is agonizing and nerve tissue may be damaged. The bends was known long before the days of high flying. Deep-sea divers and other men who worked under high pressures suffered from the bends when they moved too quickly from high to normal air pressure.

The flier can prepare himself for rising to very high altitudes. He inhales pure oxygen before his flight. In one hour he can rid himself of half the nitrogen in his body. Most large planes, of course, have pressure-sealed cabins; these keep the same air pressure no matter how high the plane goes.

What have you learned? Zoologists define respiration as consisting of two distinct processes: breathing and cellular respiration. Don't let us confuse the two. And don't let us confuse the work of the lungs with the work of the chest cavity. Can you explain how the structure of the lungs makes possible the diffusion of gases between blood and air? Do you know how you make your chest cavity larger in three dimensions and how this changes air pressures inside and out, making it possible for you to inhale? Do you know the air passages and the part each plays in breathing? Do you know what we mean by anoxia and the bends and how they can be avoided in flying? And most important of all, do you know how to give artificial respiration?

USEFUL WORDS IN BIOLOGY

pleura diaphragm larynx
bronchial tube trachea anoxia
air sac

TEST YOURSELF

1. Describe the structure of your lungs, explaining the relation to each other of pleura, bronchial tubes, air sacs, arteries, veins, capillaries.
2. By contraction of muscles you make your chest cavity larger in three directions. Tell (a) which muscles contract and (b) how each, through contracting, expands the chest cavity.
3. Using the terms *elasticity*, *muscular contraction*, and *air pressure* tell how air gets into and out of the lungs.
4. (a) Tell how the air that enters an air sac differs in composition from the air that leaves it. (b) Explain how the difference arises.
5. Describe: (a) how very high altitudes affect us; (b) how a flier can prepare for this; (c) how a person is affected by a rapid change from very high to normal air pressure.
6. Explain the back-pressure arm-lift method of giving artificial respiration. Be sure that you know how to use it.

CHAPTER TWELVE — LUNGS AND BREATHING

DO IT YOURSELF

1. Examining the breathing organs of a sheep. The butcher can provide you with sheep lungs if you ask a few days in advance. Tell him you would like besides the windpipe, a part of the food pipe with some of the diaphragm through which it passes. Feel the hoops of cartilage in the windpipe, the smooth pleura covering the lungs, the diaphragm (muscle tissue); and above all feel the soft, spongy lungs and notice their color. In spite of all the blood in the capillaries in the lungs they look pink, instead of red, because of the large amount of air in the air sacs. Lay a piece of the lung in a pan of water. Why does it float? Are these lungs collapsed or expanded? Write a full description in your notes.

2. Simple models to illustrate breathing. You can make a model that inhales and exhales. Use a bell jar with an opening on top, a rubber stopper, glass tubing, rubber sheeting large enough to cover the lower open end of the jar, and two toy balloons. See Figure 12.10. Your model can increase in size only from top to bottom, and since there is rubber at the bottom instead of a muscular diaphragm you will have to help this model work. How?

Can you make a simple three-dimensional model of the chest cavity to show how the breastbone and the ribs in rising make the cavity larger from back to front? Hint: Use strips of cardboard to represent backbone, breastbone, and ribs; hold the "bones" together with brass fasteners.

3. To discover differences between inhaled and exhaled air. Blow your breath into a rubber balloon, and note carefully how much the balloon has expanded. Permit it to empty itself under the surface of limewater in a jar. Pump air into the balloon until it reaches the size it reached before. Empty this into a jar containing the same amount of fresh limewater. Examine both jars. Now light a candle fastened to the laboratory table. Invert a jar over it. Notice how long the candle burns (use a watch). Why does it go out? Collect exhaled air in a jar of the same size by displacing water. Invert this jar over a burning candle. How long does the candle burn? What conclusions can you draw from these experiments?

4. Artificial respiration. Thoroughly prepare yourself and then demonstrate the back-pressure arm-lift method of artificial respiration. Consult the *American Red Cross First Aid Textbook*.

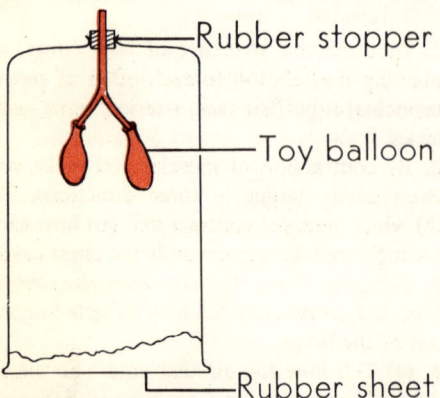

12.10 A simple model to illustrate breathing. How does this model differ from the chest cavity with its lungs?

ADVENTURES IN READING

1. *The Machinery of the Body* by A. J. Carlson and V. Johnson, University of Chicago Press, 1953. A good reference book for this chapter.
2. *The Human Body* by Logan Clendening, Knopf, 1945.

Chapter 13

Excretion

What is excretion? You have read that the products of cellular respiration are carried away from the cells by the blood and lymph. And you know that two of these, carbon dioxide and water, are excreted by the lungs. But when protein, for example, is oxidized, a number of other wastes are formed besides carbon dioxide and water, namely urea, uric acid, and other salts. This is shown in Figure 13.1. Now all these wastes, except carbon dioxide, are excreted by the kidneys, and some of them are excreted in small amounts by the skin. The kidneys, lungs, and skin, then, all excrete. The intestine does not excrete; it eliminates substances that have never been part of the body, such as nondigested foods.

The kidneys. The kidneys are our most important excretory organs. It is they that get rid of the nitrogenous wastes, urea and uric acid, various other salts, and of course, water. Since their only function is excretion the kidneys are thought of as part of the **excretory system** (ex'cree-tor-y). The excretory system shown in Figure 13.2 includes: the kidneys; two tubes, the **ureters** (you-ree'ters), leading from the kidneys; and the **bladder** into which the ureters lead.

The kidneys are attached to the back wall of the abdomen, one on each side of the spinal column, just below the diaphragm. They are shaped like the common red kidney beans which you may have eaten. If you get a veal or

13.1 The waste products formed when sugars, fats, and proteins are oxidized. Which food substance yields the largest number of wastes? What are the five wastes produced by the oxidation of this compound? But proteins are not oxidized generally.

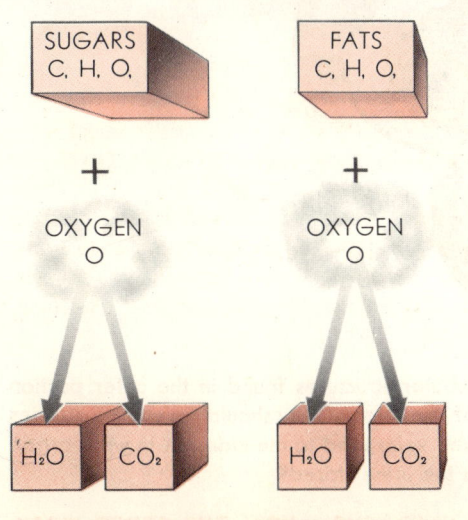

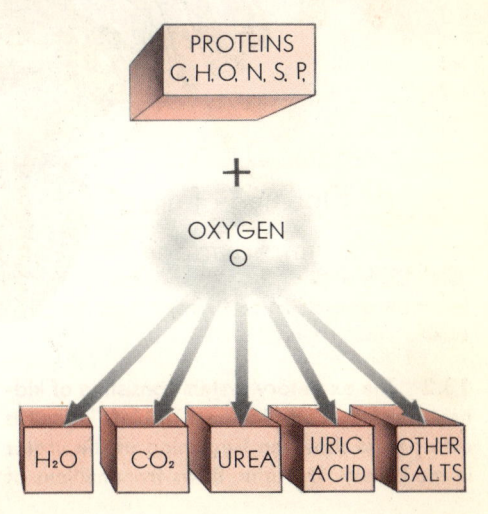

SUGARS $C, H, O,$ + OXYGEN O → H_2O + CO_2

FATS $C, H, O,$ + OXYGEN O → H_2O + CO_2

PROTEINS $C, H, O, N, S, P.$ + OXYGEN O → H_2O + CO_2 + UREA + URIC ACID + OTHER SALTS

CHAPTER THIRTEEN — EXCRETION

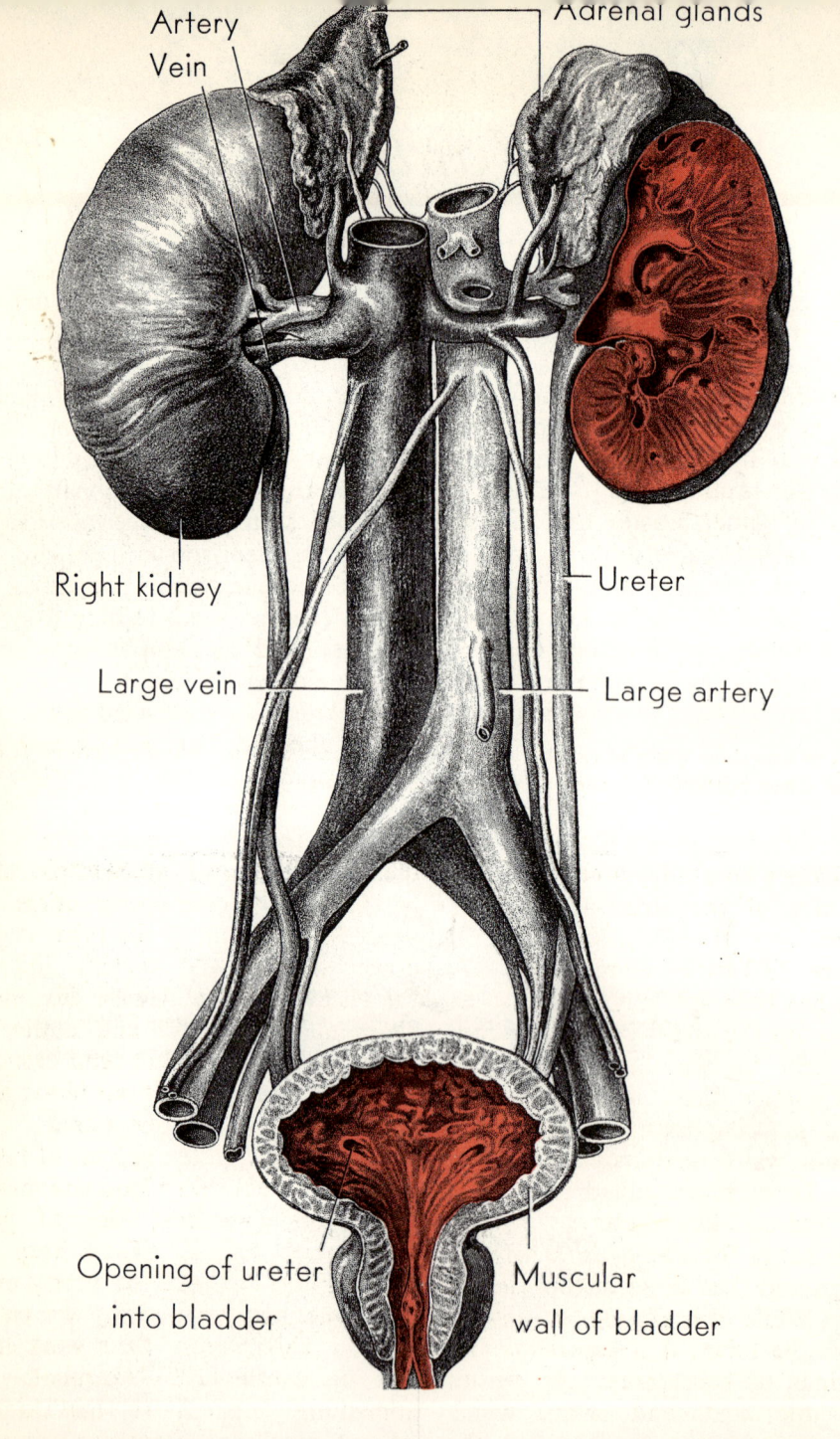

13.2 The excretory system consisting of kidneys, ureters, and bladder. The left kidney is cut open to show the beginning of the ureter in the kidney. The urine flows from millions of tubular structures found in the outer portion of the kidney. Why should such large arteries and veins lead to the kidneys? In what organ is the urine stored?

236   UNIT FOUR — HOW OUR BODIES WORK

13.3 The branched tubes which carry urine from the outer portion of a sheep's kidney toward the ureter. *Ward's Natural Science Establishment, Inc.*

lamb kidney to study, you can get a good idea of the structure of your kidneys.

Figure 13.3 will interest you. A kidney has been specially treated so as to show up the many-branched tubes which arise in the outer part of the kidney. Here there are millions of microscopic, cuplike structures with very thin walls surrounded by capillaries. Long, much coiled tubes lead out of the cuplike structures. Plasma diffuses out of the many capillaries into the cups and then flows down into the tubes. While the plasma is flowing through the tubes, it is separated into two kinds of substances: the wastes (urea, uric acid, and salts), which continue down the tubes; and the useful parts of the plasma, which diffuse back into the capillaries.

The substances from the capillaries that remain in the microscopic tubes of the kidney make up the urine. As urine flows out of all the tubes it goes down through the ureters and into the bladder, a large storage sac. Look again at Figure 13.2 and notice the big artery and vein that send branches into the kidney. All of our blood must at some time go into the kidney.

The kidneys, in the process of taking substances out of the blood and making urine, do something else of great importance to us. They keep the composition of the blood pretty much the same no matter what we eat or drink. This part of their work must not be overlooked. Fortunately, if something happens to one kidney, we can usually get along perfectly well. The remaining kidney then grows larger and does the work that normally is done by two kidneys.

CHAPTER THIRTEEN — EXCRETION

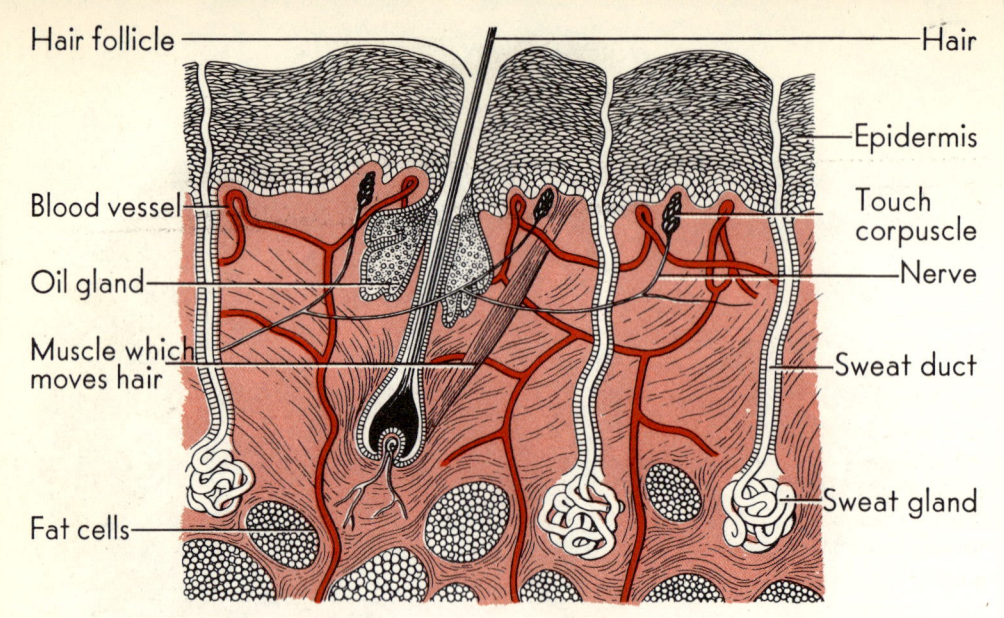

13.4 Section through skin. The top layer is epidermis. Everything else below is the dermis. In which layer do you find blood vessels and nerves? Why do the outer layers of the epidermis die? What other structures lie in the dermis?

The skin. You probably just take your skin for granted and never think of it as an organ of the body. But it is a very important organ as well as the largest. It excretes large amounts of water but it is important in other ways, too. Let's look at those first. It keeps out bacteria, and it protects the more delicate cells underneath. It can do this very well because the outermost cells of the **epidermis** are dead anyway. If you look at Figure 13.4 you will see how far from the blood supply these outer cells lie. Naturally, they keep dying off.

Under the epidermis there is a much thicker layer, the **dermis**. When a pin pricks through the epidermis and gets near the dermis, you feel pain; nerves run to the upper part of the dermis. Look carefully at Figure 13.4 and see all the other structures that lie in the dermis. Besides the nerves, you will find blood vessels, touch corpuscles, and special nerve endings that pick up sensations of heat, cold, and pain. You will find oil glands, the roots of hairs, and small bands of muscle fibers that pull on the base of the hair and make it stand straight up. You will find masses of fat cells way at the bottom, and last, but not least, sweat glands. Do you find them all?

Sweat glands. Now look at your own skin with a magnifying glass. Can you see tiny openings or pores? Most of the pores lead into a long narrow tube which widens out at its lower end. Around this lower part are coils of capillaries. This is a sweat gland. It takes large amounts of water and small amounts of sodium chloride and other salts out of the blood stream. You can see a sweat gland clearly in Figure 13.5.

UNIT FOUR — HOW OUR BODIES WORK

13.5 A sweat gland highly magnified. What are the branching white tubes? The gland looks like some digestive gland, but its secreting cells do very different work. What do they take out of the capillaries? Into what are these substances made? Where does the gland duct lead?

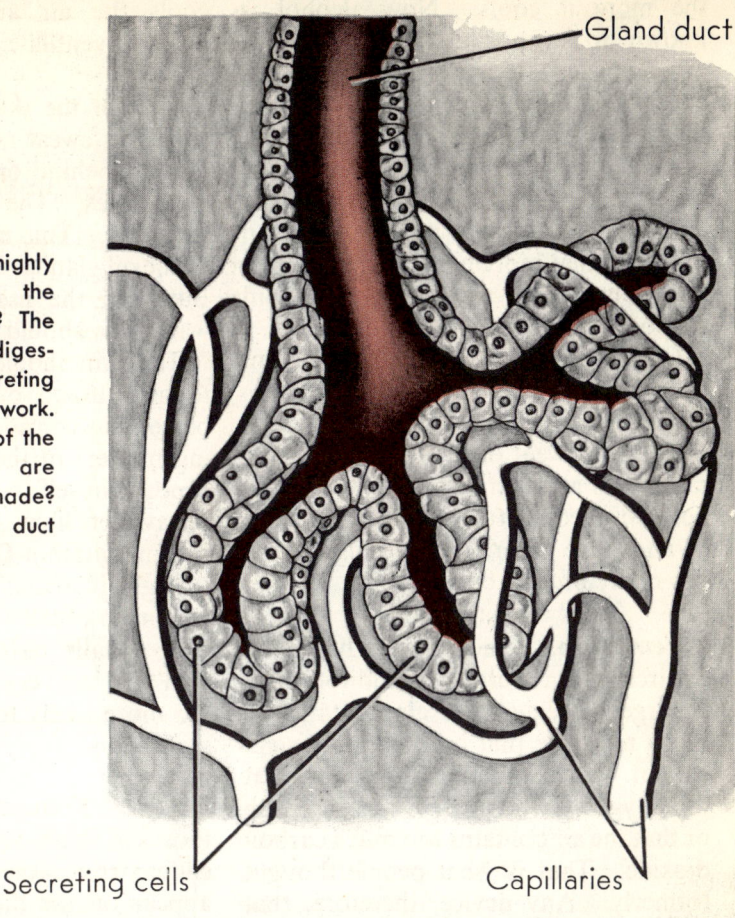

Gland duct

Secreting cells

Capillaries

These glands make and then excrete sweat all the time without your being conscious of it. You lose as much as two to four glasses of water a day through your sweat glands. And when it is hot or when you exercise, of course, you lose very much more. It will interest you to put a tightly fitting bottle or test tube over one of your fingers as you read the rest of this chapter. When you come to the end look at the inside of the bottle.

Regulation of temperature. Besides its functions of excretion, sensation, and protection, the skin provides a most efficient cooling system which works by itself, without your bothering to think about it. When you exercise hard and much heat is being released by the cells, does your blood get hotter? Does your temperature rise? Only a little, if at all. Why is this? Lots of blood is brought to the surface of the body at these times; you know how red your skin gets. What makes more blood come to the surface? It's partly that the heart beats faster, and partly that the tiny arteries leading to the skin widen, allowing more blood to flow through them. And all this extra blood passes the sweat glands; they take more water and salts out of the blood and excrete more sweat. Quantities of sweat pour out on the skin. As it evaporates it carries off heat. Evaporation from any surface cools the surface; the more rapid the evaporation

CHAPTER THIRTEEN — EXCRETION

the more it cools. Now alcohol is known to evaporate very quickly — much faster than water. Try this experiment. Put some drops of alcohol on the back of one hand. On the back of the other hand put some drops of water. The hand with alcohol on it feels cooler, doesn't it? The reason for this is that more heat is being carried away from that hand by the rapid evaporation of the alcohol.

Our cooling system breaks down, more or less, on a hot day if there is much humidity (moisture in the air). Then your sweat does not evaporate as rapidly as at other times, and you feel hot and uncomfortable. When you are ill and have fever, the cooling system has really broken down.

Ventilation. When we get headachy and restless in a crowded auditorium it is largely because the air contains so much moisture that our cooling system cannot work properly. It is not that the oxygen of the air has been used up or that the air contains too much carbon dioxide. That is what people thought formerly. Any device, therefore, that cools the air and absorbs moisture helps to ventilate.

Care of the skin. The minerals dissolved in sweat and a good deal of oil are left behind on the skin after sweat evaporates. The oil, particularly, collects dirt. This may clog up the pores of the oil glands, forming "blackheads." But with the use of soap and warm water this should not happen.

The skin should also not be allowed to get burned by the sun. Unless a person has considerable pigment (coloring matter) in the skin, he should not expose himself to too much of the sun's ultraviolet light, useful as this is in making vitamin D. In moderate doses sunlight increases the pigment, and the person gradually tans. Blondes, however, usually have little pigment in the skin and tan very little; therefore, they are more likely to be injured by ultraviolet rays.

Acne. Younger people, particularly those of high school age, sometimes suffer from **acne** (ack'nee). Pimples appear on the face and sometimes on

TABLE 14

EXCRETION OF WASTES FORMED IN OXIDATION

	Kidney	Skin	Lung
Wastes excreted	Water Urea Uric Acid Other nitrogenous compounds Salts	Water Salts	Water Carbon dioxide
Special structures	Complicated microscopic structure, with long winding tube surrounded by capillaries	Sweat glands with networks of capillaries	Air sacs with capillaries in walls
How important as organ of excretion	Necessary	Relatively unimportant	Necessary
Other function of organ	Keeps blood uniform in composition	Regulates body temperature	Supplies blood with oxygen

UNIT FOUR — HOW OUR BODIES WORK

the upper part of the body. The cause is often difficult for a physician to find and remedy. For some reason the secretion from the oil glands remains in the duct. Then, if bacterial infection sets in, a little red swelling appears. This pimple may disappear in a few days but frequently it breaks open and pus is discharged. A person with acne should consult a physician. Most cases of acne are not the result of neglect or dirt and will in time disappear. In many people worry about acne seems to make this skin condition worse.

What have you learned? Let's sum up briefly what you have learned about the three organs that excrete wastes formed in oxidation: the lungs, kidneys, and skin.

3. Regulation of the body temperature is an important function of the skin. What are three other skin functions?
4. Consult Figure 13.4 and name five structures found in the dermis.
5. Discuss: (a) the care of the skin, (b) acne and how it should be treated.

PROBLEMS TO THINK ABOUT

(a) What might be the danger of going out on a cold day immediately after a hot bath? (b) What is the advantage of a cool shower after a hot bath? (c) Why might you catch cold if you sat in a strong cool breeze after vigorous exercise has made you very hot? (d) Why does an electric fan cool you?

USEFUL WORDS IN BIOLOGY

excretory system
ureter
bladder
dermis
uric acid
sweat gland
touch corpuscle
oil gland
acne

DO IT YOURSELF

How evaporation affects the temperature. Wrap the bulb of each of three thermometers in a small wad of absorbent cotton. Hang the thermometers in the air about three inches apart. Note the temperature reading of each. With a medicine dropper put a drop of alcohol on one bulb and a drop of water on another. After two minutes again add a drop of alcohol to the first and a drop of water to the second. Repeat once. Leave the bulb of the third thermometer dry throughout. Watch the temperatures carefully. What conclusions can you draw?

TEST YOURSELF

1. Name the organs of the excretory system and state the function of each.
2. What else of importance is done by the kidneys besides excreting wastes?

Chapter 14

Ductless glands

14.1 The man in the middle is of average height. Read the text to find out why one of the others is a midget and the other is a giant. Wide World Photo

The chemical regulators — hormones. Look at Figure 14.1. How does it happen that three grown men can be so different in height? One of these men is at least twice as tall as one of the others. It is probable that as babies and growing boys these men ate much the same kind of food. The difference in their height is due to a small ball of cells, no larger than a pea, at the base of the brain. We call it the **pituitary** (pit-two'i-ter-ree) **gland.** It is a gland without a duct — a ductless gland. The secretion from this gland goes directly into the blood.

For some reason the pituitary gland of each of these men poured into the blood a different amount of a chemical substance (called **tethelin** — teth'e-lin). It is not important to remember this name. What is important to remember is that this substance is a hormone, a **chemical regulator.** You read earlier about secretin, a chemical regulator or chemical messenger, in the small intestine. We have many other hormones. Hormones are secreted in very small amounts, travel in the blood, and regulate special activities in the body. This hormone evidently regulates the growth of the bones.

Experimental proof. Rats have much the same organs as we; they, too, have a pituitary gland, and its hormone regulates growth. Scientists made an extract of pituitary glands and injected it into some young rats. Other rats were matched with these and were kept as controls; they received no injections. For five or six months all

242   UNIT FOUR — HOW OUR BODIES WORK

the rats were carefully weighed and measured. At the end of this time the controls were normal; the other rats had turned into giant rats. They were almost twice their natural size and weight.

More about the growth hormone. When the pituitary fails to secrete the growth hormone, as you might suspect, the skeleton stops growing. The result is a midget, a person whose body is well proportioned but much too small. See Figure 14.1. Feeding or injecting the hormone seems to be of little help in these cases.

Sometimes the pituitary gland becomes overactive after body growth has stopped. You may have seen people in whom only certain bones are enlarged, the bones of the face and perhaps the hands and feet. This condition (called **acromegaly**, ak′ro-meg′a-li) is sometimes treated by an operation on the gland. Sometimes, too, an oversecretion of the growth hormone (later in life) seems to be associated with one serious form of arthritis.

Ductless glands. Figure 14.2 shows the positions of the pituitary gland and the various other ductless glands. The hormones they secrete are of the very greatest importance to us. They are enzymes, constantly regulating one chemical activity or another. You are not aware of the work they are doing until, for some reason, they secrete too much or too little of some hormone. This may cause a slight disturbance but extreme undersecretion or oversecretion that causes circus freaks is rare. As more is learned about the chemistry of the body, it might well be that small groups of other ductless gland cells will be discovered.

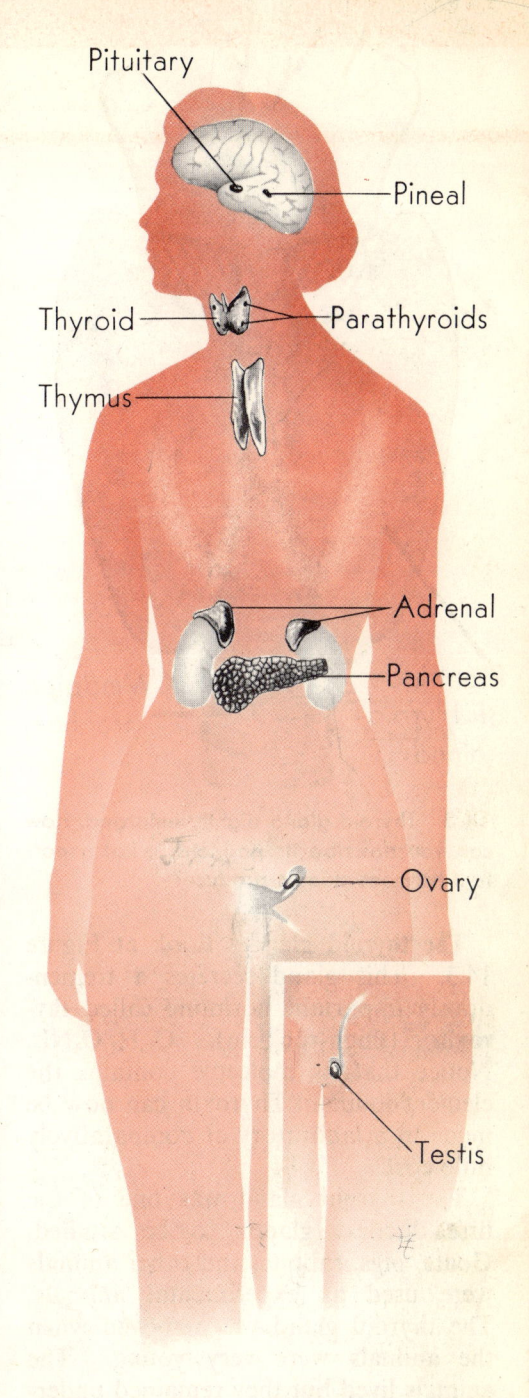

14.2 How do these glands compare in size with other organs? Can you name all the ductless glands?

CHAPTER FOURTEEN — DUCTLESS GLANDS

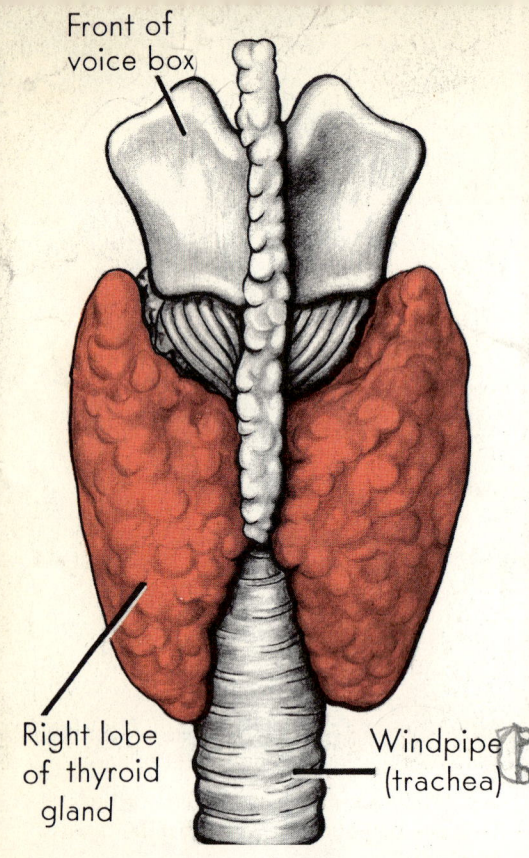

14.3 Thyroid gland slightly enlarged. How can you describe its position? What important hormone does it produce?

The thyroid gland. Look at Figure 14.3. This gland secretes a tremendously important hormone called **thyroxin** (thigh-rock′sin), $C_{15}H_{11}O_4NI_4$. Notice that its molecule contains the element iodine. Thyroxin can now be made in a laboratory at comparatively little cost.

The thyroid gland was one of the first ductless glands to be studied. Goats, pigs, rabbits, and other animals were used as experimental animals. The thyroid gland was removed when the animals were very young. The animals lived but they remained undersized; their reproductive organs did not develop; they did not play like the other animals; they were slow and sluggish. Feeding an extract of thyroid glands to these animals at an early age brought them back to normal. From these and other experiments scientists concluded that thyroxin acts as an enzyme that helps development and in general speeds up oxidation in cells.

These experiments helped to explain **cretinism** (cree′tin-ism) in children. Cretins are just like the experimental animals whose thyroid glands were removed; they are undersized and underdeveloped in every way, both physically and mentally; they are mental defectives. This condition had been recognized for a long time, but its cause was not known. We know now that cretins are born with a defective thyroid gland or without any thyroid secretion. If the lack of thyroxin is noticed at a very early age the baby can usually be helped by being fed thyroxin. But once the child has been allowed to fall too far behind, it can never catch up and will always be defective.

Frogs also seem to need thyroxin for their proper development. If the thyroid is removed in the young or tadpole stage, they never grow up to be frogs. They remain as tadpoles and their reproductive organs never form. On the other hand if you feed some thyroxin to your tadpoles, and you can do this experiment rather easily, what do you think happens? The tadpoles almost at once grow into adult frogs; they don't have a chance to grow to their full size before they change. They grow into frogs, but tiny frogs. Thyroxin is a wonderful substance! And **another** interesting thing about it is that very tiny amounts of it can help in the activities of many cells in many parts of the body. In his whole lifetime a person normally secretes only a little more than an ounce of thyroxin.

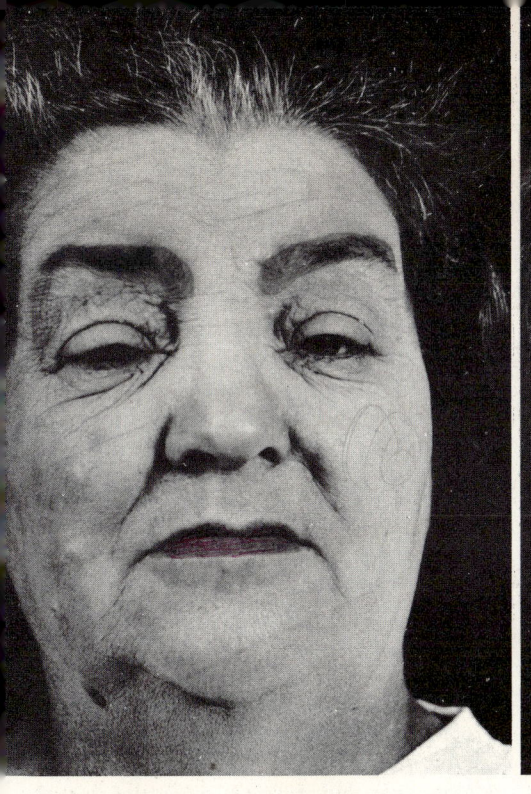

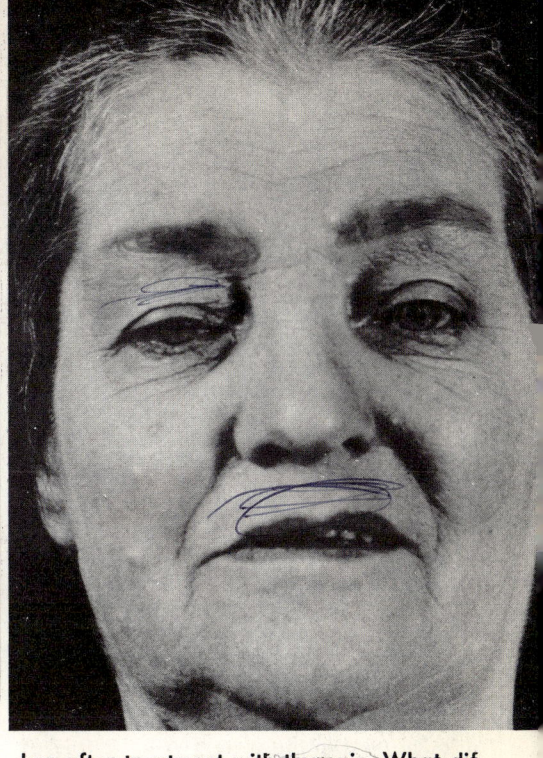

14.4 The picture on the left shows a woman in whom there was an insufficient secretion of thyroxin later in life. The other picture shows her after treatment with thyroxin. What differences do you note? *Massachusetts General Hospital*

The thyroid in later life. Figure 14.4 shows what happens when the thyroid gland becomes inactive after people have reached their full development. They become slow moving and slow thinking. Their basal metabolism is far below normal. They gain much weight. This condition (known as **myxedema,** mix-e-dee′ma) gets steadily worse if the patient is not given thyroid. Here, too, animals were used experimentally to determine the cause of this condition.

Goiter. There are two kinds of goiter. Have you ever seen people with a slight swelling, a goiter, in the region of the thyroid gland? While the thyroid grows larger, the secreting cells become less active; the body gets too little thyroxin. Of course, this is easy to treat by giving thyroxin. Figure 14.5 shows you in which parts of the United States this type of goiter occurred most often some thirty years ago. At the same time the map shows you that in these same regions the drinking water contained less than the normal amount of iodine. The number of cases of goiter has decreased very much since this map was made because nowadays health officers in such regions may add iodine salts to the drinking water or they may recommend the use of "iodized" salt. But before you use iodized salts without advice remember that, although some iodine is necessary for us, too much iodine may not be good for us at all.

There is a second type of goiter,

CHAPTER FOURTEEN — DUCTLESS GLANDS

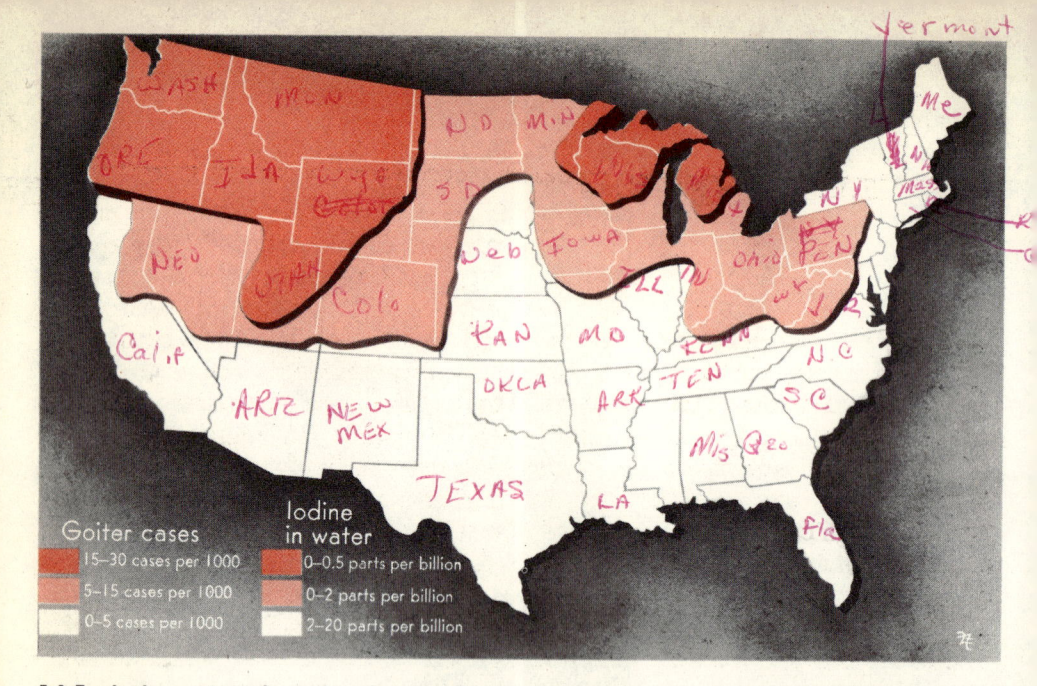

Goiter cases
- 15–30 cases per 1000
- 5–15 cases per 1000
- 0–5 cases per 1000

Iodine in water
- 0–0.5 parts per billion
- 0–2 parts per billion
- 2–20 parts per billion

14.5 In the regions shown in color, note how many cases of simple goiter appeared per 1000 people, and note what the percentage of iodine was in the water. What is true of the regions more lightly colored, and of those left white? This map shows conditions in 1923. Do you wonder that doctors suspected a relation between thyroxin and iodine deficiency?

or swelling of the thyroid gland. In this type the gland cells produce too much thyroxin. The person is likely to be restless; he loses weight; the temperature may be above normal, and the heart beats fast. All of this should not surprise you since you know that thyroxin speeds up oxidation. Sometimes the eyes become bulging with this type of goiter. But remember that only a physician, and not a layman (someone who has not studied medicine) can decide whether a person has this type of goiter. A surgeon can cut out part of the gland or he can shut off some of the blood supply to the thyroid; then its cells can't secrete so actively.

Isotopes. There is a new and interesting treatment for overactivity of the thyroid gland which is sometimes used. To understand it you must think back, for a moment, to what you learned about atoms. Do you remember that the nucleus of every atom contains one or more protons and usually one or more neutrons, and spinning around them are electrons? Every atom of an element has the same number of protons and electrons. It has been found however, that the atoms of an element are not always exactly the same. For example an atom of ordinary hydrogen has one proton and one electron. But there is a different atom of hydrogen which has in its nucleus one neutron besides its proton. And there is still another hydrogen atom that has two neutrons. These two kinds of atoms are spoken of as **isotopes** (eye'so-topes) of the hydrogen atom. Further study shows that all elements have isotopes. The only difference between an element

246   UNIT FOUR — HOW OUR BODIES WORK

and its isotopes is that they have different numbers of neutrons. You have probably heard that the uranium used for the atom bomb is an isotope of ordinary uranium. It has fewer neutrons.

Radioactive isotopes. Another important discovery was that many isotopes are **radioactive;** they give off powerful rays like those given off by radium. Some atoms can be made radioactive in atomic piles or by **cyclotrons** (sigh'clo-trons). In a laboratory, radioactive atoms can be put into chemical compounds. These substances can then be fed or injected into the body.

Now for some conditions of overactive thyroid glands, a compound containing radioactive iodine is fed to the body. It travels through the blood, and being an iodine compound, it is absorbed by the thyroid gland. While in the gland, the iodine gives off rays. These relieve the abnormal condition of the gland. A good many cases of overactivity have been treated in this way.

Radioactive isotopes are being used for many other purposes, too. Sometimes they are used in laboratory experiments with plants and animals to discover where some particular compound goes and how it is used by the body. Its travels can be easily traced by using a Geiger counter. Have you ever seen a Geiger counter being used? By its clicking it shows up the presence of any radioactive substance. In this way radioactive isotopes can be traced through the body of experimental animals. They have, therefore, been called **tracers,** or **tagged atoms.** By means of tagged atoms we should be able to learn a great deal about the metabolism of the body.

Insulin. Insulin is a hormone that regulates the amount of sugar in the blood. It is important that the amount of your blood sugar remain fairly constant, even when you happen to eat a great deal of sugar. In the normal body insulin takes care of this by removing the extra sugar. But when a person is secreting insufficient insulin the amount of sugar in the blood increases. And then the sugar begins to appear even in the urine. By testing the blood and the urine for sugar, doctors can find out whether your body is making too little insulin, in other words whether you have the disease known as **diabetes** (die'a-beet'ees). Fortunately, nowadays, this disease can be easily controlled by injecting insulin. Before this was discovered, diabetes was often fatal.

Insulin removes sugar from the blood in a number of ways, two of which you can easily understand. First, it hastens oxidation of sugar in the cells; thus sugar diffuses out of the blood into the cells. Secondly, insulin helps in the storage of glycogen (animal starch) in the liver. This also helps to take sugar out of the blood since glycogen is made from sugar.

The discovery of insulin. In Roman times physicians knew the disease we call diabetes. Naturally, they thought it was a disease of the kidneys since the urine was not normal; it always contained sugar. Hundreds of years later, around 1850, a great French scientist, Claude Bernard, had a new theory. Claude Bernard was one of the first to attempt to study the workings of the body through experiments. He was not satisfied with observation and reasoning alone; he performed carefully controlled experiments on animals. Through some of these experiments he showed that the liver takes

14.6 This girl has diabetes. She has learned to inject the amount of insulin prescribed by her physician. *Encyclopaedia Britannica Films, Inc.*

part in sugar metabolism. Then he began to wonder whether perhaps the liver, rather than the kidneys, is diseased when a person has diabetes. In time, however, this theory proved to be false.

Then, about 1890, an important discovery was made, largely by accident. Two German investigators, in order to study pancreatic digestion in dogs, removed the pancreas from some of their experimental animals. Their helper who cared for the animals in the laboratory knew no science, but he was evidently a keen observer. He noticed that large numbers of flies were always attracted to the urine of these dogs that had lost the pancreas. Many of us would never even have noticed this. But he not only noticed it; he also reported his observations. This was the first great step toward discovering the cause of diabetes. The scientists, of course, knew that flies are attracted to sugar; so they tested the urine, and they found it contained sugar. Then they asked themselves this question: Does sugar in the urine have any connection with the loss of the pancreas? More experiments followed. These showed that loss of the pancreas or damage to the pancreas always resulted in the presence of sugar in the urine — diabetes.

In the meantime, a biologist named Paul Langerhans was studying the pancreas under the microscope. He discovered scattered little patches of cells that looked different from the cells that make pancreatic juice. It was suspected that these cells which became known as the islands of Langerhans might have something to do with controlling the amount of sugar in the blood. Then came another clue. Autopsies (dissections after death) were performed on people who died of diabetes; the pancreas was carefully examined. In every case the cells in the islands of Langerhans were damaged. By this time it was known that there are ductless glands in the body. It was known that glands can pour their secretions directly into the blood. Why then should not the islands of Langerhans be little patches of ductless gland cells? The pancreas, evidently, has two distinct functions; it makes large amounts of a digestive juice which leaves through the duct; it also makes a hormone that is absorbed directly into the blood.

Almost the last step was taken by two Canadians, Banting and Best, in their chemical laboratory. Using the pancreas of animals such as the pig, they extracted the hormone from the islands of Langerhans. They called it insulin. Then they discovered how to inject insulin into a person suffering from diabetes. See Figure 14.6. The final step was learning the formula of insulin and learning how to make it in the laboratory without extracting it from animals. The discovery of the cause of diabetes is more or less typical of many scientific discoveries. The dis-

14.7 What gland becomes active in an emergency such as this? Can you state six changes going on in the cat? *Black Star*

coveries of many scientists, often from different parts of the world, must be fitted together.

The adrenal glands. The **adrenal** (ad-ree′nal) **glands** are two small glands, one on the upper end of each kidney. Small as they are they secrete a number of hormones. The hormone that interests us here is **adrenalin** (ad-ren′a-lin). Adrenalin enters your blood in increased amounts when your emotions are aroused. That is, fear, anger, great joy or excitement of any kind make the adrenal glands secrete actively. Then the adrenalin begins to act immediately. Professor Cannon, experimenting with cats at Harvard University, discovered this connection between excitement and the adrenal glands. When the cat

CHAPTER FOURTEEN — DUCTLESS GLANDS 249

14.8 The sex glands of this silver-laced Wyandotte rooster (on the left) were removed. As a result he changed into the hen-feathered bird shown on the right. What is the difference in plumage? *U.S. Bureau of Animal Industry*

is fighting or fleeing from an enemy, adrenalin circulates freely and brings about many changes in the body; all of these fit it for the emergency. And in a crisis adrenalin brings about the same changes in us. See Figure 14.7.

Now let's see what these changes are. You must look at all parts of the body for your answer. The skin becomes pale, and if you could look into the body, you would see many of the internal organs losing color, too. The adrenalin constricts (makes smaller) the arteries in all these organs; this shuts off much of their blood supply. Furthermore, the adrenalin slows up the contraction of involuntary muscle cells; thus the digestive organs slow down. The heart, on the other hand, is stimulated by the adrenalin; it beats harder and faster. At the same time blood vessels that run to the brain and the skeletal muscles are made wider. The blood that was saved in the internal organs is thus sent to the brain and skeletal muscles. In the lungs the smaller air passages widen; thus more oxygen reaches the air sacs and the blood. In the liver the adrenalin speeds up the changing of glycogen into glucose, which then enters the blood. Can you see that these six changes add up to increased oxidation and release of much energy where it is needed in an emergency — in the brain and in skeletal muscles. For this reason Professor Cannon called the adrenal glands the "glands of combat." But adrenalin does still more. If blood begins to flow, adrenalin helps it clot. It also makes the fur bristle, or feathers become ruffled. Thus the animal shows its rage to the enemy.

Physicians make frequent use of adrenalin. In heart failure it may be injected directly into the heart to stimulate it. It is also used to help clot blood and to help people with asthma, whose breathing tubes need to be widened in order to breathe comfortably.

Other adrenal hormones. Adrenal glands have an inner and outer portion. The outer part is called the cortex. The cortex secretes more than twenty hormones, some of which are of great importance. **Cortisone** (cor′ti-sone) is one of them. Cortisone is secreted in very small amounts, but it has very important effects not yet fully understood. It is made artificially and is used to treat, but not to cure, one form of arthritis, high blood pressure, and certain other conditions. Sometimes, however, by affecting the other ductless glands it does more harm than good.

Other ductless glands. First, there are the **parathyroids**. They are very small, one lying within each lobe of the thyroid. They secrete a hormone which is necessary to keep the calcium content of the blood and lymph normal. Too little of the hormone has two effects: it results in the depositing of calcium salts in some of the joints, causing swellings there; and in cases of a serious shortage, **convulsions** (violent muscle contractions or muscle spasms) result.

And then there are the very important ductless gland cells in the sex organs. They secrete hormones called **estrogens** (ess′tro-jens) and **androgens** (an′dro-jens). In male animals more of the androgens are made than of the estrogens, and in female animals it is the other way around. Physicians use these hormones a good deal in treating various diseases. As an animal grows up, or matures, these hormones are secreted into the blood and produce the changes which give the male a different appearance from the female. Figure 14.8 shows how a rooster can be made to look like a hen by removing its sex glands.

Scientists are uncertain about the use of the **thymus**, found in the chest of

14.9 Certain differences between dogs may be caused by differences in the activities of ductless glands. Can you state what abnormal gland condition might have produced each of the three breeds of dogs shown above? Do you know another breed in which you might suspect ductless glands to have played a part? *American Museum of Natural History*

children, and about the **pineal body**, found in the brain. Some experiments show that these organs produce hormones; other experiments do not. Perhaps someday we may know the truth.

Plants, too, make some hormones, although not in separate glands. Plant hormones affect the growth of the plant.

The master gland. The pituitary can be called the "master gland" because it secretes many hormones which control the other ductless glands. You surely have heard about one of these hormones, the one that is carried to the cortex of the adrenal glands. It is called ACTH, the four initials of its long name consisting of four words. ACTH, more recently named corticotropin, is easy to make in the laboratory; therefore, sometimes when people need cortisone, the physician may inject ACTH. This stimulates the adrenals to make cortisone.

The master gland certainly manages the other ductless glands pretty successfully. But some of the other glands, for example, the sex glands, in turn affect the pituitary. In fact, it seems as though all the ductless glands are interrelated. Something wrong with one gland may have very far-reaching effects.

What have you learned? Hormones play a very important part in all our body processes, and, therefore, they affect our appearance and our personality. Look at Figure 14.9 to see how hormones affect the structure of dogs, giving us different breeds.

You have read about only a very few hormones in this chapter; and year by year more are being discovered both in animals and in plants. This is a

TABLE 15

HORMONES

Gland	Location	Hormones	Effects	Abnormalities
Thyroid	Neck	Thyroxin	Speeds up oxidation and mental and physical development	Cretinism; two kinds of goiter; myxedema
Islands of Langerhans	Pancreas	Insulin	Regulates sugar metabolism	Diabetes
Adrenals	On kidney	Adrenalin Several others	In larger amounts prepares for emergency. Used as drug.	
Pituitary, the "Master" Gland	Base of brain	Tethelin	Controls growth of skeleton	Giants (too much) Dwarfs (too little)
		ACTH Many other hormones carried to other ductless glands	Stimulates adrenals to secrete cortisone	
Parathyroids	Within each lobe of thyroid	Parathormone	Keeps up supply of calcium in blood	Convulsions from lack of Ca salts
Sex glands	In sex organs	Estrogens Androgens Many others	Influence characteristics of male and female	
Thymus	In chest	?	?	

large field waiting for many more investigators. Now take a look at the simple review table which lists and describes only a few of the more important hormones.

6. Describe at least five specific effects of adrenalin on the body which would be of use in an emergency.
7. Describe briefly the effects of the hormones secreted by (a) the parathyroids, (b) the sex organs, (c) the pituitary, or "master," gland.

USEFUL WORDS IN BIOLOGY

hormone	goiter	adrenalin
pituitary gland	isotope	cortisone
	radioactive tracer	parathyroid glands
ductless gland	tagged atom	estrogens
thyroid gland	insulin	androgens
thyroxin	diabetes	thymus gland
cretinism	adrenal glands	ACTH

DO IT YOURSELF

1. The effect of thyroxin on tadpoles. In late spring, when you can find tadpoles, you will find this an easy and rewarding experiment. Place a very *small* amount of thyroid extract in the aquarium. Change the water each day before adding fresh thyroid extract. What control is necessary? Observe closely and keep a day by day record of your observations.

2. A report on ductless glands and personality. A good article with which to begin your study of this subject is "Your Glands and Personality" in *Coronet* of April 1952. Then look up "hormones" in *Readers' Guide to Periodical Literature* of the last ten years.

TEST YOURSELF

1. Tell about hormones: (a) in what kind of organs they are made, (b) where in the body they work, (c) what they do in the body.
2. Describe animal experiments which showed the function of (a) the pituitary gland, (b) the thyroid gland.
3. Cretinism, goiter, and myxedema are all associated with thyroxin. Explain how each condition is associated with thyroxin and how each may be relieved.
4. Radioactive isotopes have proved useful in science. (a) Name one radioactive isotope, and tell how it may be used in curing disease. (b) Explain a second way in which radioactive isotopes and a Geiger counter can be used in the body.
5. Most discoveries in biology and medicine are made through the contributions of many scientists. Show how this was true of the discovery of the cause and cure of diabetes.

ADVENTURES IN READING

1. *The Chemicals of Life* by Isaac Asimov, Abelard-Schulman, 1954 (enzymes, vitamins, and hormones). Has a brief and simple chapter on hormones.
2. *Science Survey* edited by Ian Cox, Sampson Low, Marston, 1948. This contains Best's own account of the discovery of insulin.
3. "ACTH and Cortisone" by George W. Gray in *Scientific American*, March 1950 (*Scientific American Reader*, 1953). If you read carefully you will learn a great deal from this rather difficult but well-written article by a famous writer on scientific subjects.

Unit Five

Why we behave as we do

CHAPTER 15

The simplest kinds of behavior

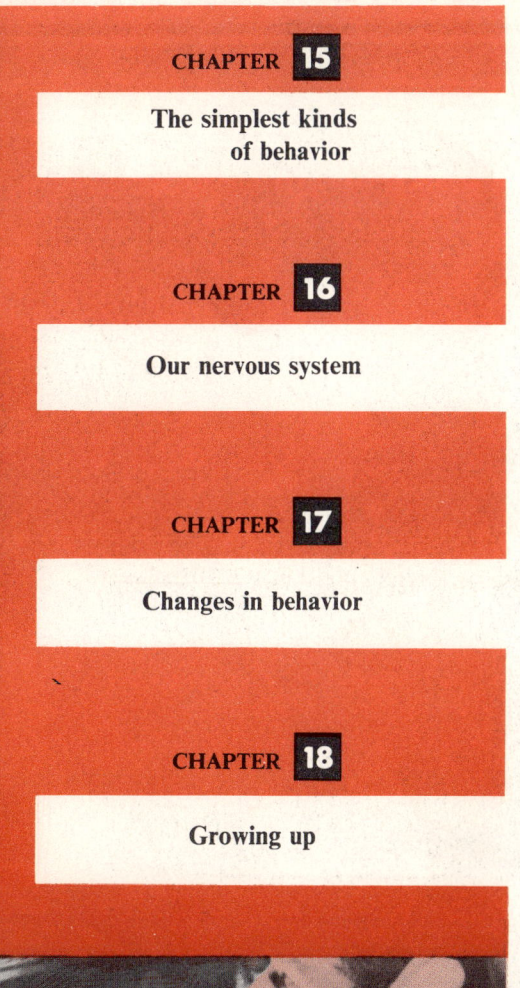

CHAPTER 16

Our nervous system

CHAPTER 17

Changes in behavior

CHAPTER 18

Growing up

Look at the picture on the opposite page. The obvious part, boys and girls talking and popping corn, is the least interesting part. What is going on in each one's mind is far more interesting, far more important, and far more difficult to study. If you look closely at one of these young people, you may ask yourself: what kind of boy or girl is this? What makes this young person "click"? That is what we'll want to find out in this unit.

We'll study about babies, whose behavior is relatively simple. Perhaps we can discover why they behave as they do. You have watched babies get red in the face and cry. Some cry a lot; some are more placid and smile a great deal. Even when they are very young they show some personality traits, although these may change with time.

We'll also study animal behavior in controlled experiments. This gives us clues to an understanding of our own behavior. From observation and experimentation on dogs and apes and many other animals, and on man himself, we have learned about reflexes and about habits. We have learned something about how we learn and how we reason. How our senses work was one of the earliest discoveries. You will read about that, too.

A great deal is still to be learned about our behavior. We are not yet able to explain fully why we behave as we do; but the chapters of this unit will give you some idea of your mental development and of the special cells in your body that make this possible. There will be new words to learn, as usual, and new ideas. But the effort will be worth your while if it gives you a better understanding of yourself and of other people.

Chapter 15
The simplest kinds of behavior

15.1 The stimulus and response are clear. Explain. "The Shamrock" St. Vincent H. S. Akron, Ohio

UNIT FIVE — WHY WE BEHAVE AS WE DO

Behavior. You stub your toe and stumble; you feel warm and take off your coat; you decide to walk to the pool for a swim; you sleep and have interesting dreams; the television is on and you watch the baseball game. Hurrah! a holiday tomorrow! You feel happy. All this and much more makes up your behavior. Behavior, in science, means all that an animal does. Behavior does not mean "good or bad conduct." In this chapter you will read about some simple types of behavior shown by you as well as by simple animals and plants. But let us stop for a moment to learn the meaning of some other words we will want to use.

Sense organs and stimuli. The honking of a horn sounds in your ears. You turn your head and see a blue car coming toward you. As it passes you feel the heat of the exhaust on your skin; the fumes strike your nose. And there are other sense organs in your skin besides those that feel heat; some feel cold, pain, or pressure. And there are sense organs in your mouth, as you know.

Now anything that excites (stimulates) a sense organ is called a **stimulus** (plural **stimuli**); light waves and sound waves, for example, are stimuli. The sense organs are also called **receptors,** since they receive stimuli.

Stimulus and response. If you hear the horn of an automobile very close to your ear, you start; that is, certain muscles in your body contract violently. A stimulus was received by your ear and this brought about a contraction of muscles. We say that the muscular contraction and your starting back was your **response** to the stimulus.

Responses are not always muscular contractions. That is, besides muscles, the body has other organs that respond. A sharp cinder in the eye (stimulus) causes two quite different responses: a muscular contraction of the eyelid (blinking), and the secretion of tears. Glands, as well as all the muscles, can respond.

And responses are not always visible. For example, in the case of the approaching car, recognizing the noise as a horn is a response; and the feeling of fright is another response. But a response is always something the body itself does. If the automobile knocks you down, this is not a response to a stimulus.

Responses in a baby. If someone puts a newborn baby's hands over a broom handle, what do you think will happen? The baby folds its hands tightly over the stick. The stick was a stimulus; the tightening of the muscles in the fingers and in the arm was the response. If something is placed in the baby's mouth (stimulus) its lips and cheeks go through sucking movements. If milk reaches the baby's throat, muscles in the throat contract and the baby swallows. The baby sneezes or coughs when its nose or throat is irritated. And it shows other responses to stimuli. These simple direct responses to a stimulus, which are inborn in the baby, are called **reflexes.** You, too, have reflexes, many of them. If someone taps just the right spot below your kneecap when your leg hangs freely, the lower leg kicks out. This is the "knee-jerk reflex." If you accidentally touch a very hot stove, you pull your hand away without thinking of what you are doing.

Why can we respond to stimuli? It is the protoplasm of which we are made that both receives stimuli and responds. Some change takes place

CHAPTER FIFTEEN — THE SIMPLEST KINDS OF BEHAVIOR

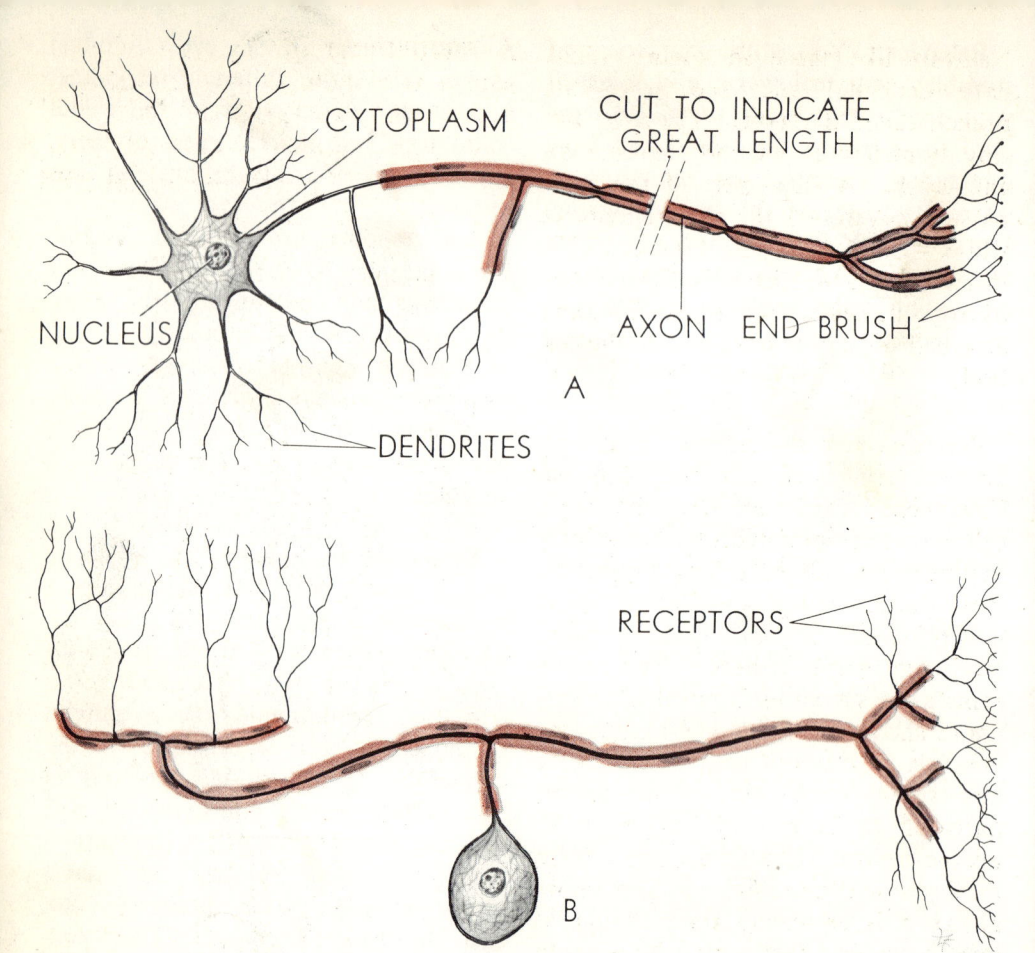

15.2 Two types of neurons, or nerve cells. A neuron is a very complex cell. What are the parts of the neuron in **A**? Notice that the axon is covered with a sheath, which is not part of the neuron, however. Cell **B** seems to have two axons. What does it lack? One of the long axons seems to take the place of the dendrites shown in **A**.

in the protoplasm when the change in the environment (stimulus) occurs. Another change in the protoplasm produces the response. This statement doesn't explain much. The best we can do is just to give a name to this property of protoplasm — **irritability**. Your protoplasm has this property, just as all other protoplasm has.

Nerve cells. You know that we and other many-celled animals have muscle cells, bone cells, nerve cells, and other kinds of cells. All living protoplasm shows irritability, but our nerve cells show a particularly high degree of irritability. Take a look at Figure 15.2A to see how a typical nerve cell, or **neuron,** looks. Even in its appearance a nerve cell, or neuron, is very different from all other tissue cells. Its cell body is large and very much branched. The branches are called **dendrites** (den drites — Greek for tree).

258   UNIT FIVE — WHY WE BEHAVE AS WE DO

Neurons like those in Figure 15.2A have dendrites and one very long branch called the **axon**. The axon has tiny branches at its end, making an **end brush**. A large part of the axon has two coverings; the outer one looks white. Some neurons, Figure 15.2B, instead of having branched dendrites, have what looks like a second axon attached to the opposite end of the cell body.

Nerve centers and nerves. You may be wondering where in the body we have these complicated neurons. Their cell bodies are gathered together mostly in the brain and in a long projection from the brain, the spinal cord. That is why we call the brain and the spinal cord the **nerve centers**. The nerve centers are shown in Figure 15.3. This figure shows, too, that the long axons you just read about arise in the brain and spinal cord and extend to all parts of the body. The axons make up the **nerves**. The axons don't leave the brain and cord singly. Remember an axon is extremely thin, though it may be several feet long. You could never see a single axon without a microscope, yet nerves can be seen as fairly thick cords. Each nerve, therefore, that you see in Figure 15.3 is a bundle of axons, many hundreds of them together. Since each nerve is a bundle of axons, nerves can branch by having some axons go in one direction, some in another. And each of these smaller branches can again separate into branches. This happens many times in each big nerve which is connected with the brain and spinal cord. Thus practically all the cells in the body are reached by one of the finest branches of a big nerve. You can see what a wonderful arrangement we have in the body for sending messages along the nervous system. First, the protoplasm

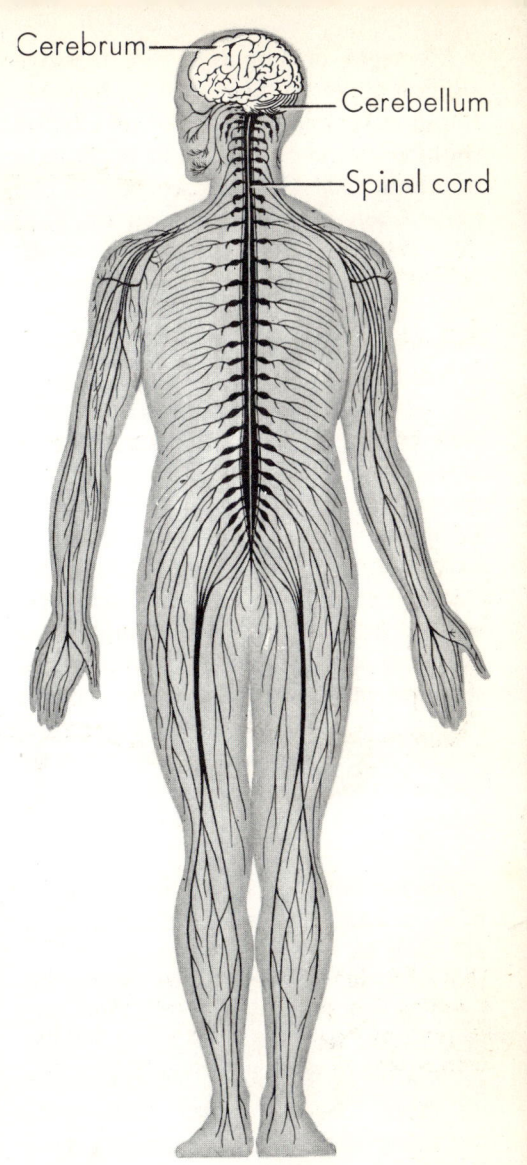

15.3 This shows the nerve centers, brain and spinal cord, and the large nerves which branch from them. This is also called the central nervous system. About how many nerves arise from the spinal cord? Notice, also, the little swellings (ganglia) on the nerves attached to the spinal cord.

of the nerve cell has the property of irritability to an extreme degree; second, this highly irritable protoplasm connects all body cells with the nerve centers, brain and spinal cord.

CHAPTER FIFTEEN — THE SIMPLEST KINDS OF BEHAVIOR

Messages or impulses. A message along a nerve fiber is called an **impulse**. Impulses travel about as fast as a bullet shot from a revolver, that is, at the rate of about 300 feet per second. The nerve fiber, after carrying an impulse, must rest for a tiny fraction of a second before it can carry a second impulse. While an impulse travels along a fiber, chemical changes go on in the fiber. It has been shown that oxygen is used up, carbon dioxide is produced, and heat energy is released. But there is more than a chemical change; an electrochemical wave, evidently, travels along the fiber. The electrical currents have actually been measured. This electrochemical wave is the same no matter how strong the stimulus is. When a strong stimulus produces a stronger response, it is partly because a larger number of nerve fibers and muscle fibers are aroused and partly because there are more impulses per second.

Tracing a reflex act. Now let's see how the baby is able to perform a reflex act such as grasping the stick. When the baby is born, its brain and spinal cord have all the nerve cells they will ever have. Many axons and dendrites grow after birth but the cell bodies are all there. In this reflex, nerve cells carry impulses from the sense organs in the skin of the hand into the spinal cord. The cord and the brain act like a telephone exchange. Whenever impulses arrive in the brain or cord, connections are made; and the impulses are relayed to other neurons. These neurons send out impulses along their axons, which end in muscle fibers. When the impulses arrive in the muscle fibers, the fibers contract.

Figure 15.4 is a very simple diagram of what goes on in the baby's body as a reflex occurs. This shows a neuron in touch with the sense organ. It is called a **sensory** neuron. The arrow shows in which direction the impulse travels. This is one of the neurons that has two long projections instead of one. Its cell body lies just outside of the spinal cord in a little swelling called a **ganglion** (gan'glee-on — plural **ganglia**). These ganglia show in Figure 15.3.

In the cord the impulse goes to a second neuron and then out along its axon, which ends in a muscle. This second neuron is called a **motor** neuron since the impulse results in motion. When the impulse reaches the muscle fiber, the fiber contracts. The reflex is completed. But it isn't a single neuron that brings an impulse into the nerve center nor a single one that takes an impulse out. The same thing goes on in a number of neighboring neurons; and many muscle fibers respond.

It is interesting to know how an impulse travels from one cell to another. When the impulse gets to the end brush of one cell it jumps across the gap into the dendrites of a second cell. The branches of the two cells do not actually touch. Figure 15.5 shows one of these junctions, called a **synapse** (sin-aps').

Reflex acts in other animals. All but the very simplest animals have neurons, even though many of these animals don't have a brain or a spinal cord. In insects, for example, small groups of neurons, or ganglia, are arranged in chains with nerves extending from the ganglia, as Figure 15.6 shows.

These neurons make it possible for the invertebrates to perform many reflex acts. In fact, reflex behavior in insects and spiders, for example, is far more complicated than ours. They often perform reflexes in chains. The

260   UNIT FIVE — WHY WE BEHAVE AS WE DO

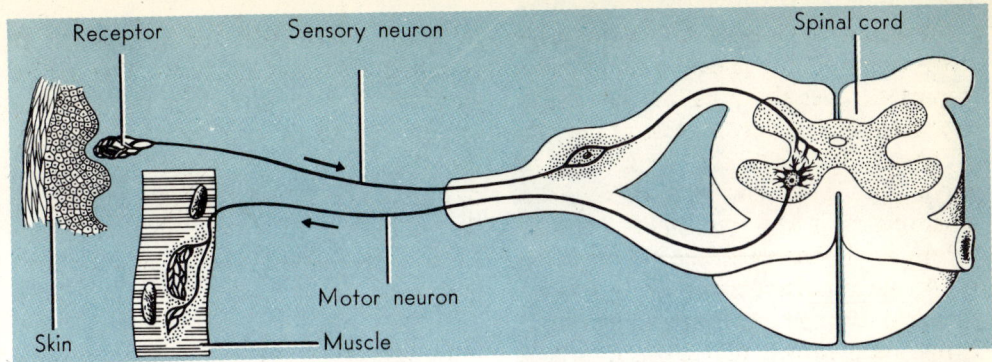

15.4 A simplified drawing of a reflex arc. No neuron is shown between the sensory and motor neurons. Note that the cell body of the sensory neuron lies outside the cord (in a ganglion). In this type of neuron the one axon acts like the dendrites in bringing an impulse into the cell body. You saw this type of neuron in Figure 15.2 B.

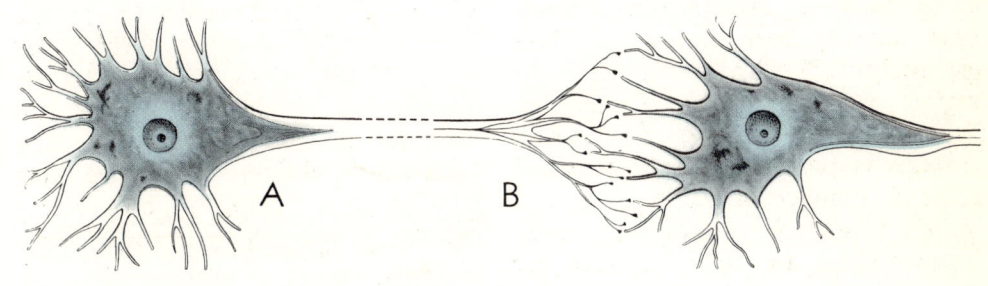

15.5 An impulse can pass from **A** to **B** across a synapse. Cell **A** is shortened (see the dotted lines). Cell **B** is incomplete. Copy this diagram. Complete cell **B** and show how the impulse would get into another cell, **C**, beyond **B**.

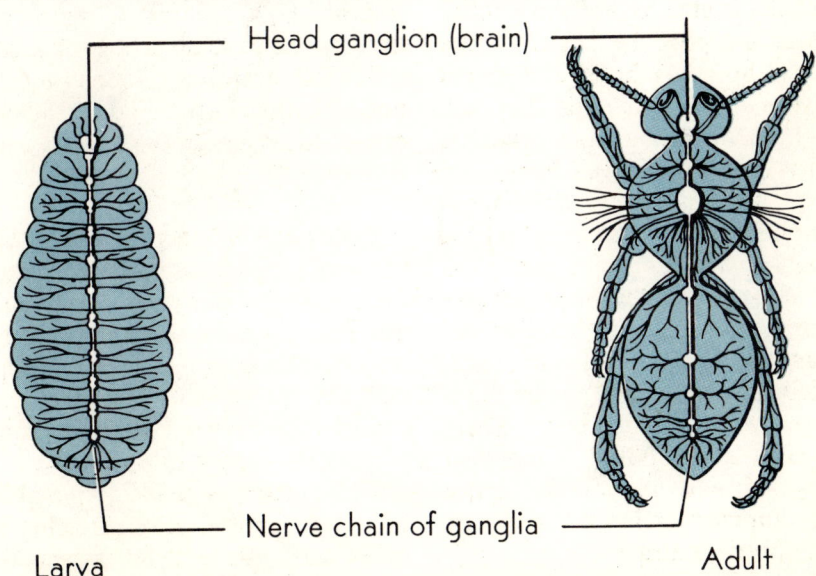

15.6 Chains of ganglia found on the ventral (lower) side of a honeybee larva and adult. Insects have no brain, but note where the larger ganglia are.

CHAPTER FIFTEEN — THE SIMPLEST KINDS OF BEHAVIOR

first reflex serves as a stimulus for a second, the second starts off a third, the third sets off a fourth, and so on. In this way the honeybee builds its hive and the spider spins its complex web (Fig. 15.7). We know that these are all reflex acts; they are all inborn. No spider ever "learns" how to spin its web. If you raise one kind of spider with spiders of another kind which spin their webs in a different design, does it imitate what goes on around it? Not at all. It spins the kind of web its parents did, a kind it has never seen. We often call behavior in which there is a long chain of reflexes **instinctive behavior.** The behavior of all invertebrates is entirely, or almost entirely, reflex or instinctive behavior.

15.7 A spider's web is built by a succession of reflex acts. How can we know that the spider's behavior is instinctive, not learned? *Ewing Galloway*

15.8 Well-constructed dams like this one can be built by beavers that have never seen a dam. You probably know that beavers dam a stream, then build a house in the pond above the dam. Here they store the food on which they live in winter. Would you call this instinctive behavior or intelligent behavior? Why? *National Park Service*

UNIT FIVE — WHY WE BEHAVE AS WE DO

15.9 Young quail in a nest on the ground, photographed from above. Where is the head of each bird? What advantage is there in this position? Did the young birds think up this good device for protecting themselves? Or do they show instinctive behavior? What reason can you give for your answer? *Gehr*

The behavior of many vertebrates, too, is largely reflex or instinctive. See Figures 15.8 and 15.9. The beavers were not *taught* to build a dam. Nor were the quail *taught* to take this position in their nest.

Behavior in protozoa. Even the single-celled animals like paramecium and ameba perform reflex acts. Their protoplasm has the property of irritability. When a paramecium meets some solid object other than food, it backs up. This is its response to a mechanical stimulus. Look for other stimuli and responses in Figure 15.10. A change in the intensity of light or in its color also acts as a stimulus to a paramecium; so does a change of temperature. You can see this for yourselves if you have some paramecia in the classroom. You can try electrical stimuli, too.

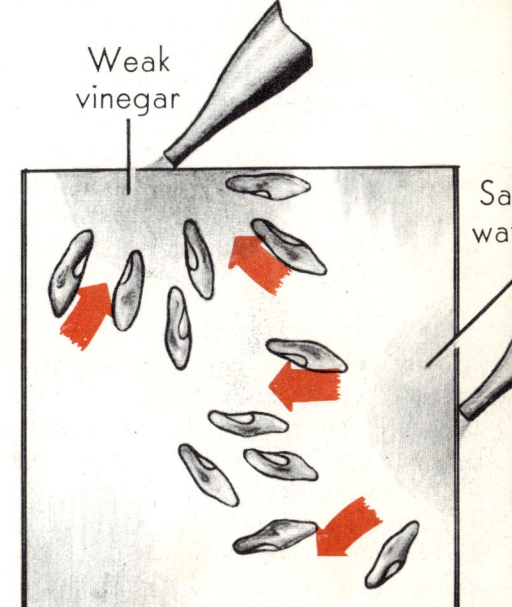

15.10 How do paramecia respond to salt water and weak vinegar?

CHAPTER FIFTEEN — THE SIMPLEST KINDS OF BEHAVIOR

stem and leafstalks, since they turn toward the light, are said to show **positive phototropism.** The turning of a part away from the source of the light is **negative phototropism.** Now look at Figure 15.13, which shows another tropism.

Tropisms are sometimes shown by animals, too. Have you seen moths at night fly directly into the light and kill themselves? These moths are showing positive phototropism. Protozoa, also, make some responses that are tropisms. But tropisms are far more common in plants than in animals. Below are listed some plant tropisms.

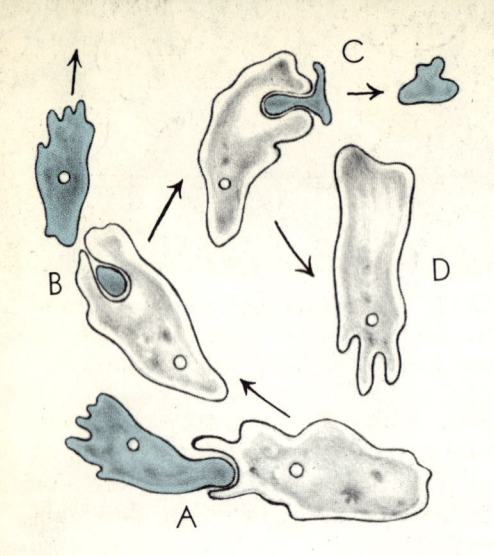

15.11 Responses in two amebas. Start at A. What is the hindmost ameba doing? Look at B. What has the hindmost ameba succeeded in doing? The foremost one received a stimulus and responded by moving away. In C the small piece that was engulfed receives a stimulus; and it responds by sending out pseudopods; thus it escapes.

Figure 15.11 shows what happened when one ameba "tried" to eat another ameba. Do you think it was really trying in the same sense as you might try to make an "A" in biology?

Plant behavior. Don't be surprised to learn that plants "behave," too; they respond to stimuli. You have certainly seen plants that turned their leaves toward the light (Figure 15.12). The turning may take a few hours, even a few days. The response does not follow the stimulus quickly, as it normally does in animals.

This kind of behavior where the plant or some part of the plant turns toward or away from the source of the stimulus is called a **tropism.** The word means "turning." When the stimulus is light, the tropism is called **phototropism** (fo-tot'row-pism), or light turning. The

By what method plants respond. Responses are slow because plants have no nerves or muscles. Tropisms in plants are the result of growth, unequal growth. Growing stem tips and leaves form a growth hormone called **auxin** (awk'sin). Auxin causes increased growth in length of stems. In roots, auxin has the opposite effect. It slows up or inhibits the growth of root cells. Auxin moves from stem tips and leaves down through the growing stem, but in moving down it is affected by light and by gravity. Light makes the auxin move along the shaded side of the stem or leaf stalk, causing the shaded side to grow faster. And the increased growth on the shaded side causes the bending toward the light. Look again at Figure 15.12. When a plant is tipped over, as in Figure 15.13, auxin is pulled by gravity to the lower side of the stem, causing this side to grow faster and to bend up.

But not all responses in plants are growth responses. Look at the curling of tendrils shown in Figure 15.14. Here other factors play a part in the response. The fringed gentian, too, in Figure 15.15 does not grow toward or away from a stimulus. It simply closes.

264

UNIT FIVE — WHY WE BEHAVE AS WE DO

15.12 Where was the source of light to which these nasturtium plants responded? How did they respond? *Blakiston*

15.13 A sunflower plant was blown down. The stem continued to grow. Explain why the stem bent up. *Schneider and Schwartz*

Another unusual plant response is shown by the **sensitive plant** (Figure 15.16), whose leaves droop as soon as the plant is jarred. These more rapid plant movements are usually caused by a sudden change in the amount of water in certain cells. In the sensitive plant the cells at the bases of the leaves and of the leaflets lose water when the plant is touched or jarred. As the cells lose water they lose their stiffness and the leaves and leaflets droop. But, in time, these cells gain water, become stiff again, and so the leaves go back to their normal position.

Figures 15.17 and 15.18 show the responses in the leaf of two so-called insect-eating plants — Venus's flytrap and sundew. Be sure to see how a small insect serves as the stimulus which leads to its being trapped and killed.

What have you learned? Your behavior, all that you are and all you do and how you do it, depends on the fact that you have nerve cells, **neurons,** that possess **irritability** to a high degree. All protoplasm in all animals and plants has irritability; that is why even protozoa can receive a **stimulus** and show a **response** to it.

Neurons are complicated cells with a cell body, a long **axon,** and many branches, or **dendrites.** The cell bodies of neurons are found, for the most part, in the nerve centers — the brain and spinal cord. Some are found in ganglia close to the cord. Nerves or bundles of axons arise in the brain and cord.

The simplest kind of behavior is **reflex** behavior. It is shown by the baby at birth and by all other animals. It is never learned; it is inborn. We keep reflexes throughout life (can you give examples of some?), but as we grow up, we have many other forms of behavior besides. Animals, especially insects and spiders, perform reflexes one after another in long chains. This **instinctive** behavior is shown in their elaborate building of nests and spinning of webs.

The simplest path of messages, or **impulses,** in a simple reflex is relatively easy to trace. A sense organ, or **receptor,** is stimulated by the environment; impulses, or electrochemical messages, are sent inward along an axon to the cord. Here the impulse is relayed across a **synapse** to another neuron. This neuron sends the message to a muscle or a gland. And so the newborn baby closes its fingers around a stick which touches the palms of its hands, and so you pull away your hand which accidentally touches a hot stove.

Plants have no neurons, but they receive stimuli and respond slowly. Very many of their responses are tropisms. In a tropism the organism turns toward or away from the source of the stimulus.

CHAPTER FIFTEEN — THE SIMPLEST KINDS OF BEHAVIOR

TABLE 16

PLANT TROPISMS

Stimulus	Part of Plant	Response	Tropism
Light	Stem and leafstalk	Positive	Phototropism
	Root	Negative	Phototropism
Gravity	Root	Positive	Geotropism
	Stem	Negative	Geotropism
Water	Root	Positive	Hydrotropism
Chemicals	Root, pollen tubes, other parts	Positive	Chemotropism
Mechanical (contact)	Stems, tendrils, other parts	Positive	Thigmotropism

15.14 Squash tendrils attached to a dead pine stem. After its tip has caught on an object, the tendril tightens up in a corkscrew. What was the stimulus that produced this response? *Schneider and Schwartz*

15.15 Fringed gentians in the daytime (left) and at night (right). What might be the stimulus that causes this response? What other plants respond in this way? *Gehr*

266 UNIT FIVE — WHY WE BEHAVE AS WE DO

15.16 Mimosa, or sensitive plant. When the photograph at the left was taken, the plant had been undisturbed for several hours. The whole plant was slightly jarred and, after a few minutes, again photographed. Which parts responded to the stimulus? How is the response made? *General Biological Supply*

15.17 Two views of a Venus's-flytrap leaf. When an insect touches the short hairs on this leaf, the leaf quickly folds up as though it were hinged in the middle. Thus the insect is trapped. Juices are then secreted and the insect is slowly digested and gradually absorbed. The "insect-eating" plants, like animals, can use meat as part of their food. They do not depend upon this source, however. *Hugh Spencer*

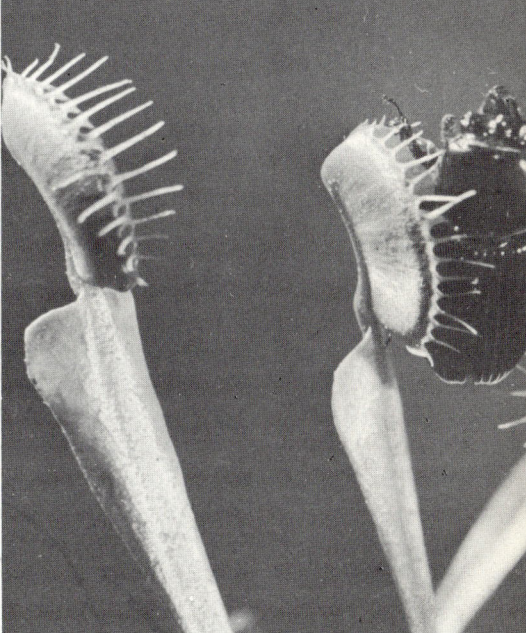

CHAPTER FIFTEEN — THE SIMPLEST KINDS OF BEHAVIOR

15.18 Sundew. The whole plant at left and a close-up of one of the leaves at right. Perhaps at some time you have found these sundew plants in a bog or at a botanical garden greenhouse. Do you see that the leaves are covered with tiny hairs, each with a drop of liquid at its tip? The photograph cannot show how these drops of sticky liquid glisten in the sunlight. Insects attracted to these leaves alight on them and are caught by the sticky substance. The tiny hairs soon respond by folding down over the prey, entangling it. Digestive juices are then secreted by the leaf, and after a time the insect is digested and absorbed. *Hugh Spencer*

USEFUL WORDS IN BIOLOGY

behavior	dendrites	tropism
stimulus	end brush	phototropism
response	nerve	geotropism
reflex	nerve centers	hydrotropism
irritability	impulse	auxin
neuron	synapse	
axon	instinctive behavior	

TEST YOURSELF

1. Copy the following sentences into your notebook, filling in and underlining the word or phrase that best completes the meaning. *Do not write in this book.* (a) The structures or organs that receive stimuli are called ——. (b) Examples of these are ——, ——, ——, ——, ——. (c) Irritability is a property of all ——. Irritability enables an animal to receive ——, and to ——. In our bodies the cells that have a high degree of irritability are called ——.

2. (a) Name the nerve centers. (b) Draw and label the most common type of nerve cell. (c) How do some neurons differ from the one shown in (b)? (d) What is the relation of an axon to a nerve? (e) How fast do impulses travel along an axon?

3. Copy the following sentences but omit those words or phrases which are incorrect. You will then have a correct description of a reflex in your notes. Reflexes are found in all animals. Reflexes are inborn. A reflex is a direct response to a stimulus. They are always slow. Both muscles and glands can respond to a stimulus in a reflex. Examples of reflexes are: blinking when a cinder gets into your eye; shaking hands with a friend whom you have not seen for a long time; starting at a sudden loud noise.

4. Draw a simple diagram to illustrate what happens when you touch a hot stove. Label all the parts.

5. (a) What is meant by instinctive behavior? (b) Give some examples of instinctive behavior in animals.
6. Give the meaning of the word "tropism."
7. (a) Name four stimuli that can cause tropisms in plants. (b) Using the words "positive" and "negative" explain how the parts of the plant respond to each stimulus. (c) Give an example of a tropism in an animal.
8. Explain why plant responses are slow compared to animal responses.
9. (a) How is a plant able to "turn" toward the light? (b) Explain what part auxin plays in this response.
10. What happens in the sensitive plant to make the leaves and leaflets droop?
11. Describe several other plant responses that are not tropisms.

each stem tip. Lay one on the cut-off top of a growing seedling. Of course, you must have controls. Observe after 24 hours, and again later. Describe. What do you conclude?

4. Geotropism in roots and stems. Sprout pea seeds. When the young plants have a main root and stem about an inch long begin the experiment. Line a wide battery jar with wet blotting paper, to give moisture and exclude light. Cover a piece of cork or cardboard with wet blotting paper. This must be wide enough to make a partition across the jar. Now pin pea seeds to the cardboard so that the root and stem will not be touching it. Pin some with the root pointing up and the stem down; some with root down and stem up; some with root and stem horizontal. Keep the blotting paper moist. Exclude light from the top. Why? Observe day by day and write up your observations. Does this experiment need a control? What conclusions can you draw?

DO IT YOURSELF

1. To see a simple human reflex. In a fairly dark room examine the pupil of someone's eye. Then direct the beam of a flashlight into it and describe what you see. How quickly does it occur? Have the person close his eyes for a minute or two and examine the eyes again. Describe.

2. Responses in paramecia. Try the effect of light and shade on a rich culture of paramecia in a test tube. (You can see the animals with the naked eye.) With a microscope you can perform a variety of experiments.

3. To show the effect of auxins on stem growth. Raise some oat seedlings. When they are 2 inches high, cut off the top quarter of an inch of half a dozen. Stand these ends, cut end down, on gelatin. (The auxin will move down into the gelatin.) Cut out a small block of gelatin under

ADVENTURES IN READING

1. "Plant Movements" by Victor A. Greulach, *Scientific American*, February 1955. Easy reading and good pictures.
2. *Plant Growth Regulators* by John W. Mitchell, 1943–1947 Yearbook of the United States Department of Agriculture. The practical applications of this work will interest you.
3. "The Language of the Bees" by August Krogh in *Scientific American*, August 1948. Good reading if you are interested in instinctive behavior.
4. *Near Horizons* by Edwin W. Teale, Dodd, Mead, 1942, has a chapter on "Insect Mystery Stories." More on instinctive behavior.
5. "The Spider and the Wasp" by Alexander Petrunkevitch, *Scientific American*, August 1952 (also in the 1953 *Scientific American Reader*).

CHAPTER FIFTEEN — THE SIMPLEST KINDS OF BEHAVIOR

Chapter 16

Our nervous system

The brain. When you figured out a difficult problem in algebra or geometry last night or when the atomic scientist figured out one step in the making of an atomic bomb, what was going on in your brain or in his? Nobody knows exactly. But we do know a good deal about the brain, and we know where the neurons lie that enable you and the scientist to reason and discover answers to problems. The neurons lie in the region known as the **cerebrum** (ser'eh-brum). Now run your hand over the top of your head. Under this whole big portion of your skull, or **cranium** (cray'nee-um), lies the largest part of the brain, the cerebrum. Tucked in under the back of the cerebrum is the much smaller **cerebellum** (ser-eh-bell'um). Attached to the cerebellum at its lower end is a third part, the **medulla** (meh-dull'uh). The medulla, or brain stem, is like a widened spinal cord. See Figure 16.1.

The cerebrum has distinct right and left halves. A deep cut (fissure) almost completely separates the two halves. Notice the deep folds, or grooves, in the outer portion of the cerebrum. The folds are called **convolutions** (con-vo-lew'shuns). The outer part of the cerebrum with its convolutions is called the **cortex**. It consists of "gray matter." In the cortex lie the cell bodies of the neurons that you will read more and more about as you continue the study of your behavior. You can imagine how many billions of neurons there must be in this much folded cortex! Beneath the cortex is the "white matter" of the cerebrum.

The cerebellum also has gray matter outside; and beneath it, white matter. And it, too, has small convolutions in its gray matter. The surface of the medulla, however, has no folds; and its gray and white matter are pretty much mixed up. You can learn a good deal from a study of a fresh sheep's or pig's brain; they are much like ours, although different, too. See Figure 16.2. You will find it interesting to compare the animal's brain with the picture of our brain.

Functions of brain and spinal cord. These different parts of the brain do different things for us. By a study of diseases of the brain and also by animal experimentation, scientists have found out pretty well what each part does. The cerebrum is — so to speak — the president, cabinet, congress, and supreme court all in one. Thinking, consciousness, and the sensations are possible because of it. We commonly think we see with our eyes. But the only reason we can see is because one portion of the cerebrum "sees." We even know which part of the cerebrum it is; it's the part in the back portion of the head. And so with the other senses — hearing, tasting, smelling and feeling. There is a definite region in the cortex of the cerebrum for each of these sensations. We have another important sense located in the cerebrum — being aware of the parts of our body so that we know what each is doing. But there is something more the cerebrum does. One part is directly concerned with bodily movement.

UNIT FIVE — WHY WE BEHAVE AS WE DO

16.1 A section through the middle of the human brain. Which region is the largest? In which of the three regions are there folds or convolutions? Notice the location of the pineal and pituitary glands.

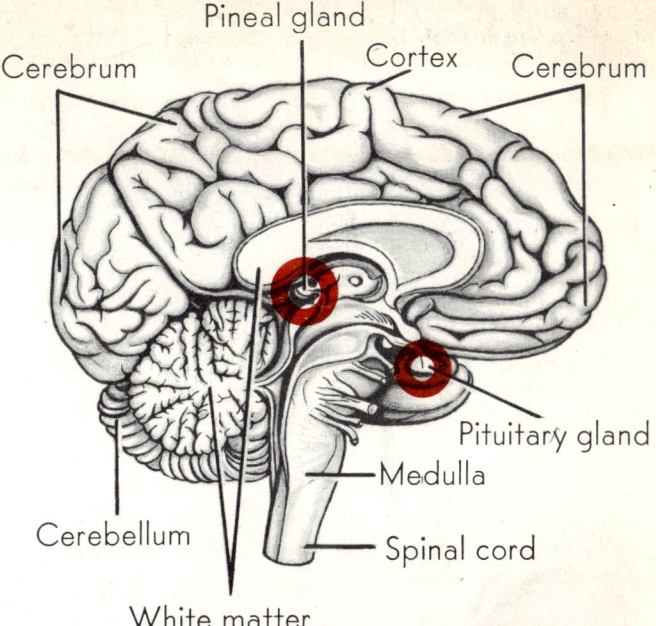

Labels: Cerebrum, Pineal gland, Cortex, Cerebrum, Cerebellum, White matter, Medulla, Pituitary gland, Spinal cord

Many impulses to the muscles seem to start in the cortex of the cerebrum. Then they continue on into neurons in the cerebellum. See Figure 16.3.

The cerebellum has neurons that relay these impulses through the medulla to the spinal cord; from here they go out to the skeletal muscles. But the cerebellum really does more than relay. It first sorts and combines these messages; we say it **coordinates** the messages. In this way the skeletal muscles in the various parts of our body work together. This enables us to sit, stand, walk, skate, and play tennis. Many different muscles in our bodies work together in performing even the simplest of these actions. But the neurons in the cerebellum never initiate impulses; they "wait for orders from above."

In the medulla, which is really a continuation of the spinal cord, are the "vital" centers, those that control the heartbeat and breathing. And through the medulla pass all the nerve fibers that extend from the rest of the

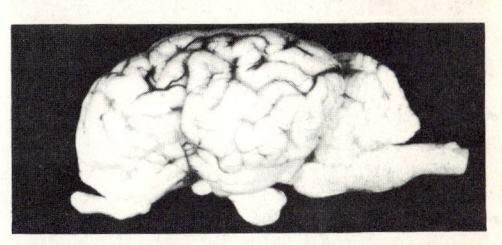

16.2 A sheep's brain. The spinal cord is at the right. Note the cerebrum (left). What two other parts of the brain are shown? The parts of the sheep's brain lie in a straight line. How does our brain differ in this respect? *Ward's Nat. Sc. Establishment*

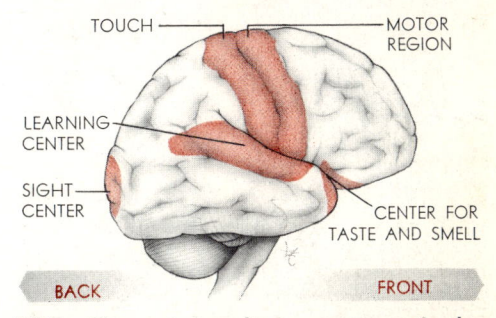

16.3 The motor and sensory areas in the cerebrum, as far as they are known, are shown above. Can you point to the part of your skull under which some of these lie?

Labels: TOUCH, MOTOR REGION, LEARNING CENTER, SIGHT CENTER, CENTER FOR TASTE AND SMELL, BACK, FRONT

CHAPTER SIXTEEN — OUR NERVOUS SYSTEM

brain into the spinal cord and, of course, those that pass from the cord to the brain.

The spinal cord, as you saw in the last chapter, is concerned with the reflexes which occur in arms and legs and all other parts of the body from the neck down.

The nervous system. The nerve centers (brain and spinal cord) with their nerves make up what is called the **central nervous system.** You saw a picture of this in the last chapter, Figure 15.3. Actually, we have two nervous systems: the central nervous system and another one called the **autonomic system.** You hear much less about the autonomic system. It controls the activities of our internal organs, and for this reason some of you may not even have been aware of its existence.

Protection of brain and cord. If you could find and examine the skull of a dog or cat or some other animal, you would see that the skull is made up of separate bones very closely knit together. The two large bones on top don't grow together in a baby for several months; that makes it easier for the skull to grow. After the closing, the skull with its rounded sides forms a wonderful protection for the brain. It completely encloses the brain except at its base where the medulla joins the spinal cord. All nerves, even those connected with the cerebrum, leave through this opening.

Inside the skull are three delicate membranes called the **meninges** (me-nin'jees). A liquid lies between the meninges and also in the inside cavity of the brain; this acts as a shock absorber.

The spinal cord has the same membranes, and outside of these is the **spinal column** or backbone. The small bones, or vertebrae, which make it up are held together by **ligaments,** cords of connective tissue. Between each two vertebrae are rings ("disks") of cartilage. A pair of nerves extends from the cord between each two vertebrae. Could you think of any better arrangement for giving both strength and flexibility to the spinal column?

The sense organs. We are kept in touch with the environment through our many sense organs, or receptors. You know that on the tongue we have taste buds and that we have nerve endings in the nose for smelling. In the skin we have tiny sense organs, some of which receive stimuli of pressure; others receive stimuli of touch or heat or cold. Nerve fibers end within these receptors and carry impulses to the brain. We get sensations of pain, not through special receptors, but through bare nerve fibers — fibers that lack the usual coverings. These are acted on by various stimuli.

Inside the body are receptors which keep us in touch with what goes on in the internal organs. For example, when the stomach has been empty for some time it contracts forcibly. You are made aware of this by special receptors in the stomach wall. As they are stimulated, impulses are sent to the brain and you feel what you recognize as hunger pangs.

But the two most interesting and complex sense organs, the eye and ear, need special study.

The eye. Most of you know how a simple camera works: it is a black box which admits light only through a hole in front which is opened or closed by the shutter. Most cameras also have a stop which is a device for changing the size of the opening in front; you

16.4 A simplified diagram showing a section through the eyeball. What are the three coats? That part of the sclera which can be seen is the white of the eye. Trace the path of light rays through the cornea, the liquid, through the hole in the iris (called the pupil), through the lens, through the liquid filling the eyeball to the retina. From here impulses are sent along the optic nerve.

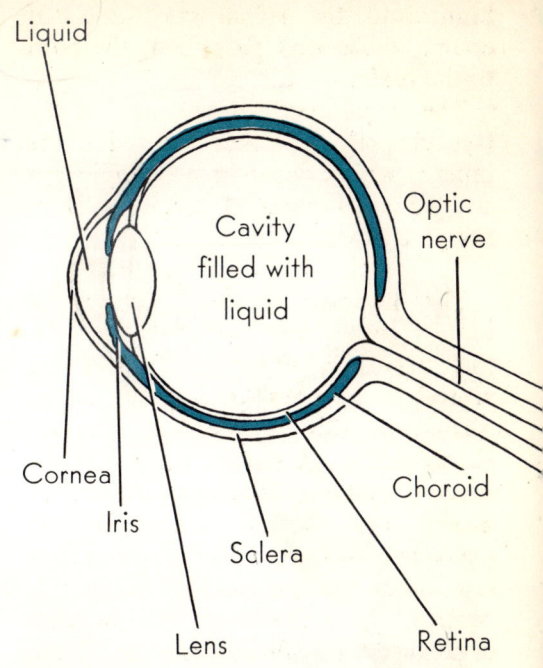

open the stop wider on a dark day than when the light is bright. Light rays enter the hole and go through the lens to the film at the back of the camera. In all but the simplest cameras the lens can be moved forward or backward so that the rays from the object you are photographing are exactly focused on the film.

Now if you look at the simplified diagram of the eye, Figure 16.4, you can see that the eye works almost like a camera. Your eyelids serve as a shutter. When they are open, light passes through the transparent **cornea** (core'nee-a) which covers the colored part of the eye. The light passes through some liquid (not needed in the camera) and strikes the lens which is, of course, made of living matter, not glass. But we have a stop, too, just as the camera has. Our stop is the colored part of the eye, the **iris**. The hole in the iris, called the pupil, is made larger in dim light and smaller in bright light. Normally, the light rays that go through the lens are focused on the inside lining of the eyeball, the **retina** (ret'in-a). The focusing, however, is not done by pushing the lens forward or backward, as in a camera. The focusing is done by changing the shape of the lens, flattening it or making it more rounded. Tiny muscles attached to the lens change its shape. Focusing is important because, if we are to see clearly, a sharp image must be made on the retina. Here are the sensitive cells (called rods and cones) which receive the image and send impulses out along the **optic** nerve. The optic nerve connects with neurons in the back region of the cerebrum.

The image on the retina is upside down as Figure 16.5 shows. But when impulses arrive in the brain we have learned to see the object right side up! It is easy enough to understand the construction of these two little cameras called eyes; it's another thing to explain why these impulses carried to the brain should result in our seeing and interpreting the object held before our eyes. We just can't explain that yet.

CHAPTER SIXTEEN — OUR NERVOUS SYSTEM

16.5 As an object (candle) is brought closer to your eye, the shape of the lens changes. How? Compare the two figures. If this change did not occur, the image would be blurred because it would not be focused on the retina.

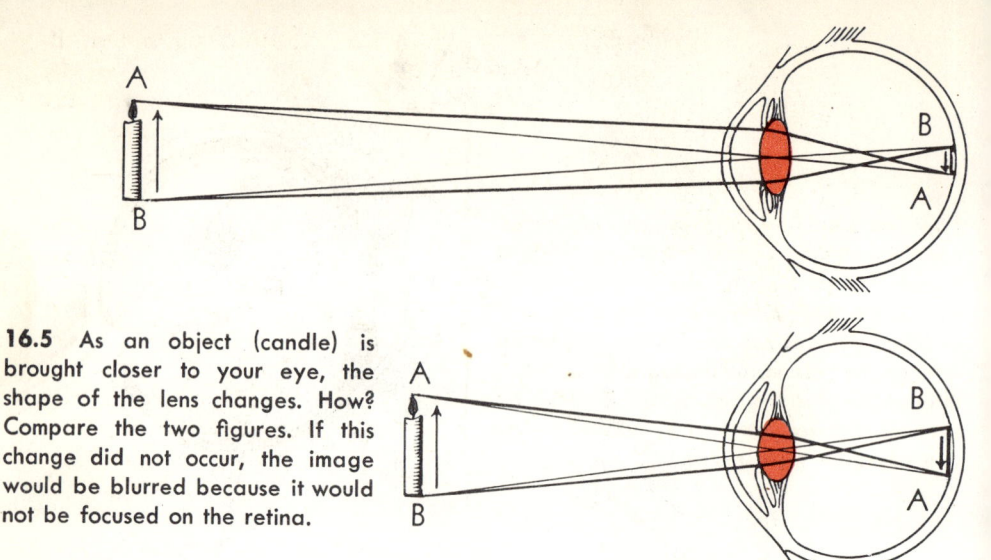

Figure 16.5 shows how the normal eye focuses. But as we get older we are unable to change the shape of the lens sufficiently and we can no longer focus as we should. We can see at a distance but not as well close up; we become far-sighted. Sometimes, however, people are born far-sighted. In these people the eyeball is too short from front to back, and the retina is too close to the lens. The eyeballs of near-sighted people, in many cases, are too long; the retina is too far back to permit a clear image unless the object they are trying to see is very close to the eye. Another common eye defect is **astigmatism** (as-tig'ma-tism). This occurs when the lens does not focus equally well from all angles. Thus, in a person who has astigmatism if the numbers 12 and 6 on a clock are clear, then 3 and 9 will be blurred. Glasses, of course, can correct all these defects.

The ear. Look at Figure 16.6 to see a diagram of the ear, the wonderful mechanism by which we pick up sound waves and transmit them to the **auditory nerve,** which connects with the brain. You will see there an outer ear with its canal; a middle ear; and an inner ear, which lies deep in the bones of the skull. Sound waves are picked up by the large outer ear and led into the canal. At the end of the canal, the sound waves hit the eardrum stretched across the opening to the middle ear. It is important that the air pressure on both sides of the eardrum be the same, both for comfort and good hearing. Normally, these pressures are equal because the middle ear is open to the outside air through the **Eustachian** (yew-stake'ee-an) **tube.** This tube connects the middle ear to the throat. But with a cold in the head the Eustachian tube may be partly closed temporarily.

As sound waves hit the eardrum, it vibrates and passes the vibrations along to three tiny bones arranged in this order: the **hammer,** the **anvil,** and the **stirrup.** Do you see the stirrup in the picture? The vibrations of the stirrup are passed along to a tiny

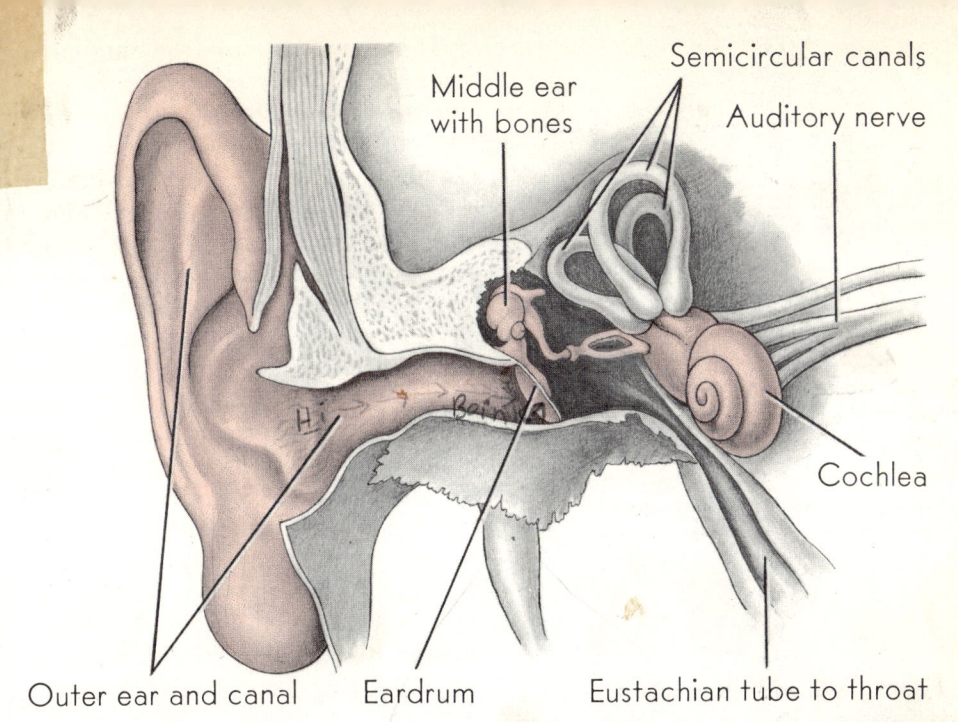

16.6 The parts of the human ear. Find the outer ear, middle ear, and inner ear. What names are given to the bones in the middle ear? To what part of the ear is the auditory nerve attached? By what passageway is the ear connected with the throat?

membrane. This lies at the entrance to a structure that looks like a snail shell (called **cochlea** — cock′lee-a). The passageway in the snail shell is filled with a liquid. The vibrations originally set up by the sound waves now set up similar waves in this liquid. The waves stimulate sensitive receptor cells lining the snail shell. These receptor cells connect with the auditory nerve, and impulses go to the cerebrum; we hear.

But the inner ear is important in another way. It helps you keep your balance. Near the snail shell are three arches, filled with fluid, and lined with sensitive cells; these are the **semicircular canals.** They lie in three planes. As your head moves and turns, first some, then others of the sensitive cells are stimulated by the liquid. Thus you are kept informed of the position of your head. When the semicircular canals fail to keep you informed in this way, you feel dizzy.

The autonomic nervous system. And now let's look at the other, the autonomic nervous system. It is closely connected with the central nervous system, and does just as important work, though not as easily seen. This system controls the involuntary (smooth) muscles and the glands. This is the nervous system over which we ordinarily have no conscious control. You don't "will" your stomach muscles to contract, or your heart to beat faster or slower, or the sweat to pour out on your skin. But some of the activities controlled by the autonomic system are the result of emotions we feel — anger, fear, great joy, and so on.

CHAPTER SIXTEEN — OUR NERVOUS SYSTEM

The structure of the autonomic system is shown in Figure 16.7. It consists of two chains of ganglia near but outside the spinal column. These ganglia are connected to the brain or spinal cord by nerve fibers. Nerve fibers in the other direction connect the ganglia to glands and to organs with involuntary muscle cells. Besides the chains of ganglia with their nerves, the autonomic system also includes networks of nerves and ganglia near or within the walls of internal organs. Such a network is called a **plexus**. If you have been accidentally struck just below the breastbone, you became painfully aware of your solar plexus. Impulses going through certain fibers of the autonomic system *stimulate* organs to activity; impulses going through other fibers *inhibit* or slow up activity.

Two chemicals seem to be associated with the action of nerves in the autonomic system — **acetylcholine** (a-seh-til-co′leen) and **sympathin**, a substance like adrenalin. Just how these chemicals work is not yet understood, but it is known that they have opposite effects.

What have you learned? You have studied the parts and the activities of the central nervous system, of the autonomic nervous system, and of the two complicated sense organs, the eye and the ear. A good way to review the parts and activities of the nervous system is to study the review tables at the top of the next page.

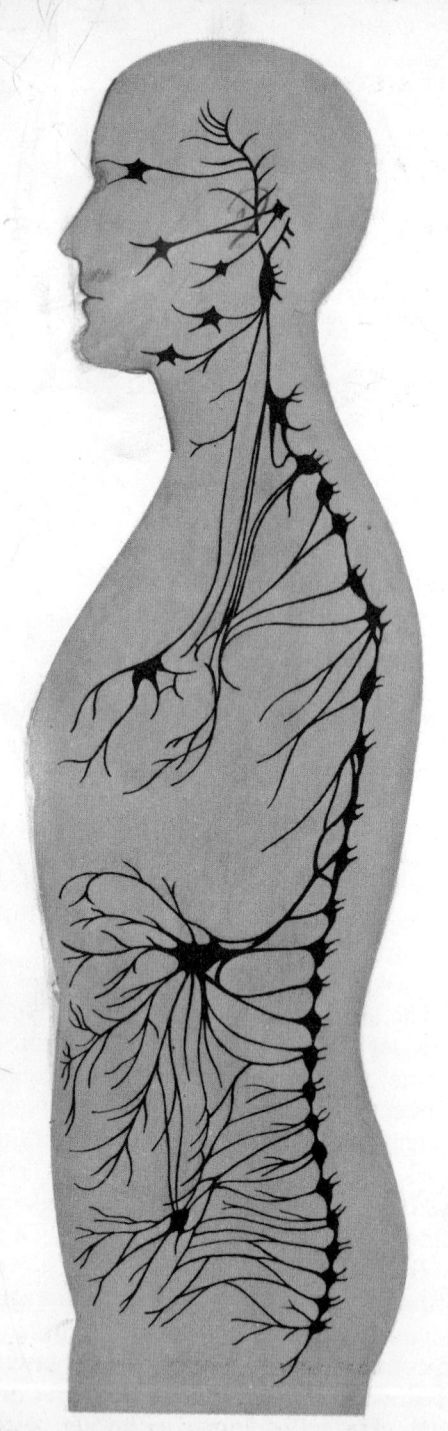

16.7 The autonomic nervous system. Can you find plexuses? Where? There are two parallel chains of ganglia like the one shown here.

UNIT FIVE — WHY WE BEHAVE AS WE DO

TABLE 17

CENTRAL NERVOUS SYSTEM

Parts		Work done	Protection
Brain	Cerebrum	Seat of consciousness; control of voluntary muscles; sensation	Skull; three meninges with fluid
	Cerebellum	Coordinates muscular movements	
	Medulla	Center for breathing, heartbeat, and other vital activities. Through it pass nerves connected with all parts of the brain	
Spinal cord		All reflexes involving parts of body below neck. Many nerves connected with brain go out through cord	Vertebrae and meninges
Nerves consisting of axons		Carry impulses to and from brain and cord	White sheath

AUTONOMIC NERVOUS SYSTEM

Two chains of ganglia, Nerves, Plexuses	Controls involuntary muscles and glands; connected with both central nervous system and internal organs. Closely tied up with emotions	

SENSE ORGANS

Senses of sight, hearing, taste, smell, touch, heat, cold, pressure, pain. Some are internal.

Eye — Light rays pass through: cornea, opening in iris (pupil), lens, to retina, which is sensitive lining of eyeball. Impulses from retina, through optic nerve to cerebrum.

Ear — Sound waves pass through: canal of outer ear causing vibrations in eardrum, hammer, anvil, stirrup, tiny membrane at entrance to cochlea. Waves created in fluid filling cochlea stimulate sensitive endings in lining. Impulses sent through auditory nerve to cerebrum.
Semicircular canals in inner ear help you to keep your balance.

USEFUL WORDS IN BIOLOGY

cerebrum
cerebellum
medulla
convolutions
cortex
gray matter
central
nervous
system

autonomic
nervous
system
plexus
meninges
cornea
iris
retina
optic nerve

astigmatism
auditory nerve
Eustachian tube
hammer, anvil,
stirrup
cochlea
semicircular
canals
inhibit

TEST YOURSELF

1. For each of the three main regions of the human brain tell: (a) location, (b) size, (c) appearance from the outside, (d) appearance in cross section.
2. What is the function of each of the three main regions of the brain and of the spinal cord?
3. Name and describe the bony and membranous protections of the brain and spinal cord.

CHAPTER SIXTEEN — OUR NERVOUS SYSTEM

4. (a) Compare the human eye with a camera, using the terms cornea, pupil, iris, lens, retina in your description. (b) Explain how the eye focuses on an object and how this differs from focusing in a camera.

5. Describe the path and the transmission of sound waves from the air to the auditory nerve, using the terms outer ear, middle ear, inner ear, and eardrum.

6. State the location and importance of (a) the Eustachian tubes, and (b) the semicircular canals.

7. (a) What are the parts of the autonomic system? (b) What is the relation of the autonomic to the central nervous system? (c) Compare the functions of the two systems.

DO IT YOURSELF

1. **Study of the brain and skull.** Ask your butcher to get a whole sheep's brain for you. Perhaps he will have to get a head. You can remove the brain by sawing the skull. Look for the meninges (you can't distinguish outer from inner). You will have no trouble in finding the cerebrum, cerebellum, and medulla. Compare with the picture of the human brain. How does the arrangement of parts differ in our brain? Cut the brain lengthwise from top to bottom and examine the cortex and white matter. Why does the brain feel soft? If you can get an animal's skull, note the number of bones and how they are joined on the rounded top.

2. **Study of an animal's eye.** Get a beef eye. Find the optic nerve in back and the place where muscles were attached. Examine the cornea and iris. With the aid of dissecting scissors find the lens, and note its composition and shape. You will find it helpful to read "Suggestions for Laboratory Study of Human Eye Structure" by Charles E. Hadley, *The American Biology Teacher*, May 1950.

3. **Learning about your touch receptors and taste buds.** Where touch receptors are located far apart you feel the two sharp points of a compass as a single point; where they are close you feel the double points. Try this experiment on a blindfolded classmate. Test various parts of the skin, the palm, the back of the hand, the cheek, etc., moving the points closer and farther apart. Now try various parts of the tongue of a blindfolded student with small drops of sour, bitter, sweet, and salt substances. With which part of the tongue does one taste each kind of substance?

4. **The sense organs of lower animals.** You can do many experiments with earthworms. Is the earthworm equally sensitive to touch at both ends? To light? How does the earthworm respond to vibrations? Where are the earthworm's organs of smell? (Use a splint dipped in xylol or some other strong-smelling substance.)

ADVENTURES IN READING

1. *Insects—Their Secret World*, by Evelyn Cheesman, William Sloane Associates, 1953. A very interesting chapter called "Sense Organs of Insects."

2. Chapter 11 of Carlson and Johnson's *The Machinery of the Body* gives you much information on your own senses.

Chapter 17
Changes in behavior

A conditioned response. As a newborn infant you performed a variety of reflex acts — sucking movements when the bottle touched your lips, sneezing, coughing when your nose and throat were irritated. And of course, internal reflexes kept you alive — breathing, beating of your heart, and secretion of digestive juices. All these were inborn, and all babies perform these acts in just the same way. But soon there came a time when your mouth began its sucking movements as you heard your mother's voice, or footsteps, or when you saw her holding a bottle. A new stimulus coming through your ears or eyes was now calling forth an old response. Your mother was very proud of you; she felt you had learned something! She was right; you had learned something; you were showing a **conditioned response**. Sometimes this is called a **conditioned reflex**.

Ivan Pavlov. The conditioned response was studied first by a great Russian physiologist Ivan Pavlov (1849–1936) about fifty years ago. Pavlov did the following experiment with dogs. Each time he fed his experimental dogs he rang a bell. Saliva flowed into their mouths; eating always makes saliva flow. After doing this over and over again, one day Pavlov just rang the bell without giving any food to his dogs. The saliva came just as promptly. As much saliva flowed as though the dog had been fed. Pavlov measured it in a bottle attached to the salivary glands. A new stimulus, traveling along different neurons attached itself to the old response. The conditioned response was learned only after many repetitions. And it was unlearned quickly; that is, the sound of the bell without the presence of food in the mouth soon stopped being a stimulus for the secretion of saliva.

Pavlov, of course, repeated this experiment many times and varied it in all kinds of ways. Instead of ringing a bell he used various other stimuli. Could you think of some ways in which you could vary this experiment?

If you have ever taught a dog any tricks, you probably used food together with the sound of your voice as stimuli at first. After the response had been learned the food stimulus could be dropped. See Figure 17.1. All the more complex animals show conditioned responses. In all animals that have a brain a new stimulus can become attached to an inborn response. Pavlov called this a conditioned reflex, since it is built on a reflex. But since this kind of behavior is learned and is not inborn it seems better to call it conditioned behavior or a conditioned response.

Activity and success learning. Have you ever tried to eat with chopsticks as the Chinese do? At your first try, no matter how you held them, the food slipped through between the sticks. As a baby, you had as much trouble learning to eat with a spoon, let alone a fork. In the beginning, when you raised your hand the food dropped off. You tried again and again. It was only after many trials and failures going on

CHAPTER SEVENTEEN — CHANGES IN BEHAVIOR

17.1 What stimulus does the wild animal trainer use when he begins to train his animals? *United Press*

UNIT FIVE — WHY WE BEHAVE AS WE DO

for weeks, that you learned to get the food to your mouth without accident. You were learning by **trial and error,** or as we say, by **activity and success.**

Experiments with animals. Both before and since Pavlov's early experiments on the conditioned reflex, there has been much study of animal behavior. An understanding of animal behavior through experimentation is often a clue to human behavior.

Even fish are used for study. In one experiment an aquarium was set up with a glass partition in the middle. In the partition was a hole just large enough for a fish to pass through. The aquarium was placed so that one half was in the sun, the other half in the shade. A shade-loving fish was put into the sunny end. Seeing the shade at the further end, the fish swam back and forth along the glass, bumping into the glass. This was a reflex act, the shade being the stimulus. When this had been going on for a long time, the fish by accident struck the hole; it darted through and was rewarded by the shade and also by food which had been placed in the shaded half. When the fish had had a rest the experiment was performed over again. After many repetitions of the experiment the fish got through the hole with fewer and fewer wasted motions and therefore in a shorter time. The fish modified its behavior; it learned. Like you, it learned by "activity and success."

Chickens and rats have been placed in what is known as a maze — a box with a confusing network of paths, only one of which leads to food at the end. Figure 17.2 shows a very simple maze. Rats were put into a much more complicated maze day after day to see whether they would learn to travel the path to the food in a shorter time. The first day it took one rat 28 minutes to reach the food; it got there purely by accident, of course. But on the second day the rat seemed to have remembered a good deal of what it had done; it got through in 11 minutes. The third day it took 12 minutes. But after that the rat ran through the maze on successive days in 4, $4\frac{1}{2}$, 5, 5, $2\frac{1}{4}$, and 2 minutes. By the thirtieth day the rat ran through in less than one-half minute. Rats learn by activity and success. Have you ever tried to find your way out of a maze? See Figure 17.3.

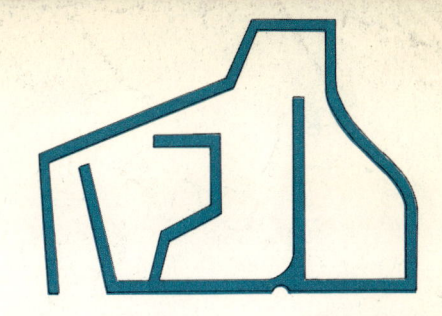

17.2 A very simple maze used by Professor E. L. Thorndike to see how fast chicks could learn. Chicks were put into the compartment at the lower end of this box. At first they fluttered about wildly and ran back and forth. But after many trials they learned to take the correct path almost without error.

17.3 In the Hampton Court Palace gardens in England a maze was constructed by planting a high hedge in an elaborate design. How rapidly can you trace the path to the center with your finger? That is easy because in the diagram you can see all the paths. In the garden this is not possible.

CHAPTER SEVENTEEN — CHANGES IN BEHAVIOR

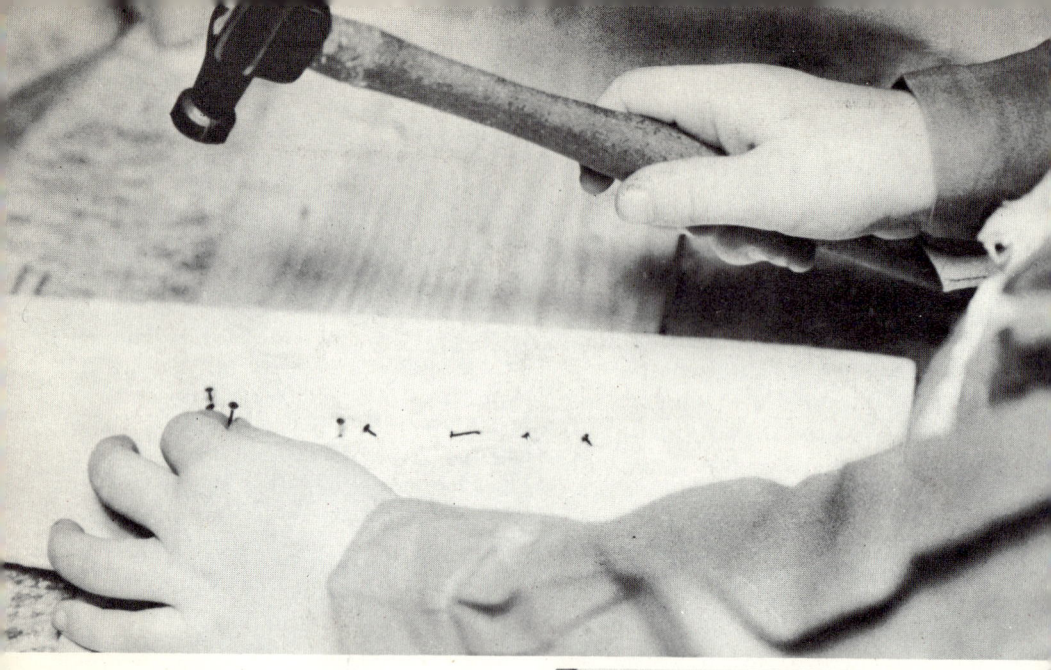

17.4 We learn by activity and success. This youngster probably hammered his fingers in the beginning, but with repetition such wasted motions become less frequent. Why is this not a conditioned response? *38th Annual Report, Supt. of Schools, New York City*

Activity and success learning continues. In the early months and years of your life you learned a great deal by activity and success. You learned to walk without supporting yourself. You learned how to use the muscles of your tongue and lips and throat to imitate the words you heard. You learned to dress yourself. It was hard work learning to put the correct foot into the correct shoe. You learned to brush your teeth. Then you went to school and you learned to write your name. Try now to write your name with your left hand (if you are right-handed) and see how long it takes and what strange letters you make. You learned to hammer nails into a board (Figure 17.4). You learned to skate and

17.5 Learning includes much that is not written in textbooks. Learning to skate and keep one's balance becomes automatic after much practice. What can we then call this kind of act? *H. Armstrong Roberts*

282 UNIT FIVE — WHY WE BEHAVE AS WE DO

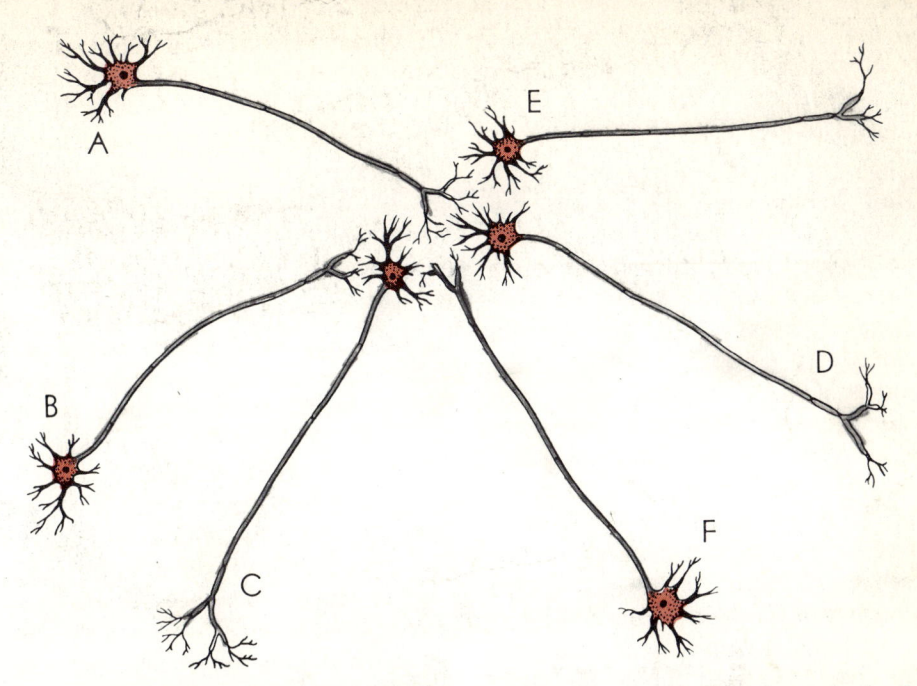

17.6 To which cells may cell **A** send impulses? From which cells may the dendrites of cell **C** receive impulses? Do you see why there can be such a large variety of responses?

to ride a bicycle (Figure 17.5). You were very busy, then, learning by activity and success. You have probably never been as busy since, but you are still learning in this same way, aren't you?

Habits. In activity and success learning there usually comes a time when you have learned completely or perfectly. Then you no longer hesitate or slip; and then you can carry on the activity without giving it your attention. You have made that activity into a **habit**. The act is performed so fast and so perfectly and has become so automatic that it may seem almost like a reflex to you. But, of course, it isn't really like a reflex at all; a reflex is inborn; it never has to be learned. The habit was learned only after many repetitions, but so well learned that it has become automatic.

Just what goes on in your nervous system when an act becomes habitual? No one knows. But look for a moment at Figure 17.6, a very much simplified diagram of just a few neurons in the gray matter of cerebrum or cerebellum. Even in this simplified diagram you can see different possible paths for impulses to travel. One cell may send impulses to several other neurons; it may, on the other hand, send impulses along only one route instead of many. Or the impulse that cell A sends out may be interfered with by impulses coming in from B and F. Impulses sent out by cell A always or nearly always take the same route, it is thought. Why does the impulse take the same path more easily the second time? Is there a change in the synapse? Is there less interference from surrounding neurons? Is there a change where the end brush connects with a muscle fiber? Is it all these things together, or is it something else? There is no explana-

CHAPTER SEVENTEEN — CHANGES IN BEHAVIOR

tion that we can give so far. This is one of the many puzzles that attract young men and women to take up biology as a lifework.

How habits help us. Think how quickly and how legibly you can now write. You have learned to do it with accuracy and speed because it has become habitual. But the greatest advantage that you gain when writing becomes a habit is that your mind is no longer occupied with how to move your fingers. Your mind is freed; you can be thinking of other things — what to write and how to express yourself. That is the great advantage of all habits. Just think what a dull life you would have to lead if your time were still occupied with struggling to do the dozens of things that have become habitual to you.

Breaking habits. You may have some bad habits, too — habits that are of no help to you and that may even interfere with your everyday living or be a nuisance to others. Would you like to break a bad habit? Forming a habit is sometimes hard; breaking a habit is often much harder. But it can be done!

How can you go about breaking a habit? How, for example, can you break the habit of cigarette smoking, if you smoke? Just making up your mind to get rid of the habit won't help much because if you smoke you probably practice the habit while you are doing or thinking of something else. Here are the recommendations of experts.

(1) Most important of all: substitute another habit for smoking. Instead of a cigarette, put a piece of hard candy or chewing gum in your mouth, preferably something that will last.

(2) Mean seriously to stop smoking. You must see good reasons for doing so.
(3) Tell your friends about your decision. Pride will help you stick to your decision.
(4) Let no exceptions occur. "I'll just smoke one" means you have failed.

Try similar rules to break some little habit. They work! But always substitute a new habit for the old.

Breaking old habits and forming new ones is worth while for its own sake. Keeping one's ability to change behavior is important. Many an automobile driver has been happy to discover that he could quickly turn from the standard gearshift to another type of drive. The people who never give up habits find, after a while, that they are unable to change, no matter how hard they try.

Thinking and reasoning. A very important part of your behavior has not yet been described. Thinking plays a large part in your life, and many of your acts involve reasoning. Experiments with animals have shown that, while they can learn, most of them apparently do little or no thinking and reasoning. The chief exceptions to this statement are the chimpanzee, the gorilla, and the orangutan. They do think and reason in a simple way. And perhaps the easiest way to show what is meant by simple reasoning is to describe an interesting experiment that was performed by Dr. Wolfgang Köhler. Dr. Köhler placed a particularly intelligent chimpanzee in a cage together with a long and a short bamboo rod. The rods were of different thicknesses, too, so that one could be fitted into the other. A banana was laid outside so far away that it could not be reached with either rod. The chimp began reaching for the banana with the longer stick. After several attempts he gave up. Later while playing with the two rods in the back of the cage he accidentally fitted the smaller into the larger. Then he jumped up, went to the front of the cage and reached for the fruit with the jointed stick he had just made. While doing this the sticks fell apart, so he again fitted one within the other. This time he reached with the jointed stick and pulled in the banana. Having made a long stick (by accident, it is true), he recognized the use to which it could be put. This shows simple thinking and reasoning. To you this kind of behavior is altogether natural, is it not? See Figure 17.7.

17.7 It would be difficult to say which part of this construction process was done through reasoning and which part was done by activity and success. *38th Annual Report, Supt. of Schools, New York City*

The value of experiments. In explaining animal behavior, we are often led into error unless we rely on experimental evidence. The bush turkey of Australia lays its eggs in a heap of decaying plant material. When the chick hatches at the bottom of this pile it wriggles up and out of the heap. How intelligent, you say! Then this experiment was performed. The young turkey after wriggling up was caught and placed again at the bottom of the pile. What happened? Nothing at all. This time it did not push its way out. The bird would have smothered had it not been rescued. We know, therefore, that it never used its cerebral cortex at all. It was hatched with an inborn reflex, a pattern of behavior for wriggling upward as it leaves its shell. But there is no pattern, no inborn reflex, for doing this a second time. You can see how easily we can be misled without experimental evidence.

Experience and reasoning. Much of what you do and see and hear is stored up in the neurons of your cerebral cortex. How, we don't know. The chimp in Dr. Köhler's experiment stored up experiences in his neurons, at least for a short time. He remembered long enough for him to put his jointed stick together a second time and to put it to practical use. Many experiments with chimps show their ability to remember and to reason. See Figure 17.8. Dr. Robert Yerkes of Yale University is a biologist famous for his studies of behavior in apes. In one of his interesting experiments chimps were taught to select their own food at "chimpomats" and pay different prices for different foods. They were given thin disks of different sizes and colors to use as coins. The chimps soon learned to distinguish between the different "coins," and they hoarded the more valuable ones whenever "coins" were distributed. Even after the chimps had been well fed and while no longer in sight of the chimpomat, they fought for the most valuable "coins"!

17.8 This chimpanzee, named Viki, discovered all by herself how to get a roll of candy out of the long wire tunnel by using a long stick. *Keith J. Hayes*

These apes stored up experiences, they remembered, and reasoned. Furthermore, they showed emotional behavior, anger and greed, or a strong desire for coins.

You behave in this way constantly, don't you? It is so large a part of your behavior that it does not seem remarkable to you. But it is remarkable that you can store in your neurons memories of experiences you had years ago and that, when the proper occasion comes, you can draw on these memories and put them together to help you solve your problems.

How we get experiences. Think of all you have done and seen in your life; you have stored up an incredible number of experiences in your memory. Add to that all you have learned about things you can't directly experience yourself, merely from listening to others! Think how speech helps us learn. Think what experiences you obtained from reading what others have written; radio and television add to our experiences. You can learn in minutes and hours what would have taken years or a lifetime of experience to learn. We humans certainly have a tremendous head start over other animals!

Rules for learning. John Hope was the best player on his college football team. John's college mates, moved by affection and gratitude, presented him at the end of the season with a large overstuffed armchair. Shortly, John's grades were seen to be going down, lower and lower. His friends guessed what was wrong, came to his rescue, and removed the chair.

A **psychologist** (a scientist who makes a study of human behavior) tells this story in giving advice to his students on how to study. It illustrates one impor-

286 UNIT FIVE — WHY WE BEHAVE AS WE DO

tant point: don't loll in an easy chair when you want to study, but sit straight up at a desk with your study materials around you. Then apply these rules for learning which seem to be of help to most people.

(1) Activity is necessary for learning. This applies not only to muscular activity as when you learn to skate. It is just as true of learning to listen to music. Something in you must be **active** if learning of any kind is to take place. Some of you may have discovered that if you make sketches when you go sightseeing, you will learn and remember much more of what you see.

(2) For the reason just given, many people take notes on what they read when learning from a book. Of course, if you merely copy from the book your fingers may be active but that is not the kind of activity that will help you. Your neurons must be active putting the thoughts of the author into your own words.

(3) Repetition or practice is most important. You have always known that. But experiments performed on college students show that repeating over and over again for a long time is less helpful than having many shorter periods of repetition. The best length of the interval varies; perhaps you have discovered what length is best for you. Steady repetition may bring fatigue, and with fatigue come bad habits.

(4) It is much easier for you to learn facts, or figures, or words that make sense. Have you ever tried to learn nonsense syllables? It takes you much longer to learn them. And if words make sense, you remember them much longer. Controlled experiments have proved this many times. For this reason, too, you can learn more easily if you are interested when you start. Your teachers try to catch your interest when they begin each lesson. They call it motivation. If you start with the wrong mind-set, your time is largely wasted.

(5) If you are looking forward to a reward at the end, you will learn faster. The young child in school is given a gold star or a high mark. But as you grow up you begin to look for other rewards such as praise and the respect of those who follow your work and the satisfaction you get when you know you have done a job well.

(6) In learning something by heart, is it better to try to learn the thing as a whole or learn it in small parts? If the whole is not so long that it brings fatigue, it is better to learn the whole. The whole makes more sense to you than little parts. But the answer depends on what you are learning and what you mean by long and short.

(7) The same rule applies in studying from a textbook. In general, reading the whole chapter (if not too long) or a whole section, or at least a whole paragraph through quickly without stopping is the best way to *begin*. Then, of course, you must go back and read each sentence carefully.

(8) Learning is helped by your reciting or using what you have learned. Reciting needs your attention and thus makes you more active. Perhaps instead of reciting, you could discuss with someone else what you learned. If no one will listen, tell it to yourself. Do it immediately after learning, and do it again after a few hours. Reciting after study helps in that it shows you what you know and what you don't know. Try it for yourself.

Memory and memorizing. What is memory? Psychologists don't really know but they do know that memorizing consists of three parts: **learning;**

retaining (keeping); and **recalling,** commonly called remembering. In short-answer tests, which questions are easier, those in which you must recognize the correct answer out of three or four choices, or those which have a blank space and you must recall and fill in? The former, of course, are easier. If you have not learned and retained perfectly, you may still be able to recognize; but you can't recall what you don't know. But in either case your neurons must be active for you to remember. In learning, too — the first step in memorizing — there must be activity, as you know.

In retaining, there is no activity. In general, you forget a lot of what you learn within the first twenty minutes, and you forget more during the rest of the day. But what you manage to retain for a day seems, usually, to stay with you for a little while at least or, if you are fortunate, for a very long time. Now what can you do to retain better? Probably not much. Some people's neurons retain well; some people retain less well. But your physical condition does seem to have something to do with retaining what you learn. Getting enough sleep and keeping generally fit will help you retain. Then is there really no way of improving one's memory? Indeed there is. While you can improve your ability to retain to only a slight degree by keeping yourself fit, you can all do much about improving your *learning*, the first step. Apply the rules given above and learn better. Then you can also find tricks for yourself which will help you recall or recognize.

What have you learned? Your behavior has changed since you were born. You came into the world with certain reflexes, and ever since the early months of your life, you have been adding other forms of behavior to your reflex behavior. First, there were many conditioned, or learned, responses built on some simple reflex. Then came much activity and success (trial and error) learning which resulted in acquiring many skills. As the activity and success learning became automatic and more perfect you were acquiring habits; many of these, like feeding yourself, writing, and performing the other routines of life are very useful since they free your mind. In the meantime, more and more of your behavior was involving thought and reasoning. Can you give an example of each kind of behavior? And are you sure you know and practice the rules for learning?

USEFUL WORDS IN BIOLOGY

conditioned response
activity and success
trial and error

habit
experience
psychology

TEST YOURSELF

1. (a) Describe and explain the results of Pavlov's conditioned response experiments on dogs. (b) Give two examples of conditioned response behavior in babies.
2. Give examples of activity and success (or trial and error) learning in (a) very young babies; (b) fish, rats, and chicks; (c) older children.
3. Define a habit and state how it differs from a reflex and how it resembles it.
4. State three ways in which habits are helpful to us.
5. Give rules for breaking a habit.

6. Describe an experiment which showed simple reasoning in an ape.
7. Explain, by using an illustration, how experience is a help to us in reasoning.
8. Give eight rules for learning that are recommended by some psychologists.
9. (a) What are three main steps in the memorizing process? (b) To what extent and by what means can you expect to improve in each of these three steps?

of inborn behavior. What examples, if any, of conditioned behavior and activity and success learning does the baby mammal show? Perhaps you can illustrate the changes by a series of snapshots. Why not compare your observations with the statements made by doctors? One of these is *The Pocket Book of Baby and Child Care*.

4. Acquire a new habit. Try writing with the hand you do not normally use. How long does it take before you show improvement?

DO IT YOURSELF

1. A conditioned response in an animal. If you have a dog, cat, parakeet, or any other pet, or if you have white rats in the laboratory, you must have observed an example of a conditioned response. Describe it. If you have not seen one, try to establish a conditioned response in an animal.

2. Activity and success learning. Construct a simple maze and try an experiment in activity and success learning, using some laboratory animal. You must plan carefully and keep accurate notes.

3. Observing a young baby or other young mammal. Watch a young baby's behavior closely. Perhaps you have puppies or kittens whose behavior you can study. List examples

ADVENTURES IN READING

1. "The Yerkes Laboratories" by George W. Gray, *Scientific American*, February 1955. Tells about Viki, a chimpanzee who was adopted by workers in the laboratory and lived with the family.
2. *Animal IQ: The Human Side of Animals* by Vance Packard, Dial Press, 1950. Has surprises in store for you.
3. *How To Make and Break Habits* by James L. Mursell, Lippincott, 1953. Contains many interesting case histories of problems like your own.
4. "What Is Memory?" by Ralph W. Gerard, *Scientific American*, September 1953. Difficult but interesting.

Chapter 18

Growing up

You as a person. In whatever you do, it is not only your brain or your muscles or your glands that work; it is every bit of you. You, as an organism, operate as the single unit you are. The cinder in your eye produces blinking and tears. It also produces emotions, such as irritation that this annoying accident should have happened to you or worry that you will not be able to play in a ball game. Muscles other than those around your eye get tighter; your digestive processes may slow up temporarily; your heart may beat a little faster for a time. The whole of you is involved.

So far, you have learned about various parts of your behavior — each separately: reflexes, conditioned responses, activity and success learning, habits, and reasoning. But, of course, all these parts of your behavior go on together in the one person that is you. You have learned, too, a little about the structure of the nervous system; you can connect your behavior with the nervous system, in a simple way. In all this you have learned very little about the emotions, which accompany all behavior and often determine it. Figure 18.1.

18.1 With twenty-five seconds left in the game, these cheerleaders wait for a member of their team to shoot for the tie-breaking point. What emotions do they evidently feel? Look at their faces and their hands. *United Press*

Your emotions. At various times you have experienced love and hate; you have been happy, sad, angry, hopeful, afraid, astonished, amused, contented. This list could go on almost indefinitely. You have a large variety of emotions. And you have felt all these emotions in various degrees. You may be lukewarm about a school team or hope passionately that it will win an important game; you may be confident of your success in an examination or approach it with dread in your heart. This very expression "with dread in your heart" suggests something important about emotions. They influence bodily activity. That is why, no doubt, we have so many expressions in our language that relate emotions to

UNIT FIVE — WHY WE BEHAVE AS WE DO

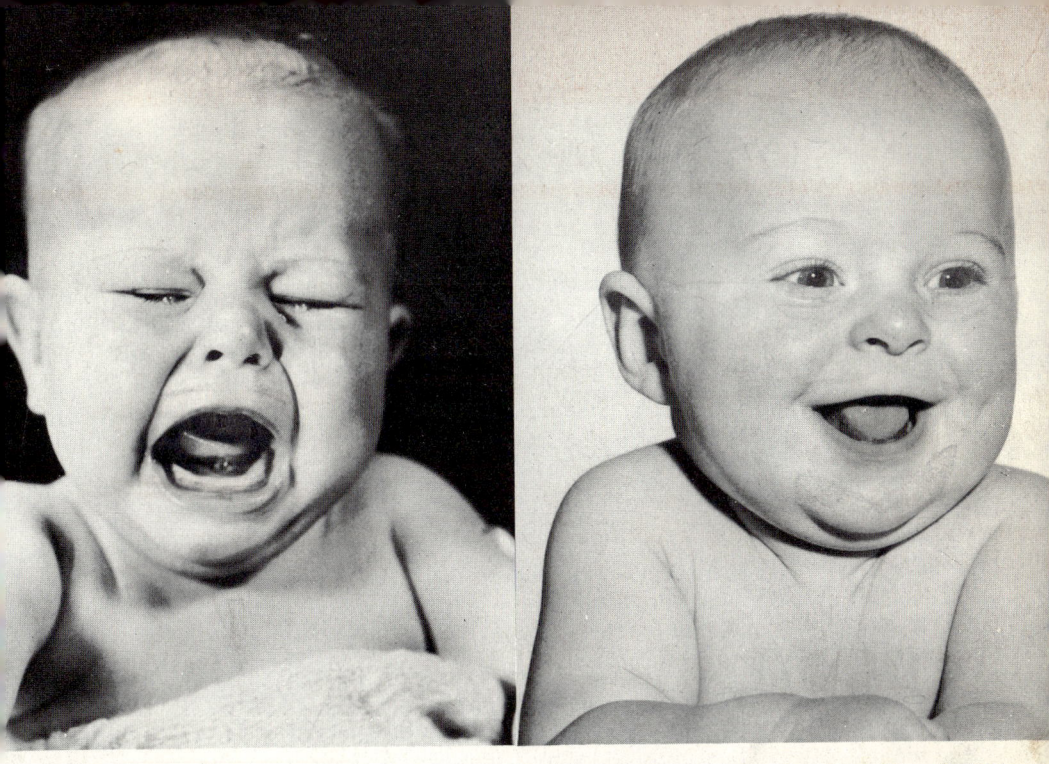

18.2 Angry, happy, strong emotions. We do not expect a baby to control its emotions. We do expect this of adults. *Don Knight (right) and H. Armstrong Roberts (left)*

the organs of the body: such as, "heavy heart"; "light heart"; "stomach tied up in knots"; "butterflies in the stomach"; "my heart was in my throat" or "in my boots"; "my blood ran cold."

The emotions can act on the organs of the body, and the organs can influence the emotions. In any case there is a two-way connection between the internal organs and the central nervous system. The connection is the autonomic nervous system, parts of which lie in the internal organs and parts of which are connected to the central nervous system. You will certainly agree that your emotions affect your behavior in very important ways.

Emotional growth. Some emotional responses are inborn. You have seen a newly born baby get angry when the movements of its arms and legs were restrained. Its face gets beet-red and it bawls with an astonishing amount of noise for so small an organism. The same baby will coo and smile and show every evidence of contentment when cuddled, Figure 18.2. And you may have seen an expression of fear in the baby at a sudden loud noise. When you were a baby, these three emotions were probably the only ones you had. The number of your emotions has grown enormously with the years; and what is more, there has been just as large an increase in the number of stimuli that call forth each emotion.

But there has been emotional growth in still another way. When you were angry as a very young child you may have thrown yourself on the floor and howled and flung your arms and legs about. When you were older and in

CHAPTER EIGHTEEN — GROWING UP

291

school, you had learned to control your anger. Even when you were very angry indeed, you waited for a proper time and place to express this anger. This is one very important form of emotional growth: learning to control the expression of one's emotions. A grown man or woman who has arrived at full emotional growth doesn't lose his temper. If you lose your temper, your emotion is controlling you. And so with other emotions, such as fear. If you are ruled by fear when alone in dense woods at night, you become panic-stricken, perhaps hysterical. Yet many a hunter in this situation has proved himself able to control the emotion and able to wait out the night with some calm despite his fears. His emotional growth throughout the years has made this possible.

Emotional maturity. There is, however, another kind of emotional growth that is even more important to our development than learning to control our emotions. This is an actual change in the emotions themselves. Perhaps the following will help to make this clear. If in your high school you have long lines waiting to be served in the cafeteria, you probably have seen an example of young people who are mature emotionally and those who are not. Every pupil is hungry; each wants his food right away. The normal young person has become accustomed to the idea that everyone else has the same feelings he has. He, therefore, takes his place in line, even though he may be far back, and cheerfully waits his turn. It is true he may be annoyed that he was delayed and didn't get to the cafeteria earlier. But he shows his emotional growth in two ways. He is able to master his annoyance. And furthermore his emotion is mild disappointment, not a towering rage. He has learned to see things in proper proportion to other things.

On the other hand there is the "chiseler" who tries to sneak into the line; he is an emotional infant. His keen desire for food immediately is so strong that he cannot stop himself from doing something that he knows will produce bitter criticism from his schoolmates. He has not only failed to master his emotions, but he has also failed to grow up emotionally. He still has the emotions of a young child; the relative strength of his emotions did not change as he grew older and as he had more experience in living with other people.

You must not get the idea that acquiring emotional maturity means that emotions decrease in intensity or in strength. Young children often love someone passionately for a short while and then lose the feeling altogether. Emotionally mature persons are less likely to have such sudden passions but their feelings of love are long-lasting and far deeper; they are just as strong. Thus there can be a lifelong friendship or a lifelong marriage between emotionally mature people, but it is most unlikely that this can happen when people are emotionally immature.

Success in life. Schoolwork is your job; certainly it is *one* of your jobs. What factors produce success or failure in jobs? Many studies have shown that success or failure is determined far less by mental ability ("brains") or by skills than it is by emotional factors. Scientists have asked employers the important question, "Why do you fire people?" The answer is almost always the same. Most people lose their jobs because they cannot get along with their bosses or with other people working in the office or factory.

18.3 This boy has asked his teacher to introduce him to a girl he wants to dance with. Explain how such an experience can contribute to his emotional growth. *Three Lions*

They cannot obey simple regulations such as coming in on time or not smoking where smoking is forbidden. Reliability, adaptability, and understanding and consideration of others are needed for holding a job. People are rarely fired because they are unable to do the work. Success on the job, it would seem, is largely a result of emotional maturity.

Emotional growth shows itself in many social situations. With experience you learn to meet people with confidence and calm. Shyness, arrogance, or aggressiveness show themselves when you are not yet emotionally mature. What can you do about it? Both your family and your school can deliberately provide you with new social experiences to help you grow emotionally in the ways mentioned above. And you can find such social experiences for yourself. See Figure 18.3.

Much the same is true of success in schoolwork. Success is possible for almost anyone who has the emotional maturity to meet the comparatively simple requirements. Do you do your assignments on time, and are they complete? Do you obey school regulations cheerfully? Can you work with others, both teachers and fellow students? If so, you are behaving like an emotionally mature person. If not, you would do well to try to grow up.

CHAPTER EIGHTEEN — GROWING UP

18.4 At work or play find opportunities to talk with others of your own age about your "problems." A little conversation can often be of much help. *H. Armstrong Roberts*

Healthy and unhealthy emotions. If you are so constantly angry or so constantly afraid that you cannot live happily and effectively, these emotions are clearly unhealthy. Some anger and some fear, on the other hand, are normal. You would be unusual indeed if you were not sometimes angry and sometimes afraid. The healthy emotions are those that you have in the right places and at the right times.

If you are very angry when you see a small child being severely beaten by an adult, you are having a healthy emotional reaction. According to our moral code such action is wrong, and anger is a healthy reaction. If you are happy when you see boys and girls showing good sportsmanship at an important high school basketball game, you are again having a healthy emotional reaction.

Common worries of young people. Many young people worry unnecessarily. Worry is often an unhealthy emotion. Often they are sensitive about variations in physical structure, about being too short or too tall, too stout or too thin. They fail to realize that they are quite "normal" even though they are not "average." The normal has so wide a range that they, too, are normal, and they would be no better off if they were average.

It is quite common also for young people to worry unnecessarily about daydreaming. All of us daydream, especially when we are young. There are times when it is particularly satisfying to think of ourselves as most handsome, bright, charming, rich, and successful. We often do so after we have failed in some job or received a rebuff. Daydreaming becomes undesirable when it interferes with the activities necessary to successful living.

You may be relieved of some of your worries by the common "bull session," in which boys or girls exchange confidences. This often serves a useful purpose in convincing you that your "difficulties" are normal and usual. You can often learn, also, how other people have overcome these difficulties. See Figure 18.4.

Mental health. The normal activities of a boy or girl include work that must be done (schoolwork, household duties), physical play (usually out of doors), a hobby, meeting with friends, engaging in family life at home, occasional parties or outings, and also some "blues" or periods of boredom and mild unhappiness. Such a young person is clearly a happy person generally, with a feeling of increasing satisfaction in growing up. Such a person is able to accept the occasional defeats that everyone experiences without suffering from a continued feeling of depression. Together with this ability there goes a growing feeling of independence of thought and action, combined with a readiness to accept increasing responsibility.

A few simple rules for achieving mental health will be useful to you.

1. Several times each week play out of doors at some game that you like and that brings you together with boys or girls of your own age.

2. Try out hobbies or learn about them until you can choose one of your own from which you get satisfaction. If possible, find a hobby that includes other persons, both boys and girls.

3. Develop friendships with boys and girls. Your joy in friendship will be great if you are thoughtful and generous and understanding of your friends.

4. Do your schoolwork to the best of your ability; work hard at it so that you can get the satisfaction of knowing that you are doing your best in your most important job.

5. Try yourself out in a new field or in new tasks of increasing difficulty. You may fail from time to time but with each success you will have a new sense of power, of independence, and of maturity. This will help you achieve mental health.

Importance of mental health. Mental health is just as important to you as physical health. **Psychiatrists** (sy-kye′a-trists), experts on mental illness, and, in fact, all physicians now believe that much physical ill health is related to emotional difficulties. Worry and fear, especially in later life, may not only interfere with the proper functioning of the organs of the body but may even be responsible for physical changes in the body.

Our greatly speeded-up life puts a great strain on the nervous system — in fact, on all the organs. As a result the number of cases of nervous disorders is increasing. They must be treated just as physical disorders are. Fortunately, sensible people no longer have the foolish attitude that mental

CHAPTER EIGHTEEN — GROWING UP

illness is something to be ashamed of. No one is ashamed of having heart disease or appendicitis; no informed person is ashamed of having a mental illness. Mental illness which is the result of emotional disturbance is called a **neurosis** (new-row′sis). Severe mental illness, **psychosis** (sy-ko′sis), is much less common. But many people formerly thought these illnesses were hereditary. When you study heredity, you will understand that heredity is so complex that such statements cannot be accurate.

What have you learned? When you learn about different forms of behavior, one after the other, you tend to get a very wrong impression of yourself. Actually you are a very complex being, a single unit, in whom these forms of behavior occur all at the same time, all shading into each other and overlapping. And closely associated with all the other forms of behavior are your emotions, those difficult-to-define feelings that we all know so well — anger, joy, love, and so on. In fact, recent experiments performed at Cornell University on goats and sheep in a maze seem to show that emotions can also interfere with activity and success learning.

As you grow up, emotions increase very much in number; they are aroused by a much wider variety of stimuli; the normal person learns to keep emotional expression under control (this does not mean suppression of emotions); and the quality of emotions changes so that they are no longer the emotions of an infant, but those of a mature person. Your success in school, on your job, in fact, your success in life, depends on whether or not you reach emotional maturity in these various ways.

All you have learned in this chapter should help you achieve mental health; it is at least as important to you as physical health. In fact, the two are very closely tied up with one another. Do you know and practice the rules for achieving mental health? Look at the rules again.

USEFUL WORDS IN BIOLOGY

emotion   psychiatrist   psychosis
maturity   neurosis

TEST YOURSELF

1. (a) Name five or six common emotions. (b) Give an example of how an emotion influences bodily activity.
2. Emotional growth is an important part of our development. (a) What seem to be the only emotional responses of a very young baby? (b) Explain how you show emotional growth in a way other than in the greater variety of your emotions.
3. Copy into your notes under *emotional maturity* only those of the following statements which are correct; omit the others: In growing up, or becoming emotionally mature, one not only keeps one's emotions under control but one does not "get emotional" over unimportant things. The person who "chisels" does so because he is an emotional infant. As one grows up all the emotions decrease in intensity.
4. What, in general, seems to be the most important factor in your success on your job?
5. What are some of the common worries of young people and what can you do about your worries?
6. State four or five simple rules to follow to achieve mental health.

DO IT YOURSELF

1. Using yourself as the experimental animal. Think back to the last time things went wrong with you. State what happened and state honestly whether you used any of the following devices for getting what you wanted: (a) Did you find an outlet such as hurting or abusing a younger child or animal? (b) Did you make excuses for yourself by saying someone else was to blame? (c) Did you try to fool yourself by saying you did not really want to win the game or John's friendship because —? (d) Did you close your ears to the person who scolded you? (e) Did you feel sorry for yourself? (f) What *did* you do?

2. Observing others. Describe an incident in which you saw someone react in each of the ways listed above.

ADVENTURES IN READING

1. *How to Be Happy Though Young* by George Lawton, Vanguard, 1949. Discusses real problems of real young people. You will find that others have the same worries and troubles as you and that often, when you understand the causes, the worries disappear.

2. *Life Adjustment Booklets* published by Science Research Associates, Inc., 57 W. Grand Ave., Chicago 10, Illinois, can be bought at a nominal price. They have titles such as these: *Getting Along with Others, Growing Up Socially, How to Get the Job, What Employers Want, Your Personality and Your Job, How to Solve Your Problems, Understanding Yourself*. Send for a list of titles.

3. *The Psychology of Development and Personal Adjustment* by John E. Anderson, Holt, 1949.

CHAPTER EIGHTEEN — GROWING UP

Unit Six

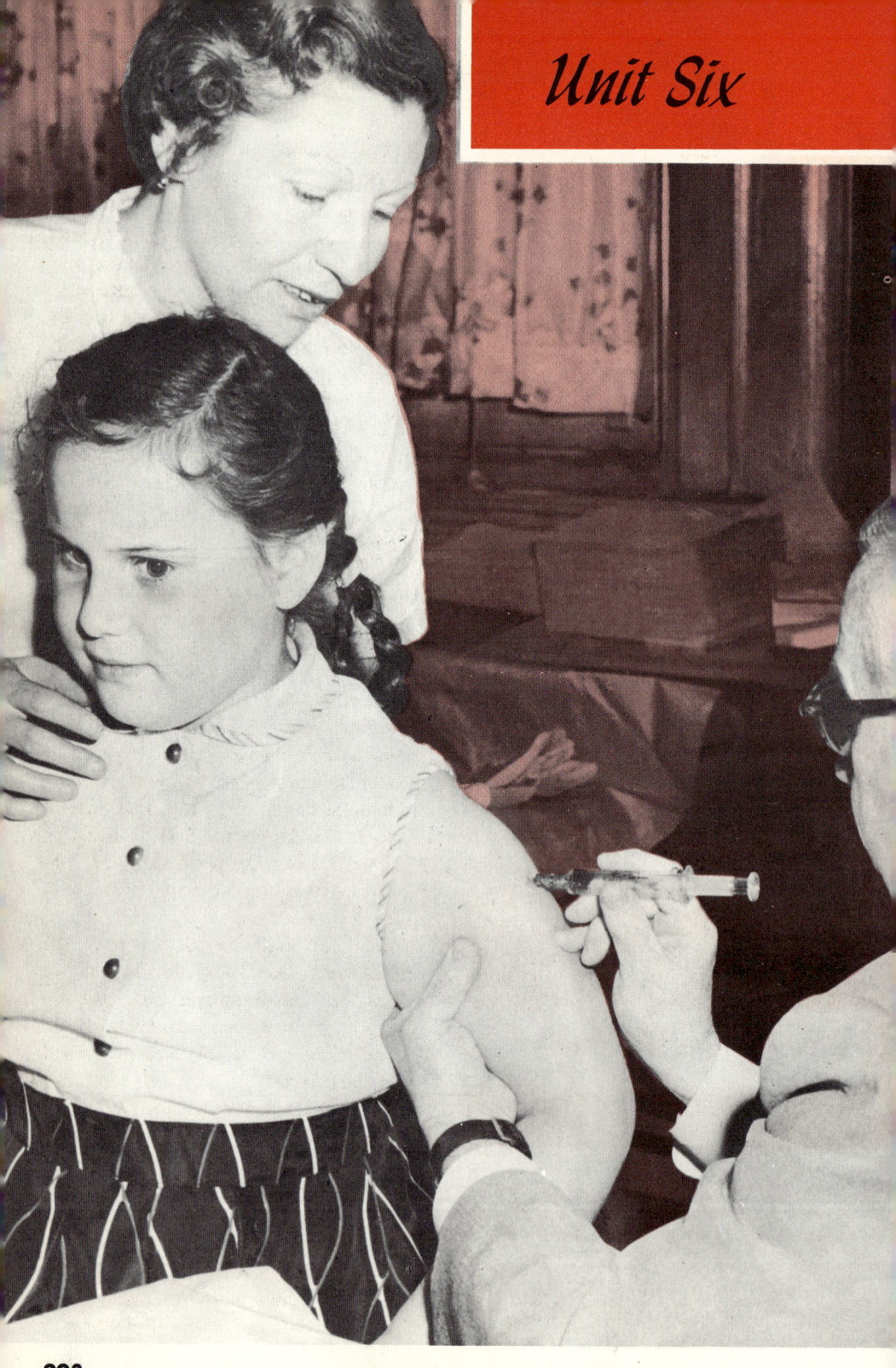

Bacteria and health

CHAPTER 19
Bacteria and disease

CHAPTER 20
Body defenses against disease

CHAPTER 21
Some recent discoveries

CHAPTER 22
Stopping the spread of disease

CHAPTER 23
Building health

In the spring of 1955 the results of experiments on the use of a vaccine against polio were announced. The development of the vaccine by Dr. Jonas Salk and the experiment that followed were outstanding examples of the methods used by scientists.

Hopes and fears were not allowed to enter into this experiment. Facts were wanted, favorable or unfavorable, to answer the question, "Does the Salk vaccine protect children from the polio virus?" The investigators used controls. Many thousands of children took part in the experiment. Even the parents of the children did not know whether the "shot" given was vaccine or a neutral salt solution. Only the doctors in charge of the official records knew. By spreading the experiment across the country the investigators made sure that no local condition might change the result. They checked every possibility of error. And this experiment could be repeated and thus double-checked if any responsible group of scientists thought it necessary. And when the investigators reported they told exactly what they found: that the Salk vaccine was effective in preventing polio for about 70–80 per cent of the children to whom it was given.

Note, too, that the discovery of the vaccine itself was the work not only of Dr. Salk and the many men and women in his laboratory; it was also the work of hundreds of scientists who prepared the ground for this last step.

Testing the Salk vaccine was the largest experiment on human beings ever performed. But in this unit you will read of many other experiments and exciting discoveries in our efforts to prevent and cure disease. These are fascinating tales of flashes of insight, patient plodding, and at last success. Millions of us owe our lives and our good health to these discoveries.

Chapter 19

Bacteria and disease

Diseases. You "catch" a cold. You "catch" measles. Some diseases you catch; they are the **infectious** diseases caused by some living organism. You pick up the living organism directly or indirectly from other people or even from other animals.

At times your body or some part of it doesn't work properly — you have a disease — but it's not one you caught from anyone else. You may have a deficiency disease like rickets or scurvy. You may have an organic disease like having something wrong with your kidneys or heart or some other organ. But let's find out more about the infectious diseases. The more we know about them the easier it will be for us to avoid getting them.

Parasite and host. Do you remember that **parasites** are those organisms that make their home in or on some other living thing, getting their food that way? We call this type of food-getting **parasitism**. It is a very common method. Many thousands of different kinds of parasites live in plants and in animals.

You may be the "host" to a number of parasites! Many kinds of worms can live as parasites in people; insects like lice and fleas are external parasites. Protozoa, too, can live in our bodies; it is a protozoan that gives us malaria. Molds give us athlete's foot and ringworm; but by far the most common parasites to which we play host are the bacteria and viruses.

"Microorganisms that cause disease" is very long to say or write. Instead of it let's use the word **germ** for organisms that cause disease. Sometimes, in other books, germ is used to mean any microorganism.

What are bacteria? Bacteria (singular, **bacterium**) are very small single-celled plants. They have a firm cell wall of cellulose and mostly for this reason they are classified as plants. Bacteria are related to the molds and yeasts in that they, too, lack chlorophyll. Bacteria have no nucleus but they do have chromatin granules scattered through the cytoplasm. Figure 19.1 shows bacteria magnified about 3000 times. Here you can see clearly the three common shapes: the rod-shaped **bacillus** (ba-sill'us); the spherical **coccus** (cock'us); and the twisted **spirillum**.

As for their activities, bacteria can do just about what the cells of your body can do: they secrete enzymes, digest food, absorb what they digest, change food to protoplasm, carry on oxidation and release energy, and reproduce. They do this by dividing in two. A very few carry on locomotion in a liquid by means of long hairlike projections (**flagella**) as shown in Figure 19.2. Now look carefully at Figure 19.3. When certain kinds of bacteria settle on a piece of meat, they send out enzymes into the meat and absorb the digested foods. The figure shows that this bacterium grows and reproduces. Figure B shows that it has reproduced and has consumed a part of the meat.

Bacteria of many kinds. Of the many kinds of bacteria only a relatively

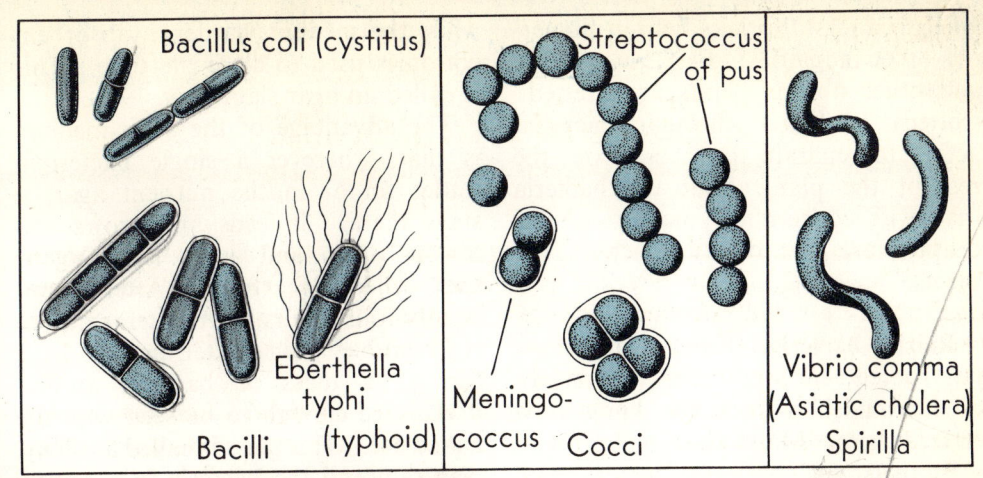

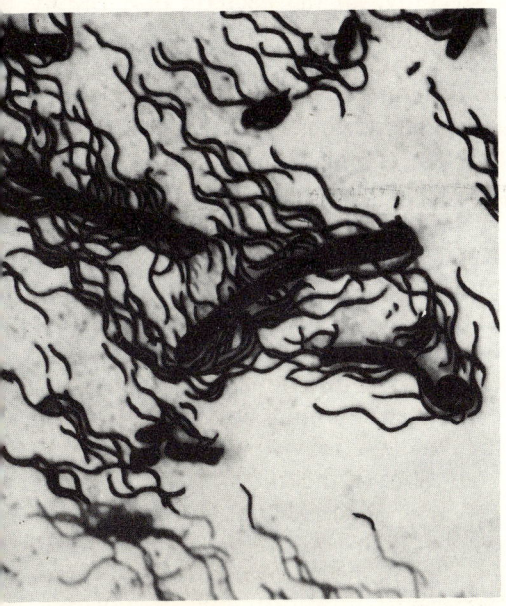

Bacillus coli (cystitus)

Streptococcus of pus

Eberthella typhi (typhoid)

Meningococcus

Vibrio comma (Asiatic cholera)

Bacilli | Cocci | Spirilla

19.1 This shows several bacilli, cocci (cock'-sye) and spirilla. What shape is the germ found in pus? the cholera germ? Note how some bacteria hang together in chains or small groups.

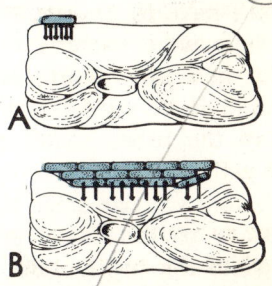

19.2 Typhoid bacteria. Only a few bacilli are shown. The wavy lines are flagella. *General Biological Supply*

19.3 A illustrates what may happen when a bacterium settles on a piece of meat. Arrows indicate that something is leaving and something is entering the bacterium. Can you explain what? Drawing B represents the same piece of meat some time later. What has happened to the bacterium and to the meat? What would be the last chapter of this story?

few kinds cause disease in us and other animals. Many kinds live on dead animal and plant parts, or the products of plants and animals, causing changes in the substances on which they feed. These are saprophytes, and they are helpful or harmful to us according to what they happen to be living on and the changes which they cause. If they are living on food or building materials we want, of course they are harmful. If they are decaying sewage or plant and animal parts in the soil, they are helpful. Some kinds cause changes in foods that suit our taste. Milk changes to cheese through the action of bacteria or molds. And when meat is allowed to "hang" bacteria make it more tender and bring out the taste we like. Other kinds of bacteria change alcohol to

CHAPTER NINETEEN — BACTERIA AND DISEASE

vinegar, and still others help in numerous other industries. Flax, jute, hemp, and other fibrous plants are "retted" (rotted) in water through bacterial action to separate the fibers from the rest of the plant. But the bacteria that will concern us mostly in this chapter are the disease bacteria, or germs.

Raising bacteria. Raising, or culturing, bacteria for study is easy; you can do it yourself if once you know how to feed them. Many kinds will grow in a broth (soup) containing water, some peptones, some beef extract, and salt. This is called a *culture medium.* Put a little in a test tube and keep it warm (about 80° F). But where will you find the bacteria to grow in this medium? You won't have to go out to look for them; there were bacteria in the test tube and there are bacteria in the air, riding on invisible particles of dust and settling in the tube. After a day or two you will see how your broth has changed; and you can smell the change too! Decay bacteria have grown and multiplied in the broth. But unfortunately, you can't see them; even a school microscope does not magnify them enough.

A solid culture medium. A solid culture medium is often more satisfactory than broth. You can mix the broth with gelatin, which, as you know, hardens when it cools. Instead of gelatin we usually use agar-agar. The mixture is then often called **nutrient agar.** While the nutrient agar is still hot and liquid it can be poured into flat glass dishes, Petri dishes. They give a large surface for the growth of bacteria and can be covered to exclude other bacteria. The hot nutrient agar may also be poured into a test tube which is kept in a slanting position while the medium hardens; absorbent cotton is used to close the tube. This is called an agar slant (Fig. 19.4).

The advantage of the solid medium is that, wherever a single bacterium settles on or in the nutrient agar, it stays there. It feeds and grows and divides again and again right in the spot where it settled. After about twenty-four hours, if the temperature is favorable, each bacterium will have formed a mass of bacteria around itself large enough to be seen with the naked eye. This mass is called a **colony.** Naturally, all the bacteria in a colony are of the same type; they all grew from a single bacterium. Figure 19.5 is a picture of a number of colonies of bacteria growing on agar.

Most colonies are round. Some are white, but others have a distinct color such as yellow or red. Some look rough, others smooth. But generally one cannot be sure of the kind of bacterium from the looks of the colony. If your school has dishes or tubes of nutrient agar, you could experiment to find out whether there are bacteria in water, in the soil, on your skin, in the air. What else might you test? Slices of potato placed in an empty Petri dish can also be used as a medium for raising some kinds of bacteria.

Sterilization. If you want to do these or any other experiments with bacteria, you must be sure that the nutrient agar you use is free from bacteria before you begin. In other words, the agar must be **sterile.** All utensils and instruments used must be carefully sterilized. For this you need extremely high temperatures; boiling water (212° F or 100° C) is not sufficient. Really to sterilize or rid something of all living bacteria, an object may be passed through a flame or it must be

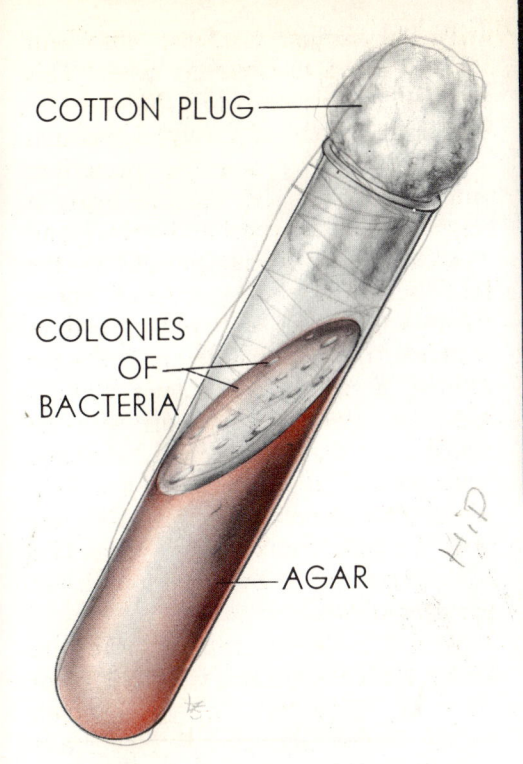

19.4 Colonies of bacteria growing on agar in a test tube. The tube is closed with a cotton plug, which allows gas exchange but filters out air-borne bacteria.

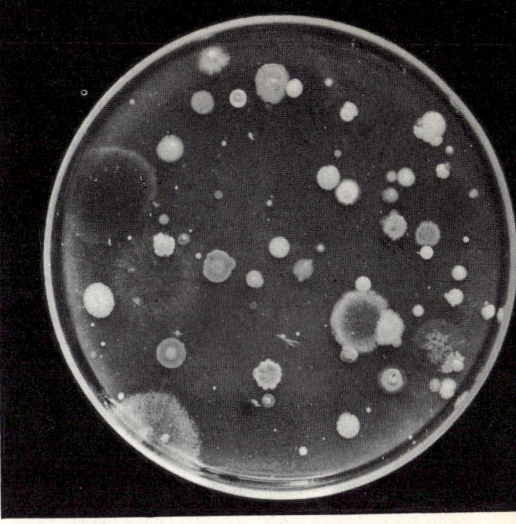

19.5 How many colonies of bacteria can you find on this agar plate? How many bacteria were introduced? This plate also contains some mold colonies—the fuzzy ones. *Brooklyn Botanic Garden*

exposed to steam under pressure. This makes it possible to raise the temperature far above the boiling point of water. When you can or preserve fruits or vegetables at home you are likely to use a pressure cooker to kill all bacteria.

Some kinds of bacteria secrete a very tough wall around themselves when temperature or other conditions are not favorable to their growth. Such a tough-walled bacterium is called a **spore**. Spores can stand several hours of boiling and many days of drying, as a rule. Fortunately, only a few germs form spores.

You can also destroy bacteria with strong chemicals, known as **disinfectants**. When strong enough, disinfectants kill even the spores. The chemicals known as **antiseptics** do not as a rule kill bacteria; they produce conditions that are unfavorable, so that the bacteria do not increase in number. Tissue cells are injured less by antiseptics than by disinfectants, as you would expect. For this reason you use antiseptics rather than disinfectants on a wound.

Conditions for growth. These are the conditions favorable to the growth of bacteria: (1) The presence of manufactured food; they can't make their own food from simple compounds. (2) Plenty of moisture. Nutrient agar is mostly water. If you are raising bacteria, you must keep the Petri dish closed or the test tube plugged with cotton so that little water evaporates. (3) Warmth, to hasten all the activities of protoplasm. Those germs that are parasites in us grow best in a temperature of 98 or 99 degrees, approximately our body temperature.

CHAPTER NINETEEN — BACTERIA AND DISEASE

You know that disinfectants and extreme heat kill bacteria. But extreme cold, even below the freezing point, kills some but not all. As the temperature goes down, bacteria become less and less active, and cell division stops. That is why you keep food in a refrigerator. At refrigerator temperatures many decay bacteria stop their activities, or grow very slowly. In a deep-freeze, however, no bacterial growth whatever takes place.

Even before people knew about bacteria and their role in spoiling foods, they had learned how to preserve foods. The American Indians, for example, smoked and dried meats and fish. For hundreds of years Europeans packed meat in barrels of brine (strong salt water) to preserve it for long voyages at sea. In the East as well as in Europe, vinegar, sugar, and spices had been used to keep foods from spoiling. Francis Bacon, the 17th century scientist, did an experiment to prove that cold preserves meat. But he, too, didn't know why.

Now we know that in canning foods and pasteurizing milk, in freezing, in drying, and in adding preservatives like salt, sugar, and spices, we are producing unfavorable conditions for the growth of decay bacteria. We sometimes use chemicals such as benzoate of soda to preserve foods, too. Examine the labels on jars, bottles, and cans of food to discover whether any contain chemical preservatives. Everything used must be listed on the label, according to the Federal Food, Drug, and Cosmetics Act.

But the conditions that are suitable for bacterial growth are so common in the environment that we are constantly struggling to protect not only foods but other kinds of substances from the action of bacteria, molds, and other fungi. Thus we paint wood to protect it, or use creosote or other chemicals. None of these methods is always sure. The more we learn about bacteria, the better we can use and control them.

Robert Koch. The study of bacteria, or **bacteriology,** has grown to be an important science since the latter part of the last century. Many scientists devoted themselves to the study of bacteria at that time but perhaps the man of those early days to whom we owe the greatest debt was Robert Koch (1843–1910). Robert Koch was a German physician and the first great bacteriologist. Being a physician his interest lay, naturally, in disease and he turned his attention to trying to find bacteria which he suspected might be the cause of disease. He realized that in this new field of dealing with invisible microorganisms new methods of study would be needed. Koch, after much experimentation, showed how to make solid culture media with gelatin and how to raise bacteria on them. He taught us the **technique** (tek-neek′), or method, of sterilization and showed the necessity of sterilizing everything in the preparation and handling of a culture medium to be used for study of bacteria. It was he, also, who first made pure cultures — only one kind of bacteria in a test tube or Petri dish. Koch did this by touching a sterile needle to a colony of bacteria he wanted to study, then passing this needle lightly over a sterile mixture in a fresh test tube. In other words he learned to "transplant" bacteria. If you have nutrient agar you, too, can make a pure culture, perhaps of some brightly colored colony.

But Koch did something more that helped greatly in the study of germs. Microscopes in those days had been improved to magnify 1000 times or more but even so it was difficult to

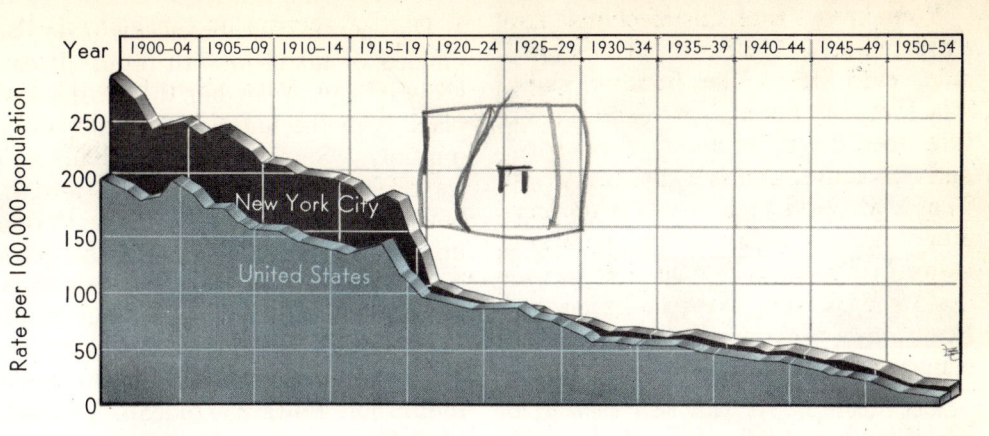

19.6 A graph showing the tuberculosis death rates in New York City and in the United States as a whole since the year 1900. Compare the early death rates with the recent ones. What has been done to cause the change in rate of death from tuberculosis?

study bacteria because they are transparent and scarcely visible. You can't see them on a slide with blood and other tissues. Koch, and later other bacteriologists, worked long and patiently to discover special chemicals that dyed or stained particular bacteria but did not stain the other cells. All of these techniques helped him and many others to make important discoveries.

Koch's four postulates. In 1876 after his long preliminary work Koch published an important paper describing the cause of anthrax. Anthrax is a disease which rarely attacks man, but it was formerly a common disease of sheep and cattle, killing them in large numbers. Other scientists had found a germ in the blood of some cattle ill with anthrax. Koch had found the same germ in all the diseased cattle he examined. Healthy cattle did not have this germ. Then he succeeded in raising the germ outside the animal's body, and injecting it into healthy cattle. This gave them the disease. Thus he proved that this germ and it alone caused anthrax.

Koch believed that finding a particular germ in all animals that suffer from a disease is not proof that this germ is the cause of the disease. He was too good a scientist to jump to that conclusion. He knew that the germ always present may merely accompany the disease and not be the cause of it. He decided that four steps must be taken before one can be sure that a particular germ is the cause of a disease. The four steps are called Koch's **four postulates.** Here are the steps:

(1) The same germ must be found in every animal that has the disease. Of course, no one can examine *all* the diseased animals, but a large number must be examined.

(2) The germ must then be grown in pure culture so that it can be definitely identified.

(3) When these germs grown in pure culture are injected into healthy animals, these animals must get the disease.

(4) The germ must be recovered from these sick animals and must be shown to be the same type of germ as the original ones.

CHAPTER NINETEEN — BACTERIA AND DISEASE 305

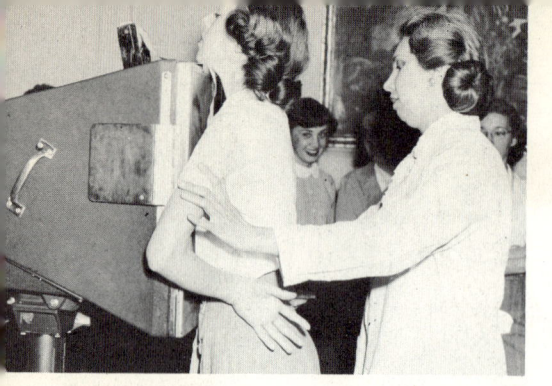

19.7 Chest x-rays are being taken at school. Chest x-rays plus new methods of treatment have reduced lung tuberculosis significantly in the United States. *Bloom from Monkmeyer*

In 1882 Koch announced that he had found the germ that causes tuberculosis. He had actually taken these four steps and was therefore sure he had found the tuberculosis germ. It was at this time that he announced his four postulates.

Tuberculosis. Tuberculosis was once called the "great white plague." During Koch's lifetime (and for many years after that) it took an enormous number of lives. With the coming of the industrial revolution more and more people got tuberculosis and more and more died of it. As people left their farms and settled in towns and small cities, as they began to work long hours indoors and in crowded factories, the germ spread rapidly from one to another. Even into this century tuberculosis was a major killer all over the world including our country. At present, in spite of the great decline in tuberculosis, far too many people in the United States have the disease — more than a half million people. Turn back to Figure 19.6; note the decreasing tuberculosis death rates in the United States and New York City since 1900.

The germ of tuberculosis may be inhaled or taken in with food. It can grow in any organ but the most usual place is in the lungs. Here the germs multiply. Some are coughed up and leave the body through the mouth. Since people with tuberculosis are often up and about and at work, the germ is spread by coughing, by carelessly washed dishes, by towels and other objects touched by the sick. Formerly the usual treatment was rest and good food. Dr. Edward Trudeau, who was himself a tuberculosis patient, devoted his life to curing others by this method. Nowadays, the treatment for advanced cases often includes the temporary collapse of a lung to rest it, or removal of a lung or part of a lung by surgery. Many cases can be successfully treated by drugs such as streptomycin and isoniazid (eye-so-neye'a-zid), a substance similar to the vitamin niacin. Sometimes these drugs are used together. So successful have these new methods been that in recent years many tuberculosis sanitariums have been closed, including the one that Dr. Trudeau himself founded.

Doctors can now detect the disease in its very early stages by chest x-rays. All people should have these x-rays taken frequently as part of a regular medical checkup. Figure 19.7 shows how simple it is to have this x-ray taken. Tuberculosis is usually easy to cure in its early stages. Tuberculosis can also be prevented in children who are particularly exposed to it. They can be vaccinated against it somewhat as we are all vaccinated against smallpox.

Pasteur and fermentation. Surely you have heard of Louis Pasteur, haven't you? Louis Pasteur (1822–1895) was a Frenchman. He started as a chemist, not as a physician. It is interesting to know how a chemist came to study the problem of disease. Pasteur lived in the south of France where the making of wines was an important industry. He had known for some time that wines are made from grapes by living yeast cells. The yeast cells cause **fermentation.** This is an incomplete oxidation of sugar into alcohol and CO_2. But every once in a while the wine growers were in trouble. The wine went bad; it turned sour or bitter or had some strange taste. Pasteur wanted to know why. He used his microscope on such mixtures and found besides the yeast cells other much smaller objects. Working on the hypothesis, or guess, that these were living cells, he put a tiny drop of the soured wine into a fresh barrel of wine. In time, this wine, too, turned sour; and Pasteur found large numbers of the same tiny objects in this barrel. Evidently these objects were living cells, microorganisms, that had reproduced. They had got into the first batch of wine, no doubt, from the air or from the skin of grapes. In the wine that had turned bitter there were also microorganisms but of a different kind. In every case there was a particular bacterium that caused the wine to become "diseased."

Pasteur was soon convinced that if particular bacteria can cause definite changes in wines, other bacteria can bring about changes in the animal's body, causing disease. After a while, therefore, he turned his attention to the study of disease. You will read more about Pasteur's work on disease.

The germ theory. Throughout this chapter it has been made clear that there are some diseases which are caused by germs. You have been hearing about germs for as long as you can remember. But your great grandfather did not know that there were

19.8 One African tribe treats all aches and pains by bleeding the patient. The "doctor" makes a cut over the affected part. He then places a goat horn over the cut and sucks the air from the horn. These people know nothing of the germ theory of disease. When was the germ theory established? *Chicago Natural History Museum*

infectious diseases that are caused by germs. When the early settlers came to this country, medical students were being taught that disease was caused by some position of the planets. There must be many ignorant people in this world who still do not know that germs exist and cause diseases. See Figure 19.8.

This idea that a specific germ causes each infectious disease is known as the **germ theory of disease.** Of course, it is no longer a theory; there is so much evidence for it that no physician doubts it. Credit for the establishment of this very important idea goes to Robert Koch and Louis Pasteur. You have already read how they came to discover it. But other scientists, too, contributed to the establishment of the germ theory of disease. For example, far back in 1837, an Italian scientist (Bassi) had proved that a disease that was killing off silkworms was caused by a moldlike fungus that could be transferred from one silkworm to another. In his experiments he found the fungus only in the diseased silkworms; all of them had the same fungus, without exception. Bassi concluded, therefore, that the fungus was the cause of the disease. But his proof was not as complete or convincing as the proofs submitted by Koch and by Pasteur.

What have you learned? We will continue in the next chapter with Pasteur's work; but let's sum up what we have learned thus far. The germ theory of disease states that each infectious disease is caused by a particular microorganism. This microorganism lives as a parasite in the body of the diseased animal or plant. This theory was developed only within the last seventy or eighty years; there are several reasons why it was so slow in coming. Chief among them was the fact that techniques for raising and studying bacteria were required. Robert Koch did much of this spadework. He raised bacteria on gelatin containing much water and food for bacteria; he learned how to raise each kind by itself in pure culture; and he developed stains which would dye one special kind of bacterium and no other cells. Sterilization of all materials, of course, was necessary. Thus, in time, by using these techniques, Koch discovered the germ of anthrax and the germ of tuberculosis — but only after going through the four steps known as his four postulates.

In the meantime, Pasteur, in studying the diseases of wines and beers, discovered that in each case a particular germ caused the undesired change — a germ which accidentally entered the vat in which fermentation was going on. This gave strength to what was to become known as the germ theory of disease.

You also learned that a very large majority of bacteria are not the kind that cause infectious diseases. Many bacteria live not as parasites but as saprophytes; they feed on dead matter. The life activities of bacteria are much like ours: they eat, digest, make protoplasm, oxidize, and reproduce. In feeding on dead matter, they break it down or decay it. Depending on what they live on, these saprophytic bacteria may thus be very helpful to us. Can you give an example? Or they may interfere with us by spoiling our foods and other products. To keep bacteria from spoiling foods, we have devised various ways of hindering their growth and reproduction, even killing them. Name some of the conditions we create that are unfavorable.

USEFUL WORDS IN BIOLOGY

germ	nutrient agar	disinfectant
bacillus	infectious	bacteriology
coccus	sterile	fermentation
spirillum	sterilization	germ theory
culture medium	antiseptic	of disease

TEST YOURSELF

1. Explain the differences between infectious, organic, and deficiency diseases.
2. Parasites may be external or internal. They belong to various groups of animals and plants. Give examples to show the truth of those statements.
3. (a) Describe the structure and shape of bacteria. (b) Describe their life activities.
4. Discuss the importance to us of saprophytic bacteria.
5. Describe the steps in the preparation of nutrient agar, giving the reason for each step.

6. (a) What is a bacterial spore? (b) Of what importance are spores to us?

7. (a) Name the conditions favorable to the growth of bacteria. (b) Explain in some detail how we make practical use of this knowledge of favorable and unfavorable conditions.

8. (a) Tell what you know about the life of Koch. (b) Name four important contributions made by Koch toward the raising and studying of bacteria.

9. State the four postulates that Koch said must be followed if a particular germ is to be proved to be the cause of a disease.

10. Explain about tuberculosis: (a) how the germ enters, (b) where it settles, (c) how it leaves, (d) how the disease is often successfully treated.

11. (a) Define fermentation. (b) Explain how Pasteur's early work on wines and beers led to his belief in the germ theory of disease.

DO IT YOURSELF

1. **Where are bacteria found?** Make nutrient agar by boiling in a quart of water 10 grams of powdered peptone, 10 grams of Bouillon cubes, 10 grams of salt, $\frac{1}{4}$ teaspoonful of baking soda. Filter while still hot through thick absorbent cotton lining a funnel, into clean Petri dishes. Cover the dishes at once and place them on a rack in a pressure cooker to steam for an hour. Be careful to keep the dishes closed as you remove them from the cooker. (Wrap four or five carefully and set them aside for later experiments.) A rather thick slice of raw potato in a Petri dish can also be used as a culture medium. Add a little water, cover and sterilize as described above.

To discover where bacteria live expose one dish to the air in your classroom, one in the school corridor while students are moving about, one in the gymnasium, and one in your bedroom. Expose dishes three minutes. Test tap water (three drops), milk (three drops), meat (a small piece), and bread (a small piece). Use a toothpick on your teeth, then rub it over the agar. In opening a dish to introduce some object raise the cover as little as possible and hold it so that dust cannot fall into the dish. Keep the dishes at 80° or 90°F for 48 hours. What will you use as a control for your experiments? Write up your observations and conclusions carefully.

2. **To find favorable conditions for bacterial growth.** Perform an experiment to discover the best temperature for bacteria. Devise another experiment to discover the effect of drying on bacteria. (Hint: nutrient agar is mostly water.)

3. **Making a pure culture.** If you have any colony of brightly colored bacteria make a pure culture of it by passing a dissecting needle through a flame, letting it cool, and then passing it lightly through the colony. Then use the needle for scratching your initials lightly in the agar of a sterile dish. Only the scratches should show. Keep warm for 48 hours or more. Describe.

4. **Bacteria under the microscope.** Most bacteria are so small that you will see very little unless you have a microscope with an oil immersion lens. In any case the bacteria must be stained. Smear a drop of broth containing bacteria over a slide and let it dry. Then pass the slide through a flame rapidly three times. Add a few drops of methylene blue or gentian violet stain; let it stand for two minutes. Wash the dye off with water.

5. **Preparing a book for the class library** on "Bacteriologists, Past and Present." Begin now to write up briefly in an interesting way the life and work of famous bacteriologists. Continue as you read the following chapters.

ADVENTURES IN READING

1. *Microbe Hunters* by Paul de Kruif, Harcourt, Brace, 1926; also Pocket Books. Contains biographies of Koch and Pasteur.

2. *The Microbe's Challenge* by Frederick Eberson, Jacques Cattell, 1941. Also helpful on the earlier bacteriologists.

3. *Microbes Militant* by Frederick Eberson, Ronald, 1948. A more recent book by the same author on bacteria and disease.

4. *Microbes of Merit* by Otto Rahn, Ronald, 1945. Information on helpful bacteria.

CHAPTER NINETEEN — BACTERIA AND DISEASE

Chapter 20

Body defenses against disease

Where germs enter the body. There was no longer any doubt about it after about 1880. A specific germ is the cause of each infectious disease. By "specific," we mean of a particular kind. But where do these germs come from? How do germs enter the body?

In general, germs come from the people who have the disease. They may come to us directly from the person or they may come indirectly. They may be on our food, or in the water we use, or in the air we breathe, riding on particles of dust. They may be on objects used or touched by the person who has the disease.

How do germs get into the body? Mostly through the nose and mouth. Another common door is a break in the skin, as when we cut or scratch ourselves. You know how often you have been told to use an antiseptic on a cut or scratch, even though it seemed so small as to be unimportant. See Figure 20.1.

How the body keeps out germs. Your body is protected by some remarkable gadgets. To begin with, your body is covered with a tough, dry epidermis; germs can't live long on those dead cells. Normally, the skin has no openings. The pores lead into sweat glands or oil glands; germs are usually stopped right there. The nose and mouth have a sticky coating of mucus. This catches the particles of dust on which the bacteria may be riding. Also the cells lining some of the air passages have cilia. They beat upward and sweep out any particles that did not get

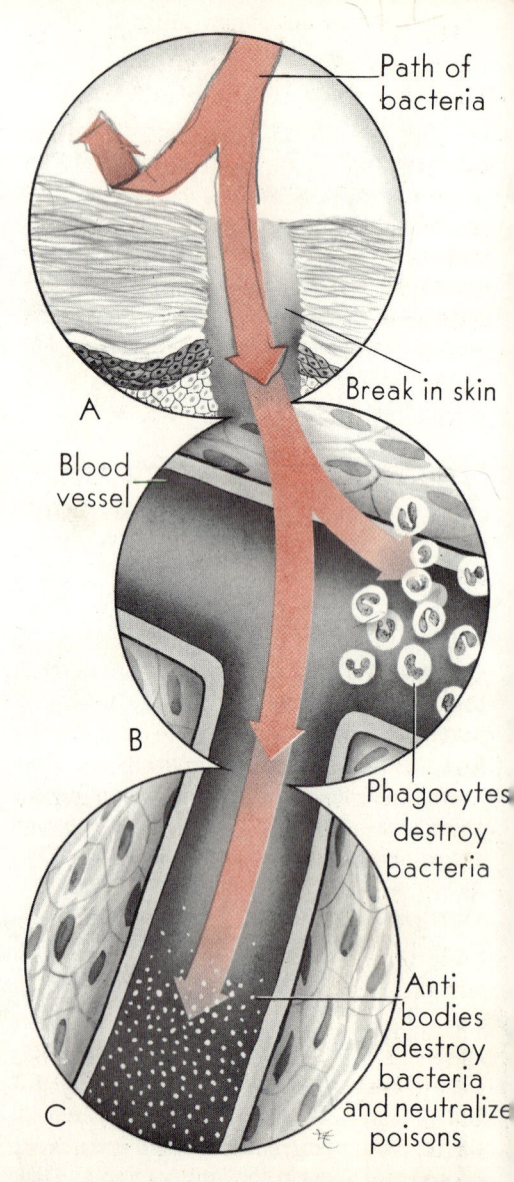

20.1 The three "lines of defense" against disease. **A.** The skin and lining of nose and throat keep out most germs. **B.** Many of the germs that enter the body are destroyed by phagocytes. **C.** Antibodies neutralize poisons produced by germs.

310   UNIT SIX — BACTERIA AND HEALTH

caught in the mucus. Some bacteria reach the throat and are swallowed. Some of these are killed by the hydrochloric acid of the gastric juice; many kinds can't harm us in any case.

The second line of defense. But some germs get past these protections. Then the white corpuscles get busy. Do you remember that the phagocytes eat bacteria? The blood carries them to the region where bacteria have settled. Here they leave the capillaries and devour bacteria and particles of dead cells. Other kinds of white blood cells are made in the spleen and lymph glands. As blood carrying bacteria passes through the lymph glands, the germs are strained out and destroyed.

The last line of defense. The phagocytes are good workers and there are many of them. But they often need help. For germs, as they grow in the body, may produce substances that poison the host. Such poisonous substances made by germs are called toxins. Each kind of germ produces its own kind of toxin. We say, therefore, that toxins are specific. The toxin usually remains in the germ; sometimes the toxin leaves it. It does as much harm to the host one way as the other.

If the toxin leaves the germ, your body cells sometimes make a chemical substance that neutralizes (makes harmless) the toxin. We call this an **antitoxin.** The antitoxin gets into your blood and is carried throughout your body. An antitoxin neutralizes a particular toxin and no others; it, too, is specific. You will read later how doctors make practical use of antitoxins. Do you remember that in connection with blood types A, B, AB and O you read about agglutinogens and agglutinins in the blood? Those occur normally in the blood. But it was discovered that bacteria or any other foreign cells when they enter tissues sometimes stimulate the body to form agglutinins or other **antibodies** which work against the foreign cells. Among the antibodies there are not only agglutinins which clump bacteria; there are also **lysins** which dissolve bacteria; and there are **opsonins** which change bacteria in such a way that phagocytes can more easily eat them. The antitoxins, of course, are antibodies, too. Do not, however, make the mistake of thinking of phagocytes and other white corpuscles as antibodies. Antibodies are chemical substances, not cells.

Providing antibodies in advance. But the body does not always make antibodies as rapidly as it should. Fortunately, thanks to Pasteur, and later to other scientists, we don't have to depend only on the body's defenses you just read about. You remember that Pasteur became interested in animal diseases after he had discovered why wines often spoil. With the help of his assistants he began raising pathogenic germs of many kinds. Among others he had pure cultures of the germ that causes **cholera** (coll'er-a) in chickens. You may have read of people having cholera, an intestinal disease. Pasteur had been injecting cholera germs into chickens to study the effects of the germs; thus he hoped some day to find a cure. One day, largely by accident, he injected an older culture than usual. Ordinarily the injection of germs killed the chickens. These chickens became ill, but strange to say, they recovered.

This gave Pasteur an idea. Being a scientist with imagination, he needed no more than a hint. Perhaps the

CHAPTER TWENTY — BODY DEFENSES AGAINST DISEASE 311

germs in the old culture had grown weaker with age. Perhaps the chickens that had recovered from an inoculation of weak germs could now be given a dose of strong cholera germs and survive. Pasteur tried it. They did. His guess was right. These chickens did not die. Perhaps he could purposely raise and weaken germs and make a practice of inoculating these into healthy chickens. If later, cholera germs appeared in the poultry yard, chickens that had had a mild form of the disease could resist the disease. Pasteur tried this again and again. Inoculated chickens did not catch cholera. They were no longer **susceptible** (suss-sep'ti-ble) to the disease; or, as we say, they had been given **immunity** to cholera. Pasteur had made the body ready to fight a germ before the animal was exposed to the disease. In those days antibodies had not yet been discovered. You who know about antibodies can explain how these chickens became immune.

Immunity to anthrax. Pasteur asked himself whether the method that worked with chicken cholera would work with another disease, anthrax. He weakened anthrax germs by keeping them in a high temperature (108° F) for some days. When he injected these weakened germs into healthy sheep the animals contracted anthrax but in a mild form. When the sheep had recovered entirely from the attack he inoculated them with the most **virulent** (strong) anthrax germs he could obtain. Most of the animals had become completely immune to anthrax; they did not become sick. A few had a mild attack. In this case, as in the case of chicken cholera, we now know that the animal's tissues had been active in making antibodies. So we say that these animals had developed **active immunity**.

Pasteur reported his experiments. But many people, scientists as well as sheep owners, refused to believe that one could prevent a disease by giving a disease. They would not accept the new idea; their minds were closed. They demanded that Pasteur give a public demonstration of his discovery. He did and the demonstration was successful. Even then some went home unconvinced. They refused to admit the facts, even though they had seen the demonstration.

Rabies. **Rabies** (ray'bees) is rare now. Formerly it was a fairly common disease among dogs and wolves and related animals. When a rabid animal bites a person (or another animal), rabies germs found in its salivary glands are left in the wound. These germs multiply and make a strong toxin which is carried to the brain. There it causes the throat muscles and other muscles to become paralyzed, making swallowing impossible. Death is sure to follow. Formerly people believed that an animal with rabies was afraid of water and for that reason the disease was long called **hydrophobia** (fear of water).

Pasteur could not find the organism that causes rabies. (We know now that it is a virus.) But he suspected that it lodges in the brain or spinal cord. Therefore, in order to weaken the germs, he decided to dry the spinal cord of an animal that had just died of rabies. He succeeded and finally was able to make a healthy dog immune to rabies by injecting such weakened germs. Pasteur had learned to prevent another disease in animals by immunizing.

Then one day a nine-year-old boy who had been bitten by a mad dog was brought to Pasteur. The parents pleaded with him to use his treatment on their child. Pasteur hesitated because this case was different in two ways. First, he had never experimented with people. And second, he had given the weakened virus to dogs *before* they had been bitten by a rabid animal. Now he was asked to give **inoculations** (injections) to a child who had already been bitten. However, Pasteur knew that rabies develops very slowly; usually the disease does not show itself until many weeks after the bite. Possibly his inoculations could do some good before the disease really developed. Also he knew that without treatment the child could not possibly recover. So Pasteur let himself be persuaded. After many anxious days of inoculating and watching, the boy left the hospital, cured.

The so-called "Pasteur treatment" has been used ever since that time. In fact, in order to play safe, health officers inoculate all people bitten by a dog, unless the dog is caught and shows no signs of rabies. Nowadays, fewer inoculations are given, and the virus is weakened with chemicals or ultraviolet rays.

Immunity to smallpox. Have you ever had a smallpox vaccination that took? Then you will remember the intense itching in that spot. A smallpox patient has such spots all over his body. The spots itch and get sore; frequently deep pits or "pocks" are left when the sores heal. You have probably never seen people with faces disfigured with pock marks because in our part of the world smallpox is rare indeed. Yet, up to about 1800, few people escaped it. Even today smallpox is a common disease in some parts of the world, particularly in southern China and India (Figure 20.2).

It was Edward Jenner (1749–1823), an English physician, who taught us how to keep from getting smallpox. Smallpox caused thousands of deaths annually in England in the late 1700's. Cows had a similar disease called cowpox. Jenner learned that dairymaids who milked these cows often came down with cowpox, too. Cowpox is a much milder disease than smallpox. What interested Jenner particularly was that the dairymaids who had had cowpox did not catch smallpox even when exposed to it. Why not give everybody cowpox? Then no one would get smallpox. Jenner got permission to try his theory on a boy. He took material from one of the sores or "pustules" of a cow that had cowpox. After lightly scratching the boy's arm he rubbed the material into the scratch. The boy became mildly ill with cowpox, and as Jenner had hoped, this boy became immune to smallpox.

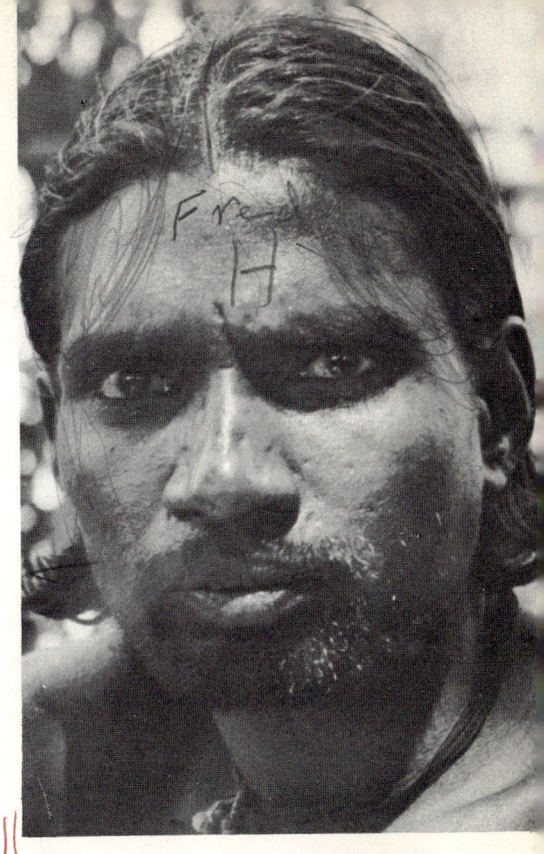

20.2 In India a great many people are marked by smallpox. *Black Star*

CHAPTER TWENTY — BODY DEFENSES AGAINST DISEASE

Jenner said he **vaccinated** the boy because he took material from a **vacca**, the Latin word for cow. The material he used was called **vaccine** (vak-seen').

Vaccination became fashionable in England. The practice spread to France and Germany. Jenner was honored and feted by kings and adored by all the people. And yet in those days severe illness often followed vaccination. See Figure 20.3.

Nowadays, vaccine is carefully prepared in laboratories. Healthy calves are inoculated with cowpox virus. As cowpox develops, material is taken from the pustules. The material contains a virus closely related to the smallpox virus. This is later purified in the laboratory and then tested for purity and strength on experimental animals. When the doctor vaccinates you he makes sure that his instruments are sterile. Thus vaccination has become safe.

Why be vaccinated? It is almost true that in the United States "no one has smallpox any more." In a recent year only eleven cases were reported in the whole country. In 1939 almost 10,000 cases were reported. The reason for this good record is that many states require vaccination of children before they enter school. And no one may enter the United States without a vaccination certificate. If we failed to enforce such rules, there is little doubt that smallpox would increase. Some years ago some smallpox cases suddenly appeared in a state which was very proud of its good smallpox record. Why? A woman, visiting from another state, was mildly ill with a disease not diagnosed until later. Sixty-five cases of smallpox were traced to this one woman! And it was discovered later that all sixty-five had either never been vaccinated or had not been vaccinated

for a very long time. Immunity after vaccination often lasts for a good many years, but sometimes for only a year or two. When a few smallpox cases were discovered in one of our largest cities a few years ago, the Board of Health offered to vaccinate free everyone who requested it. Thousands were vaccinated both for their own protection and the protection of the community.

Typhoid fever. It is quite possible that you have never known anyone who had typhoid fever. This is another disease that in the United States is becoming rare. Only about 2,000 cases were reported in 1950 and 1951 compared with almost 10,000 cases in 1940. The germ enters our bodies with food or drinking water. It multiplies in the digestive tract, causing a severe illness with high fever, often severely damaging the intestines. Germs pass out with the excretions and are later found wherever the sewage goes, in the soil, or in streams and lakes. Public water supplies in the United States are probably free from typhoid germs, but private water supplies may be contaminated. For that reason everyone in the United States armed forces is immunized against typhoid, as a matter of routine. Other people, too, who travel and who cannot be sure of the source of their drinking water and their food are often immunized. Dead typhoid germs are used for immunization, or "vaccination," as it is sometimes loosely called. Immunity lasts for only a few years. Figure 20.4 will interest you.

Polio and its prevention. Soon polio, or **poliomyelitis** (po'lee-oh-my-e-lye'tis) may be as rare a disease as smallpox. You have read and heard so much about polio in connection with the Salk

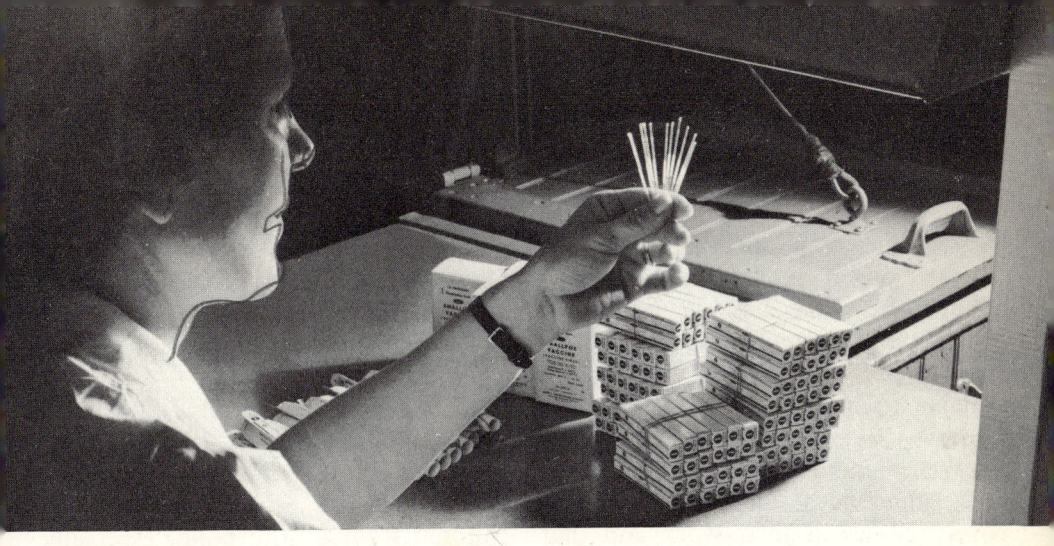

20.3 The final step in preparing a vaccine is inspection. Here a laboratory worker inspects the capillary tubes containing smallpox vaccine. Each tube contains vaccine for one immunization. Contents, of course, cannot be exposed to air. *Lederle Laboratories*

vaccine that you probably already know many of the important facts about this disease. You know that it is caused by a virus which affects the nervous system and sometimes causes paralysis. Polio, also called infantile paralysis, usually attacks children under ten. Often, no doubt when polio does not result in paralysis, the disease is not recognized. Although only a relatively few of us are ever known to have polio, physicians now think that most of us have had mild cases of the disease. They think that these mild cases caused us to develop antibodies which remain for life, thus making us immune. That would explain why relatively few older people get polio.

Polio seems to be spread directly from one person to another, just as a cold is spread. Even a well person who is immune to polio may spread it if the virus is lodged in his nose and throat. More cases of polio occur in the spring, summer, and fall months than in the winter.

When you studied about the blood, you read that the plasma contains protein substances called gamma globulins which act as antibodies. Gamma globulin (GG) from the blood of people

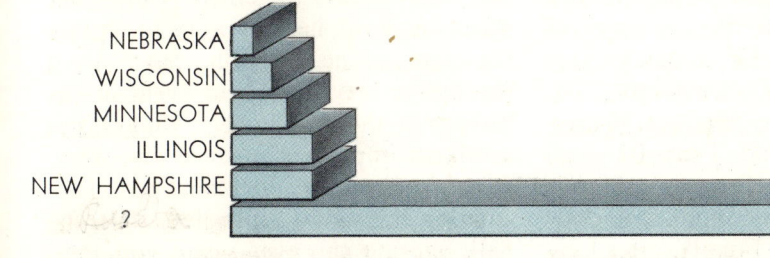

20.4 This shows the number of cases of typhoid (and the related disease, paratyphoid) in six states in a recent year. Which five states showed an excellent record? What might explain the poor record of the unnamed state?

CHAPTER TWENTY — BODY DEFENSES AGAINST DISEASE   315

who have had polio has been used as a preventive in children who have been exposed to the disease. That is, the child is given passive immunity. But gamma globulin doesn't remain in the body very long, and therefore, this passive immunity lasts only a short time. Really to reduce the number of polio cases, a vaccine was needed for giving active immunity.

Polio vaccine. In 1949, Dr. John F. Enders with two colleagues, Dr. Thomas H. Weller and Dr. Frederick C. Robbins, announced an important discovery based on their work and that of a large number of researchers who preceded them. After years of patient experimentation they had finally succeeded in making the polio virus multiply in test tubes. This was considered of such importance that they were awarded a Nobel prize. Dr. Enders, in appreciation of the contributions of the many scientists who had helped to bring him success, is quoted as saying this about his and all other scientific discoveries: "The one who places the last stone and steps across the terra firma of accomplished discovery gets all the credit. Only the initiated know and honor those whose patient integrity and devotion to exact observation have made the last step possible."

Now Dr. Enders himself, in successfully growing polio viruses in test tubes, made possible the discovery of the polio vaccine by Dr. Jonas E. Salk of the University of Pittsburgh. Dr. Salk raised the three different viruses, Type I, Type II, and Type III — all of which give some form of polio — on tiny bits of living monkey kidney tissue in test tubes. Finally, after long experimentation he succeeded in making the viruses inactive by the use of formaldehyde; yet they were still able to stimulate the production of antibodies in the body. In 1953 he reported the results of his investigations. Dr. Salk was so confident that the vaccine would not cause polio and was so hopeful that it might make children immune to the disease that he injected his own children with it in 1954. And in this year the greatest medical experiment in all history was begun. This experiment involved — with the large number of controls — 1,830,000 school children. This great experiment proved, as you know, that in a large majority of cases the vaccine can protect children from getting polio, especially the crippling kind.

You can imagine that when the vaccine was given to hundreds of thousands of children, every precaution had to be taken to make it safe. But the laboratory experiments have not ended. Dr. Salk and many other scientists believe that the vaccine can be further perfected so that it will give immunity in an even larger percentage of cases and will give even more nearly complete immunity.

On April 12, 1955, some of you read the large newspaper headlines and perhaps the many pages describing this important discovery. You may have read, too, about the training and the life of this quiet, unassuming scientist who worked with infinite patience and tremendous perseverance for many years together with other scientists until he was able to "place the last stone." You have lived through a very important event in the history of the world. Not that this is the most important medical discovery. Jenner's discovery of smallpox vaccination has saved more lives than the Salk vaccine can ever save; von Behring's discovery of diphtheria antitoxin, followed by Schick's discovery of active immunization against diphtheria, saves the lives of thousands of children every year. But now for the first time a controlled experiment was performed on an enormous scale; thousands of tests were made and records kept with the greatest accuracy. Nothing like this had ever been done before. When the experiment was reported, the whole world, not only we in the United States, learned the exact results.

Other immunizations. Measles, too, is caused by a virus. A vaccine is now made by growing the measles virus in fertile hen's eggs. Figure 20.5 shows how this is done, though the virus being injected here happens to be that of another disease. Many children have already been given measles vaccine. Vaccines have also been made against scarlet fever and whooping cough. These vaccines do not always give complete immunity, but they at least protect you from a serious case of the disease.

You read earlier that children can be vaccinated against tuberculosis. This vaccine is called BCG, the initials of the three Frenchmen who discovered it. Ten million people throughout the world have probably been given BCG. Controlled experiments on animals and people have been performed for many years to test it. It is safe and, in general, prevents tuberculosis. Influenza vaccines are also being experimented with and used to some extent.

Antitoxin as a treatment. Way back in 1892 a German physician, Emil von Behring (1854–1917), made a wonderful discovery. His discovery saved children from dying of diphtheria. In those days it was one of the worst children's diseases. Diphtheria germs enter through the nose or mouth and settle in the throat. You can see how easily the germs could be transferred to other people. The throat swells and is very painful. The germs excrete a very powerful toxin which enters the blood, causing high fever. Now von Behring discovered that, when a person has diphtheria, the tissue cells make an antitoxin. Sometimes this helped the patient to recover. Often it did not. So von Behring asked himself why not have some animal make diphtheria antitoxin and use that to help out? Perhaps he could give antitoxin, readymade and in large quantities, to the diphtheria patient. He tried it and was successful. This is what he did. He raised diphtheria germs in broth; here they made toxin. He gave a small dose of this toxin to a healthy horse. He injected more and more toxin at intervals. During all this time the tissues made antitoxin; the horse was building up active immunity to diphtheria. Later he took the antitoxin from the horse, and as soon as a child

20.5 A stage in the preparation of typhus vaccine. The young woman is injecting virus into an egg. How? Then the eggs are incubated (kept warm). What is the advantage of using eggs instead of an animal in preparing vaccine? *Wide World*

CHAPTER TWENTY — BODY DEFENSES AGAINST DISEASE

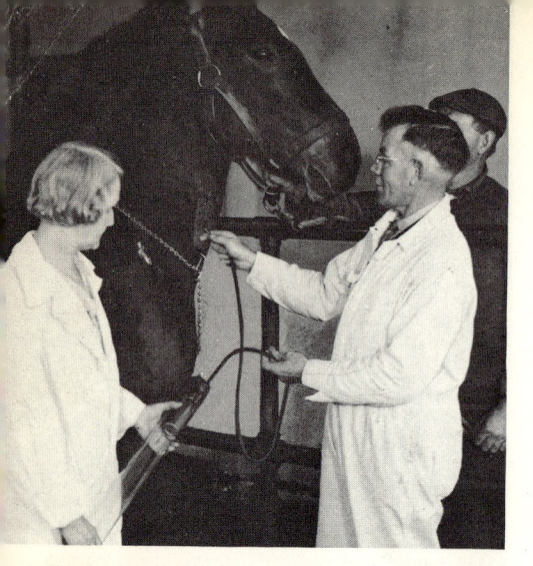

20.6 Bleeding a horse for antitoxin. Why is this horse able to supply antitoxin? *New York City Board of Health*

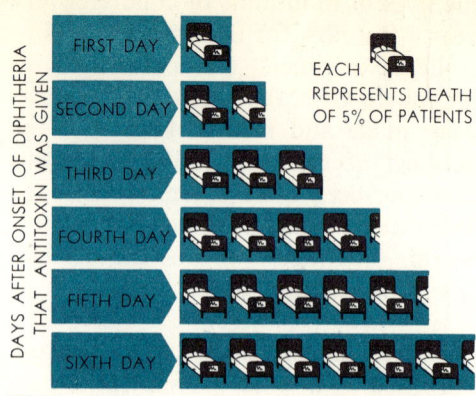

20.7 Each bed means 5 per cent of the patients died. What per cent died when antitoxin was not given until the sixth day? What per cent died when it was given the first day?

showed symptoms of diphtheria, von Behring injected this ready-made antitoxin. When given promptly, it was a cure. Figure 20.6 shows how the blood containing antitoxin is drawn from a horse. Figure 20.7 shows how important it is to give antitoxin promptly.

Passive immunity. Then von Behring tried something else. He injected diphtheria antitoxin into the children who had been playing with the sick child, but had not yet been taken ill. He tried antitoxin as a preventive against diphtheria; the antitoxin really gave immunity. This is called **passive immunity** since the tissues of the inoculated child did no work; its cells remained inactive (passive). The advantage of giving passive instead of active immunity is that the person can be made immune within a few hours. The disadvantage of passive immunization, however, is that it lasts only two or three weeks. The injected antitoxin quickly disappears from the blood. All immunity to be lasting must be active. That is why the use of gamma globulin against polio is only temporarily helpful.

Active and passive immunity are both acquired. But some people seem to have a natural immunity to disease. Very recently a special protein (properdin) has been found in the blood of some people and some animals which seems to act under certain conditions to give natural immunity. Unlike antitoxin and other antibodies, it is not specific.

Active immunity against diphtheria. Dr. Bela Schick, a Hungarian doctor who became a citizen many years ago, found a way of giving active immunity to diphtheria. He injected a small amount of toxin into the child and mixed some antitoxin with it to make it safe. This gave lasting immunity. Nowadays, you would be given two or three injections of **toxoid** to give you lasting immunity. Toxoid is made by growing germs in sterile broth and weakening their toxin with chemicals.

UNIT SIX — BACTERIA AND HEALTH

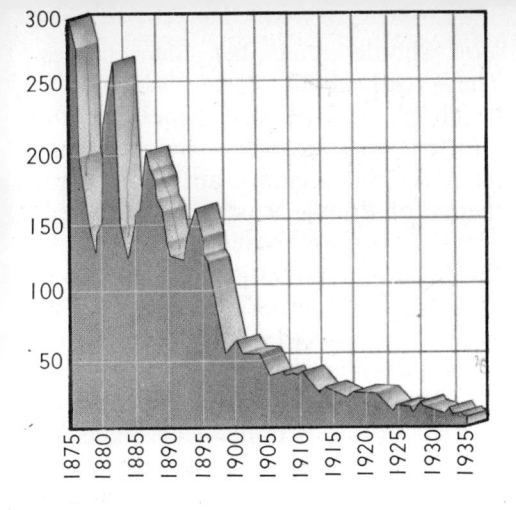

20.8 Death rate from diphtheria per 100,000 people in New York City. Explain why diphtheria is now a rare disease.

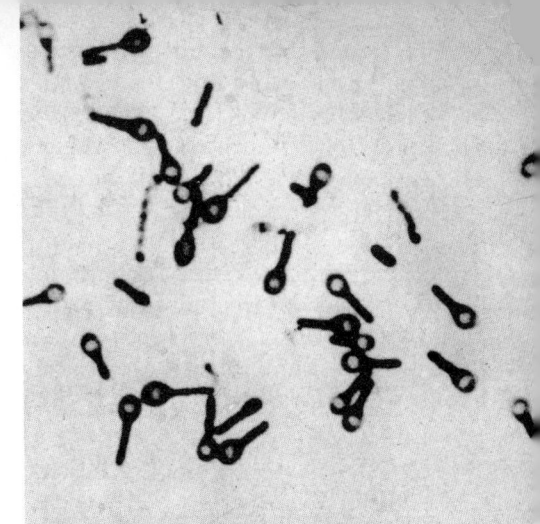

20.9 The rod-shaped germ that causes tetanus forms a spore at one end. Of what importance is this to us?

The Schick test. A few children seem to have natural immunity to diphtheria and don't need immunizing; all others should be immunized. But the question is who does and who does not need it? Dr. Schick discovered a test, the "Schick test," for answering this question. Many of you have probably had it. A very small amount of toxin is put into the skin of your arm. After about twenty-four hours if the doctor finds that the skin around this spot has a peculiar red look, he says the results are "positive"; you are susceptible. Then, of course, you should be immunized with toxoid. Figure 20.8 shows what von Behring and Schick have done for us.

Tetanus or lockjaw. Tetanus (tet′anus) is frequently a fatal disease. But you need never get tetanus. You can be given lasting immunity with a toxoid made from tetanus germs. In fact, babies are often immunized against diphtheria and tetanus at the same time. The tetanus germs make a very powerful toxin which reaches the brain and causes severe contraction of many muscles, especially of the jaw, therefore its name "lockjaw."

You almost never hear of people having tetanus; and therefore, you may wonder what keeps the disease from dying out. The germs are kept alive by living and growing in the digestive tracts of horses and some other animals, without doing any harm to the animal. There they multiply and constantly leave with the excretions. Once out of the body and in the soil, they form spores. The tetanus germ is one of the very few kinds of disease bacteria to form spores. Look at the strange spores in Figure 20.9. These spores can live a long time in the soil without the food and warmth of an animal's body. Other horses in grazing swallow some of the spores. Thus the germ goes from horse to soil to horse to soil, as long as there are horses. Soils which have been fertilized for a long time with horse manure contain lots of them; such soil is particularly dangerous to get into a wound.

CHAPTER TWENTY — BODY DEFENSES AGAINST DISEASE

Deep wounds are the most dangerous. Tetanus germs grow and form toxins only when little oxygen is present. They grow better without free oxygen. They are **anaerobic** (anay'-row'bic).

If there is a possibility of your having been infected with tetanus germs and you have not been immunized, you can be treated with tetanus antitoxin. This is prepared in the same way as diphtheria antitoxin, and, like it, works immediately.

"Borrowing" antibodies. Diphtheria and tetanus are the only diseases you would be likely to hear about against which the tissues make antitoxins. But antitoxins are not the only antibodies; remember all the other kinds. When you recover from a disease these antibodies sometimes remain in the blood and give immunity for a lifetime. That is why doctors sometimes "borrow" serum containing such antibodies from people who have had a particular disease. This is done in measles, scarlet fever, some types of pneumonia, polio, and some other diseases. Of course, since the work done by Dr. Edwin Cohn on blood fractionation, doctors don't use the whole serum but only some fraction of it, some particular protein, like gamma globulin.

Blood poisoning. Formerly one heard frequently about blood poisoning. In fact, in the early days hot tar or red-hot irons were applied when an arm or leg was amputated. And this was still being done as recently as 100 years ago! It was supposed to stop "blood poisoning," and it did sometimes, if the patient survived. This blood poisoning which took so many lives was very puzzling. But the Hungarian doctor Ignaz Semmelweiss (1818–1865), and the Scotch surgeon Sir Joseph Lister (1827–1912) found an explanation. You should remember their names. They read about Pasteur's work in which he showed that wines become infected with invisible living things from the surrounding air. The germ theory of disease was being accepted. Their own experiments seemed to show that blood poisoning, too, was caused by bacteria in the air. The puzzle was solved, but how to stop blood poisoning?

Lister's first idea was to kill all bacteria with carbolic acid when he operated. He washed his hands and instruments in carbolic acid. He sprayed it on the part operated on. Later he covered the wound with gauze soaked in carbolic acid. This was called **antiseptic surgery.** Blood poisoning set in much less often. But the antiseptic injured the tissue cells; wounds healed slowly or not at all. Evidently this was not satisfactory. Then Lister tried to keep germs from entering the wound, instead of killing them after they were in. He sterilized his instruments with heat; he sterilized his hands and operated in a room as nearly sterile as he could make it. He practiced **aseptic surgery,** which was much more successful. In our time many improvements have been made so that during operations everything is completely sterile. An infection nowadays after an operation is a rare exception. See Figure 20.10.

What have you learned? The story you have just read of scientists conquering one infectious disease after another is an exciting one. And the story is far from finished. But let us pause and sum up. The cause of infectious disease was known; then came the problem of how to destroy the germs and their poisonous products. First, scientists worked on guesses and hunches, as when Jenner in 1796 vac-

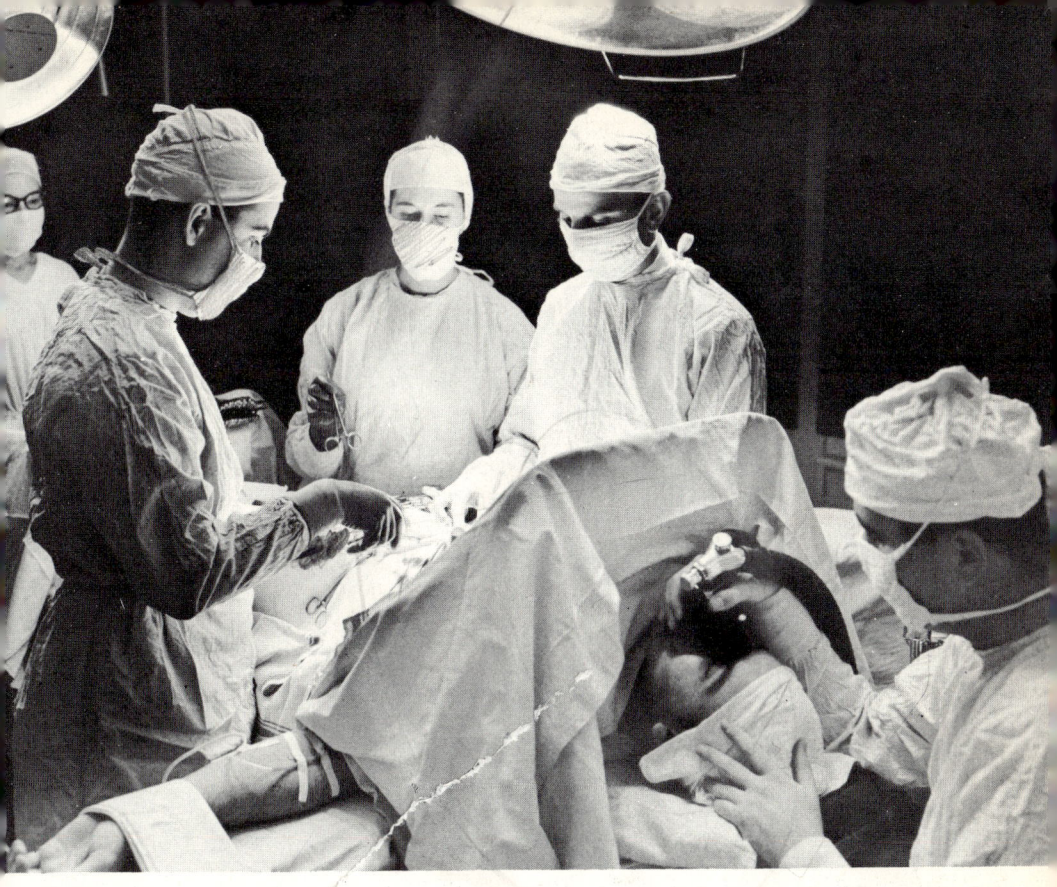

20.10 Make a list of the precautions taken to assure that the patient will not become infected during this operation. *Harold M. Lambert Studios*

cinated against smallpox by putting cowpox material into a person and when Pasteur immunized animals against cholera, anthrax, and rabies by injecting weakened germs. Thus we had the beginning of active immunization, in which the body makes its own antibodies. Active immunization is used to prevent smallpox, rabies, typhoid fever, diphtheria, tetanus, and other diseases.

But in the meantime bacteriologists were beginning to understand how active immunization worked. They were learning more and more about antibodies. First, in 1892 von Behring discovered diphtheria antitoxin. He used the antitoxin made by a horse to *cure* diphtheria. Then he used it to *prevent* diphtheria. He was giving passive immunity, which acts almost immediately but does not last. The diseases for which we use antitoxin or other antibodies taken from animals or from other people are diphtheria, tetanus, measles, scarlet fever, polio, and various other diseases. You should know something about all of the diseases mentioned. Do you?

Toward the end of the last century came another great discovery: the part that bacteria play in causing wounds to become infected. Aseptic surgery was developed.

You should know, too, all the following names and connect them with

CHAPTER TWENTY — BODY DEFENSES AGAINST DISEASE

some important discovery. Can you do that? Jenner, Pasteur, Lister, Semmelweiss, von Behring, Schick — these are but a few of the many physicians and bacteriologists who devoted their lives to saving the lives of others.

USEFUL WORDS IN BIOLOGY

toxin	susceptible	inoculation
antitoxin	vaccinate	toxoid
antibody	vaccine	anaerobic
lysin	virulent	aseptic
opsonin	active immunity	
agglutinin	passive immunity	

TEST YOURSELF

1. How is each of the following fitted for keeping many germs out of the body: (a) the skin, (b) the lining of nose and throat, (c) the lining of the air passages below the throat?
2. The blood has two ways of dealing with bacteria and their products once they get by the first barriers: by means of white blood cells and by means of chemical substances. Describe each of these methods in detail.
3. Explain how Pasteur immunized (a) chickens against cholera and (b) cattle against anthrax.
4. State about rabies: (a) how the virus enters; (b) where it settles, causing paralysis; (c) how it leaves the body; (d) the treatment.
5. (a) Explain how Jenner was led to practice vaccination against smallpox. (b) Where did he obtain his vaccine?
6. Name all the precautions taken in the preparation and use of smallpox vaccine.
7. Explain: (a) how typhoid germs enter and leave the body; (b) how large numbers of people have been immunized against typhoid.
8. Tell all you read about: (a) how the polio virus seems to be spread; (b) where it settles; (c) why older people rarely get polio.
9. What did Dr. Enders contribute to Dr. Salk's discovery?
10. (a) What is in Dr. Salk's vaccine to give immunity? (b) How is it supposed to work?
11. There is both active and passive immunization against diphtheria. In tabular form tell about each: (a) what substance is injected; (b) how quickly it takes effect; (c) how long the immunity lasts; (d) which has done most to cut down the number of cases of diphtheria.
12. What was Dr. Schick's important contribution to the conquest of diphtheria?
13. The tetanus germ is different from practically all other disease bacteria in that it is anaerobic and in that it forms spores. How do both of these characteristics enable us to explain some unusual features of the disease?
14. Lister practiced both aseptic and antiseptic surgery at different periods. Explain the difference.

PROBLEMS TO THINK ABOUT

1. What do you think of these two arguments presented by people opposed to vaccination? "The health records of a large city in which vaccination of school children had long been required show that between 1930 and 1935 not one case of smallpox occurred, but there were three deaths following vaccination." "Vaccine is made from material taken from a calf and scratched into human tissues. This is unclean and unsafe."
2. What do you think of the truth of this statement: "Pasteur saved more lives than Napoleon lost in all his wars"?
3. Remembering that Jenner practiced vaccination long before Pasteur, why is Jenner given so much less credit than Pasteur?

DO IT YOURSELF

1. Building up a class library. Each member of the class could take on one job. Write to the following addresses and perhaps to many others for booklets and leaflets giving you reliable and useful information on infectious diseases.

Metropolitan Life Insurance Co., New York 10, N.Y.; *Superintendent of Documents*, United States Government Printing Office, Washington 25, D.C.; *Public Affairs Pamphlets*, 22 East 38, N.Y. 16 (small charge); *Blue Cross Plans of U.S. and Canada*, 425 North Michigan, Chicago, Illinois. (Ask to be put on the mailing list of the quarterly called *Blue Print for Health*.) Drug manufacturers, too, publish reliable articles. (Ask your druggist for names and addresses.)

2. Bacteriologists, past and present. You can add to your booklet on bacteriologists by writing up the lives of Jenner, Lister, and Semmelweiss. The Metropolitan Life Insurance Co., New York 10, N.Y. will send you a free copy of the biographies of Jenner and Lister.

ADVENTURES IN READING

1. *Eleven Blue Men and Other Narratives of Medical Detectives* by Berton Rouche, Little, Brown, 1953. Do you like detective stories? Read how medical detectives tracked down and stopped these diseases in various places: typhoid, smallpox, psittacosis, leprosy, trichinosis, botulism.

2. "Tracking the Killer" by Robert Coughlan, *Life*, February 1954. The killer is polio.

3. "Botulism—Food Poisoning" in *Blue Print for Health*, Blue Cross, summer 1954. An interesting article on this rare but sometimes fatal disease.

Chapter 21

Some recent discoveries

21.1 Dr. Alexander Fleming in his laboratory examining some mold cultures in test tubes. You will read more about his great contribution to the world. He discovered the drug penicillin. Which mold was in the test tubes? *Wide World*

Penicillin. Have you ever seen a bright, bluish-green mold on cheese or bread or other foods? From that common mold (*Penicillium*) the drug **penicillin** (pen-i-sill'in) is made. Since its discovery in 1929, a whole new chapter has been written in the treatment of disease. The idea of using as drugs substances that were extracted from simple fungi like molds or soil bacteria was an entirely new idea, but one that has resulted in many dramatic discoveries. See Figure 21.1. This is the way it started. A Scotch bacteriologist, Alexander Fleming (1881–1955), saw blue-green molds (*Penicillium notatum*) growing in some of his culture dishes. Spores of the mold had fallen there by accident. Then he noticed that none of the bacteria he was raising in the dish were growing near the mold. Evidently, the mold gave off a substance harmful to the bacteria. He reported his observations, but at the time no one was particularly interested in Fleming's culture dishes. With the coming of the war, however, there was great need for drugs to prevent wound infections, and scientists turned back to the study of the blue-green

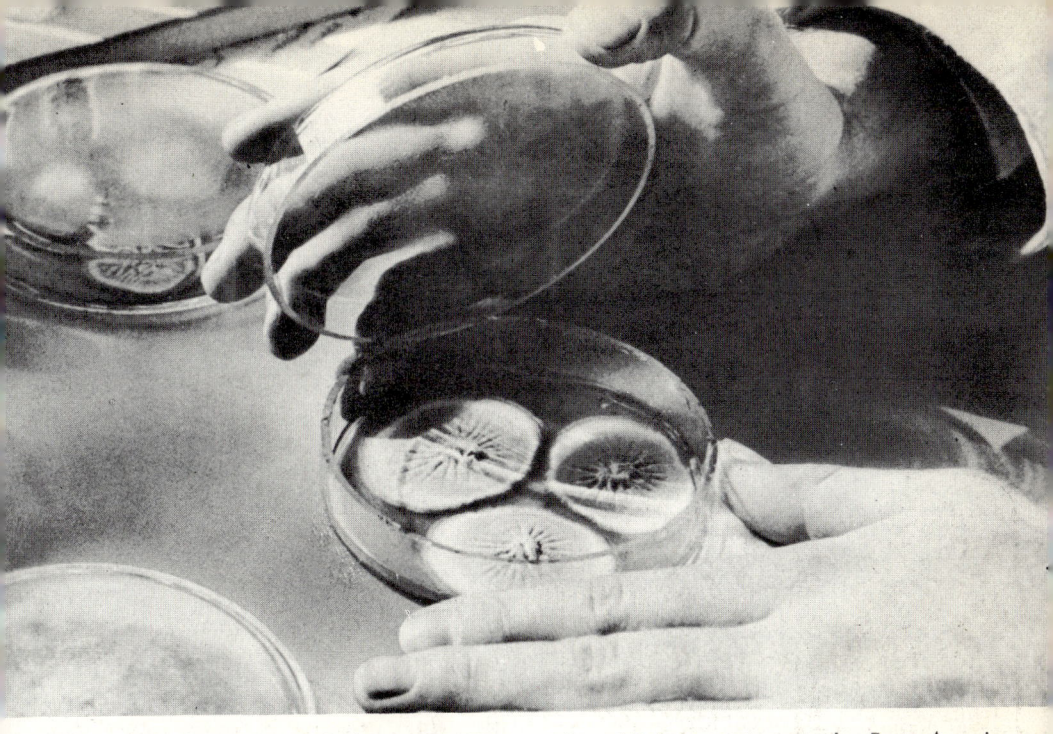

21.2 Colonies of one of the molds that produce penicillin. Commercially the mold is cultured in huge vats or tanks. *Press Association Inc.*

mold. See Figure 21.2. At great cost they collected small amounts of penicillin and began to use it. Penicillin was so dramatically successful in killing some germs that Fleming was awarded a Nobel prize for his discovery.

Nowadays, penicillin is prepared on a large scale from a mold closely related to the one Fleming discovered. It may be injected, taken by mouth, or used externally to cure infections of many kinds. But, of course, no powerful drug should ever be used unless prescribed by a physician. Penicillin sometimes causes serious allergies.

Antibiotics. Penicillin was the first of the **antibiotics** (anti-bye-ot'iks) used by doctors. Antibiotics means "against living things." Antibiotics are substances made by microorganisms, and they work against other microorganisms. They are not specific as antibodies are. Each antibiotic has a variety of uses.

Antibiotics all work fast and, in general, they are not harmful to the body. But here again only a physician can decide whether or not to use them. They have this disadvantage. The bacteria that cause disease in time develop strains that seem to be resistant to the antibiotic that was used, so that the drug becomes useless. Also, through the use of antibiotics, this interesting discovery was made about disease germs. One kind of germ in the body may keep down the growth of others. You know that in all communities one kind of organism often crowds out others, and, furthermore, that destroying one kind may make it possible for other kinds to increase. As soon as an antibiotic

CHAPTER TWENTY–ONE — SOME RECENT DISCOVERIES

21.3 Selman Waksman handling flasks containing the right culture medium for raising the soil microorganisms that give us antibiotics. Can you see how the flasks are kept closed? *Wide World*

kills off one species the others grow rapidly and may begin to make trouble for the patient. In spite of all this, antibiotics perform miracles in cases of pneumonia, influenza, rheumatic fever, and other infectious diseases.

Antibiotics are useful to us in still another way, a very different way. They are used on the farm. Cows and chickens and other animals grow faster and healthier when certain antibiotics are added to their food.

Waksman and streptomycin. When he was a young man, Dr. Selman Waksman came to the United States from Russia. As a student at the New Jersey Agricultural Experiment Station at Rutgers, he began to work on soil bacteria. There are many kinds of soil bacteria, and all are of great importance in agriculture. They look quite different from the bacteria that cause disease, and of course, they are very different in their habits. After the use of penicillin was discovered, Dr. Waksman hoped to find that soil bacteria, like molds, would produce substances that could be used as drugs. He worked for years with his assistants to develop the drug **streptomycin**. He was awarded the Nobel prize in medicine for preparing this antibiotic. Streptomycin is used against tuberculosis, as you read earlier, and against many other disease germs. See Figure 21.3.

Perhaps some of you have been treated with one of the many kinds of drugs made from soil bacteria. You may have heard of aureomycin, chloromycetin, terramycin, magnamycin, or many others.

The early wonder drugs. But before antibiotics became known, other drugs had been discovered that had equally dramatic effects. They are still being used in the treatment of many diseases. These drugs were chemical substances prepared in a laboratory. After long experimentation, shortly before Fleming discovered the effects of the blue-green mold, some German scientists patented a powerful drug (called prontosil — pron'toe-sil). In the body this could kill one of the most dangerous kinds of germs we know, **streptococcus** (strep'toe-cock'us), which causes many kinds of infections. Before long some French scientists discovered which part of the patented drug brought about the cures. They gave this substance to the public. It is now called **sulfanilamide** (sul-fa-nil'ah-mide), the first of the sulfa drugs.

Now sulfa drugs don't kill germs in any usual way. In their chemical make-up sulfa drugs are almost, but not quite, like one of the substances germs normally absorb from the body and use in making their own protoplasm. When the sulfa drug is present, it is absorbed by the germ "by mistake," so to say, in the place of the needed substance. The germ then cannot build its protoplasm and it dies.

Sulfa drugs came into common use just in time for use in World War II. They saved countless lives by keeping wounds from becoming infected. Sometimes, however, they have harmful effects on some organs of the body. For that reason they must never be used except under the direction of a physician. By this time there is a long list of sulfa drugs: sulfadiazine, sulfapyridine, sulfathiazole, sulfasoxizole, and others.

Paul Ehrlich. Some credit for the discovery of the sulfa drugs you have just read about really should go to Paul Ehrlich (1854–1915), a German physician. It was he who started this type of research when he was looking for a cure for the disease known as syphilis. He experimented with one chemical after another, trying to find one that would kill the germ of syphilis, and yet not harm the patient. He was a tireless worker who refused to admit defeat. It was during his 606th experiment that he found a compound containing arsenic and bismuth which would cure most cases of syphilis. He called the drug "606," but it is now more generally known as "salvarsan." Although it is now seldom used since other drugs have replaced it, 606 saved many lives. And more important still, Ehrlich had found a new way to treat disease.

Drugs, of course, had long been used; but very few drugs were used to kill a specific germ. One of these drugs was discovered by Mexican Indians a long time ago. Early explorers found them treating malaria with the bark of the cinchona (sin-koh'na) tree. This bark yields the drug known as quinine. Up until recently, quinine was the only drug known that could control the malarial protozoan in a human being. Now new and better drugs have been discovered. Atabrine is used extensively, and many others were tried during the war (chloroquine, pentaquine, paludrine).

Venereal diseases. Syphilis is one of the venereal diseases, that is, diseases commonly spread through the sex organs. The first symptom of syphilis is usually a harmless-looking sore which heals. Then the germ (a spirochaete) makes its way into the nervous system. Eventually it causes death. Syphilis in the mother has caused the death of many babies. For this reason many of our states, before issuing a marriage license, require a Wassermann or similar blood test. This is a simple test for detecting syphilis. In states that do not require a test, many people ask for the test and, if necessary, receive treatment before being married.

Gonorrhea (gon-o-ree'ah) is another venereal disease. Gonorrhea in the mother often results in blindness in the baby. Fortunately both gonorrhea and syphilis can now be successfully treated.

Viruses and Rickettsiae. The wonder drugs, both antibiotics and sulfa drugs, are not the only achievements of modern research on disease that are exciting. The study of viruses has been just as exciting. We now know that many diseases — smallpox, rabies, measles, polio, influenza, and the common cold — are caused by viruses. You have heard about viruses often.

21.4 Influenza virus photographed with an electron microscope. The white spheres which look like balls of cotton are the virus particles. *R. C. Williams and R. W. Wycoff*

Sometimes the doctor just says, "You have a virus infection."

Now, what is a virus? Actually we cannot yet answer this simple question satisfactorily. Some important facts are known, however. A virus is so small that it can pass through a filter made of porcelain through which no bacterium can pass. A thousand of them may together be only the size of a typhoid germ. See Figure 21.4.

Dr. Wendell M. Stanley of the Rockefeller Institute for Medical Research was one of the first to study viruses. It was he who showed that a virus which caused a serious disease in tobacco plants (tobacco mosaic) was a protein molecule. That does not mean that all viruses are like this one; but the discovery showed how complicated the study of viruses can be.

Viruses are difficult to study because they cannot be grown on nutrient agar. They grow only in living tissue cells, which are difficult to raise outside the body. Some viruses will grow in fertile hen's eggs, which, of course, are living cells. You saw a picture of eggs being used in this way in Figure 20.5. This discovery has greatly helped in the study of viruses.

It is not clear whether or not viruses are living; perhaps some are and some are not. Some years ago smallpox virus was grown on a tissue culture. A very tiny amount was transferred to a second culture and so on, eleven different times. After that there was 50,000 times as much virus as at the beginning of the experiment. Had it reproduced? If so, it must be living. Or did the tissue cells keep making new virus? There is still much to be learned about viruses. Radioactive elements are being used to study their activities and growth. Perhaps that will produce results.

Less important than the viruses, since they are much less common, are the Rickettsiae, named after Howard Ricketts who discovered them long before viruses were known. They are known to be the cause of several diseases, two of which you sometimes hear about, typhus and Rocky Mountain spotted fever. In size they are halfway between a virus and a small bacterium. But they resemble viruses in that they can be raised only on living cells.

Bacteria have diseases too. Long before viruses were discovered, a Frenchman (D'Herelle) discovered that certain bacteria in one of his culture dishes were being preyed upon by something invisible. He called it **bacteriophage** (bak-tee'ree-oh-faj), which

21.5 High school students can carry on many interesting experiments in the biological laboratory. The girl is holding the Petri dishes used for raising bacteria. The boy is keeping a careful record of their observations. *Three Lions*

means devouring bacteria. We now think that this mysterious something is a virus which attacks bacteria. It was hoped that it could be made use of in killing certain germs. But so far it has not proved useful.

What have you learned? Recent research has been largely on drugs, and less on immunization against disease. After Paul Ehrlich made his famous 606 for treating syphilis, other chemicals gradually came into use. These are the sulfa drugs. Then came the antibiotics, the drugs extracted from molds and soil bacteria. The first antibiotic was penicillin, discovered by Alexander Fleming; the others with names ending in *mycin* or *mycetin* followed in quick succession.

But the ultramicroscopic virus claims the attention of many bacteriologists. Is it always or can it be a lifeless protein molecule? It is known to be the cause of many infectious diseases — smallpox, rabies, measles, polio, influenza, and a score of other diseases — and it is known to be transferred from person to person much as bacteria are. Much remains to be done in this field.

Those of you who will later study medicine may continue the research on this important subject. Figure 21.5.

CHAPTER TWENTY-ONE — SOME RECENT DISCOVERIES

USEFUL WORDS IN BIOLOGY

penicillin
Penicillium
antibiotic
atabrine
streptomycin
streptococcus
sulfa drugs
cinchona
sulfanilamide
Rickettsia
bacteriophage

TEST YOURSELF

1. How and by whom was penicillin discovered?
2. (a) Explain what is meant by antibiotics and state two disadvantages in their use against disease. (b) For what very different purpose are antibiotics sometimes used?
3. Explain: (a) how the preparation of sulfa drugs differs from that of antibiotics; (b) how the two kinds differ in their method of killing bacteria.
4. Tell about the work and discoveries of Selman Waksman.
5. Paul Ehrlich probably deserves most of the credit for starting research on drugs. Tell all you know about his discovery of a drug for treating syphilis.
6. Virus, Rickettsia, and bacteriophage are comparative newcomers in the field of bacteriology. (a) What is the importance of each, and (b) what are the problems that still remain to be settled about each? (c) Which of the three is most important to us? Explain.
7. Sum up your understanding of a virus in a table under the following headings: Characteristics of a Virus; Reasons for Believing a Virus Is Living; Reasons for Believing It Is Not Living; Virus Diseases Against Which We Have a Vaccine; Well-known Diseases Caused by a Virus.

DO IT YOURSELF

1. **Bacteriologists, past and present.** After writing up the biography of Ehrlich (see also De Kruif's *Microbe Hunters*), add biographies of more recent bacteriologists, such as Fleming, Waksman, and others you may read about. You can find out about them by reading some of the books mentioned below and consulting *Readers' Guide to Periodical Literature*.

2. **Making a chart.** Many classes of biology students have enjoyed making a chart showing new discoveries. If preceding classes have begun such a chart, continue their work. If not, this is the time for a committee to start one.

ADVENTURES IN READING

1. *Magic in a Bottle* by Milton Silverman, Macmillan, 1948. Contains the life of Ehrlich, Fleming, Domagk (and sulfa drugs).
2. *Yellow Magic; the Story of Penicillin* by J. D. Ratcliff, Random House, 1945.
3. *Miracles from Microbes; the Road to Streptomycin* by Samuel Epstein and Beryl Williams, Rutgers University, 1946.
4. "The Drugs of Microbial Origin" by K. B. Raper and R. G. Benedict, in the 1950–1951 Yearbook of the United States Dept. of Agriculture, *Crops in Peace and War*.
5. "Rickettsiae," an article by Marianna R. Bovarnick, *Scientific American*, January 1955. Gives a simple account of these puzzling organisms.
6. "Viruses Within Cells" by Joseph L. Melnick, *Scientific American*, December 1953. Contains photographs showing viruses within cells. It is difficult reading.

Chapter 22

Stopping the spread of disease

Epidemics of former times. The Black Death (bubonic plague) spread over Asia, Africa, and all of Europe in 1348. Probably one fourth of all the people in Europe died of it at that time. When an infectious disease spreads like this to large numbers, we have an **epidemic.** Later came epidemics of smallpox which killed many millions. In the 19th century, epidemics of cholera swept through India, westward, and over Europe. Even as late as the twentieth century an epidemic of influenza killed hundreds of thousands in Europe and the United States. Compared with earlier epidemics, this one was mild. We no longer have epidemics like those of early days. Do you know why?

Even when men believed that devils, evil spirits, or the stars caused disease, they were afraid to be close to the sick. They had noticed that contact brought disease. So they did the easy thing. They fled to escape and in fleeing they spread the germs to new communities. Nowadays we know better; we don't run away; we keep those who have an infectious disease apart from the well. We **isolate** the patient. Thus we prevent the disease from spreading.

People must work together. To keep disease from spreading the whole community must act; people must work together. In the Middle Ages people realized something of this sort when they got together and decided that lepers must carry a bell so that they could be recognized as people to be avoided. Then in the Middle Ages, too, the Italian city of Venice took a further very important step. The city isolated those suspected of possibly being sick. Every vessel arriving from the East, where there were always cases of bubonic plague, was kept at anchor, outside the port. There it waited for forty days. If by that time no case of plague had developed, the ship was allowed to dock. Thus the Italians began the practice of **quarantine** (kwar'an-teen), isolating those who might be developing a disease. The word itself means "forty"; but of course, the quarantine period may not be forty days. Every community now uses quarantine to protect its citizens.

Health officers. As you read about tuberculosis, diphtheria, typhoid fever, tetanus, rabies, polio, and smallpox, you found answers to three questions about each disease: (1) through what channels do the germs of this disease enter? (2) Through what channels do the germs leave the sick person? (3) Where and how long will the germs of this disease live outside the body of the sick person? All of us should have this information to protect ourselves and others. But each of us alone can't control disease. We need help from the community. For this reason communities appoint a health officer or a board of health. Health officers have many duties: First, they collect data on disease and death. Such data, along with data on births and marriages, are called **vital statistics,** and can be used in many ways. Second, having gotten facts about disease from physi-

22.1 A sewage disposal plant at Durham, North Carolina. In breaking down the sewage, all disease bacteria are killed. Does this look like a cheap or costly method?

cians and workers in laboratories, the health officers must make practical use of these facts to control the spread of disease. They also make regulations about the isolation of the sick, reporting of disease, or quarantine. But health officers must work for the health of the community, too, by controlling the environment. This is called **sanitation**. And so the health officers or the board of health must also make regulations about sewage disposal, treatment of drinking water, safeguarding the milk supply, and many other factors of the environment. While every town has a health officer or board of health, each state, too, has a health department; and besides all this we have the United States Public Health Service with the Surgeon General at its head.

Could your class make a list of the many duties of a board of health? Then if you grouped yourselves into committees, each committee could prepare a report on one or more of the functions of the health board. In fact, some of these committees could perhaps even take over this function in your own school.

Sewage disposal. Some germs, like those causing typhoid fever, cholera, and dysentery, are taken in with food or drink. They multiply in the digestive tract and leave the body with the wastes. Now most germs die very soon after leaving the tissues and fluids of the animal's body, but not the typhoid germ. It can live in sewage, or in water containing tiny particles of sewage, for weeks or months. Though it is not a spore-former, it can survive even the freezing of water. That means that the greatest care must be taken in the disposal of sewage. Otherwise some germs may find their way into streams or wells. From these, the germs may reach food supplies. Water or food that contains disease germs is said to be **polluted** (pol-loot'ed).

Sewage can be disposed of in various ways. On farms and in villages cesspools and septic tanks are used. The temperature in these tanks must be kept high enough (minimum 60°) for decay bacteria to grow. They decompose the waste into liquids. When these liquids seep into the soil, other bacteria in the soil destroy the remaining harmful substances. In towns sewage is sometimes treated in plants such as the one shown in Figure 22.1. Since flies may carry germs and thus pollute food, it is important when indoor toilets are not available to guard the outdoor privy against this danger. Fly-tight privies have been devised and are widely used on farms.

22.2 The interior of the Dalecarlia filtration plant. In this plant, which supplies water for Washington, D.C., are long rows of rapid sand filters. *C. J. Lauter*

A modern sewage disposal plant can even be profitable. Part of the waste can be used as fertilizer, the gas formed can be burned to supply heat or power, and the water left over can often be used in various industries. But there are still cities that dispose of their sewage by leading it into large bodies of water. If these waters are far from the drinking water supply and far from bathing beaches, this method protects the community against disease. But pollution of water kills off much of the animal life it would otherwise support. This destruction of fish and shellfish that we could eat costs us money and reduces our food supply.

Pure water. If your drinking water comes from a well, you can have it tested for possible pollution. Send a sample at regular intervals to your local health board or to the State Health Department. In cities the problem of supplying pure water is a difficult one. Some cities, such as Boston, Los Angeles, New York City, and many others, construct large reservoirs many miles from the city. The region supplying water to the reservoirs is known as the **watershed.** If the whole watershed could be controlled we would know that the water was pure. However, control is partial at best; so to make doubly sure, the water is usually **chlorinated** (klor'in-ated). The small amount of chlorine used is harmless to us but kills germs which may be injurious. The water also may be **aerated** (mixed with air) and then piped to the city. Other large cities, such as Washington, Chicago, St. Louis, and others, may purify their water by filtering it, through large sand filters. See Figure 22.2. The sand by itself is much too coarse to filter out microscopic germs. But a film of diatoms and other algae forms around each grain of sand. This film catches the bacteria. By these and other methods, such as the use of special chemicals to cause suspended silt and bacteria to sink to the bottom, many communities seek constantly to maintain a supply of pure water.

Pure milk. Milk is a good home for disease germs, and it is likely to become contaminated. The cow may have tuberculosis, or undulant fever, or some other disease that attacks man; and these germs may get into the milk. Then, too, the person who milks the cow, or later handles the milk, may transfer germs from his body to the milk. For this reason, in cities, most milk sold to the public is **pasteurized.** In pasteurization, milk

CHAPTER TWENTY-TWO — STOPPING THE SPREAD OF DISEASE

is heated to a temperature of about 150° F for about half an hour (the boiling point is 212° F) and then cooled rapidly. This procedure is enough to kill any disease bacteria which may be present. The process was named after Pasteur since he treated wines and beers in much the same way to keep them from spoiling. Pasteurization kills many of the bacteria that sour milk and those that cause decay, but not all; some of these can form spores. The temperature of pasteurization only stops the growth of the spore formers, and under favorable conditions the bacteria multiply again. That is why, after being heated, the milk must be immediately cooled and kept cool. After cooling it is immediately put into sterile containers and sealed. See Figure 22.3. Where pasteurized milk is not available, it can be made safe by boiling. This, however, makes it less digestible for babies and changes the taste.

A simple test applied by boards of health in large cities shows whether pasteurized milk has been heated enough to kill all the disease bacteria. Raw milk contains a certain enzyme (phosphatase). This is destroyed by the amount of heat applied in correct pasteurization. So if pasteurized milk still contains this enzyme, the pasteurization evidently was not satisfactory. The whole plant is regularly inspected for cleanliness, too, as are the dairy farms which supply the milk. See Figure 22.4. Here the cattle are tested for disease. In many cities samples of milk are tested for the number of bacteria. See Figure 22.5. In New York City, for example, no more than 400,000 bacteria are allowed per half thimbleful before pasteurization; no more than 30,000 at the time of delivery. In some communities the selling of raw milk is forbidden unless it is "certified"

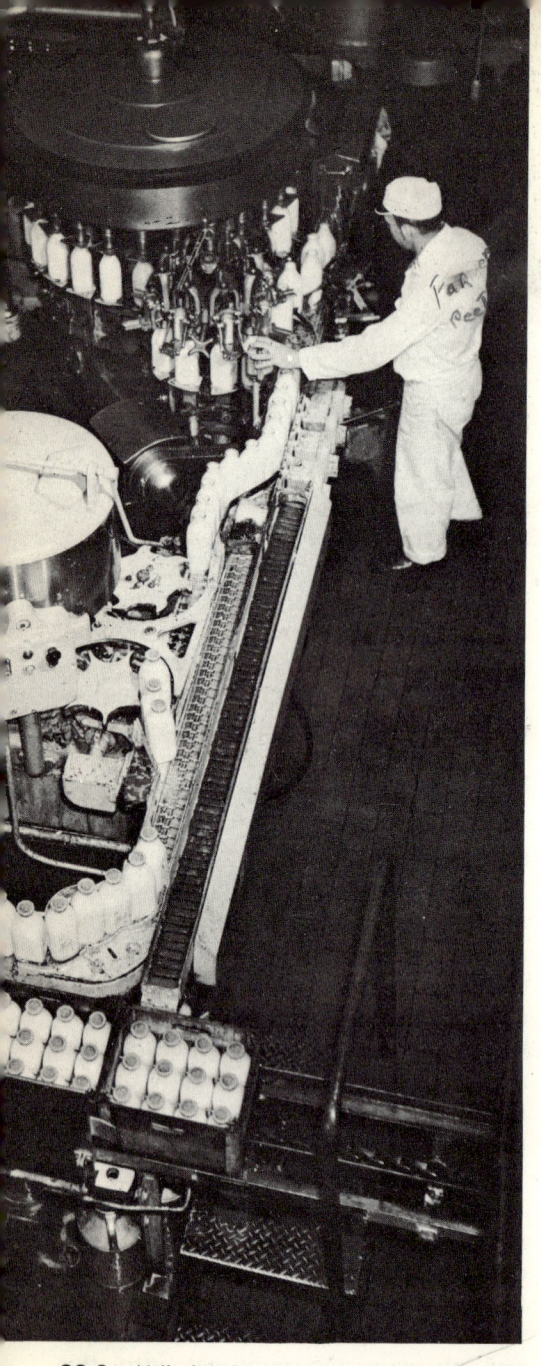

22.3 Milk bottling in a modern dairy. In the machine at the top of this picture, pasteurized milk is put into clean sterile bottles, which are capped as they leave the machine. Pasteurization of milk and sterilization of bottles is done in adjoining rooms. *Hudson Studio*

UNIT SIX — BACTERIA AND HEALTH

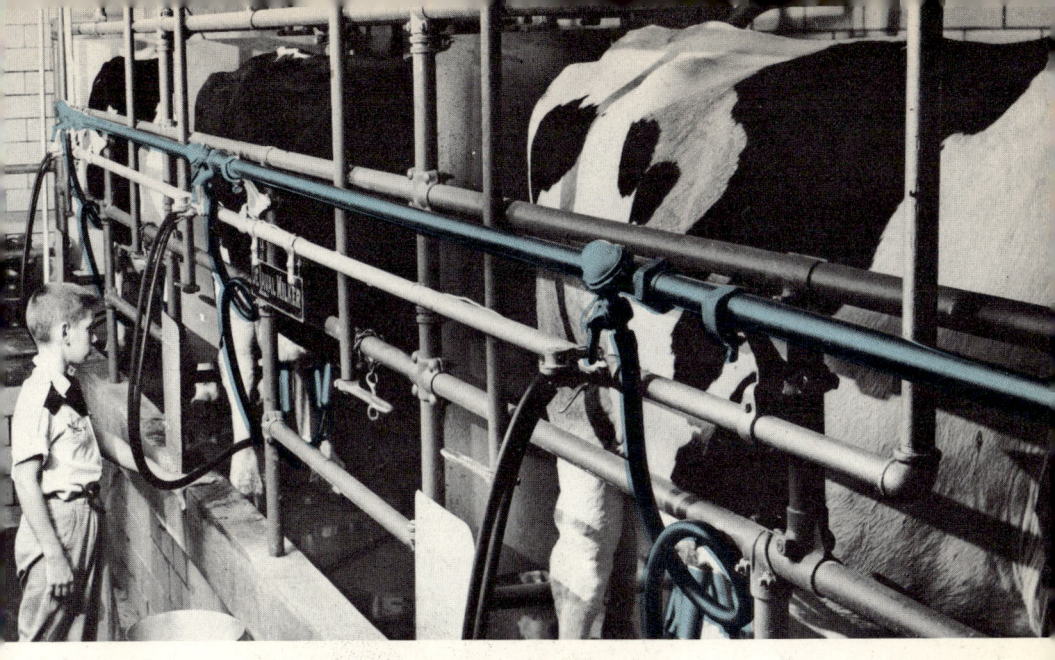

22.4 On a modern dairy farm the cows are kept clean. They are milked by machine in a clean room called a milking parlor. Milk goes through a pipe to a milk room where it is cooled immediately in sterile vessels. *H. Armstrong Roberts*

milk. Certified milk must meet far higher standards than ordinary milk.

Keeping other foods pure. Cases of infectious disease must be reported to the health officer. Sometimes those who were exposed must be quarantined; and those who are ill must be isolated. But some illnesses, like tuberculosis, are often not diagnosed immediately and even after detection a person who has tuberculosis may be permitted to be up and about and mingling with others. For this reason there must be many kinds of regulations to protect the public. Places that serve food and drink must be licensed; these places are regularly inspected to see that they and the help employed meet high standards of cleanliness and health. Food poisoning, of which we hear so much, is now believed to be caused usually by germs that come directly from someone handling the food. Formerly it was thought that the food itself in decaying formed poisonous substances, such as **ptomaines** (toe'-mains). This is probably rare.

The laws provide that foods which are eaten uncooked must be protected from dust on which bacteria ride and from flies which carry germs on their feet. Paper towels must be supplied in washrooms. Common drinking cups have mostly been replaced by drinking fountains and paper cups.

Oysters and clams may be gathered only in waters that are not polluted by sewage. Animals in slaughterhouses and meat sold by wholesale distributors should be inspected to make sure that diseased animals are not being used as food. This is a short list of regulations and practices. There is no end to the measures a health officer must take to protect the people in his charge.

Pure food and drug laws. In some cases the United States Government rather than a local health officer

22.5 This technician is helping guard your health. He is counting the bacteria in milk. Only milk that is up to standard is marketed. *H. P. Hood and Sons*

protects our health. About fifty years ago people recognized the need for protecting the public from impure foods and from misleading advertisements of both foods and drugs. Congress passed the Pure Food and Drug Act, providing for the honest labeling of packaged and canned foods, in regard to the contents of the package or can. Formerly chemicals were commonly added as preservatives. The manufacturer was obliged to state which preservatives and how much of each had been added; certain injurious preservatives were completely banned. In the same way manufacturers of patent medicines were required to state which drugs and how much of each had been used in the preparation of the medicine.

Since this law did not always accomplish what it was designed to remedy, the Federal Food, Drug, and Cosmetics Act was passed in 1938. It provides for:

(1) Stating on the label the contents or the ingredients of the article being sold.
(2) Prohibiting advertisements of foods or drugs which carry false claims.
(3) In the case of drugs, stating on the label full directions for their use and warning of the dangers in using them.
(4) Labeling habit-forming drugs conspicuously as such.

Where products are shipped across state borders or where false claims are made in advertisements either by mail or by radio, the Federal Trade Commission can summon the offender to court.

Carriers. Have you heard of Typhoid Mary? Many years ago Mary had typhoid and recovered. The germs, however, were not all killed off. These germs no longer harmed her; she was immune. But they were still virulent and could infect another person. Mary thus became a **carrier** of typhoid for the rest of her life. She was given strict orders by the health officer never to handle food which would be eaten by others. But Mary, who did not know much about germs anyway, needed a job. Suddenly typhoid broke out in a hospital. Health officers investigated and found that Mary was the cook! When she refused to cooperate she was finally put into an institution.

The health officer keeps a list of typhoid patients who have become carriers. Fortunately, not many do. Recently a carrier was responsible for an outbreak of typhoid in one of our large cities, but through no fault of her own. Several cases of typhoid appeared in close succession within one small area. Health officers soon traced all the cases to the purchase of fruit in a store located in the house in which a registered carrier lived. An unfortunate leak in the plumbing had spread the germs to the store.

Some people are diphtheria and polio carriers, too. These carriers may not even have had the disease, and yet they carry the germs. Ordinarily such carriers are not detected.

Insect carriers. Flies that breed in filth may have germs stick to their

22.6 The circular shields on the hawsers are rat guards. Use of rat guards is required by the Public Health Service as a measure to protect against introduction of bubonic plague. *Public Health Service*

feet and these may be left on our food. But flies are not true carriers. True insect carriers are those that carry a particular kind of germ sucked up with the blood of a person or animal. They inject these germs into the next victim. Fleas, for example, carry bubonic plague germs from one rat or ground squirrel to another. Or they may carry the germs from the animal to a person, especially when the diseased rat or squirrel dies of the disease. Then all of the fleas leave the body, carrying the virulent plague germs with them. Do you wonder that formerly there were terrible epidemics of bubonic plague? Figure 22.6 shows how we try to stop the spread of this disease.

The body louse carries typhus fever (this is not the same as typhoid fever); a species of African fly (the tsetse fly)

CHAPTER TWENTY-TWO — STOPPING THE SPREAD OF DISEASE

carries the germ of African sleeping sickness. And mosquitoes are carriers of malaria and yellow fever.

The importance of malaria. Malaria has almost disappeared from our country, but not in Asia, the Near East, and parts of Africa. Some three hundred million people will get malaria this year. Of these about three million will die. Many of the others will be unable to work. Poverty, malnutrition, and unrest follow. Fortunately, worldwide organizations and local agencies are attacking malaria on a large scale. In Italy, for example, the number of cases was reduced in six years from more than 400,000 to fewer than a thousand. And there were no deaths in that last year. How was this done? By killing mosquitoes with DDT and other chemicals. The cost is enormous. But in a short time the country earns more than that amount through greater production. The island of Corsica and other parts of the world have been just as successful as Italy in reducing cases of malaria.

The mystery of malaria. How does one catch malaria? This mystery was finally solved — one bit of the solution in northern Africa, another bit in India, a third bit in England, and the final bit in India. The pieces were put together, and this is the story. In 1880 a French army surgeon (Alphonse Laveran) was stationed in Algeria where there was much malaria. He examined the blood of many malaria patients and found in the blood of all of them the same tiny protozoan. How did it get there? What connection, if any, did it have with malaria? In time, researchers in France, Italy, and elsewhere saw the same protozoan and learned its life history. The protozoan glides into a red corpuscle, feeds on it, and grows so rapidly that in a day or two it fills the corpuscle. Now it divides into about a dozen small bodies. These burst the membrane of the corpuscle and get into the blood plasma. Each of the dozen finds itself a new corpuscle, feeds, grows, reproduces; each one multiplies itself by twelve. Do you wonder that the person in whom this is happening looks pale and anemic and that he feels tired? Oxygen for oxidation cannot be carried around in large enough amounts. And worse than that, when a corpuscle bursts open a toxin is given off into the blood stream. This gives the chills and fever that malaria patients have at such regular intervals.

But the question "How do the protozoa get into the blood in the first place?" still was not answered. An English physician (Patrick Manson), reading about the protozoan found in the blood of malaria patients, made a guess. It had been known for centuries that malaria occurs where it is warm and damp and swampy, just the best place for mosquitoes to breed. The name malaria means "bad air." Do mosquitoes, perhaps in biting, pick up the protozoan from the blood of a malaria patient and put it into the blood of the next victim? Manson merely mentioned his guess: he did nothing else about it. A British army surgeon in India (Dr. Ronald Ross) set himself the task of looking for these protozoa in the mosquito. It took two years of the most thorough and patient research to find them in the mosquito. Why did it take so long? First, hundreds of different kinds of mosquitoes live in India, and only about thirty kinds carry malaria. It is only some species of the ANOPHELES (an-off'el-ees) mosquito which can carry the malaria protozoan and only the female, at that. Figure 22.7 shows you how an *Anopheles*

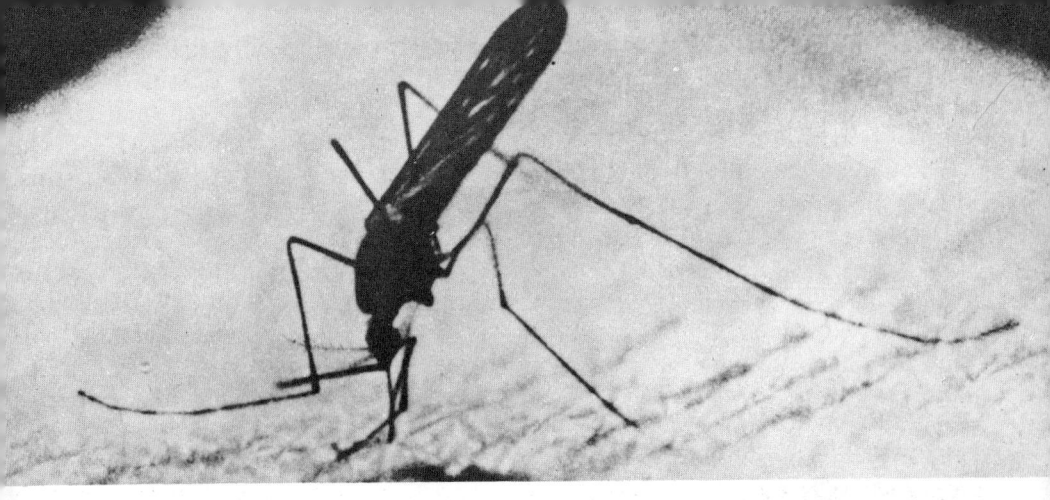

22.7 The female malaria-carrying mosquito (Anopheles) sucking blood. It "stands on its head" when biting. The common mosquito (Culex) holds its body parallel to the surface of the skin. Which kind of mosquito is common in your area? *Science Service*

mosquito looks. Secondly, Ross, naturally, was looking for the protozoan that had been found in the blood and red corpuscles of malaria patients. But this protozoan looks quite different while it lives in the mosquito. Study Figure 22.8 to see the protozoan in man and in the mosquito. After feeding for some time in the mosquito, it reproduces and some of the offspring find their way into the salivary glands of the mosquito. The protozoan's reproduction in the mosquito is by a more complicated method. When the mosquito bites the next person some of the protozoa are introduced. It can bite quite a number of people and put some protozoa into all of them.

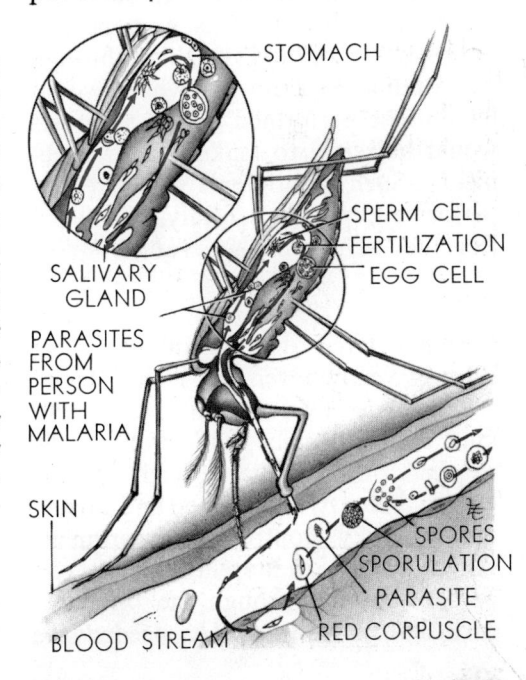

22.8 A mosquito introducing the malarial protozoan. Look first at the section of the skin (below). Do you see a protozoan entering a corpuscle? What happens to it in time? When "spores" are formed, where does each spore go? Now look at the mosquito's stomach. You can see some of the same parasites, but they soon get into the wall of the stomach where they reproduce. This mosquito had sucked up parasites from a malaria patient some time before. Later the parasites wriggle into the salivary glands. This mosquito is injecting the protozoa into the skin of a new victim. In a day or two another mosquito may suck his blood and fill its stomach with parasites.

CHAPTER TWENTY-TWO — STOPPING THE SPREAD OF DISEASE

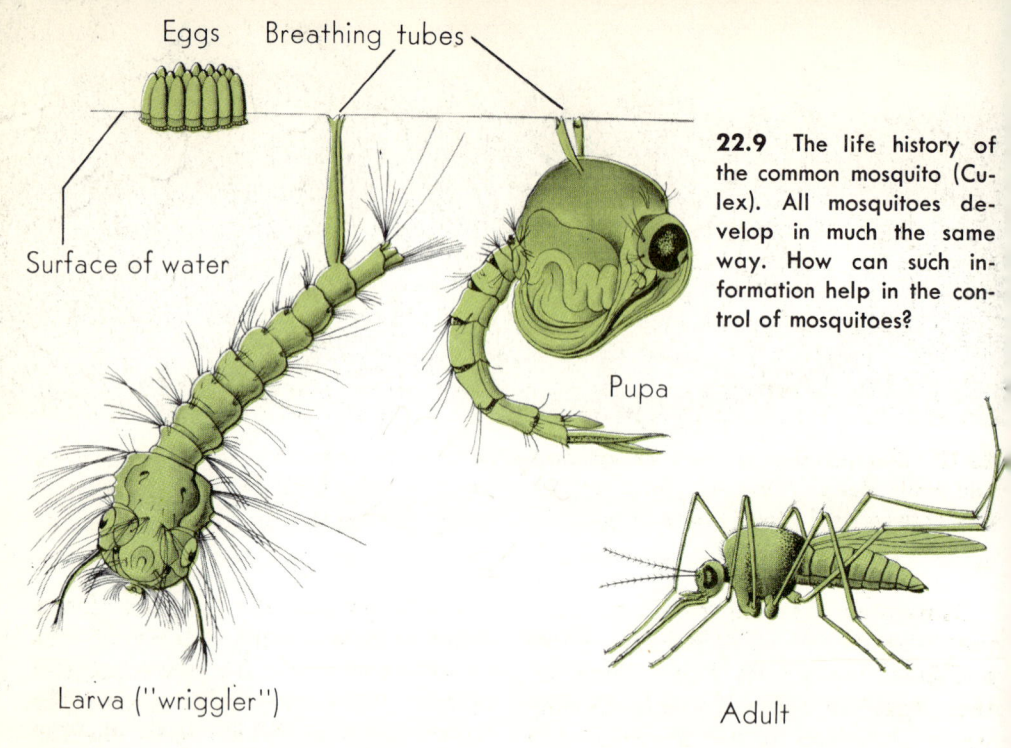

22.9 The life history of the common mosquito (Culex). All mosquitoes develop in much the same way. How can such information help in the control of mosquitoes?

Putting all these pieces of evidence together into one story was still not proof that malaria is always caused by a protozoan carried by an *Anopheles* mosquito, and that it is caused in no other way. Experiments were needed to prove this. Could you think through and outline experiments which would have to be performed before scientists would be ready to make such a statement? Such experiments were actually performed, partly in Italy, partly in England. The proof was found.

Yellow fever and mosquitoes. The germ of yellow fever or "Yellow Jack" is also carried by a mosquito, a different kind that is usually found only in the tropics. Dr. Walter Reed of the United States Army planned and carried out carefully controlled experiments which proved that yellow fever can be spread only through the bite of a particular mosquito. He needed the help of volunteers for these experiments, brave men who were willing to risk their lives, since yellow fever is very often a fatal disease. Two privates in the United States Army (John R. Kissinger and John J. Moran) allowed themselves to be bitten by yellow fever mosquitoes which had just before sucked the blood of yellow fever patients. Both men came down with bad cases of the disease. They suffered horribly for days but finally recovered. Other army volunteers slept for twenty nights in a screened hut with the bedding and belongings of patients who had just died of yellow fever. None of them got yellow fever. Of course, more experiments had to be performed before it could be stated with certainty that a person gets yellow fever only when a particular kind of mosquito introduces the disease-producing organism, in this case a virus. It is clear that mosquito extermination is an important sanitary measure.

340 UNIT SIX — BACTERIA AND HEALTH

22.10 This old creek is being straightened and made deeper. How will this affect the flow of the water? Would the small wrigglers and pupae, with their delicate breathing tubes, be more likely to survive in still or in rapidly flowing water?

Mosquito extermination. To exterminate mosquitoes, we must know where and how mosquitoes live. They lay their eggs on still or slowly moving water. In a week or two the eggs hatch into tiny larvae called wrigglers. Look at Figure 22.9 to see how both larva and pupa breathe air above the surface of the water. To kill them we need only to spread the thinnest film of any oil, such as kerosene, over the surface of the water. This cuts off the air supply from both larva and pupa. Sometimes it is easier to fill in or drain the stagnant pools, as shown in Figure 22.10. Then no mosquitoes can reproduce. Or we can stock the waters with small fish that feed on mosquito larvae and pupae.

But to kill malaria mosquitoes on a large scale, mosquito breeding grounds and houses are sprayed with DDT or some other material. Within several years a region can be cleaned up by this method. The difficulty with this method is that mosquitoes may develop strains resistant to the poison. Then it fails to work. It is therefore important that *all* mosquitoes in these areas be killed before resistant strains develop.

The larger parasites. Health officers certainly have a large variety of jobs as we have seen. But there are still others. They protect us against the larger parasites which give disease. Of these the most common and perhaps the most serious in our part of the world are the hookworm and the trichina worm. The **hookworm** has for centuries undermined the health of people living in warm climates. It belongs to the group of roundworms and looks like a tiny white thread, hardly visible to the naked eye. It starts its life in the soil and enters the skin of the foot of anyone walking barefooted. Then it travels far: first it gets into the blood stream; next it bores through the lungs, sometimes damaging them badly; then, up through the windpipe; down through the food pipe; and into the intestines. Here it fastens itself to the wall of the intestine, pierces a blood vessel, and secretes a substance which keeps blood from clotting. Thus the worm has a steady flow of blood on which it feeds. The constant bleeding causes anemia and tiredness, which was generally mistaken for laziness before the hook-

CHAPTER TWENTY-TWO — STOPPING THE SPREAD OF DISEASE

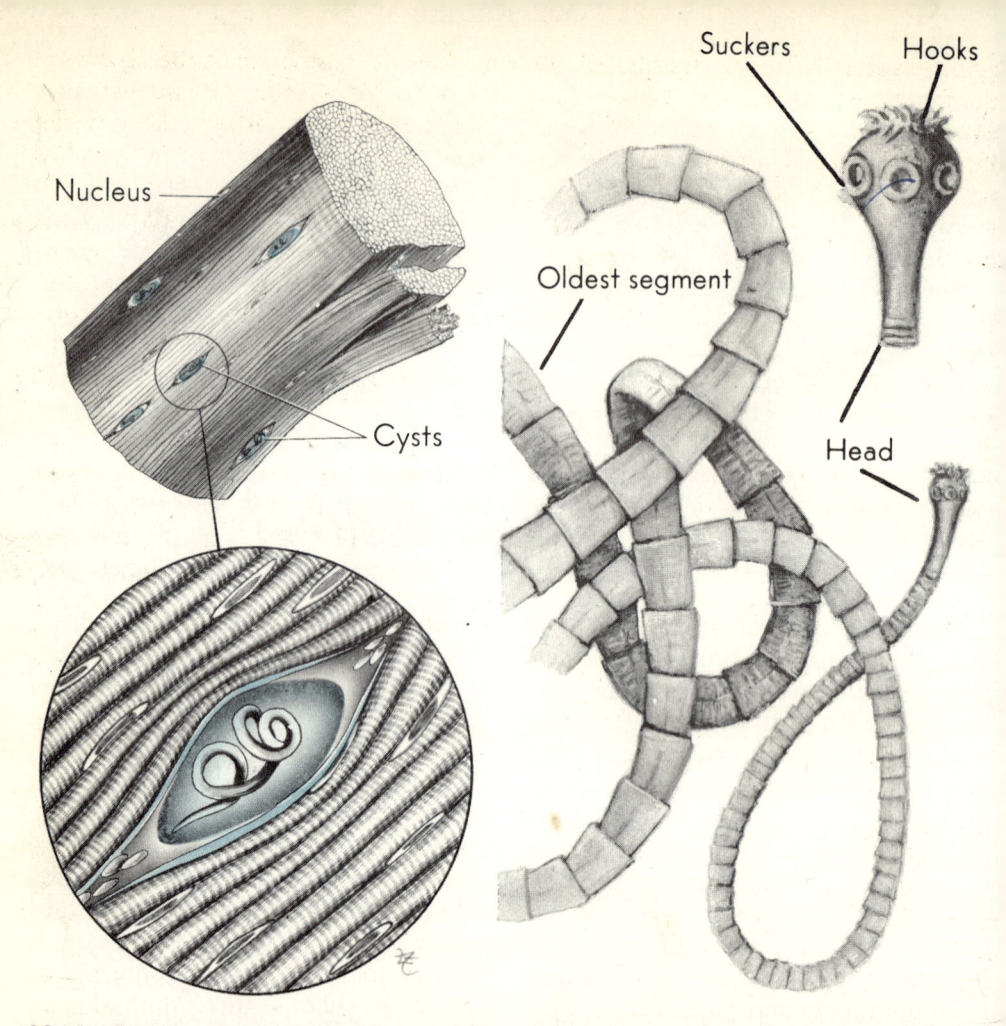

22.11 Trichina cyst in muscle, below. The muscle above shows many cysts.

22.12 The tapeworm is an ugly-looking visitor. How does it cling to its host?

worm was discovered. The worm grows and reproduces rapidly. The eggs pass out of the intestines with the excretions and get into the soil. You can well see that poverty and lack of sanitary measures allow the hookworm to spread from person to person. Wearing shoes is the best way to escape hookworm infection. Recently, drugs have been discovered which kill the worm in the host.

The trichina worm. Another roundworm is the **trichina** (tri-ky′na) worm.

It lives in the intestines of two hosts, the pig and man. In both hosts the young get into the muscles and there the worm forms a hard coat around itself. We call this a **cyst** (sist). You can see one in Figure 22.11. A small portion of infected pork may contain many thousands of these cysts. In pork that has not been thoroughly cooked the young worms are still alive. After the food reaches the intestines the worms come out of their cysts and reproduce. Shortly the young worms travel to the muscles and form cysts

UNIT SIX — BACTERIA AND HEALTH

again, especially in the muscles of the diaphragm, tongue, and eyes. This causes a great deal of pain and fever, but the disease is rarely fatal. Fortunately, if the pork has been in cold storage for several weeks, the worms are dead before the meat is cooked.

But how does the worm get into the pig? Pigs probably get it from eating garbage with infected pork scraps. The United States Government inspects meat sent from one state to another, but there is little inspection of meat sold within the state. That is why we must all know the danger of eating pork or pork products which have not been thoroughly cooked. And the farmer must know the danger of feeding his pigs garbage which has not been cooked enough to kill the trichina worm.

The tapeworm. The tapeworm, one of the flatworms, is still another parasite that may make trouble for us, but much less serious trouble. Several kinds of tapeworms can live in our intestines. They develop from young, or larval, stages which live in the muscles of some other animal. One kind lives in a cow, another in a pig, a less common kind in some fresh-water fish. In the muscles of these animals the tapeworm larva forms a cyst. If we eat such infected meat or fish which has not been sufficiently cooked, we swallow a living young worm. This attaches itself to the wall of the intestine and begins to eat our food. It grows rapidly, adding more and more segments. A twenty-five foot tapeworm was once found. Figure 22.12 shows how it is able to cling to the intestinal wall. The picture also shows some of the oldest segments which are filled with eggs ready to hatch. These segments break off and leave the body with the excretions. In the soil each egg changes into a larva which may be picked up by a grazing cow or pig. Tapeworms are easy to get rid of with drugs. With proper meat inspection there should be no tapeworms in the meat we buy.

What have you learned? This table is far from complete, especially in citing examples, but it may help you recall some of the many important things you have read. The most important measure a community can adopt against the spread of disease is the education of the public. This might therefore be mentioned in every case.

TABLE 18

	HOW DISEASE IS SPREAD	MEASURES AGAINST SPREAD	EXAMPLES
1	Through contact or air	Quarantine; Isolation	Smallpox, diphtheria
2	Through water	Sewage disposal, supplying unpolluted water	Typhoid, cholera, other intestinal diseases
3	Through milk	Pasteurization; Inspection at all stages of production	Tuberculosis, septic sore throat
4	Through other foods	Inspection and licensing of restaurants, food handlers	Tuberculosis, influenza
5	Through carriers (no longer ill or never ill)	Registration of known carriers	Typhoid, many other diseases
6	Through insect carriers	Mosquito extermination	Malaria, yellow fever
7	Through infected meat	Meat inspection	Trichina worm, tapeworm
8	From polluted soil	Raising standard of living	Hookworm

CHAPTER TWENTY-TWO — STOPPING THE SPREAD OF DISEASE

USEFUL WORDS IN BIOLOGY

epidemic	watershed	carrier
quarantine	chlorinate	Anopheles
vital statistics	pasteurize	trichina worm
polluted	ptomaine	cyst

TEST YOURSELF

1. Give several reasons why epidemics are not now so widespread as they frequently were in former times.
2. (a) What must be known about the germs of an infectious disease if it is to be kept from spreading? (b) What facts do you know about typhoid and tuberculosis, for example, which should help you protect yourself and others?
3. (a) Explain how some communities have solved the two important problems of sewage disposal and supplying pure water. (b) What is done in your community?
4. There are several reasons why milk, more than most other foods, should have special attention by health officers. (a) What are they? (b) What measures are usually taken to make sure that the milk we buy will not give us diseases?
5. Licensing restaurants, control of oyster beds, and inspection of slaughterhouses are a very few of the functions of health officers. In each of these cases explain fully which disease or diseases the health officers are attempting to control.
6. By what act does the Federal Government attempt to protect our health? Explain the major provisions of this act.
7. (a) Name one disease that may be transmitted by a human "carrier" and another transmitted by an insect carrier. (b) Explain in what sense people and insects are really different types of carriers.
8. Describe each of the many discoveries that were pieced together to explain the cause of malaria.
9. Describe the experiments which definitely established the fact that yellow fever is transmitted by a mosquito.
10. Describe three ways of controlling mosquitoes other than by the use of DDT.
11. Under what conditions does DDT fail to exterminate mosquitoes?
12. Show in table form about these worms—hookworm, trichina, and tapeworm: (a) how one gets the worm; (b) where and how it harms the body; (c) how one can get rid of the worm.

DO IT YOURSELF

1. An eminent physician interested in public health, has listed five of the six important services of a board of health: vital and disease statistics; control of common infectious diseases; sanitation of housing and workplaces, water and milk supplies; laboratory services to physicians; health education. After consulting with the principal of your school you may be able to take on one or more functions of a health department in your own school community.
2. **A visit to a food market, milk distributing plant, model farm, sewage disposal or water purification plant.** If any of these trips are possible, use all your powers of observation, take full notes and write a report. Before you go prepare questions which you will want answered.
3. **Comparing the number of bacteria in different kinds of milk.** In Chapter 19 you learned how to prepare nutrient agar. Perhaps you were able to keep some of the unexposed dishes. Use them now. Test equal amounts of pasteurized and raw milk (if it is obtainable) for the number of bacteria contained in it. Compare also fresh pasteurized milk with milk two or three days old. In each case dilute a small amount of milk with ten times the amount of sterile, distilled (or freshly boiled) water. You must use a separate dish for each sample. Everything you use must, of course, be sterile. Do you need a control?

4. Could a housefly contaminate food? Catch a housefly and let it walk over the sterile nutrient agar in a Petri dish. Do you need a control? Examine the dish after 48 hours. Describe your results.

5. My career. If you have found the subject of bacteria and disease interesting you will want to look into the large number of careers open to you besides the obvious ones of doctor and nurse. Many physicians devote themselves to research in pathology (the study of the origin and nature of disease). Local, state, and federal public health offer a large variety of careers. The large drug companies employ many research workers and technicians. Laboratory technicians are needed by hospitals and doctors. The Institute for Research, 537 South Dearborn St., Chicago, Illinois, publishes a large number of pamphlets under the heading "Careers." Research Bulletin #3 is *Biology as a Career*. Science Research Associates, Chicago, Illinois, publishes a pamphlet called *Careers in Public Health*, by Adrian Gould. Rice Research Associates, Chicago, Illinois, publishes *Biology Careers Manual*. *Outlook for Women in Biological Sciences* is a Women's Bureau Bulletin 223-3, 1948, U.S. Dept. of Labor. There is also *Veterinary Medicine as a Career*, American Veterinary Medical Association, Chicago, 1947. Get a list of titles on careers from the Superintendent of Documents, Washington, D.C. You will find other suggestions under "Adventures in Reading."

ADVENTURES IN READING

1. *Malaria; the Biography of a Killer* by Leon J. Warshaw, Rinehart, 1949. Also contains chapters on quinine and on the work of Gorgas and yellow fever.
2. "The Eradication of Malaria" by P. F. Russell, *Scientific American*, May 1952. Tells in an interesting way how malaria was practically wiped out in Italy within five years.
3. *DDT, Killer of Killers* by O. T. Zimmerman and I. Lavine, Industrial Research Service, Dover, New Hampshire, 1946. Contains two interesting chapters on epidemics and how DDT was discovered and first tried out.
4. *Yellow Jack*, a history by Sidney Howard in collaboration with P. de Kruif, Harcourt, 1934.
5. *History of the Plague* by Daniel Defoe was written early in the 18th century. It is a most exciting account of the great epidemic of bubonic plague which swept over Europe and Asia.
6. *Careers in Science* by Philip Pollock, Dutton, 1945.
7. "Career Opportunities in Natural Science Education" by Dorothy E. Alfke, *The American Biology Teacher*, April, May 1954.

Chapter 23

Building health

Length of life. For four hundred years, see Figure 23.1, the average length of man's life has been increasing. Note how short a distance the "average" man walked in the 16th century before he was stopped by death. Of course, even in the 16th century some people lived longer than nineteen years; many lived much longer. But so many died as babies and young children that the *average* length of life was only nineteen years. Now look at the long road a man has ahead of him in 1955. Why is this? If you were to review and summarize what you have learned during the past few weeks, you could answer that question. We have learned how to immunize people against many infectious diseases, how to cure many diseases with wonder drugs, how to keep many infectious diseases from spreading, and how to avoid many deficiency diseases. We have better food, better housing, more leisure for rest, and greater security. All this makes it possible now for more people to live to middle or even old age. But when so many people live to old age there is a great increase in the population, which is already growing rapidly because of the large number of births. This increase makes it more necessary than ever for us to develop all of our resources, our supplies of food, which depend on the soil, our water supplies, our forests and wildlife.

And as the average length of life is increased, new problems arise for the health authorities, too. As more people reach old age the "old-age diseases" become more common and need more attention from research scientists. Let us look at those diseases next.

23.1 The gradual increase in average length of life. Note how in four centuries the "stop" signs have been moved farther and farther along the road. In which century or half century has there been the greatest increase?

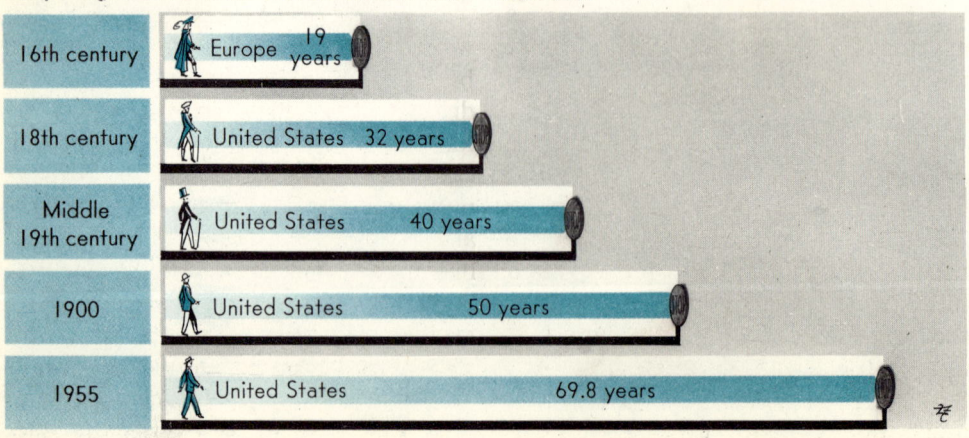

16th century	Europe	19 years
18th century	United States	32 years
Middle 19th century	United States	40 years
1900	United States	50 years
1955	United States	69.8 years

UNIT SIX — BACTERIA AND HEALTH

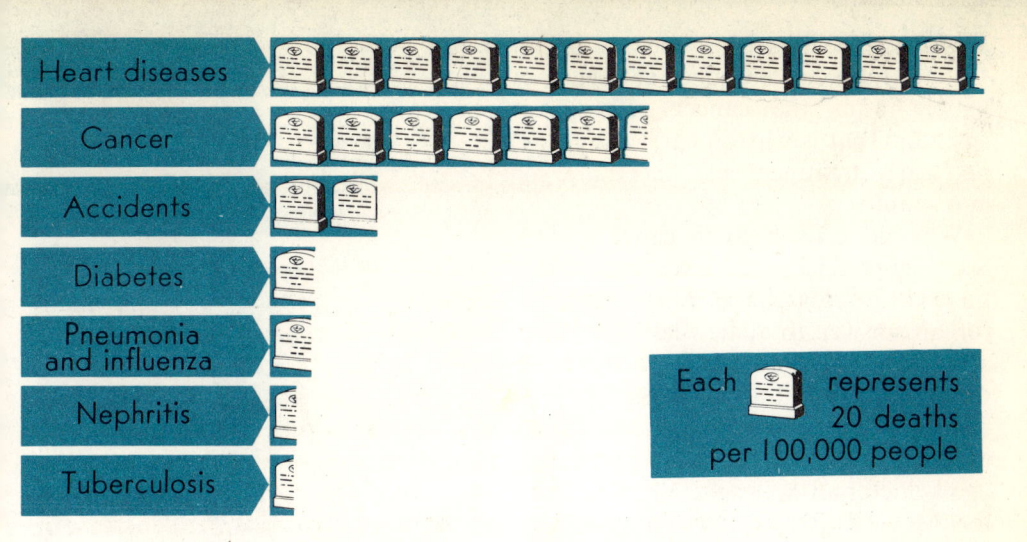

Heart diseases	🪦🪦🪦🪦🪦🪦🪦🪦🪦🪦🪦
Cancer	🪦🪦🪦🪦🪦🪦
Accidents	🪦
Diabetes	🪦
Pneumonia and influenza	🪦
Nephritis	🪦
Tuberculosis	🪦

Each 🪦 represents 20 deaths per 100,000 people

23.2 Causes of death among the Metropolitan Life Insurance Company policy holders during 1955. You can see at a glance which are the major killers. Some years ago this picture would have looked different. For what two reasons?

The worst killers today. The worst killers nowadays are diseases of the circulatory organs and cancer, Figure 23.2. Fifty years ago pneumonia and influenza would have been in the top row with the largest number of deaths. In the second row would have been tuberculosis. Both are germ diseases. Naturally, since we have learned to prevent or cure infectious diseases more successfully, more people reach old age. But this is the time when organic diseases strike, such diseases as cancer and diseases of the heart and blood vessels.

Cancer. We certainly hear a great deal about cancer now. You just saw one good reason why that should be. There are other reasons. Much has been learned about cancer today; many more cases are recognized. And then, too, people are no longer afraid or ashamed to speak about cancer. And that is a good thing! Cancer cures are much more common today since many people consult a physician as soon as they suspect cancer. Early diagnosis and early treatment are of great importance.

What is cancer? You know that in children growth and division of cells is normal. Even in adults, cells in such tissues as skin and blood divide throughout life; but most tissue cells stop dividing early in life. Cancer is an abnormal growth and division of cells in any organ or tissue. Cells that would normally have stopped dividing begin to divide again and continue to divide; thus they form a lump, or tumor. Not all lumps or tumors are cancers — far from it. Many, perhaps most, are not dangerous. Such tumors are said to be **benign** (be-nine′), or harmless; they can usually be removed by a surgeon. A cancer, however, is a **malignant tumor** — some of the cancer cells may break off and be carried by the blood or lymph to other parts of the body, where new cancer tissues

CHAPTER TWENTY-THREE — BUILDING HEALTH 347

start. At the time this book is being written, little can be done for a cancer patient after the cancer cells have spread. That is why an early diagnosis and early treatment of cancer are so important.

Why do cells become cancer cells? See Figure 23.3. All over the world there are research scientists looking for an answer to that question. The answer may well be a clue to the cure of cancer. But this much is known: cancers are not all alike, nor caused in the same way. Some forty years ago a doctor at the Rockefeller Institute for Medical Research (Peyton Rous) mashed malignant chicken tumors and filtered the mashed cells through a porcelain filter. He then injected the clear material that went through the filter into healthy chickens. These chickens developed tumors. Some kinds of cancer in mice, too, can be caused by a filterable substance present in the milk of the mother mouse. Although these cancers seem to be caused by a virus, they are not spread in the way virus diseases are ordinarily spread. And we still have no evidence that any kind of cancer in people is caused by a virus.

Cancers can be caused by continued irritation from ultraviolet light, heat, or chemical substances such as coal tar products. Workers with dyes, tar, luminous paint, and a variety of other substances, unless properly protected, are often affected. It is believed that injury causes cells to lose their power of respiration. They then get energy from fermentation, and in time become cancer cells. Since tar compounds are formed in cigarette smoking, some people think smoking may be responsible for the increase in lung cancer. Experts disagree. Much research is going on.

Does the pituitary gland have any

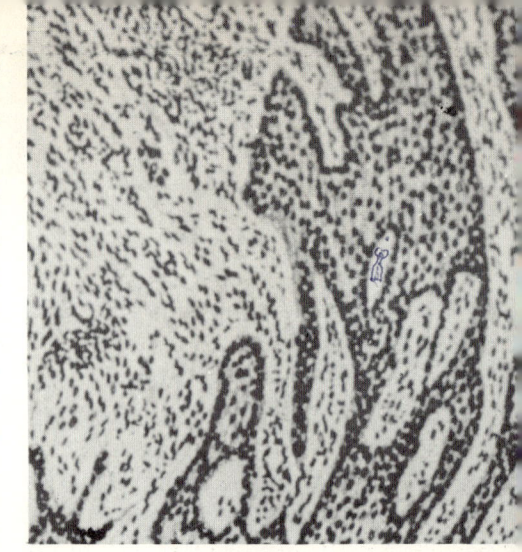

23.3 The dark colored groups of cells are cancer cells. *American Cancer Society*

connection with cancer? It stimulates normal growth and it seems to stimulate the growth of certain tumors. When the pituitary is removed from rats they do not develop cancer even when treated in ways which normally bring about malignant tumors.

Another question that bothers people is this: Is cancer inherited? It sometimes seems to run in some families more than in others. But the question of the inheritance of cancer in man has not yet been settled.

Possible cancer symptoms. Often there are no definite symptoms of cancer in its early stages. But lumps anywhere, especially in the breast or on the lips should always be looked on with suspicion. So should unusual bleeding, persistent hoarseness, and persistent indigestion. Moles and sores that do not heal should be watched. In no case should moles be tampered with; you must consult a physician if moles begin to change. Cancers of the skin are not uncommon, but if treated promptly and in the right way, they need not be a cause for worry.

Treatment of cancer. Certain kinds of cancerous tissues can be removed by surgery. Other kinds may be treated with x-rays, which kill the cancerous cells. Radium, which gives off rays similar to x-rays, can be used to treat some internal cancers. A radioactive substance is placed in a capsule near the cancer cells. Radioactive isotopes of calcium and phosphorus have been used in certain cancer treatments.

Cancer is everyone's business. The search for the cause and cure of cancer goes on constantly. Trained men and women are employed for this work by the United States Public Health Service, state and local cancer societies, and by universities and medical schools. But public education, too, is an important part of our attack on cancer. And this is where all of you can help. You can help teach people to be on the lookout for the first signs of cancer, and if necessary, to start treatment promptly. A regular medical checkup once a year is important.

Circulatory diseases. You may have heard of a "nervous heart." People sometimes feel the heart beating too fast, or too slowly, when there is really nothing wrong with the heart or blood vessels. A thorough medical examination and an **electrocardiogram** (electro-car'de-oh-gram) can usually be depended upon to show whether there is a defect in the heart or blood vessels. You read about some of these defects in Chapter 11. Sometimes infectious diseases in children weaken the heart for a time. This is especially true of rheumatic fever. The aftereffects may last for some years, and during that time the child needs special care. Some communities provide free care for such children when they need financial help and until they have outgrown the heart condition.

Careful living according to a doctor's advice often makes it quite possible for people with serious circulatory disease to live to old age. Diet is important, too; you know the danger of putting on weight as you grow older. Salt-free diets and diets with little fat are often prescribed.

Appendicitis. Inflammation of the appendix is called **appendicitis.** See Figure 23.4. Bacteria cause an inflammation in the wall of the appendix. (Of course, these are not germs that one catches from anyone else.) White blood cells are left there by the blood.

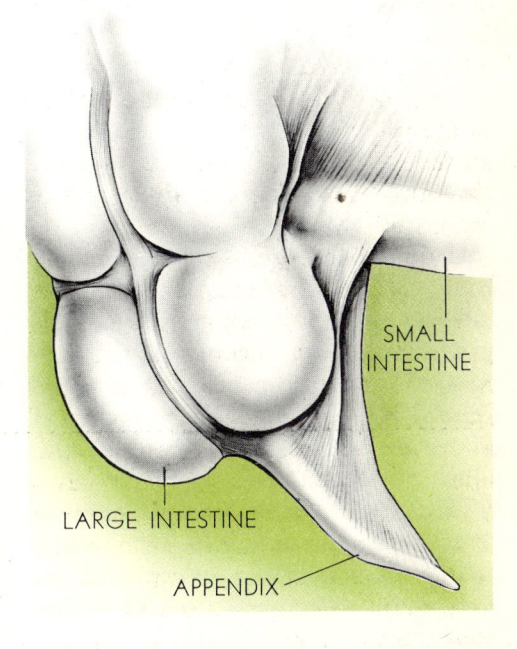

23.4 The appendix projects from a pouch of the large intestine. It seems to have no use. Food remaining in it may cause trouble.

CHAPTER TWENTY-THREE — BUILDING HEALTH

The appendix swells, and there is pain. You know where your appendix lies — in the lower right part of the abdomen. The pain is not always in this region, however. Any abdominal pain, especially if it occurs at intervals, may mean that the appendix is infected. This is particularly true of young people of high school age. Appendicitis is most likely to occur in these years.

You should never use hot pads or laxatives if you have an abdominal pain. If home treatment seems necessary, rest and use an ice pack. You know why — bacteria grow more slowly at lower temperatures than at higher temperatures. If an abdominal pain lasts more than a few hours, call a doctor! The doctor can tell how serious the infection is by taking a blood count; with any serious infection the white blood cells increase two or threefold very quickly. Antibiotics are used for this, as for other infection. If attacks of appendicitis are frequent, even though mild, an "interval" operation — an operation between attacks — is often recommended.

Accidents. Accidents cause more than one fourth of all deaths among children of school age. They cause more deaths than pneumonia, tuberculosis, influenza, rheumatic fever, and appendicitis combined. And almost all accidents can be prevented. Ask yourself the questions in Figure 23.5. If you or your family have not yet corrected a faulty condition listed here and an accident occurs, you can blame it on your own carelessness and not on "bad luck." Automobile accidents, too, are rarely the fault of the car. Foolish, selfish, and often law-breaking people cause these, though it may be the innocent person who suffers most.

PREVENT FALLS:

1. Do you use a nonslip rug or heavy towel in the bathtub or shower?
2. Do you have nonslip backing under small rugs?
3. Do you immediately clean up food, grease, or liquid spilled on the floor?
4. Do all members of the family put away hobby materials or toys to prevent falls?

PREVENT BURNS AND POISONING:

5. Do you use only noninflammable cleaning fluids?
6. Do you make sure no member of the family smokes in bed?
7. Do you make sure curtains and drying laundry are hung away from stove or heater?
8. Do you make sure ammonia, bleaches, cleaning fluids, lye, rat, and roach poisons are stored away where children cannot get them?
9. Do you make sure there are no peeling paint flakes or plaster (lead poisoning) which young children can get and chew?

PREVENT OTHER ACCIDENTS:

10. Do you avoid putting electric cords under rugs?
11. Do you have frayed electric cords repaired?
12. Do you avoid touching electric fixtures or switches when your hands or body are wet?
13. Do you have first aid supplies located where they can be reached easily?

23.5 The Board of Education of New York City, with The Greater New York Safety Council, and the Police Department, issues a blank (modified here) to all school children. Of which practices are you guilty?

23.6 A safety suit worn by a technician working with radioactive materials. *General Electric*

23.7 The ragweed leaf is easily recognized. Do you see the small flowers in spikes? *Hugh Spencer*

Accidents in industry are, also, still too common. Labor unions and employers, however, have done much to reduce accidents. And progress in making use of safety devices continues. See Figure 23.6.

Allergies. Are you **allergic** (al-ler′jick), or unusually sensitive, to any substance? A specific food may be the cause of an allergy; even dust, feathers, fur, or almost any substance which can be blown about in tiny particles may be responsible. The symptoms are varied, too. There may be a running nose, watering of the eyes, or a cough. There may be a skin rash or itch, diarrhea, asthma, or some other reaction which you yourself can tell about. The reaction usually comes on rapidly. It may be mild or violent; it may pass off soon or be lasting. It may become less troublesome as the person grows older, or it may appear suddenly at any age.

Hay fever is the result of an allergy, caused by pollen from the flowers of a particular plant. **Ragweeds** give the worst form of hay fever, not hay! You find them along roads, around cultivated fields, and in city lots in many parts of the country, especially in the Middle West and in the East. Look at Figure 23.7 so that you will recognize this troublesome weed. Perhaps you can help get rid of it. In many parts of the country ragweed flowers open and begin to discharge their pollen in the middle of August. They continue to spread pollen until frost comes.

Other pollens cause allergies at different seasons: in midsummer, the pollen of grasses such as timothy and redtop; in spring, the pollen of oak, maple, elm, birch, and other trees. Goldenrod

CHAPTER TWENTY-THREE — BUILDING HEALTH

23.8 Testing for allergies. Do you see the many small scratches that have been made? What might be in the many bottles in the background? The doctor knows later from the appearance of the skin to which substances she is allergic. *Parke, Davis and Co.*

and roses, in spite of their bad reputation, do not cause allergies; their pollen is sticky and is not carried by the air. Both flowers are showy, and we overlook the less conspicuous flowers blooming and discharging pollen at the same time. Thus many people jumped to the conclusion that roses and goldenrod cause "rose fever" and "hay fever."

Tests for allergies. The girl in Figure 23.8 is getting a skin test. She is allergic to something, and the doctor is trying by this means to find out what causes her trouble. Pollens, various foods, dust, and other substances may be scratched lightly into the skin. The doctor can later judge from the appearance of the skin around each scratch to which substance she is allergic. Skin tests for food allergies are not very satisfactory, however.

If he finds the cause, the doctor may treat the person by injecting some of the offending substance in increasing doses. Or if it is food, it may be fed in very tiny amounts daily. This may give some relief for a while. Some drugs, too, **antihistamines** (an-tee-hist′te-means), sometimes relieve hay fever or skin allergies, such as hives. If you suffer often from asthma, eczema (ek′se-ma), or hives, you will, of course, consult a physician. These may be allergies or they may be symptoms of some other trouble. It is sensible to let a physician decide.

Other causes of poor health. The common cold causes more absences from school or work than any other infectious disease. And a cold is often followed by more serious illness. In

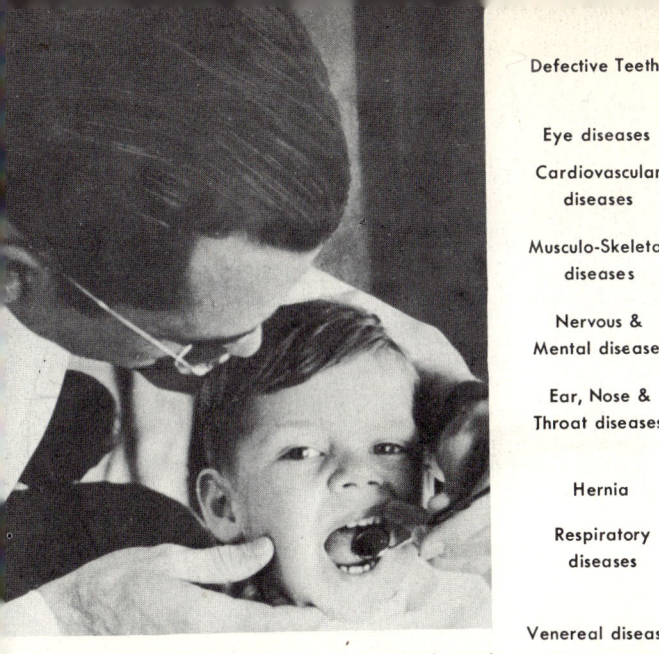

23.9 Checking on the teeth. An infected tooth may have consequences more serious than a toothache. Can you explain what might happen? *Hygeia*

many places much research is being done to find the cause and prevention of the common cold. There seem to be several different viruses and also some bacteria that are responsible for colds; this is what has made their prevention and cure so difficult. If you suffer a great deal from colds, a vaccine can be made for *you* from your own nasal discharge. This is called **autogenous** (aw-toj'en-us) vaccine. But, in general, the best we can do now is to build up our resistance by means of correct diet and sufficient exercise and rest.

Malnutrition, or the lack of sufficient vitamins, minerals, or other food compounds, is still far too common, even among people who can afford the very best food. Malnutrition causes fatigue and lack of energy, even if the person escapes a deficiency disease. But worse than that, it increases susceptibility to germ diseases.

Defective Teeth
Eye diseases
Cardiovascular diseases
Musculo-Skeletal diseases
Nervous & Mental diseases
Ear, Nose & Throat diseases
Hernia
Respiratory diseases
Venereal diseases
Foot diseases
Overweight & Underweight
Unfit & Defective
Other Causes

Each symbol represents 1% of those medically examined under the Selective Service System (1941)

23.10 Causes of rejection of draftees during World War II. How many causes for rejection are indicated? What caused the most rejections?

Then there are the tonsils, the teeth, and the sinuses (cavities in the bones of the head) that may make trouble for us. Bacteria may cause inflammation in these regions, and pus may be formed. Sometimes, too, toxins and bacteria may spread from that point to other parts of the body. **Sinusitis** (sigh-nu-sigh'tis) is an infection of the membranes lining the sinuses; it is painful and is often difficult to cure. If tonsils become infected frequently, they can, of course, be removed without

CHAPTER TWENTY-THREE — BUILDING HEALTH

harm. Infected teeth can be treated or pulled. See Figure 23.9.

Among nine million men examined for the United States Armed Forces during World War II, 43 out of every 100 were found physically or mentally unfit. See Figure 23.10.

As you read about keeping yourself in the best of health, some questions may have come to you — questions about the effects of alcohol and tobacco. Unfortunately, there is still much that is not known on these subjects; on the other hand there are some things we do know.

Smoking and length of life. Professor Raymond C. Pearl of Johns Hopkins University gathered figures some years ago in an attempt to find out whether smokers die earlier than nonsmokers. He compared the length of life of men in three groups: those who were heavy smokers, those who were moderate smokers, and those who never smoked. He found that a higher percentage of the nonsmokers and the moderate smokers than of the heavy smokers lived to the age of sixty. But Professor Pearl knew that figures or "statistics" of this kind do not serve to prove a case. Controlled experiments can give us real proof, but controlled experiments to find the effect of tobacco smoking on length of life seem impossible. He, therefore, did not say that smoking makes people die at an earlier age; he stated his conclusions only in very general terms: heavy smoking seems to have some connection with shorter life span. You already know about the possible connection between cigarette smoking and lung cancer. It is true that since the great rise in cigarette sales there has also been a rise in the number of cases of lung cancer. Also, some kinds of lung cancer are almost never found in people who do not smoke. As science students, however, you know that these facts do not *prove* that cigarette smoking caused the rise. Many other conditions of life changed within this same period. These may be responsible. We shall have to wait for an answer; but until we have that answer, the best advice is, "Do not smoke!"

What do we know about tobacco? Tobacco contains **nicotine**, a very powerful poison if injected directly into the veins. If you smoke a cigarette to the end and inhale the fumes, you may get into your body from one to two milligrams of nicotine. A fatal dose would be 60 to 120 milligrams. Even a small amount of nicotine in your blood affects the autonomic ganglia, causing a constriction of blood vessels and a quickening of the heartbeat. But tobacco smoke contains, besides nicotine, a number of other harmful or irritating substances in small amounts. Athletes while in training are advised not to smoke. Smoking is also forbidden to people with serious circulatory diseases and sometimes to those with sinus trouble, throat irritations, or certain allergies.

Yet a great many boys and girls in high school are eager to begin to smoke. Why? It is natural for young people in their teens to want to grow up and to want to prove to themselves and to others that they are growing up. Are there, perhaps, other and better ways of showing this?

Alcohol in the body. Unlike most other substances we eat or drink, alcohol is absorbed into the blood from the stomach. Absorption is especially fast if the stomach is empty. Alcohol circulates in the blood to all the body cells, where it is oxidized rapidly. However, it should not be

23.11 Four young people died when this car collided with a truck. Many such "accidents" have "happened" after the driver has been drinking. *Wide World*

used in place of food for giving energy. In the walls of arteries alcohol causes the muscles to relax; for this reason small amounts of alcohol are sometimes recommended for people with high blood pressure. Brain tissue absorbs more alcohol than the other tissues. For a very short time, therefore, immediately after being taken, it acts as a stimulant. But this does not last; it soon acts as a **depressant;** that is, it slows down reflexes and other bodily activities.

In the brain, alcohol affects the higher brain centers first; a person thinks less clearly, his judgment is not as good, and he sees less clearly. As more alcohol reaches the brain, it affects the centers that control the skeletal muscles, those that help you coordinate. The person can no longer speak clearly and he stumbles or sways as he walks. With still more alcohol, the nerve cells in the medulla become affected, those that control breathing and other internal functions. By this time the person has become unconscious. Death may result. How much alcohol is needed to bring about each of these changes varies with the individual. It even varies in the same individual at different times.

You can easily understand how drinking makes the driver of an automobile a less reliable driver. A definite relationship between the use of alcohol and automobile accidents has been shown. And that is why many states suspend or cancel a driver's license if the driver in an accident is shown to have been drinking. Good citizens, of their own accord, will stay away from the wheel after taking alcohol. See Figure 23.11.

Alcoholism. Heavy drinking of alcoholic beverages by a person who does not seem able to stop is a serious illness

CHAPTER TWENTY-THREE — BUILDING HEALTH

known as **alcoholism.** The illness seems to have several possible causes, a common one being emotional illness. Some researchers now think that in some cases the desire to drink has some connection with a food deficiency, or with secretions of the adrenal glands. We do not blame the alcoholic; he is the victim of a disease, just as a diabetic is.

Alcoholism is a disease which is on the increase. About six of every hundred people who drink become alcoholics. The disease presents serious problems not only to the person himself but also to his family and community. That is why the American Association for the Advancement of Science and many other organizations are studying alcoholism. They are trying to find the causes of this excessive desire to drink, how best to treat the patients, and how to educate people so that they may seek help from doctors. Some years ago the Yale Center for Alcohol Studies showed what alcoholism does to industry. Of the 35,000,000 men and women in industry 2,000,000 are alcoholics and another million or more are borderline cases. By alcoholics they mean the men and women who are absent from work because of drinking, whose accident rate at work is high, and who cannot work as efficiently as they should.

The group of men and women who call themselves "Alcoholics Anonymous" have brought about many cures. This much is sure, an alcoholic, to be cured, must never again drink any alcoholic beverage. Most of our states now have institutions for treating alcoholics.

What is a narcotic? A narcotic is a substance that dulls the senses, relieves pain, and brings on sleep. Few drugs are more useful to man than narcotics, and they are not harmful when properly used under a doctor's supervision. Many narcotics are habit-forming and may be the cause of much suffering and misery. The most common habit-forming drugs are opium and drugs, such as morphine, that are made from it. Codeine, too, comes from opium but it is a much milder narcotic. The doctor may have prescribed it to you in cough medicines.

Opium is made from the juice of a poppy plant. Poppies are raised on a large scale chiefly in China, India, Turkey, and Russia. Since these narcotics are so dangerous and yet are so much needed by people in all countries, there must be careful regulation of their sale, and smuggling must be prevented. International groups are working to control the lawful production and sale of narcotics.

Another habit-forming drug that has become well known is marijuana (mahr-i-wah′na). This comes from the common hemp plant, whose fibers are used for making rope. And there are many other substances used by doctors to quiet people; these may be habit-forming, too, but much less so. Most of these are chemicals called **barbiturates** (bar-bit′tew-rates).

Drug addicts. Drug addicts are people who have acquired the habit of taking one of these dangerous narcotics. They cannot break the habit without treatment. In spite of the suffering which they know will follow, addicts cannot keep away from the drug. The immediate effect of the drug is to make the person "feel good." This does not last long; it is followed by terrible suffering.

There have always been drug addicts. But recently drug peddlers, who are usually themselves drug addicts, have begun to sell narcotics to young people. Wise teen-agers know the danger of even one experience with narcotics. Instead of allowing themselves to become an easy mark, they will report to the police or to school authorities at once any attempt to sell or give them so-called "reefers" (cigarettes containing narcotics) or any other unusual material that is not on open sale in respectable stores.

Health — a conservation problem. Much more money is needed for research — research on alcohol and tobacco, especially research on cancer, circulatory diseases, and on mental illness. It is important that we conserve our men and women, as well as our soil, our water, and our fuel. Conservation costs the government vast sums of money, but in the end we get back what we spend. Man power can be conserved, not only here, but the world over. Health has become an international problem.

Health organizations and health officers can do only a small part of the job of building healthy people. In general, poor health and low income go together. Look at Figure 23.12. It was once popularly believed that both poor health and lack of ability to earn a good income were inherited. But now it seems that low income from whatever cause is likely to result in poor health. During the great depression which started in this country in 1929, it was shown that in general, when people lost their wealth, they soon lost some of their health. The increase in illness came when their income became too low to provide good housing, food, and medical care. Poor housing, poor food, not enough clothing, and worry brought on illness. If we want to conserve human lives, we must raise the standard of living for all people.

What have you learned? You learned much in this Unit. Think of the many important discoveries in medical science: antibodies, immunization, antibiotics, and other drugs. These discoveries are widely used by doctors and health officers. But they alone cannot keep us in good health. Therefore you learned about germs and how infectious diseases are caught (Chapter 19); for which diseases you can be immunized, and how you are immunized (Chapter 20); that bacteriologists directed their attention from immunization to new fields, drugs of various kinds and to the viruses, which

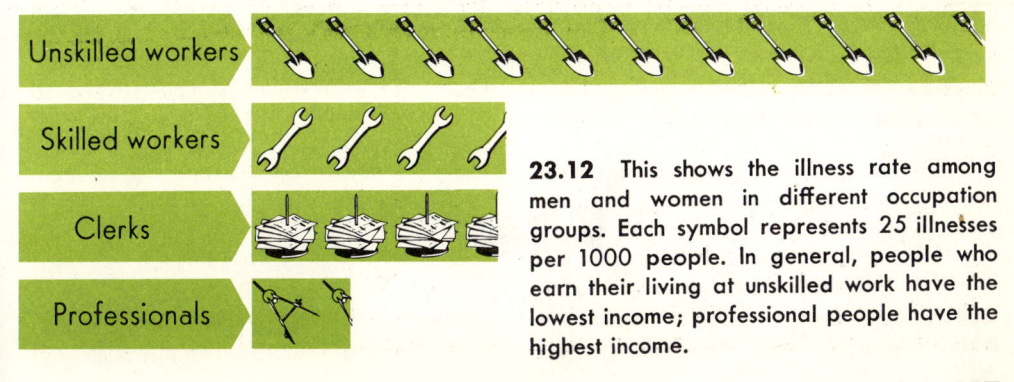

23.12 This shows the illness rate among men and women in different occupation groups. Each symbol represents 25 illnesses per 1000 people. In general, people who earn their living at unskilled work have the lowest income; professional people have the highest income.

CHAPTER TWENTY-THREE — BUILDING HEALTH

are now known to be the causes of many common diseases (Chapter 21). You learned that diseases are spread through polluted water, raw milk, infected foods, and human and insect carriers (Chapter 22); and that we have added many years to our lives, thus making more common the old-age diseases of the circulatory organs and cancer. You learned that allergies and other factors, including alcohol and tobacco, may at times interfere with our health (Chapter 23). All this is information that should be common knowledge. It is the responsibility of all of us to keep ourselves informed and help spread the information to all other people.

USEFUL WORDS IN BIOLOGY

benign tumor	antihistamine	stimulant
malignant tumor	autogenous	depressant
electrocardiogram	malnutrition	alcoholism
allergy	sinusitis	barbiturate
ragweed	nicotine	

TEST YOURSELF

1. What are five factors which have increased the length of life of people in the United States?
2. (a) Which group of diseases is responsible for the largest number of deaths in this country? (b) Give one reason why these diseases have increased so much of late.
3. About human cancer tell: (a) some probable causes; (b) suspicious symptoms; (c) treatment; (d) your responsibility in the fight on cancer.
4. Explain how diet can affect heart disease.
5. (a) What are two measures to be taken for suspected appendicitis before a doctor arrives? (b) What two practices are dangerous?

6. What proportion of deaths among children are caused by accidents? Name five practices you know of in your home or in the homes of friends which may result in accidents.
7. Tell about allergies: (a) What is an allergy? (b) What are some possible symptoms? (c) How can you be tested for the cause of an allergy?
8. (a) Name five common causes of poor health. (b) What can *you* do for yourself about each of these?
9. What evidence is there that a shorter life and heavy smoking are related?
10. What are some of the injurious effects of nicotine and some of the other substances in tobacco or tobacco smoke?
11. Explain the effects of considerable amounts of alcohol on the body, using the words depressant and stimulant in your explanation.
12. (a) What are some of the causes of alcoholism? (b) Where can an alcoholic get help to cure the disease?
13. What is a narcotic and what is the danger in using narcotics?

DO IT YOURSELF

1. **Life expectancy.** Prepare an interesting and original chart, based on Figure 23.1, showing life expectancy and the principal causes of death. Or you might make a life expectancy chart and relate it to the important medical discoveries you read about in the earlier chapters.

2. **Tobacco and narcotics.** Prepare your own booklet on tobacco or on narcotics. You will have no trouble finding articles in journals such as these: *Scientific American, Science News Letter, Look, Time, The Ladies' Home Journal, Collier's, Harper's. The Readers' Guide to Periodical Literature* will be of help.

3. **Adding to your class library.** The American Cancer Society Inc., 521 West 57, New York 19, N.Y., and the American Heart Association, Inc., 44 East 23, New York 10, N.Y., distribute a great deal of reliable literature which is easy to read. All pamphlets should

be bound as you receive them, and charts mounted on cardboard.

4. A study of accidents and their causes. Different committees can study automobile accidents, playground accidents, accidents in the home, accidents in school shops, accidents in industrial plants. The National Safety Council Inc., 405 Lexington Ave., New York 17, N.Y., should be able to give you help. Summarize your findings by listing recommendations for avoiding accidents. This might be duplicated and given to the other students in the school.

ADVENTURES IN READING

1. *The Facts of Life: From Birth to Death* by Louis I. Dublin and Mortimer Spiegelman, Macmillan, 1951. Answers innumerable questions we all want answered on the various common diseases—our length of life, public health, mental diseases, diseases of childhood, accidents, and so on.

2. *Good Health for You and Your Family* edited by E. Patricia Hagman, Barnes, 1951. This is a practical and reliable book prepared from the publications of the Health and Welfare Division of the Metropolitan Life Insurance Company.

3. "Alcohol in the Body" by Leon A. Greenberg, in *Scientific American*, December 1953. This gives up-to-date information on the effects of alcohol; it is simple and interesting.

4. *Alcohol Talks to Youth*, School and College Service, Columbus, Ohio, 1947.

5. *Tobacco and Health* by A. H. Steinhaus and F. M. Gunderman, Association Press, New York, N.Y., 1945. An important subject for all.

6. *Magic in a Bottle* by Milton Silverman, Macmillan, 1948. Contains an interesting chapter on opium and a chapter on atomic medicine.

7. "The Common Cold" by Christopher H. Andrewes, *Scientific American*, February 1951 (also in Scientific American Reader, 1952). Naturally, concerns us all.

Unit Seven

Reproduction

CHAPTER 24

Reproduction in some simple organisms

CHAPTER 25

Plant reproduction

CHAPTER 26

Animal reproduction

You started life as a single cell, a cell formed by the union of two cells. This cell grew into millions of cells; tissues and organs formed. Approximately nine months later you were a baby. The story of reproduction of all the vertebrate animals is much the same. The pig held by the girl in the picture was born after four months of development from a cell formed by the union of two cells.

Reproduction in flowering plants, it may surprise you to learn, is basically like that in vertebrate animals. The organs used in reproduction are found in the flower; and ordinarily each plant starts life as a single cell formed by the union of two cells. Just how flowering plants reproduced puzzled biologists for a long time. It has been understood for much less than a hundred years.

And all the simpler animals and plants? They, too, reproduce, although they often reproduce in the simplest way possible. The paramecium, for example, divides in two. In this reproduction there is no parent and no child. Does it occur to you that the paramecium you see today is, therefore, a part of the first paramecium that lived on this earth? We won't ask you to say how small a part; this division has gone on steadily for more than a billion years!

A general outline of reproduction in living things will be found in the following chapters; but, of course, there are many interesting variations which you may want to read about. Only some can be included in this short account.

Chapter 24
Reproduction in some simple organisms

Can living things arise from lifeless matter? The ancient Egyptians were sure frogs and mice came from the mud left in the fields when the river Nile overflowed its banks; they saw it happen! Some few people may still tell you that horsehairs left in water turn into tiny snakes. Some may tell you that small white worms arise from decaying meat; they, too, have seen worms come out of decaying meat! But all of you know that cannot be. Living things can arise only from other living things.

It took a good scientist to prove that such things do not happen and to explain why it seemed as though white worms (really maggots, the larvae of flies) were made out of rotting meat. Redi (ray'dee), an Italian biologist, performed the following experiment about the middle of the 17th century. He put decaying meat into three jars as you can see in Figure 24.1. He left one open; he covered the second with gauze; and the third he covered with parchment (sheepskin), which was so thick that no odor from the meat could pass through. Flies normally lay their eggs in decaying meat, and of course, they were at once attracted by the odor of the meat. They laid their eggs in the first jar; soon maggots appeared in that jar. Naturally, they were attracted to the second jar, too. They laid their eggs on the gauze and maggots appeared on the gauze. The third jar attracted no flies and no maggots appeared either in the jar or on its cover. After repeating this experiment several times, he drew this conclusion: maggots develop only from eggs laid by flies, they do not come out of the meat.

After this simple and carefully controlled experiment, other scientists were much more ready to believe that **spontaneous generation** does not take place. This is the idea that living things can arise from lifeless matter.

Must microorganisms have parents? Just a few years after Redi's work, microorganisms were discovered by Leeuwenhoek. It seemed natural to think that these tiny organisms could be formed out of stagnant water or other lifeless matter, without parents. The argument started all over again. This time, in the nineteenth century, Louis Pasteur in France and John Tyndall in England performed just as convincing experiments to disprove spontaneous generation among microorganisms. Let us see what Pasteur did.

Pasteur prepared many flasks (bottles) of liquid food material for bacteria. After bacteria had appeared in the liquid, he boiled it, killing the bacteria. While the liquid was boiling, he sealed some of the flasks by melting the glass necks; he left others open (see Fig. 24.2). After some days Pasteur found that the open flasks were full of bacteria which were decaying the food. In the sealed flasks, however, there were no signs of decay. Then, Pasteur broke the seal of a few of these flasks and let them stand open. Very soon bacteria appeared in the flasks, and the food began to decay. It was clear that bacteria did not develop from the lifeless food. Pasteur decided

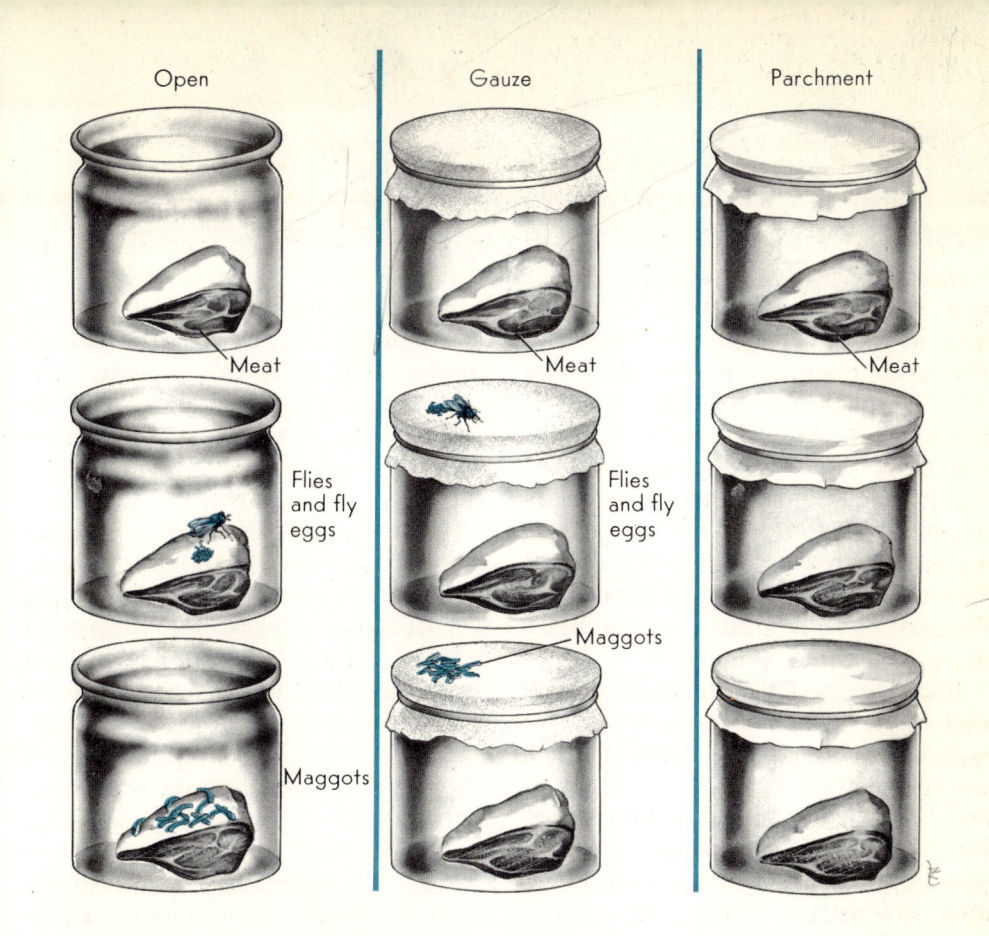

24.1 Here is Redi's experiment in diagram. Explain it. How did this experiment and many others like it change men's thinking about spontaneous generation of living things?

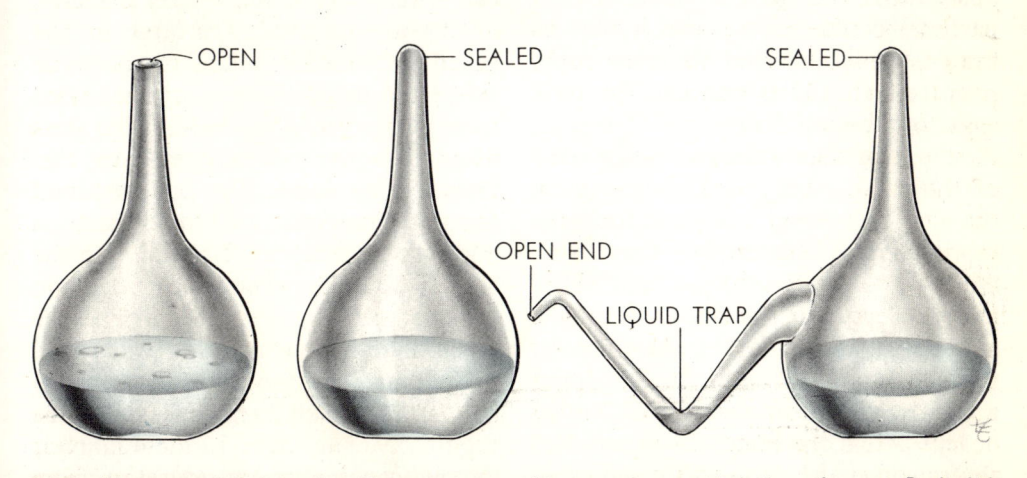

24.2 Here are drawings that illustrate one of Pasteur's experiments. Explain it. How is this experiment related to the one Redi did with flies?

CHAPTER TWENTY-FOUR — REPRODUCTION IN SOME SIMPLE ORGANISMS 363

24.3 Paramecium dividing. Which is the later stage? What happens to the nucleus? What is the name of this type of reproduction? *General Biology Supply House*

that bacteria on the dust in the air had settled in the open flasks and multiplied there, causing decay. You can try this experiment for yourself.

To check his theory that bacteria entered with the dust from the air, Pasteur took some of his sealed flasks to the top of a high mountain; he opened them there, where the air was almost free from dust. He found that bacteria rarely appeared in the flasks opened on the mountaintop.

But some scientists objected. They said that when Pasteur boiled the liquid and sealed the flasks he had driven out most of the air. The lack of air, they said, kept bacteria from arising out of the lifeless material. Perhaps so! Another experiment! This time, after boiling the broth in the flasks, Pasteur did not seal the flasks. Instead he softened the neck of the flasks and drew it out sidewise into a zigzag, open tube. Air could enter but no bacteria could drop in. Again he heated the flasks, then set them aside. Even after four years, no bacteria were found in the flasks.

This convinced the scientists that even the simplest living things arise only from other living things, by reproduction.

Reproduction in Protozoa. In a rich culture of PARAMECIUM, you are sure to find some that are reproducing. Under a microscope you can see them dividing in half across the middle. Figure 24.3 shows you that both nucleus and cytoplasm divide. The ameba reproduces by splitting in half in the same way. See Figure 24.4. Usually the process takes about half an hour. When it is over, the new amebas feed and grow to full size. Later each reproduces again.

This method of reproduction in a one-celled organism is called **binary fission** (by'na-ree fish'un). In binary fission the whole organism makes the two offspring. These two are often spoken of as the daughter cells and the parent as the mother cell. But no mother cell remains after the daughter cells are formed. Other protozoa and many single-celled plants reproduce by binary fission.

Yeast reproduction. Some single-celled organisms, but not many, reproduce by dividing into unequal parts. The yeast plant does this, as Figure 24.5 shows. The nucleus divides into two equal parts, but the cell body divides at one end. The larger cell is called the mother cell, the smaller is called the daughter cell, or **bud.** This method of reproduction is called **budding.** Usually, the bud breaks off and grows. Sometimes the daughter cell remains attached and grows until it buds, so that a small chain of yeast cells is formed. They soon separate, however. Yeasts reproduce by another method, too, of which you will learn.

Budding occurs in a few many-celled animals. One of them is *Hydra*. See Figure 5.9, page 86. In these animals the bud is composed of several to many cells.

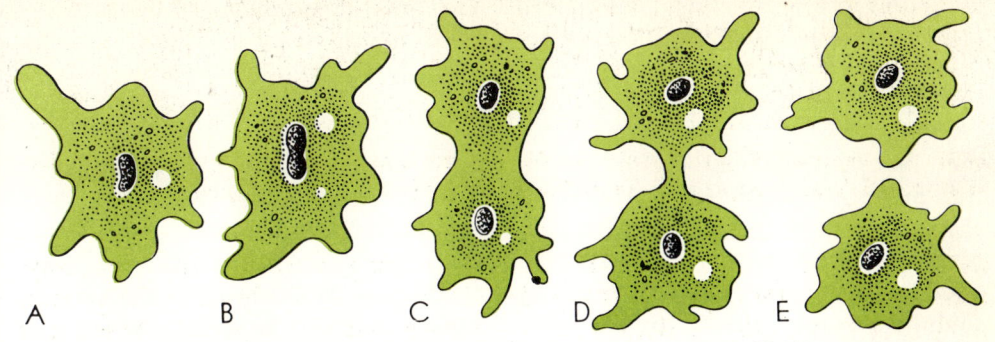

24.4 Five stages in the reproduction of an ameba. How does **B** differ from **A**? What changes are shown in **C**? What is happening in **D**?

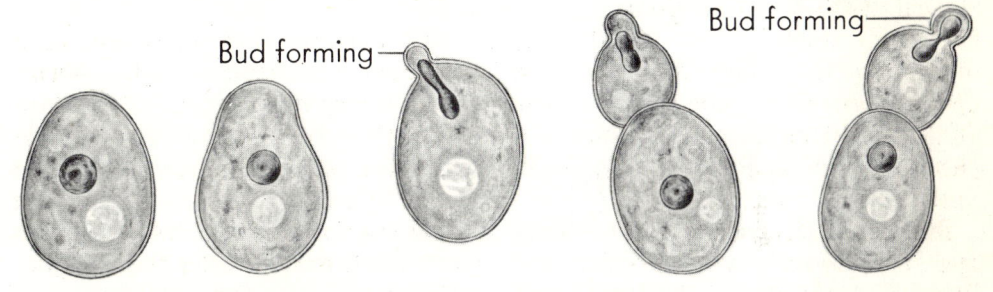

24.5 The common yeast used for baking. How many cells are in the process of budding? Where is the nucleus when the cell is budding?

Reproduction in bread mold. Bread molds, and for that matter molds in general, reproduce in still another way. In these plants the cells that are concerned with reproduction divide again and again until many small cells are formed. Each small cell (as a rule) develops a thick, protective wall. A reproductive cell formed in this way is called a **spore**. The method of reproduction is called spore formation, or **sporulation** (spore-you-lay′shun).

Figure 24.6 shows the process in the common bread mold (*Rhizopus* — rye′zo-pus). Bread mold is a fuzzy white plant that appears to turn gray and finally black when the spores are ripe. A spore develops into slender white threads (**hypha** — plural **hyphae**) which grow and branch many times. Some of the threads grow upward into the air. These are the ones that are

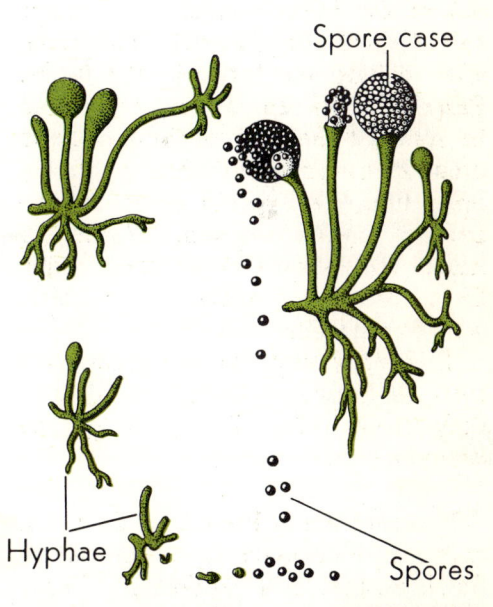

24.6 Spores of the bread mold (Rhizopus) grow into hyphae (shown on the bottom and on the left). How do the hyphae change? Where are the spores produced?

CHAPTER TWENTY–FOUR — REPRODUCTION IN SOME SIMPLE ORGANISMS

later used in reproduction. They swell at the tip into a ball, which is later called a spore case (**sporangium**). It is in this spore case that sporulation takes place. As more and more spore cases form, the white plant gets darker and darker, for the spores are black. All this is shown in Figure 24.6. The spore case breaks open when the spores are ripe, and the tiny spores are carried by slight movements of the air for some time before they settle.

Certain protozoa and a few of the simpler invertebrates reproduce by spore formation, too. It is an effective method, for it provides very large numbers of offspring in a short time. Sporulation is rare in animals but is found in many plants.

Asexual and sexual reproduction. Binary fission, budding, and sporulation are all forms of reproduction in which only one parent (or parent cell) is needed to produce offspring. This is called **asexual reproduction.**

In most species of plants and animals, however, two parents or two parent cells take part in reproduction. This is called **sexual reproduction.** Some organisms reproduce sexually at one time and asexually at another time. But let's study sexual reproduction first in a simple plant, such as Spirogyra.

Reproduction in Spirogyra. Spirogyra is one of the algae, a simple green water plant consisting of a long thread (filament) of cells, end to end. If you look at Figure 4.2, page 59, you can see how beautiful the pattern of the spiral chloroplasts is.

If you collect Spirogyra in the spring months, you will probably find it reproducing.

If reproduction is to occur in their cells, two Spirogyra filaments must happen to lie next to one another. The spiral chloroplast (or chloroplasts) in each cell loses its shape, and the mass of cytoplasm begins to shrink away from the cell wall. In the meantime, each cell in each filament sends out a projection toward the cell opposite it in the neighboring filament. These projections grow toward one another until they meet. Then the cell walls dissolve at the point of contact. This makes a continuous passageway, or bridge, from the cell in one filament to a cell of the opposite filament.

Then the protoplasm from one cell streams into the opposite cell, or into the opposite protoplasm, which remains inside its cell wall. The two cell masses fuse, nucleus uniting with nucleus. The cells that fuse are called **gametes** (gam'eats). The protoplasm that flows across the bridge into the other cell is called an **active,** or **supplying,** gamete; the one which remains within its cell wall is the **passive,** or **receiving,** gamete. What has been described happens in every pair of opposite cells, so that in time one filament is empty. The other filament now holds all the fused cells. Each fused cell loses water, shrinks, and secretes a heavy wall around itself. It is now known as a **zygospore** (zy'gospore). See Figure 24.7. The plant's cell walls gradually decay, and the zygospores sink to the bottom of the pond.

The story of reproduction in Spirogyra is not yet complete. It ends weeks or months later when, with favorable conditions, the living protoplasm within the zygospore wall absorbs water and bursts open its covering. The chloroplast manufactures sugar, the cell absorbs water and minerals, makes proteins, and grows. When the cell has grown to normal size, first the nucleus and then the cytoplasm divides. After repeated divisions there is a whole new filament — a new Spirogyra plant.

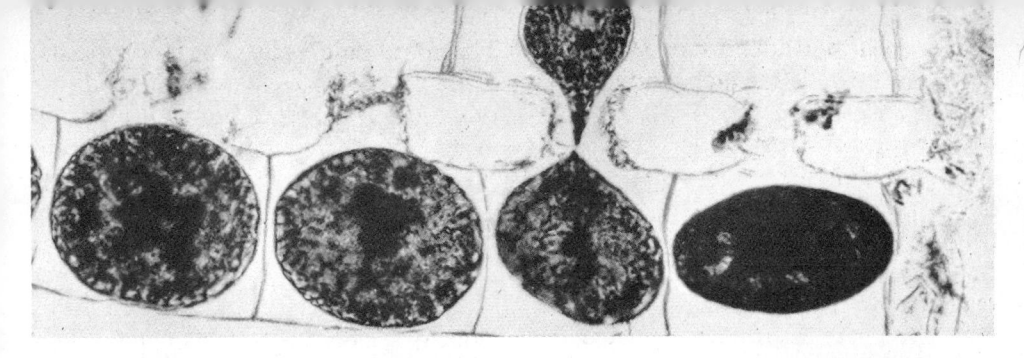

24.7 Two filaments of conjugating Spirogyra. Conjugation is complete in three pairs of cells. In one the gamete from the upper filament is passing into the lower. Which is the latest stage? *Ward's Natural Science Establishment*

Where the gametes are alike in appearance, as in Spirogyra and some other organisms, we use a special name for this type of reproduction; we call it **conjugation**. But you will see that in most organisms that reproduce sexually the gametes are not alike. In all cases of sexual reproduction there is a single cell formed from the fusion of two. This is called a **zygote** (zy′goat). But in conjugation the zygote goes by the special name of **zygospore**.

Conjugation in other organisms. Molds may reproduce by conjugation, too. Figure 24.8 shows how this happens. The two molds must be of different strains, usually called **plus** and **minus** strains. Conjugation in *Paramecium* is different. Although two paramecia unite they don't stay united; no zygospore is formed. The legend of Figure 24.9 tells you what happens.

Unlike gametes. Do you remember learning about the protozoan that causes malaria? Figure 24.10 shows that in the mosquito's stomach the protozoan changes into two forms. The protozoa that remain spherical are called **female cells;** those that become whiplike and smaller are called **male cells**. When one of the male cells

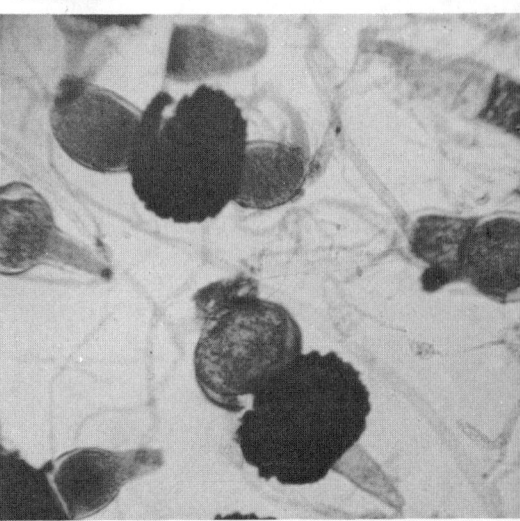

24.8 Conjugation in bread mold. The filaments from two plants swell at their ends (lower left corner), meet, fuse, and form a large zygospore (right). *Kline*

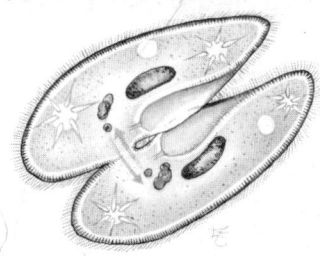

24.9 Paramecia sometimes conjugate. When they do, the large nucleus (macronucleus) disappears. Equal parts of the small nucleus (micronucleus) are exchanged and fuse with one another. New macronuclei are formed, the organisms separate, and then continue reproduction by binary fission.

Fertilized cell

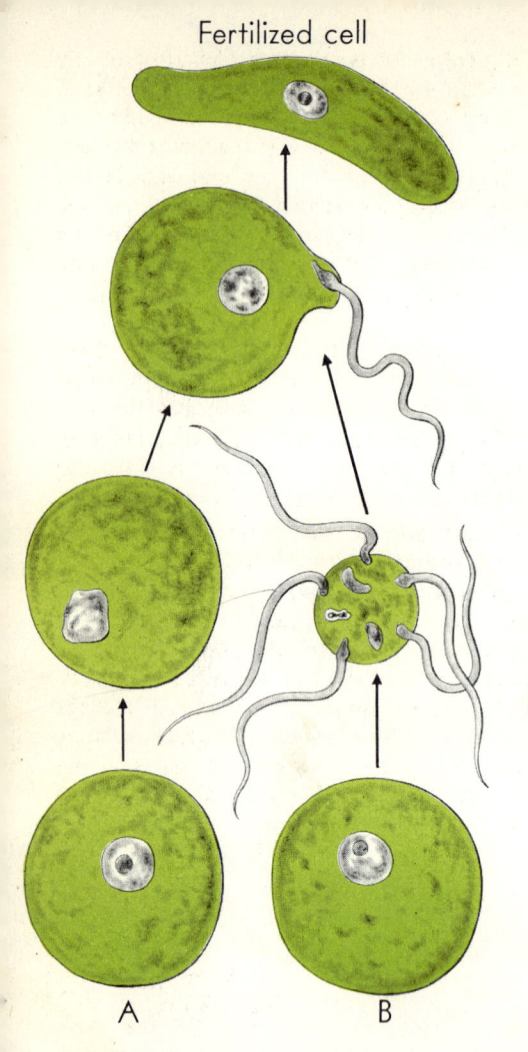

24.10 How the malaria protozoan changes in the mosquito's stomach. Does **A** change into male or female? Where are the male and female cells shown fusing?

gametes; a male cell unites with a female cell. That is, reproduction is by fertilization, not by conjugation.

What have you learned? Plants and animals make more of their own kind in several ways. Sexual reproduction requires two parents, one male and one female. The organism causing malaria reproduces by this method in the mosquito's stomach. Another sexual method, conjugation, requires two parents but the parents or parent cells are so much alike that we cannot speak of male and female. We indicate a difference between the parents or parent cells by calling them "plus and minus" or "active and passive." The other reproductive methods — binary fission, budding, and sporulation — are asexual; that is, only one parent or parent cell is needed. Can you describe these three methods of asexual reproduction? And can you name some organism that reproduces by each method?

USEFUL WORDS IN BIOLOGY

spontaneous generation
binary fission
budding
spore
sporangium
sporulation
asexual reproduction
sexual reproduction
zygospore
zygote
conjugation
fertilization
gamete

TEST YOURSELF

enters a female cell, the nuclei and cell bodies unite. This union is called **fertilization**. The new cell is called the fertilized egg cell. It goes on to produce more cells like itself. You read that fertilization is a much more common form of sexual reproduction in animals and plants than conjugation. In the reproduction of higher animals and plants there is always a union of unlike

1. Redi performed a simple but important experiment with flies and meat. Describe it.
2. How was it proved that what is true of the origin of maggots is just as true of the origin of microorganisms?

UNIT SEVEN — REPRODUCTION

3. Name and describe the methods of reproduction in (a) paramecium, (b) yeast, (c) bread mold.
4. Define and give three examples of asexual reproduction.
5. Describe sexual reproduction in spirogyra, using the terms active and passive gamete, and zygospore.
6. How does conjugation in bread mold differ from conjugation in spirogyra?
7. In what ways are fertilization and conjugation alike? How are they different?

DO IT YOURSELF

1. Watching paramecia reproduce. You will need a rich culture of paramecia. In Chapter 5 under "Studying paramecium" you read how to get a particularly rich culture. Be sure to have a large number of protozoa on your slide and some shreds of lens paper or cotton to slow them down. Use the low power and hunt until you find one dividing. Perhaps you could stain some slides with Lugol's solution (potassium iodide and iodine in water); then you could look for the dividing nucleus under high power.

2. The budding of yeast. Put a teaspoon of molasses or corn syrup into a small tumbler of water. Crumble a small amount of yeast into this solution and let it stand in a warm place for twelve or more hours. By that time the yeast cells should be growing and dividing actively. Find mother and attached daughter cells under the high power of the microscope.

3. Conjugation in spirogyra. You will probably have to use prepared slides from a biological supply house. See whether you can find all the stages in the process from the first to the last. Draw and label them. You may find the last stage first; if so, make a sketch of it and then move your slide around until you find an earlier stage, and so on until you have found four or five stages in the process of conjugation.

Spirogyra conjugates in the spring. Open roadside ditches and small ponds in the country are likely places to collect it. If you have living spirogyra plants keep a small jar of them in a basin of iced water and examine the plants under the microscope at intervals.

4. Sporulation in molds. Start with a flourishing bread mold which is not so old that it is dark and sooty. Examine some of the hyphae with a magnifying glass or two magnifying glasses, one held above the other at the correct distance. Look at a ripe sporangium and look for sporangia that are forming and are not yet filled with black spores. Describe and draw what you see. Make a rough guess at the number of offspring your bread mold would have if all the spores lived.

ADVENTURES IN READING

1. *Biology and Its Makers* by William A. Locy, Holt, 1915. Has a section on "The Spontaneous Origin of Life," which is full of valuable information presented in rather old-fashioned language.

Chapter 25

Plant reproduction

A preview. When farmers want to raise fields of oats, wheat, rice, corn or beans, they plant seeds. Flowering plants reproduce by making seeds. But before seeds appear, the plant always bears flowers. The flowers are necessary for reproduction, too. This is what happens: The seed grows; in time, the plant produces flowers; certain parts of these flowers change into seeds. The seeds are the beginning of a new generation of plants.

Just a little more information will make this simplified story complete: there is a tiny plant (an embryo) in the seed. To find out how it gets there, we must study flowers and what goes on within them.

A close look at flowers. Perhaps many of you have thought of flowers only as decorations, and flowers have been used as decorations for as long as we have any record. In the life of the plant, however, flowers are important because they hold the cells that enable the plant to reproduce.

If you examine a flower, usually you will first see white or brightly colored leaflike parts. We always think of these when we speak of flowers. They are called **petals** (pet′uls). The petals are arranged in a circle and together are called the **corolla** (co-rol′la). Outside of the petals are the **sepals** (see′pels) which are usually green and smaller than the petals. This outer circle is called the **calyx** (cay′lix). The sepals of some plants, especially many of the monocots, are much like the petals (Fig. 25.1). Together, the calyx and corolla make up the **perianth** (per′ee-anth). Inside the perianth is a circle of **stamens** (stay′mens). In Figure 25.1 each stamen consists of a threadlike part thickened on the free end. In the very center of the blossom is a single **pistil**. The number, shape, size, and color of all flower parts are different in different kinds of plants.

Stamens and pistils. Stamens and pistils are called **essential organs** because they produce the gametes necessary in sexual reproduction. A flower may have one pistil (lily) or many (buttercup); it may have six stamens (lily) or many (apple). The other flower parts, the sepals and petals, may attract insects or otherwise be useful in sexual reproduction. But in some species sepals or petals or both are much reduced in size, or lacking altogether.

Some kinds of plants, such as corn and the willows, have stamens and pistils in separate flowers. A flower that has stamens but no pistil is called a **staminate** flower. A **pistillate** flower is one that has one or more pistils but no stamens. In corn the staminate and pistillate flowers occur on the same plant, Figure 25.2. Among willows, the staminate and pistillate flowers are found on different trees.

The pistil. A pistil consists usually of three parts: a top that may be flattened and broad, called the **stigma**; a stem or neck below the stigma, called the **style** (this may be long or short); and a large thickened lowest part, the

25.1 In this lily you can find three sepals and three petals (they are much alike). You can find six stamens and the one pistil. See Figure 25.3 for a diagram of a lily flower. In the diagram all the parts are labeled. *Horace McFarland*

25.2 The corn plant has two kinds of flowers. The staminate flowers are found at the top of the plant in the "tassel." They are tiny green flowers which lack the pistil. The ear of corn which grows lower down on the stalk is a collection of pistillate flowers. These flowers which don't look much like flowers to you are wrapped in the husks; only the ends of the pistils stick out. *U.S. Department of Agriculture*

CHAPTER TWENTY-FIVE — PLANT REPRODUCTION   371

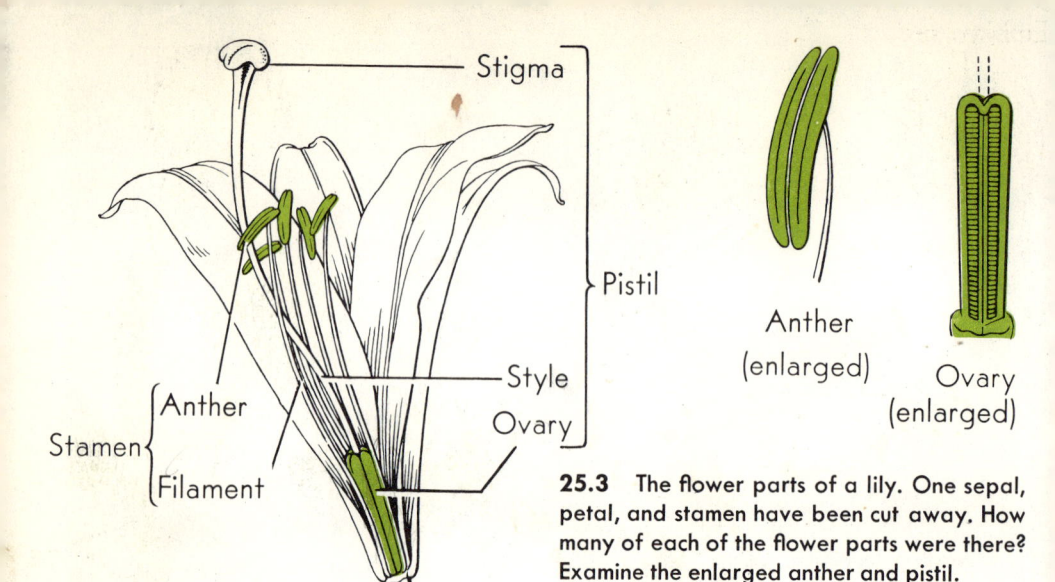

25.3 The flower parts of a lily. One sepal, petal, and stamen have been cut away. How many of each of the flower parts were there? Examine the enlarged anther and pistil.

ovary. Examine Figure 25.3 to see these three parts. If you cut into the ovary, you will find **ovules** (oh'vules). In some kinds of flowers the ovary contains only one ovule; in others there are hundreds of tiny ovules.

Now the ovule in the ovary is worth looking at very closely, for it is the ovule that in time becomes a seed. It is here that fertilization, or the union of two unlike gametes, takes place. Let us see what happens in a young ovule. In Figure 25.4, A is a diagram of a young ovule containing the large cell called an **embryo sac**. In B the nucleus of the embryo sac has divided, and a second ovule coat has grown outside the first. In C and D the ovule and embryo sac are growing ever larger, and the nuclei have divided until there are eight. Each nucleus has cytoplasm around it, and therefore, is often thought of as a cell, even though it may not be surrounded by a membrane. The large cell near the top is the female gamete, or **egg cell**. Two of the other nuclei usually move to the middle of the embryo sac where they fuse, forming the fused, or **double**, nucleus. Notice that we have discovered the female gamete, the egg cell, used in sexual reproduction. Now we will find the male gamete.

The stamen. The stamen consists of a more or less slender stalk (**filament**) with a bulky **anther** (**pollen case**) on top. If you shake a ripe stamen, many **pollen grains** will fall from the anther. The grains are so small that pollen feels like a fine powder. Each grain contains two nuclei. Pollen grains are usually spherical, but not always. Now if a pollen grain happens to fall on the stigma of the pistil next to it or on the stigma of some other flower of the same species, a tube grows out of the pollen grain. It seems to be nourished by a sugary substance on the stigma. Figure 25.5 shows you how this tube grows. As the tube lengthens it pushes down through the stigma and style, toward the ovary. In C, you can see that something is happening to one of the nuclei, the one called the **sperm nucleus**. In D you can see that the sperm nucleus has divided, forming two sperms. These are male gametes. The other original nucleus is now way at the end

UNIT SEVEN — REPRODUCTION

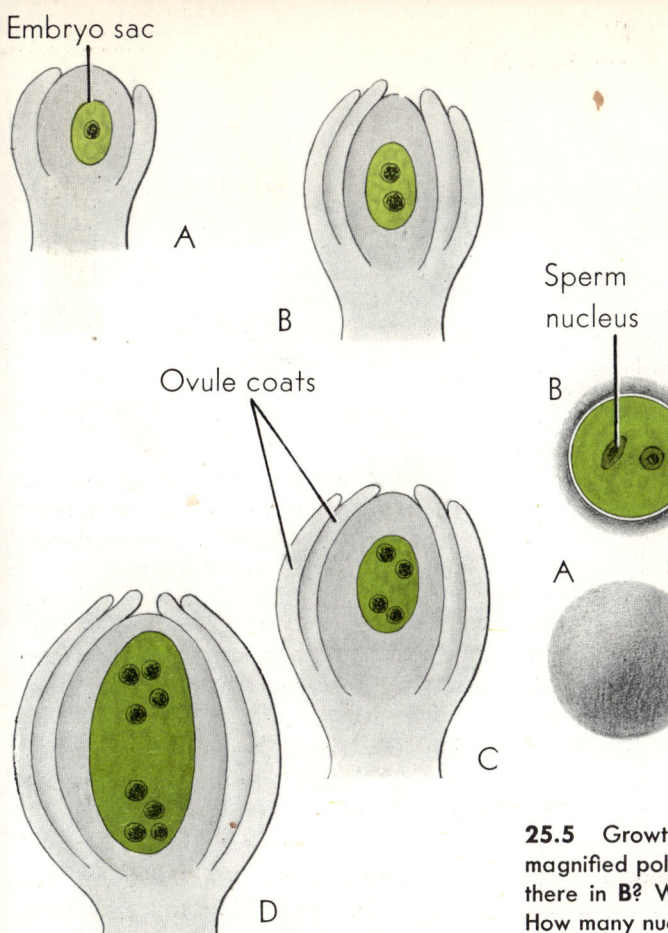

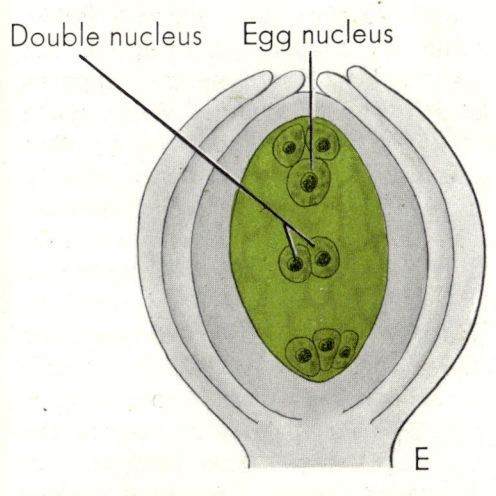

25.4 Diagrammatic sections showing a young ovule growing into a large ovule. Note what happens to the nucleus of the large cell (embryo sac) in **A**.

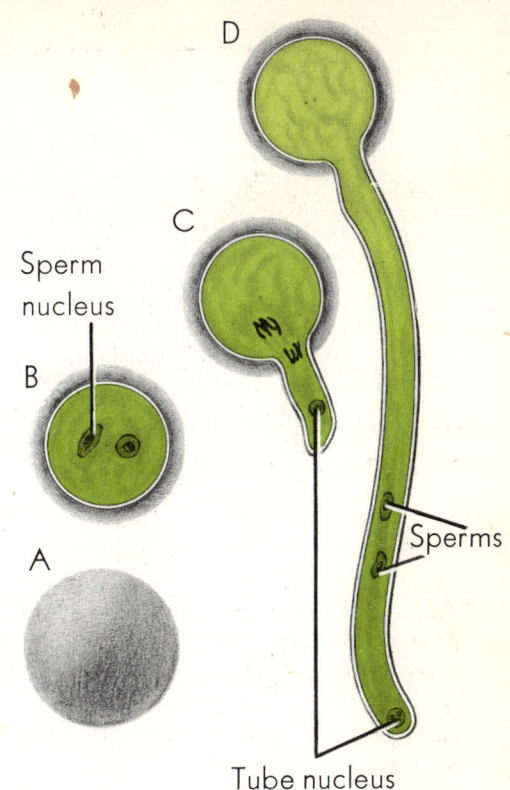

25.5 Growth of pollen tube. **A** is a much magnified pollen grain. How many nuclei are there in **B**? What is happening in **C**? In **D**? How many nuclei are there in **D**? Which ones of these are gametes?

of the tube; it is called the **tube nucleus.** One of the male gametes will unite with the female gamete. The other gamete plays a different part.

Thus we have found the two gametes needed for sexual reproduction: the male gamete (sperm) hidden within the pollen tube and the female gamete (egg cell) hidden within the embryo sac of the ovule. As the tube grows the male gamete approaches the female gamete.

Pollination. If the two gametes are ever to get together you can see how important it is that the pollen grains reach a stigma; it must be the stigma of a flower of the same kind. The

CHAPTER TWENTY-FIVE — PLANT REPRODUCTION 373

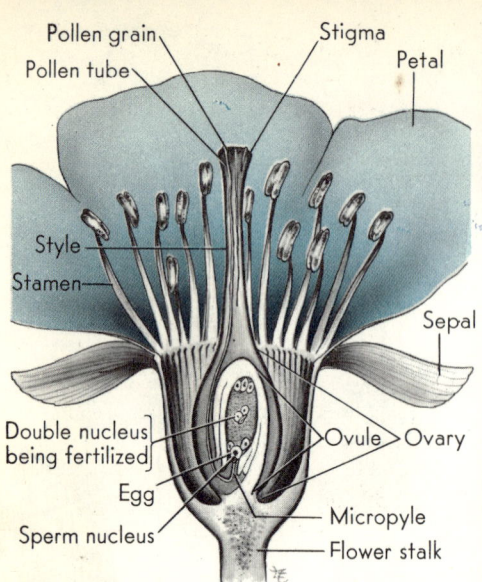

25.6 A section through a flower during fertilization. Only one ovule is shown. Where is the micropyle? What has entered through it? Where is the egg cell? What becomes of the second sperm nucleus?

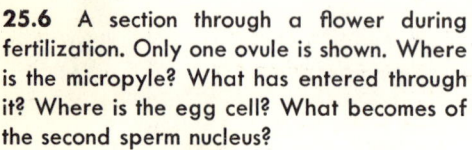

25.7 As they gather nectar, bees and other insects accidentally also carry pollen from one flower to another. How else may such flowers be pollinated? *U.S. Department of Agriculture*

transfer of pollen from the stamen to the pistil is called **pollination.** In pollination the pollen may be blown by the wind or may be accidentally carried by insects flying from one flower to another as they gather nectar (Fig. 25.7). Thus, by wind, insects, birds, or other agents, the transfer of pollen from anther to stigma is made. Transfer of pollen from an anther to a stigma in the same flower or a stigma in a flower on the same plant is **self-pollination.** If pollen is transferred to the stigma on a different plant, the process is **cross-pollination.** If the pollen is carried to flowers of another species the pollen usually dies. Much of the pollen never reaches the right kind of flower.

Fertilization. The gametes in the growing pollen tube approach the egg nucleus. Having gone through stigma and style, the tube grows into the ovary and finally enters the ovule, Figure 25.6.

The growth of the pollen tube may take from several hours to many days; the time varies from plant to plant. Hundreds of pollen grains may fall on the stigma. Many develop tubes which grow toward the ovules in the ovary. When a tube reaches an ovule it usually enters through an opening called the **micropyle.** The pollen tubes which do not enter dry up and disappear. When the pollen tube reaches the embryo sac, the cell wall at the end of the tube dissolves. The sperm nuclei enter the embryo sac, and one of them fuses with the egg nucleus, producing the fertilized egg cell. Fertilization has now taken place. A new plant has begun.

In some species of plants the second nucleus unites with the double nucleus lying in the center of the embryo sac. This union does not result in a fertilized

374

UNIT SEVEN — REPRODUCTION

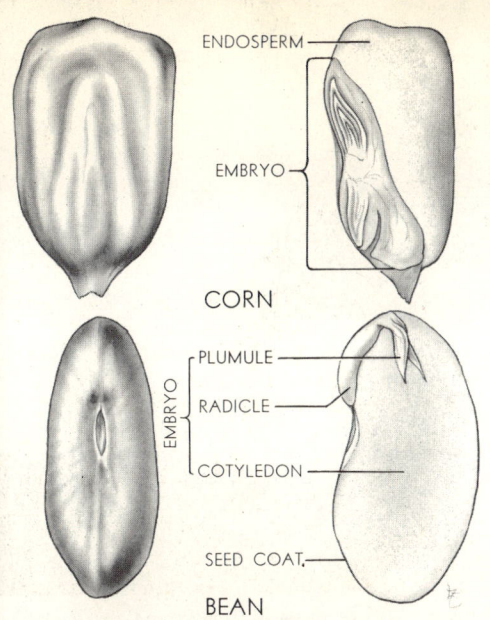

25.8 All the tissues within the seed coats of the bean are part of the embryo. In corn (above) the embryo lies alongside the food-storage tissue (endosperm).

25.9 Development of an ovary into a fruit. This normally takes place after pollination and fertilization. What happens to each ovule? To the parts of the pistil?

egg cell. It results in a large group of food-storing cells called **endosperm.** In other species the second sperm nucleus does not unite with the double nucleus. In that case, no endosperm forms.

Changes within the ovule. Fertilization has taken place. What happens next? Two kinds of things happen. (a) The fertilized egg divides. Then the daughter cells divide, and divisions continue until there are thousands of cells. (b) As these divisions go on, most of the cells, which are all alike at first, begin to change and form the different tissues of the embryo plant. This process is called **differentiation.**

By these two processes, cell division and cell differentiation, some groups of cells become pith, some become phloem, some xylem, some epidermis. Soon the small root, stem, and leaf become apparent. This tiny plant, formed from the fertilized egg cell, is the **embryo.** Although embryos are small and often curled up, the new plant parts can usually be recognized in the seed. The food necessary for growth from fertilized egg to embryo comes from the surrounding tissues of the plant.

Seed and fruit. The development of the embryo takes many days or weeks. In the meantime, as a rule, the flower petals have dried up and fallen off, leaving only a few shriveled flower parts and the ovary attached to the flower stem. As the embryo increases in size, so does the ovule. The ovule changes too, especially its outer layers. After these changes we no longer speak of an ovule; the developed ovule containing an embryo plant is a **seed.** The bean in Figure 25.8 is a seed. This seed, like many others, consists of two

CHAPTER TWENTY-FIVE — PLANT REPRODUCTION

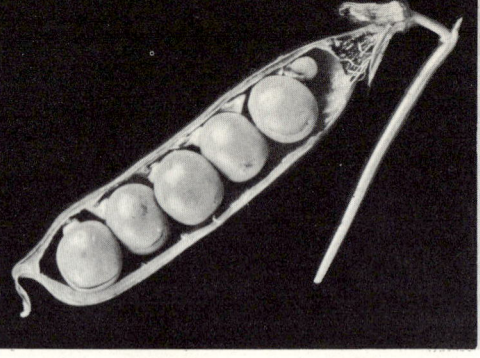

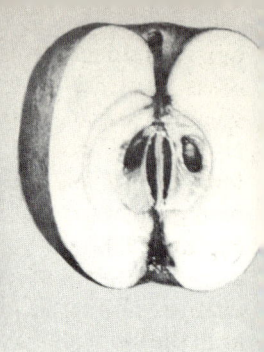

25.10 Three ripened ovaries or fruits. In the apple, the core is the ripened ovary. From what does the fleshy part grow? Brooklyn Botanic Garden and Schneider

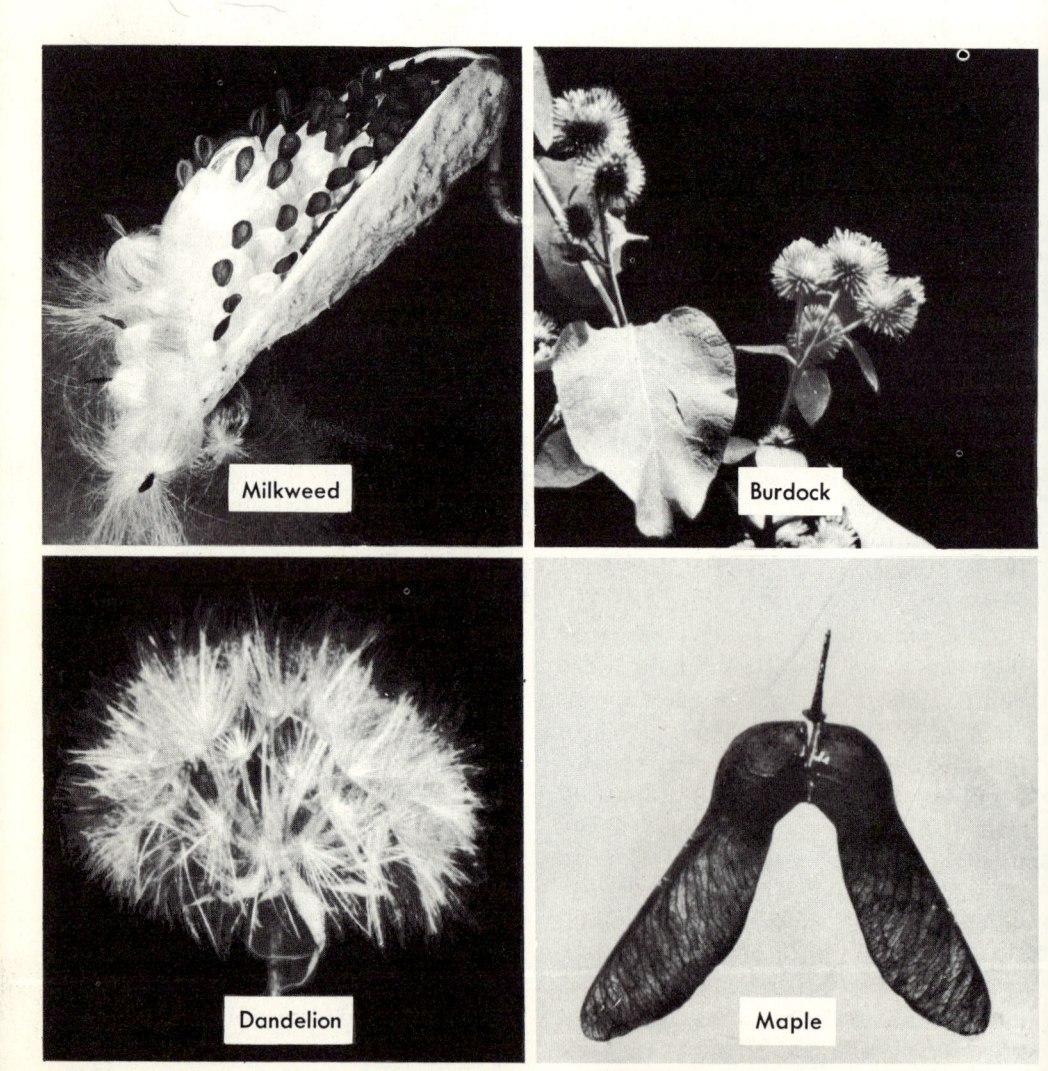

25.11 Fruits and seeds. By what agent may each kind be dispersed? American Museum of Natural History; Schneider and Schwartz; Brooklyn Botanic Garden

UNIT SEVEN — REPRODUCTION

parts: seed coats and embryo. Some seeds contain, also, extra food (endosperm) around or alongside the embryo.

Not only does the ovule grow after fertilization of the egg cell, but the ovary grows, too, as you can see in Figure 25.9. If you examine a bean or pea flower and pod, you can see the changes for yourself. The bean pod and the pea pod are enlarged ovaries, enclosing seeds. They are fruits, just as are peaches, plums, tomatoes, watermelons, and avocados. The corn grain (Fig. 25.8) is a fruit. Each ovary of the ear contains one ovule. As the embryo and endosperm grow, the ovule coats and ovary wall grow fast together.

The fruit of some plants is much more than the enlarged ovary. Sometimes other flower parts enlarge along with the ripening ovary, Figure 25.10. You do not eat an ovary when you eat an apple; the core, which you throw away, is the ovary. You eat the top of the flower stalk, the part to which the petals and sepals are attached. This becomes enlarged and makes the fruit.

From seed to seedling. After the fruits containing the seeds ripen, the seeds are often moved far from the parent plant. This is called **seed dispersal**. See Figure 25.11. Some fruits or seeds are light and are blown far and wide by the wind, or they may float on water. Some grow in fruits that have hooks or spines that catch on the fur or hair of animals or in man's clothing.

Some wild animals bury seeds after carrying them some distance from where they grew. Nowadays, man carries seeds of many kinds to all parts of the earth. Some are carried on purpose for planting crops. Some are accidentally carried by railroads, ships, airplanes, and automobiles.

25.12 This oak seedling has burst open the seed and fruit coats that covered it. It is growing on the food stored in the seed. *American Museum of Natural History*

Seeds have played a large part in making seed plants the dominant plants of the earth.

Seeds may travel great distances and may lie a long time in conditions not favorable to their growth, for the seed is nearly always **dormant** when it is first formed. It may stay dormant until another growing season comes or for a much longer time. Some seeds can stay alive but inactive for a great many years (40 or 50), but most will live only one or several years. Later, when water and warmth are supplied, the embryo again begins to grow; we say that the seed **germinates**. Germination produces a seedling. See Figure 25.12. If you soak some pea or bean seeds to break their dormancy and put them in a covered dish on moist blotting paper, you can watch them germinate. Then you can watch the further growth of the seedlings if you plant them in moist sawdust or sand.

Vegetative reproduction. If you have a geranium or begonia at home and

CHAPTER TWENTY-FIVE — PLANT REPRODUCTION

25.13 Three uprooted strawberry plants, two of which have grown from runners. The parent plant is in the center. What kind of reproduction is this? *Brooklyn Botanic Garden*

would like to have more of it, you don't wait for seeds to develop. All you need to do is to cut off one of the leafy stems and place the cut end in water or moist sand for a few weeks. You will find that roots grow from the sides of the stem and that soon you have a complete plant — roots, stem, and leaves — which will bear flowers just as the original plant did. You can see that this kind of reproduction is not at all like the sexual reproduction you have just been studying.

Since it is a vegetative organ in this case that produces a new plant, and *not* a reproductive organ, this process is called **vegetative reproduction** or **vegetative propagation.** Many of our food and ornamental plants are propagated in this way. The piece of stem or leaf that is used in propagation is called a **slip,** or a **cutting.**

Sometimes new roots and branches form from plants without their becoming separated from the parent plant. From the strawberry plant, Figure 25.13, a long stem known as a **runner** grows along the ground. When the runner is several inches long, it produces at its end a short upright stem with leaves and roots. Each plant holds hands, so to speak, with its mother plant and in time stretches out a hand to its daughter. In the black raspberry a drooping twig, or **layer,** takes root where it touches the ground.

Other examples of vegetative reproduction. Still other plants reproduce vegetatively from stems, but in some the stems are not easily recognized as such. The white potato, Figure 25.14, is an enlarged underground stem, as you read earlier. The buds on this

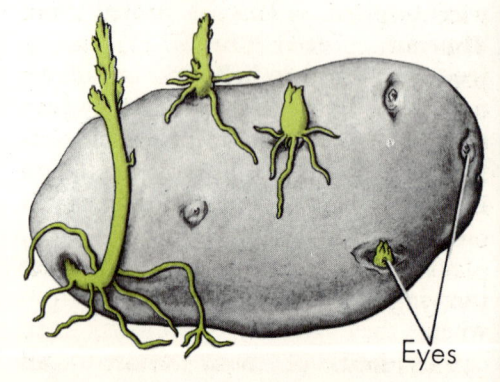

25.14 When he wants a new potato crop, the farmer cuts up the potatoes and plants the pieces. What must he be sure to include in each piece?

378

UNIT SEVEN — REPRODUCTION

stem are in little depressions called "eyes." Such a fleshy underground stem is known as a **tuber.** When the tuber or a piece of it containing an eye is planted, the bud begins to grow again. Soon a complete plant develops.

Other stems, usually produced underground also, are very much shortened and compressed. The leaves which ordinarily are found along the sides of a stem are thus very close together. They lack chlorophyll and become fleshy. Such a compressed stem with its attached leaves is known as a bulb. An onion is a bulb. Of course, you know about tulip bulbs, Figure 25.15. The bulb you plant is used for food in producing the flower, but it also produces another large bulb and usually several small ones. This is another example of vegetative reproduction.

Some roots, too, can be used in vegetative propagation. Sweet potatoes are roots. If you set one end of a sweet potato in a jar of water and put the jar on a window sill, both roots and shoots will grow from it. The leaves of some plants, kept moist, will produce new roots and stems and leaves. African violets and bryophyllum (Fig. 25.16) are good examples.

Gardeners and nurserymen make wide use of vegetative propagation. They often make use of **grafting,** a process that you will read about in detail later. Much time is saved through vegetative propagation in growing new plants. Furthermore, since in vegetative reproduction there is only one parent you are sure to get a plant exactly like that parent. This, too, you will read about later.

Variations in reproduction. An exceptional type of reproduction takes place in quite a number of plants — the common dandelion is one. In these the unfertilized egg or some other cell

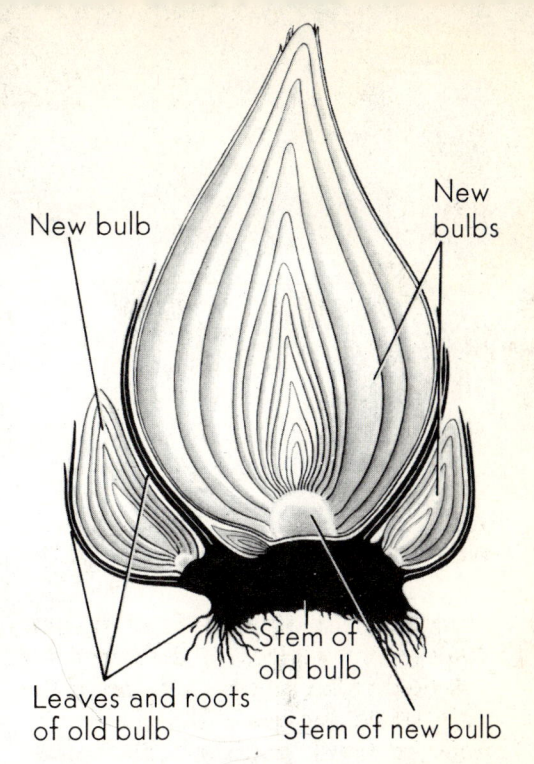

25.15 Tulip bulbs increase in number. Several buds within the old bulb enlarge forming new bulbs. Portions of the old bulb are shown in black.

25.16 Vegetative reproduction by a bryophyllum leaf. The leaf was removed from the stem, then laid on soil. How many new plants are growing from this single leaf?

in the ovule begins to divide just as a fertilized egg would. Divisions continue until there is an embryo in the seed. This process is known as **parthenogenesis** (par'-then-oh-jen'eh-sis), which means development of an egg into an embryo without fertilization.

25.17 The lower surfaces of parts of three fern leaves. At each spot there are many tiny spore cases. What is in the spore cases? *Brooklyn Botanic Garden*

Most of us have eaten seedless oranges, grapefruits, and grapes (raisins are dried grapes). Occasionally we may have seen seedless tomatoes, apples, or pears. Probably none of us has seen seeds in bananas or pineapples. You might well ask why seeds do not develop in these fruits. To answer this question we would have to study each plant carefully. In certain kinds of oranges the blossoms have stamens and stigmas but the pollen tube that is produced is defective. Other kinds of oranges fail to form seeds because either no embryo sacs are produced or the embryo sacs are imperfect. In some seedless grapes pollination and fertilization occur, but the embryos die when they are very young and the ovules do not grow into seeds. The hundreds of black specks you see in bananas are ovules, not seeds; as a rule, in the banana flower neither the pollen nor the embryo sacs are perfect. Commercial seedless fruit varieties are reproduced vegetatively by one means or another; so are many of our ornamental shrubs.

It is interesting to know that ordinarily the ovary does not grow into a fruit unless the stigma is pollinated. Even though the ovules fail to become seeds, the presence of pollen and the growth of the pollen tube is enough to cause the ovary to start growing. Dr. Felix Gustafson of the University of Michigan and many others have found that pollen contains a growth-promoting hormone. In recent years much experimental work has been done with plant hormones and hormonelike chemicals. When sprayed on the

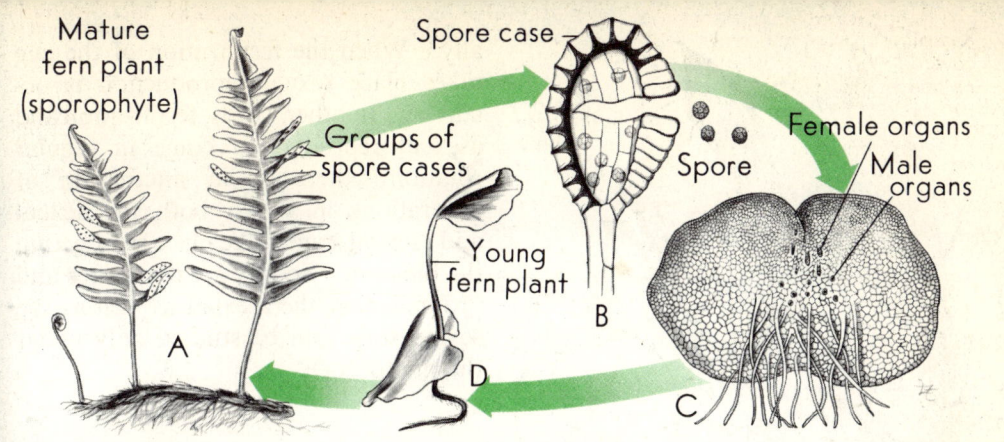

25.18 A. The fern plant (sporophyte) has spore cases on the lower side of the leaf. B is a magnified spore case split open. A spore grows into C, a green prothallus. On it are formed sperm cells and egg cells. D. A fertilized egg cell grows into a young fern plant. This grows into a mature fern plant, A.

stigma or ovary, they cause the ovary to grow but not the ovules. Seedless tomatoes, eggplants, cucumbers, and squash have been produced in this way.

Reproduction in ferns. Ferns never bear blossoms. In their life cycle, they produce spores by asexual reproduction. At certain seasons the masses of spore cases show clearly on the lower surface of the frond, as you can see in Figure 25.17. When the spores ripen, they fall out of the cases and are scattered on the ground. If they land where it is moist, they germinate.

But a spore does not grow into a new fern plant. There is produced a small, heart-shaped, green body called a **prothallus**, which does not look at all like the parent plant. This tiny plant lies flat on the ground; hairlike structures absorb water from the soil. Since it contains chlorophyll and can make its own food, it grows, but never grows much larger than a fingernail. After a few weeks, certain groups of cells produce sperms; other groups produce egg cells; or in some species sperms are produced in one prothallus and eggs in another. The sperms swim through the thin film of water on the lower surface of the prothallus and fertilize the eggs. Sexual reproduction has taken place. Each fertilized egg develops a small stem and root, and in time the characteristic fern leaves rise up into the air. See Figure 25.18. There is always asexual and sexual reproduction in regular rotation in the life history of the fern. This is called an **alternation of generations**: the fern plant produces spores asexually; these grow into a prothallus; the prothallus produces male and female gametes; fertilization occurs, and from the fertilized egg grows a fern plant like the original one.

Alternation of generations in the flowering plant. Close study of the reproduction of a flowering plant shows that it, too, goes through an alternation of generations. In the anther the pollen grain develops from a spore, a small spore (**microspore**). And in the ovule the embryo sac develops from a large spore (**macrospore**). The pollen grain with its tube and nuclei is thought of as a three-celled prothallus,

CHAPTER TWENTY-FIVE — PLANT REPRODUCTION

ally. When the fertilization of the egg takes place sexual reproduction is occurring. In other words, fertilization and asexual reproduction come in regular rotation; there is an alternation of generations in which both the sexual and asexual stages take place right within the blossom. So tiny are the spores and prothalli that the asexual as well as the sexual stage can be studied only under the microscope.

Reproduction in the mosses. Mosses, too, reproduce by asexual and then by sexual reproduction in regular succession; that is, they also have an alternation of generations. At certain times of the year a tall stalk with a spore case (sporangium) at its top grows out of the leafy moss plant. The spore case is filled with many spores which form by asexual reproduction. On the moist earth a spore grows and produces a green, branching chain of cells (called a protonema). This green thread looks like some of the simple algae. Buds form on this thread, and each bud can grow into a leafy moss plant. So far there has been no sexual reproduction. But in time two kinds of microscopic reproductive organs are produced at the top or along the sides of the leafy plant. One kind produces eggs and the other kind produces sperm cells. The sperm cells, like those of the fern, can move about in a film of moisture. They swim to the eggs, and fertilization occurs. From the fertilized egg cell develops the stalk, bearing the case in which spores are produced. Although the spore case and its stalk looks like a true part of the leafy moss plant, it is really a separate plant which lives as a sort of parasite, getting part of its food from the leafy moss plant on which it grows. See Figure 25.19.

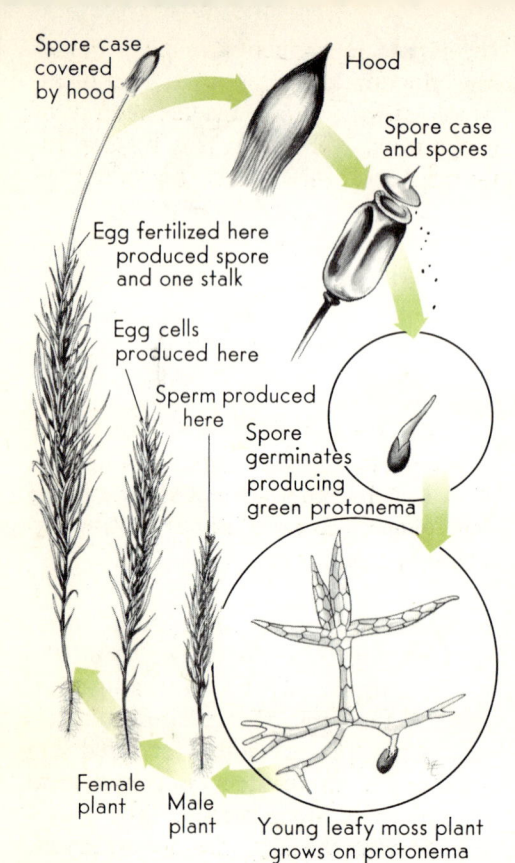

25.19 The two generations in pigeon wheat moss. The spore case on its stalk is really a separate plant which lives on the green moss plant. Spores are produced asexually. When they germinate, they produce the protonema. Buds on the protonema grow into the leafy, green moss plant, which in time produces two kinds of gametes. The result of fertilization is the stalk bearing the spore case.

tiny and colorless, but a prothallus just the same because it produces the sperm cell. In the same way the developed embryo sac is a prothallus which produces the egg cell. Here, as in the fern, the gametes are formed in prothalli which grow from spores. Male and female gametes form in separate prothalli; this is true of some ferns too. The prothalli were formed asexu-

What have you learned? Perhaps the easiest way for us to review this chapter is by means of this table. Let us begin with sexual reproduction in flowering plants. Then will come asexual reproduction in flowering plants, often called vegetative reproduction. Last comes reproduction in ferns and in mosses, which clearly show an alternation of generations. This means a regular rotation of sexual and asexual reproduction.

TABLE 19

SEXUAL REPRODUCTION IN FLOWERING PLANTS

1. Production of flowers with essential organs: stamen (filament; anther, which produces pollen); pistil (ovary, style, stigma).
2. Production of gametes: (A) egg cell, one of cells in embryo sac which lies in ovule, in ovary. (B) sperm cell in pollen tube growing out of pollen grain but only after pollination.
3. Pollination or transfer of pollen to stigma. Cross- and self-pollination.
4. Fertilization or union of egg cell and sperm nucleus in ovule in ovary.
5. Development of embryo by cell division and differentiation within ovule.
6. Growth of ovule into seed which is dormant for a time.
7. Growth of ovary and certain other flower parts into fruit.
8. Seed dispersal by insects, other animals, wind, water.
9. Germination of seed into young plant, or seedling.

ASEXUAL REPRODUCTION OR VEGETATIVE REPRODUCTION

1. New plants from leaf, stem, or root of many kinds of plants.
2. Cuttings (or slips), tubers, bulbs, rhizomes, layers, runners, grafts.
3. Advantages to us: offspring produced more quickly; offspring always like parent.

REPRODUCTION IN FERN — ALTERNATION OF GENERATIONS

1. Spores formed by asexual reproduction on fronds.
Spores develop into small, green, leaflike prothallus. This produces eggs and motile sperms.
2. Sexual reproduction by union of egg and sperm.
3. Development of embryo which grows into new leafy fern plant.

REPRODUCTION IN MOSS — ALTERNATION OF GENERATIONS

1. Spores formed in tall spore case growing out of top of moss plant.
Spore develops into tiny green protonema which buds into moss plants.
2. Sexual reproduction by union of egg and motile sperm formed at top or side of moss plant.
3. Fertilized egg grows, producing the spore case which forms spores.

CHAPTER TWENTY–FIVE — PLANT REPRODUCTION

USEFUL WORDS IN BIOLOGY

sepal (calyx)
petal (corolla)
perianth
stamen
anther
filament
pistil
stigma
style
ovary
ovule
pistillate
staminate

egg cell
embryo sac
pollen tube
sperm nucleus
tube nucleus
pollination (cross- and self-)
micropyle
cotyledons
hypocotyl
plumule
embryo

differentiation
endosperm
germination
seedling
fruit
vegetative reproduction
slip or cutting
tuber
bulb
parthenogenesis
alternation of generations

TEST YOURSELF

1. Describe the four circles of parts in a typical flower, beginning with the outside circle.
2. Which of these parts are essential for the making of seeds?
3. (a) Name the parts of a pistil. (b) Describe in detail (or make a large drawing of) a lengthwise section through the lowest part of a pistil.
4. (a) What is pollination? (b) Explain how cross- and self-pollination take place.
5. Tell what happens to a pollen grain after it reaches the stigma and how the sperm nuclei get to the embryo sac.
6. Explain how endosperm is formed in some seeds; state its use.
7. Into what does an egg cell normally develop after fertilization? Explain these changes.
8. Explain the changes which occur in ovule and ovary while the embryo develops.
9. Dormancy, seedling, germination, seed, fertilization. Use these five words to show that you understand their relationship to each other.
10. (a) Explain asexual reproduction in higher plants. (b) Describe four examples.
11. Explain parthenogenesis.
12. What is the relation of plant hormones and similar chemicals to the development of fruit and seed?
13. Ferns have a regular alternation of asexual and sexual reproduction. Explain how and where each takes place.
14. Flowering plants, too, have an alternation of generations. What is the prothallus which bears the sperm? The egg?
15. Mosses, also, have an alternation of generations. (a) Where and how does their sexual reproduction take place? (b) What is the appearance of the part of the plant that is produced asexually?

DO IT YOURSELF

1. **What is in a seed?** Kidney bean or lima bean seeds are best to study. Soak the seeds overnight. Find the scar made by the breaking off of the tiny stalk which attached the bean to the bean pod. If you press the seed gently you should see the micropyle, a tiny hole at one end of this scar. Remove the seed coats; thus you uncover the embryo. First you will see the two large fleshy seed leaves or **cotyledons**. The cotyledons are attached to a stemlike part called the **hypocotyl**. Now look for very small leaflike parts pressed together between the cotyledons. This is the **plumule**. Draw the opened seed and label these three parts. You will be interested to find out what these parts grow into when the seed is allowed to germinate.

2. **How the seed grows into a seedling.** Lay some of the unopened soaked seeds on moist blotting paper in a covered pan and watch them from day to day. Also plant some in moist sawdust or soil to see how they push their way up through soil. What part of a seedling appears first above ground? You will see that the growth of the plumule produces the stem and leaves. The root grows from the end of the hypocotyl. Draw and label a seedling after it has appeared above ground. Can you guess of what use the fleshy cotyledons might be to the small plant? You can find out

by experimenting. Plant several beans. When the cotyledons reach the surface remove one cotyledon from some seedlings, both from others.

3. Do bean seeds right themselves when they germinate? Plant soaked bean seeds in moist sawdust in different positions. Lay six seeds horizontally; plant six vertically with the hypocotyl pointing up and six with hypocotyl pointing down. Make a note of when each seed appears. (Be sure to water all parts of the pan equally.) When the cotyledons appear above the surface dig up the seedlings and describe.

4. Study of a flower. After the class has studied one kind of flower, study some other kind. Draw and describe what you see. Share your experiences with the other members of the class. If possible, someone should study a sweet pea blossom because the ovary closely resembles the pea pod.

5. Pollen tubes. If you have a microscope you can perform several experiments with pollen. Try to grow some pollen in sugar solutions; try a 10% solution, and a stronger and a weaker solution. If you have tulip blossoms you can grow pollen tubes in a more interesting way. Put some *ripe* pollen on the *ripe* stigma of the pistil with a toothpick. After about four hours cut off a piece of the top of the stigma and crush it on a slide. Under the low power you should see many pollen tubes.

6. Favorable conditions for seed germination. Using several kinds of seeds, try out different conditions of temperature, moisture, and light. Have controls. Write up your experiments.

7. Fruits and seeds. Start a collection of fruits and seeds and notice the many devices by which they are spread.

8. Vegetative reproduction. Your classroom or your home can be made into a greenhouse. There is no end to the number of plants you can raise from slips, bulbs, and tubers. You can raise begonias and African violets by planting leaves; plant the leafstalks in soil. Raise geraniums, coleus, and tradescantia from slips (stems) planted in water or moist sand. Raise potato plants from pieces containing "eyes." Put one end of a sweet potato in a glass of water. Cut off the top half inch of carrots after the leaves have been removed. Lay the pieces in a flat bowl and add enough water to cover the bottom about one fourth inch deep. Your friends may have some plants of which they would give you slips. Experiment with new plants. But remember you will never have a "green thumb" unless you give your plants regular care. Plants are living things just as animals are.

9. A plant exhibit. Could you arrange for a display of your plants in some central part of the school? This would give the other students an idea of the large variety of plants that can be raised at no expense. In time every possible window sill in every classroom could be made into a small garden.

10. Reproduction in ferns. You can raise prothalli from the spores of ferns but it takes time. Mix equal parts of garden loam, leaf mold, peat moss, and sand. Almost fill a small flower pot with this mixture. Bake the pot containing the mixture in a hot oven for three hours. Why? Moisten the soil with boiled water. Sprinkle spores which you have shaken onto a sheet of white paper onto the soil. Cover with glass and keep the pot standing in water, in a moderately light place for some weeks. Many people, however, recommend raising fern prothalli on specially prepared nutrient agar. You will find complete directions for this in "Growing Fern Prothallia" by Herbert M. Clarke, *The American Biology Teacher*, December 1954.

11. Raising Moss Protonemata. You will find simple directions in *The American Biology Teacher*, May 1950.

ADVENTURES IN READING

1. *Textbook of Botany* by E. N. Transeau, H. C. Sampson, and L. H. Tiffany, Harper, 1953. Many pages on plant reproduction.
2. "Honey Bees as Agents of Pollination" by George H. Vansell and W. H. Griggs, *Insects*, 1952 Yearbook of the United States Department of Agriculture.
3. "Seed Time and Harvest" by Edward Salisbury, *Science Survey* edited by Ian Cox, Sampson Low, Marston, 1948. The rate at which plants can spread and how long some seeds can remain alive will amaze you.

Chapter 26

Animal reproduction

A preview. Reproduction is basically the same in many-celled animals. Even in its details it is very similar in all vertebrates, particularly so in mammals. We can study the principal steps in reproduction first in a short preview. Then we can learn details later in a number of different animals, noting the similarities and the differences.

(1) When animals are sexually mature they produce gametes. The eggs (**ova** — singular, **ovum**) are produced by the females; the males produce the sperms. See Figures 26.1 and 26.2. The reproductive organs that produce eggs are **ovaries** (usually two in each female); the organs that produce sperms are **testes** (the singular is **testis**), or **spermaries** (usually two in each male). In a very few kinds of many-celled animals, ovaries and spermaries are in the same individual; the earthworm is one of these.

(2) In the male, tubes or ducts permit the discharging of the gametes to the outside of the body. These are called **sperm ducts.** In the female there are tubes called **oviducts,** one for each ovary. In some animals the eggs are discharged through the oviducts to the outside; in others, the eggs are retained in a portion of the oviduct.

(3) Fertilization, or union of gametes, takes place outside the female's body in some animals or inside the female's body in other animals.

(4) The fertilized egg or zygote becomes an embryo, as in plants. Many cell divisions take place, and then groups of cells become differentiated. In some species of animals the embryo develops outside the body of the mother; in some, the embryo develops inside.

(5) In man, the differences between men and women in general bodily structure, size, strength, voice, and so on, are well known to you. These characters are called **secondary sex characters.** In many animals, but by no means in all, the two sexes are different in structure and appearance. In most species of birds, for example, the feathers of the males are more brightly colored than those of the females. Among deer, the males are distinguished by horns. See Figure 26.3.

From fertilized egg to young embryo. A new individual begins when a sperm and egg join. After this, a series of remarkable changes results finally in an adult animal. What changes go on to make the fertilized egg of a fish turn into a fish, the fertilized egg of a bird into a bird, the fertilized human egg into a human being? The beginning of the process is the same in all many-celled animals; let's see what happens in one of the simple forms which can be studied easily. The fertilized starfish egg is easy to study. You can study the early stages yourself if you have a microscope.

The first thing that happens after fertilization is a series of divisions of the egg, one right after the other. This is called **cleavage** (clee'vej); cleavage produces a solid ball of cells. Then the cells in the ball arrange them-

Frog   Hydra   Human

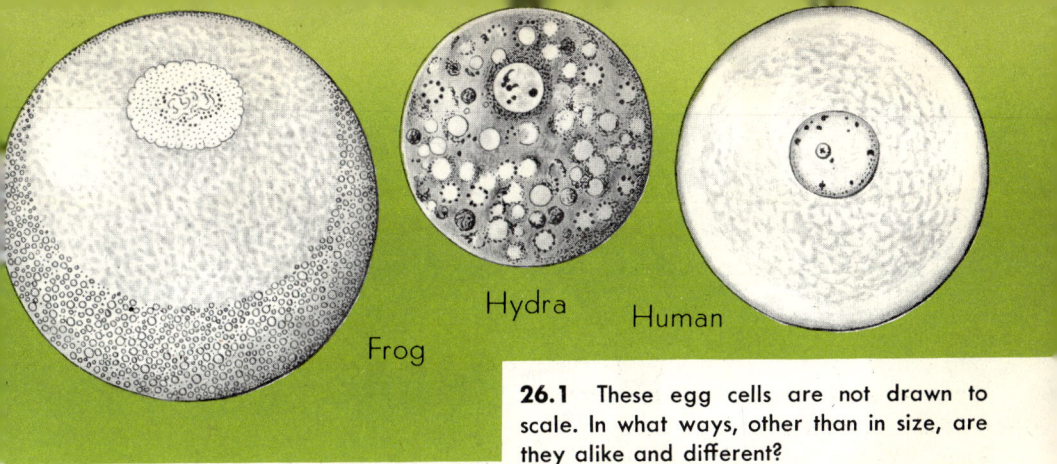

26.1 These egg cells are not drawn to scale. In what ways, other than in size, are they alike and different?

WORM   FISH   FROG   SNAKE   MAN

26.2 Sperm cells from five kinds of animals. In what respect do these five sperm cells resemble each other?

26.3 Mule deer from the Rocky Mountain region. What is the secondary sex characteristic which distinguishes male from female? *Canadian Travel Bureau*

CHAPTER TWENTY-SIX — ANIMAL REPRODUCTION

387

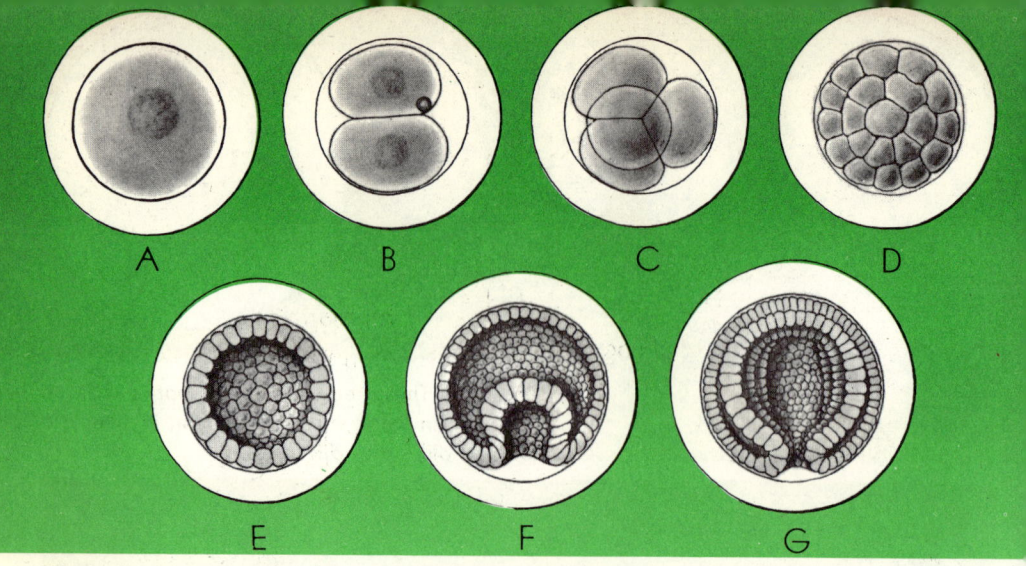

26.4 Development of the fertilized egg of a simple animal. **A, B, C,** and **D** show cleavage of the egg. **E, F,** and **G** are sections of later stages. What do they show? How do you explain the fact that there is only a very slight increase in size?

selves into a larger hollow ball (the **blastula**). The hollow ball of cells grows in on one side, so that it is no longer spherical but forms a double-walled cup (the **gastrula**). All this is shown in Figure 26.4.

Tissues and organs appear. The double-walled cup has two layers of cells; then it develops a third layer between the first two. There are now three layers, called **primary germ layers.** The outer germ layer is the **ectoderm,** the inner is the **endoderm,** and the middle layer is the **mesoderm.** It is from these three germ layers that the tissues and organs form.

Further development is more complicated. As in the development of a plant embryo, however, two things happen: further cell divisions and cell differentiation. Development of tissues and organs from the three germ layers is similar in all animals. From the ectoderm come the body covering and the nervous system. From the endoderm are formed the lining of the alimentary canal and several important organs, such as the liver, the pancreas, the thyroid gland, and the respiratory system. From the mesoderm are formed the muscles, bones, blood vessels, the sex glands, and some other body parts. When the tiny animal has organs of digestion, breathing, locomotion, and other organs that enable it to keep alive by itself, the embryo stage has ended. This development takes various amounts of time in different animals.

Fertilization in the fish. At certain seasons, often in the spring, egg cells develop in the ovaries of the adult female fish. They become separated from the other cells in the ovaries in one or several large masses; sometimes there are as many as several million eggs during the mating season. The egg cells enter the oviducts and are pushed along by cilia lining the tubes. They leave the body by an opening on the lower (ventral) surface. In fish, this releasing of egg cells is known as

UNIT SEVEN — REPRODUCTION

26.5 This fish, Telapia, has already spawned. See the eggs in the cleared spot (nest) on the bottom of the aquarium. *American Museum of Natural History*

spawning (Fig. 26.5). While the female is spawning, the male releases the sperm cells, always close to the eggs.

If you could place fresh fish eggs and sperms on a slide under the microscope, you would see the sperms lash their tails and move among the egg cells. Many sperms gather around one egg as if in response to a chemical stimulus. Soon one sperm cell pushes through the cell membrane into the cytoplasm of the egg. The sperm nucleus moves toward the nucleus of the egg and fuses with it. Fertilization has been accomplished; the egg is now a fertilized egg. As soon as one sperm has entered the egg, a tough membrane known as a **fertilization membrane** forms around the egg, and now no other sperms can enter. The fertilized egg (or zygote) is the beginning of a new individual. It can now grow up.

From fertilized egg to young fish. Figure 26.6 shows you the chief stages in the life history of the fish. It also reveals something else that needs explanation. The fish egg has a large amount of food in it. This food is called **yolk.** The embryo uses the food in the yolk as it grows. By the time the yolk has been used up, the developing fish has reached a stage where it has a mouth and a digestive system. It is then able to feed itself. The remains of the yolk can be seen

CHAPTER TWENTY-SIX — ANIMAL REPRODUCTION

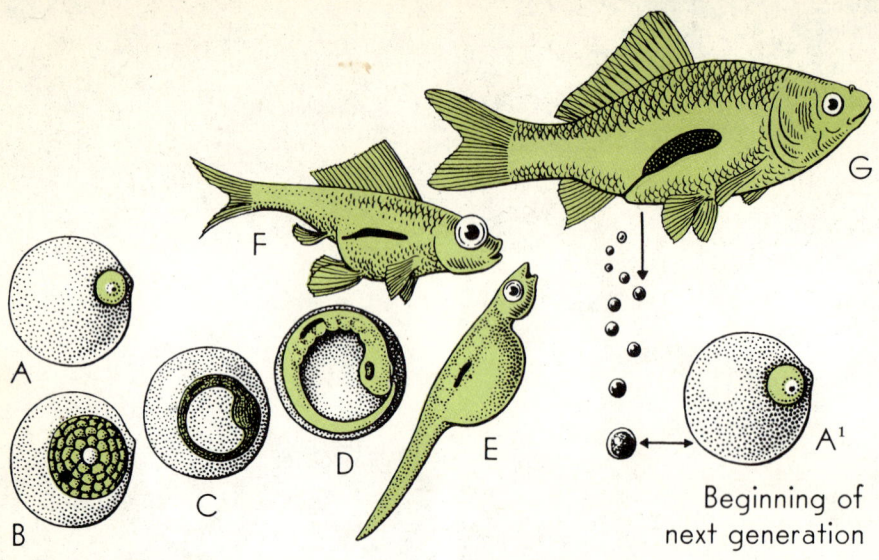

26.6 From fertilized egg, through embryonic stages, to adult fish. In **E** the "yolk sac" is seen even after the egg hatches. Of what use is it to the growing animal? Note the solid black spot in **D, E, F,** and **G**. The cells here remain undifferentiated at first. What organ do they grow into, later, in **G**? **A¹** is the beginning of a new generation.

in E and F of Figure 26.6 as the "yolk sac."

The living part of the fish egg sits like a cap on the yolk. All the early stages of embryonic development take place as in the starfish. Differentiation of cells occurs; gradually the organs develop from the three germ layers. It takes about two weeks for all this to happen in some kinds of fish, more in other kinds. The young fish can now carry on all its activities except one — reproduction. The ovaries and spermaries begin their development but don't finish it at this time.

Formation of sperms and eggs. The ovaries and spermaries, like other organs, consist of several tissues. One of these tissues, the group of cells that will later form sperms or eggs, remains undifferentiated in the sex organ for quite some time. Later, when these cells begin to form eggs or sperms, we say the fish becomes sexually mature. While sperms and eggs are found only in the fully developed fish, the cells from which the gametes came were already present in the very young embryo. Look again at Figure 26.6. The black spot represents this undifferentiated tissue.

Some fish protect their young. A few kinds of fish scoop out a small depression in the sand or gravel where they deposit eggs and sperms. See Figure 26.7. Figure 26.8 shows even better parental protection furnished by the stickleback. As a rule, however, fish eggs and sperms are deposited near each other but without protection. Probably many eggs fail to develop because no sperms reach them. Of those that are fertilized countless numbers are destroyed, for the parents rarely protect the young. Some of the exceptions are interesting. In one kind of fish, embryos are carried about in the mouth of the male parent.

390   UNIT SEVEN — REPRODUCTION

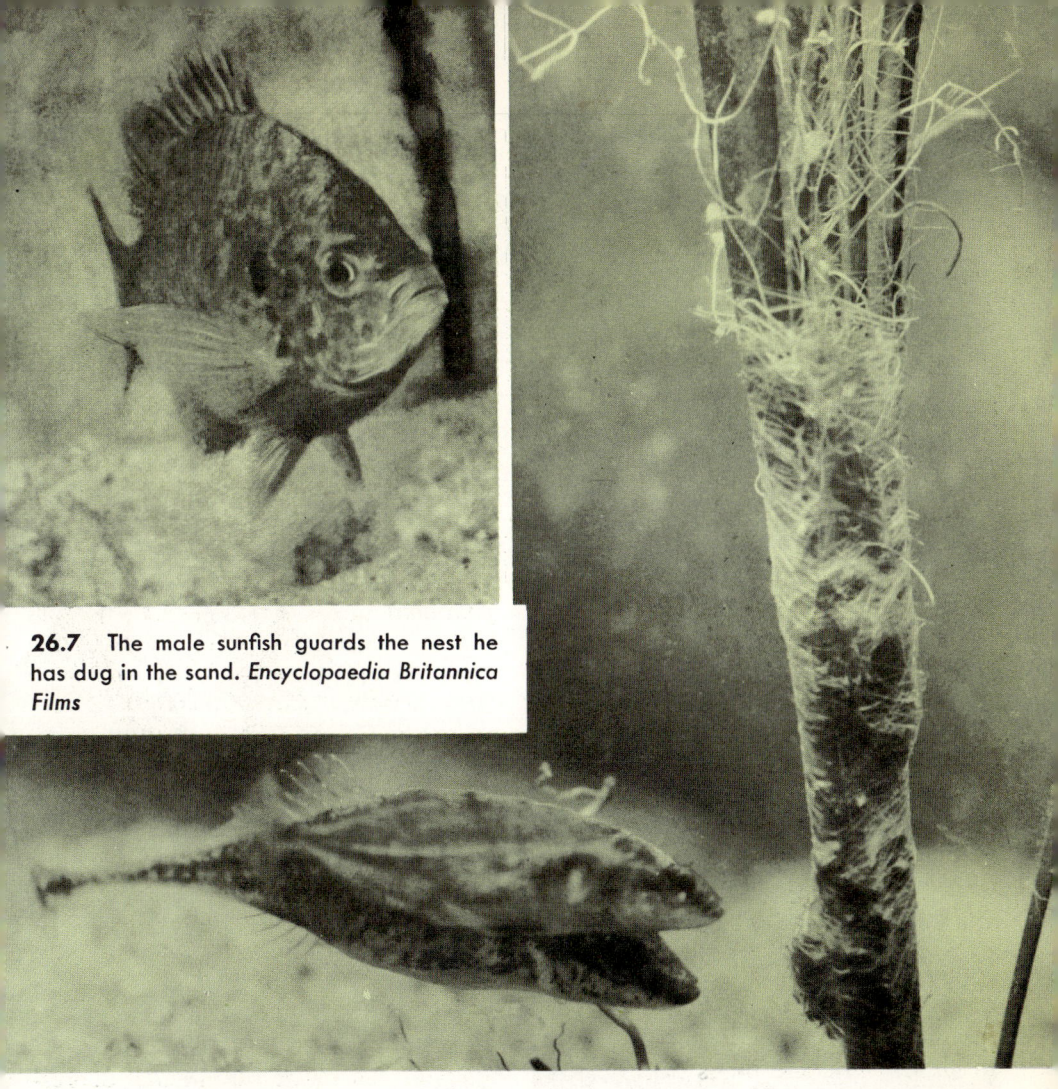

26.7 The male sunfish guards the nest he has dug in the sand. *Encyclopaedia Britannica Films*

26.8 The nest of the stickleback is made of water weeds glued together with a sticky substance secreted by glands in the body of the male. The male stickleback also guards the eggs that the female places in the nest. *New York Aquarium*

Even after they are sizable fish they keep returning to his mouth when danger threatens. How often he yields to the temptation of hunger no one knows.

Frog reproduction. In the early spring, both frogs and toads lay their eggs in quiet water. Figure 26.9 shows you the reproductive organs of the male and female frog. When mating occurs, the male frog is above the female so that as the eggs come out, the sperms are deposited on them. As each egg passes through the oviduct it is coated with a thin jellylike material. The sperms pierce this layer. The jellylike material swells as water is absorbed. It protects the eggs by holding them together. The large slippery mass of eggs and jelly is difficult to grasp and is not easily eaten by

CHAPTER TWENTY-SIX — ANIMAL REPRODUCTION

Female ♀

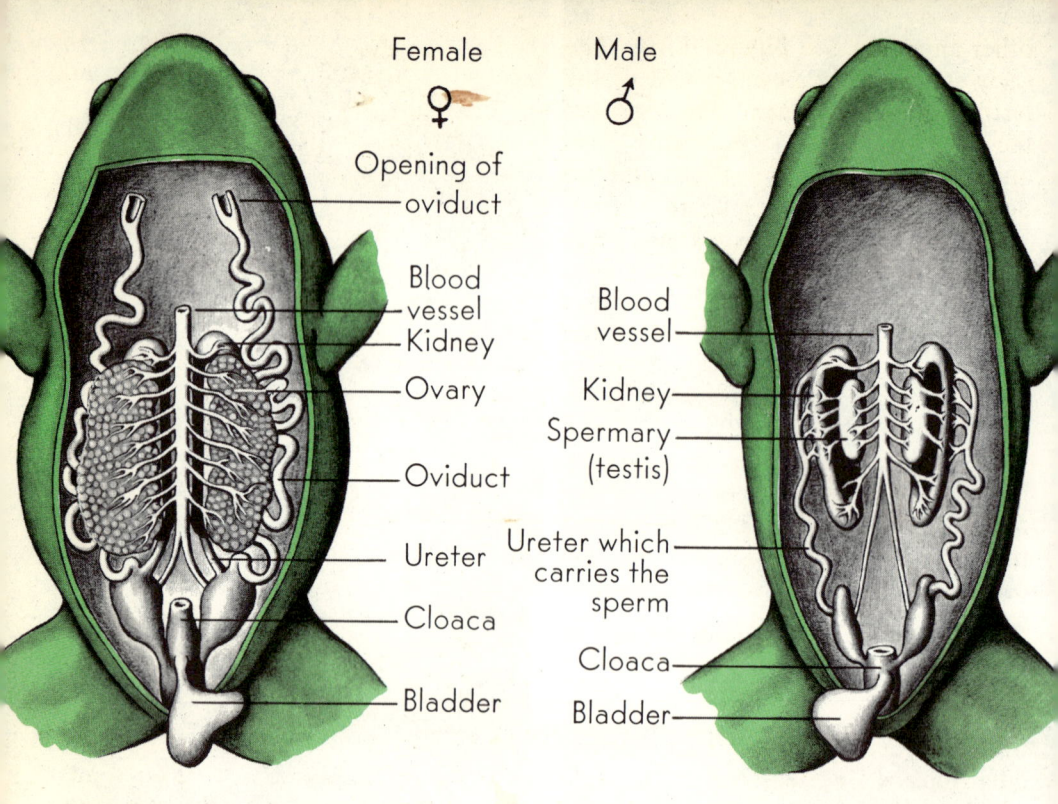

- Opening of oviduct
- Blood vessel
- Kidney
- Ovary
- Oviduct
- Ureter
- Cloaca
- Bladder

Male ♂

- Blood vessel
- Kidney
- Spermary (testis)
- Ureter which carries the sperm
- Cloaca
- Bladder

26.9 Reproductive and excretory organs of the male and female frog. When the eggs are full grown, just before being laid, the ovaries are twice as large as indicated in this drawing. How do the male and female organs compare in size?

26.10 Eggs laid by a frog. You can see the thick jelly around each egg. *American Museum of Natural History*

26.11 A tadpole changes into a frog. What is the first sign of its becoming a frog? *New York Zoological Park*

UNIT SEVEN — REPRODUCTION

other animals. See Figure 26.10. The early stages of the development of the fertilized egg are much like those of the fish. But when the organs form and the body takes shape, the embryo does not resemble the parent frog. We call it a **tadpole** or a **pollywog**. This tadpole eventually changes into the frog or toad. When striking changes of this sort occur between the embryo stage and the adult, the development is called a **metamorphosis**. See Figure 26.11.

The tadpole gets dissolved oxygen from the water by means of two feathery gills which project just back of the head. Young tadpoles wriggle occasionally or hang quietly, attached to water plants by means of a sucking organ at the front of the head. Soon the tadpole swims by means of its tail; a mouth forms, with horny jaws well fitted for eating plants; and internal gills replace the external gills with which it began. In the early spring, if you gather frog's eggs with plenty of water, they will hatch indoors, and you will see tadpoles developing.

After living this way for several months, or longer in some species, the tadpole goes through other changes. Two lumps appear near the hind end of the tadpole's body, one on either side of the tail. Slowly, legs push out here. If you cut the tadpole open at this time, you will find the little front legs already formed under the skin. Its organs of digestion and circulation are different from those of the parent frog; they too undergo changes. Within the two-chambered heart a wall grows, making three chambers. The long, coiled digestive tube gradually forms a true stomach and intestine, much shorter than the original tube. Lungs form; the gills disappear. The tail gradually grows shorter. It is absorbed, used as food, while the

26.12 The male midwife toad. Though called a toad, it lives in the water. The male carries the eggs about with him until they hatch into tadpoles. *American Museum of Natural History*

tadpole is changing. Tiny teeth appear in the mouth; the long tongue attached in the front also develops. The animal now feeds on insects and spends part of its life on land. When it is swimming and floating in the water, it must come to the surface from time to time to breathe, even though it gets some oxygen through its skin. In its habits and its appearance it is very different from the tiny tadpole that hatched from the egg. There is little parental care among the amphibia (frogs, toads, newts, etc.). Figure 26.12 shows one exception.

Bird reproduction. Among animals that live entirely on land, fertilization takes place inside the body of the female. Internal fertilization is essential to land-living, since eggs and sperms dry up and die when exposed to air. In internal fertilization, the male puts the sperms directly into or near the oviduct of the female. The sperms are in a liquid medium when they are introduced.

In birds only one of the two ovaries matures. Perhaps you have had a chance to see the ovary in a chicken. It usually contains several eggs of different sizes, all yellow in color.

26.13 Baby snapping turtles. Reptiles have internal fertilization. In some kinds the eggs hatch inside the female's body, but most reptiles lay eggs that are covered with a leathery shell. *American Museum of Natural History*

Normally, as each egg cell reaches its full size, it leaves the ovary and passes into the oviduct. All of you have seen the egg cell of the chicken. You eat it when you eat an egg; it's the yolk of the "egg."

In the oviduct the egg cell meets the sperms that came from the male bird. By one device or another, including the lashing of their tails, they have traveled up the oviduct to a pouch near the upper end. When they are brought close to the egg one of them enters the egg. There may be one or more eggs fertilized at one time. The fertilized egg cell then travels farther along the oviduct on its way to the exterior. In passing, it is wrapped in coverings of various kinds. It is surrounded first by the white of egg (albumen). This not only helps to protect the developing embryo but later serves as food for it. Farther along, the oviduct secretes two thin but tough membranes around the albumen. Finally, the oviduct secretes a limy shell which becomes hard. You can see all these parts in a hen's eggs.

In the meantime, the fertilized egg cell has begun to divide. The greater part of the development, however, occurs after the egg has left the body of the mother. This development does not take place unless the egg is kept warm during an **incubation** (in-cue-bay′shun) period. Almost all kinds of birds incubate their eggs by sitting on them. One of the parents, usually the female, does the sitting; but the male and female of some species "take turns." A few kinds lay their eggs in the nests of other birds. The incubation period of chicken eggs is about three weeks. During this time the food from both the yolk and the albumen covering has been absorbed, and the organs of the young chick have been formed. The chick cracks the shell with its bill and pecks its way out into the world.

Reptiles also have internal fertilization, and most of them lay eggs which are then left to hatch. See Figure 26.13.

Parental care among birds. Baby chickens, ducks, turkeys, gulls, and the young of some other birds need relatively little attention from the parents. They leave the egg fully equipped to go out with the mother in search of food. They are covered with downy feathers, their muscles are well de-

26.14 Young grouse hatching from eggs laid on the ground. How will the feathers look when the birds are a few hours older? *Frank Gehr*

26.15 Pelican feeding its young. In what respects is the young bird undeveloped? The birds at the extreme left are gulls. *American Museum of Natural History*

veloped, their sense organs are complete. See Figure 26.14.

The young of many other kinds of birds, such as the songbirds and pigeons, are immature when they hatch. They are completely dependent on their parents' care for several weeks. Newly hatched sparrows are naked, their eyes are closed, and the muscles of their wings and legs take days to develop. Their appetites are enormous, and the parent birds make hundreds of excursions every day in search of food for them.

When the young birds get a little older, they must learn to fly. The parents often force the young to make their first attempt by pushing them out of the nest. But growth and development are slow. Thus among some birds there is a type of family life in which, usually, both parents play an equal part. See Figure 26.15.

Reproduction in mammals. In the mammals fertilization is internal, even in those few species, like the whale, that spend their lives in water. Development of the embryo is also internal. We say that their young are "born alive." In some reptiles and some fish the young are "born alive," too. But their development within the mother's body is not like the development of the embryo of a mammal. The mammalian mother and the developing embryo have special organs, Figure 26.16, by which food and oxygen are supplied to the embryo and wastes are removed from it.

Reproduction in rabbits. Let us study rabbit reproduction as an example of reproduction in a mammal. The female rabbit has two ovaries and two oviducts. When the male and female have mated, the presence of the sperms and fluid in the lower part of each oviduct induces the ovaries to release egg cells. From one to ten mature eggs are released and enter the oviducts. The sperm cells travel up the oviducts, and fertilization occurs in the upper part of the ducts. Fertilized egg cells begin cleavage, going through the same stages — hollow ball, two-layered cup, and formation of three germ layers — that occur in the development of other animals.

During the early development stages, the embryos come down to an expanded portion of each oviduct, a sac

CHAPTER TWENTY-SIX — ANIMAL REPRODUCTION

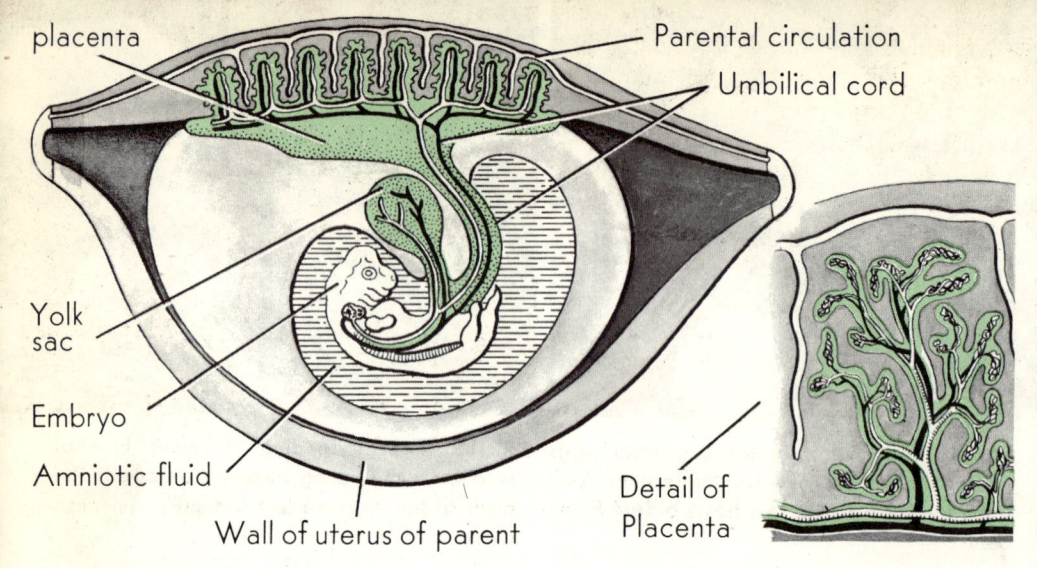

placenta — **Parental circulation** — **Umbilical cord**

Yolk sac

Embryo

Amniotic fluid

Wall of uterus of parent

Detail of Placenta

26.16 In all mammals except a few in Australia, the young develop within the mother's body. The embryo becomes attached to certain membranes of the uterus by a placenta. The text tells you how the developing embryo obtains food and oxygen and gets rid of waste products.

called the **uterus** (you'ter-us). The rabbit embryos, surrounded by membranes, become attached to the walls of the uterus. The region of attachment is called the **placenta** (pla-sen'ta). It is formed partly from the membranes of the embryo and partly from the lining of the uterus. If several embryos develop at the same time, which is what commonly happens in rabbits, each usually has its own placenta.

The embryo is attached to the placenta by means of the **umbilical cord.** Very early in the embryo's development a simple heart and blood vessels form. Several large blood vessels arising in the embryo run through the cord and end in capillaries in the placenta. These capillaries lie close to other capillaries which are part of the mother's circulatory system.

Between these two sets of capillaries there is an exchange of food, oxygen, and wastes. That is, in the placenta food and oxygen diffuse from the mother's blood through the capillary walls into the embryo's capillaries. At the same time carbon dioxide and other wastes diffuse out of the embryo's blood into the mother's blood. Blood from the mother never flows directly into the embryo; there is no direct connection between the two circulatory systems.

In this way the rabbit embryo is nourished and continues growing for about thirty days. At the end of this period the muscular walls of the uterus contract violently. The contractions cause the young animals, each with its placenta, to be detached from the uterus. Through further contractions the embryo and the placenta are pushed through the **vagina** (va-jeye'na), the passage which leads from the uterus to the outside of the body.

In all mammals, development and birth occur in the same way. But the period of internal development, called **gestation** (jes-tay'shun), varies in length. For example, on the average, it is 12 days in the opossum, 267 days in humans, 337 days in the horse and 645 days in the Indian elephant.

Mammals care for their young. The amount and kind of care mammals give their offspring varies with the species, but all feed their young on milk produced in **mammary glands.** Milk is not secreted by the mother until after the young are born. You may know that farmers cannot expect to milk a cow until after the cow has a calf.

Kangaroo and opossum babies are very immature when born. The mother kangaroo puts the babies into her pouch, into which the mammary glands open. You can see an older baby in the pouch in Figure 26.17. Young opossums climb into their mother's pouch themselves. There they receive warmth, protection, and a constant supply of food. The young of most mammals are more mature than kangaroos and opossum babies when they are born. But in many, such as the dog, cat, mouse, guinea pig, and rabbit, the young are born blind and are almost helpless. On the other hand, the babies of grazing animals are much more independent. They are able to stand, even to walk awkwardly, and are well protected by a coat of hair.

Human reproduction. Human reproduction is much like reproduction in other mammals. The differences, however, are important to us. The human female has two ovaries; and the oviducts leading from them are called **Fallopian tubes.** These are united at the base, forming a single uterus. Generally, only one mature egg cell is produced at a time. This happens at fairly regular intervals, once sexual maturity has been reached. The sperms meet the egg cell in one of the Fallopian tubes. The fertilized egg then moves down to the uterus, where it attaches itself to the wall. A placenta forms and the embryo develops. The period

26.17 The kangaroo mother carries her child in a pouch. When the baby was younger it fed from mammary glands inside the pouch.
H. Armstrong Roberts

of gestation is about nine months (267 days).

When birth occurs, it is normally because contractions of the wall of the uterus push the baby out of the mother's body through the vagina, which expands, permitting this to happen. The placenta is ejected shortly after the baby is born.

How we care for babies. Human care of babies starts long before the baby is born. In clinics or by consulting private physicians, **pregnant** women receive advice on diet, rest, and other ways in which they may provide the best possible environment for the developing embryo. Since the pregnant woman is "eating for two" there are substances, like calcium salts, of

CHAPTER TWENTY-SIX — ANIMAL REPRODUCTION 397

which she may need more than the usual amount to provide for the needs of the embryo. Frequent tests of her urine may be made to check on the work of the kidneys, which must serve both embryo and parent.

Once the baby is born, the mother and father turn to the physician for advice on diet and daily routine for the baby. Physicians, in general, prefer that the baby be breast-fed for several months if that is possible. But each baby should receive individual consideration.

As human children grow up, in countries like ours, not only their families but their communities and the nation help provide for their welfare and their development in many ways. These provisions have reduced the death rate of infants, improved the health and well-being of children, and produced increased size and strength. You might look again at the pages of Unit Six to help you recall how this has been done. Your school is another agency of society designed to help you to become an adult capable of living successfully and happily in our world.

Successful reproduction. As you read about the different methods of reproduction in simple and complex animals and plants, you may have wondered which was the "best."

There is no "best" and no "worst." To the biologist the important question is "Can the species maintain itself?" If, in a certain species, the number of organisms remains the same, its method of reproduction is successful. If the species dies out we know that its method of reproduction was not really successful. The difficulties of the physical environment may have been too great or its enemies may have killed it off.

All species living today must have had successful methods of reproduction or they would have died out. Where no parental protection is given the young, species survive because they reproduce in enormous numbers. A female cod, for example, may lay 8,000,000 eggs every season. If only one male and one female of that 8,000,000 grow up and reproduce, the number of cod remains the same.

Unfortunately, we sometimes destroy certain plants and animals faster than they can reproduce. When we do this we destroy the species. It was in this way that the passenger pigeon, which once was so common, the heath hen, and the great auk became extinct.

What have you learned? Sexual reproduction in all vertebrates is similar; the differences are minor. The sex organs are usually in different animals, the male and the female. Male organs are testes or spermaries with tiny sperm ducts that lead sperms to the exterior. Female organs are ovaries with oviducts. Depending on the animal, eggs are released into the oviduct as a rule singly (in the human), in small groups (in the bird), or large masses (about 8 million from one codfish every spring).

In all land-living animals the male puts sperms in a fluid directly into or near the lower end of the oviduct. The sperms travel and meet the egg or eggs. In most water-dwelling animals eggs and sperms are released close to each other. Many eggs and sperms are lost. But these animals survive because they produce eggs and sperms in enormous numbers.

Internal fertilization may be followed by the formation of protective coverings on the fertilized egg and the external development of the embryo into a young animal (birds and most reptiles). Or it may be followed by internal development in some reptiles, even a few fish, and in all mammals. But in mammals, and only in mammals, the embryo develops while attached to a placenta, which is part of the wall of the uterus. The placenta has two sets of capillaries, the embryo's and the parent's. At birth the attachment between embryo and parent is broken, and by muscular contraction of the walls of the uterus (the lower part of the oviduct), the young animal and the placenta are forced out of the body.

The care given to the offspring in each group of animals makes an interesting story. Are you prepared to explain that, especially in the mammals?

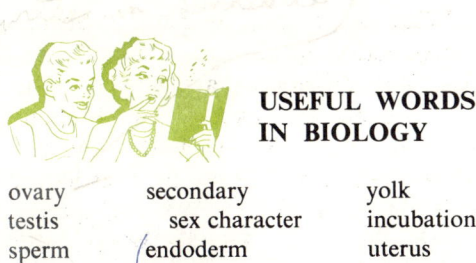

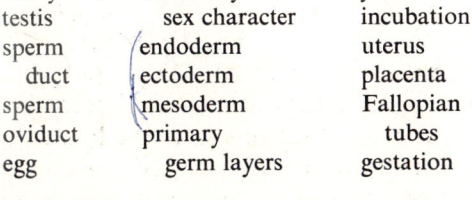

USEFUL WORDS IN BIOLOGY

ovary	secondary	yolk
testis	sex character	incubation
sperm	endoderm	uterus
duct	ectoderm	placenta
sperm	mesoderm	Fallopian
oviduct	primary	tubes
egg	germ layers	gestation

TEST YOURSELF

1. In many-celled animals: (a) What is the name of the male gamete and of the organ in which it is produced? (b) What is the name of the female gamete and the organ in which it is produced? (c) Into what tube does the male gamete pass? (d) Into what tube does the female gamete pass?
2. Fertilization differs in different animals. In which respect?
3. Give examples of secondary sex characters in man and in some other animal.
4. Describe by means of words or labeled diagrams the development of a fertilized egg into an embryo. Use these terms in your description or diagrams—cleavage, hollow ball, hollow cup, ectoderm, endoderm, and mesoderm.
5. Describe egg laying and fertilization in the fish.
6. After fertilization the embryo develops into the young fish and finally into the mature fish. Make one continuous story of this development, describing the important changes in each step.
7. Describe the metamorphosis of a frog, telling about the changes in body shape, in organs of locomotion, circulation, food getting, digestion, and breathing.
8. Explain how reproduction in the bird differs from that in the frog or fish.
9. Reproduction in the rabbit is similar in many ways to human reproduction. Describe it in detail.
10. Tell about the birth and care of the young in humans.
11. What has been discovered about the relation between numbers of offspring in animals and care of the offspring? Give examples to illustrate what you say.

DO IT YOURSELF

1. **Frog reproduction.** You will want to examine the reproductive organs of mature dissected male and female frogs. In the early spring you can collect eggs. You will be interested in their color. Can you see how the color protects the floating eggs from animals both above and below? Estimate the number of eggs laid by one frog. Put a few eggs into a large battery jar of pond water and keep the water well stirred and aerated. Examine the developing tadpoles several times a day. Take full notes. Include the time of day and date.
2. **Development of an embryo.** If you have a microscope and prepared stained slides of the early development of a starfish or sea urchin you can get a very good idea of what occurs after fertilization in all the higher animals.

CHAPTER TWENTY-SIX — ANIMAL REPRODUCTION

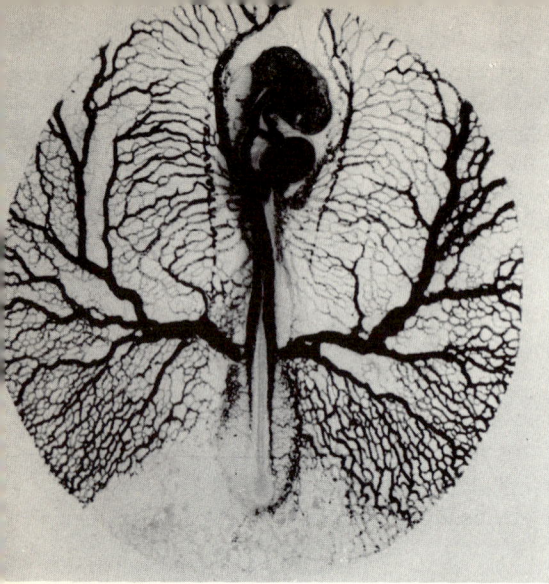

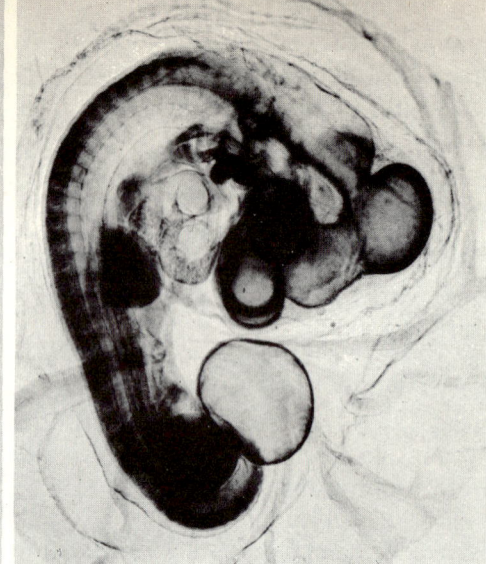

26.18 If you can incubate a hen's eggs and study developing chicks, you will find stages such as are shown in above. How old was the egg which is shown on the left? How long after that did it look like the figure on the right? Note the complex network of blood vessels spreading out over the yolk and note the chick beginning to take shape in the figure at the left. In the figure on the right you see the large head and you can see clearly the backbone beginning to form. Do Number 4 below to answer the questions.

3. The ovary and egg of a bird. Get the reproductive organs of a female chicken from a butcher. Note that the eggs in the ovary (there is only one ovary) are of different sizes. They are not all laid at the same time. How many can you count? What makes the older egg cell so large? Sometimes you find an egg partially covered in the oviduct. Describe fully what you see.

You have seen and eaten the egg with its large egg cell (yolk) many times but have you ever examined it closely? Crack a raw egg into a saucer. Examine the shell at the blunt end. How many membranes do you find inside the shell? As an egg from the ovary passed through the oviduct much seems to have been added to it. Describe all you see. If this egg was fertilized by a sperm where and when did fertilization occur? The red spot you sometimes see on the yolk is not the beginning of the developing embryo. It got there by accident and in no way affects the egg. Most of the eggs you eat have not been fertilized.

4. The development of the chick. This is a rather difficult but most rewarding project to be performed by the class, or at least by a committee. First you will need to construct an incubator. In *Methods and Materials for Teaching Biological Sciences* by D. F. Miller and G. W. Blaydes, McGraw-Hill, 1938, you will find instructions. Consult also "Embryological Studies for the High School Biologist" by Mark L. Menzel in *The American Biology Teacher*, January 1954. This gives simple directions for an incubator and also for candling store eggs to find which are fertile. It might be simpler to buy two dozen **fertile** eggs from a poultry hatching farm. Incubate the eggs at a temperature of 103°. Turn the eggs every twelve hours. After twenty-four hours of incubation open one; examine and describe it carefully. The next day open a second egg. Use a magnifying glass. What changes do you see? Repeat this every day and take full notes. Why do you need twenty-four eggs? Compare what you see with Figure 26.18.

6. Fish that bear the young alive. Raise guppies in a small aquarium. You can get full instructions for feeding and taking care of the fish from General Biological Supply House, Inc., Chicago 37, Illinois, or other supply houses or from dealers who sell guppies.

ADVENTURES IN READING

1. "Fertilization in Mammals" by Gregory Pincus, *Scientific American*, March 1951. This will interest you. Dr. Pincus got rabbit eggs to develop without their being fertilized by sperm cells.

2. "The Embryologist and the Protozoa" by Paul B. Weiss, *Scientific American*, March 1953. Rewarding to the student who is willing to work for what he gets. The article shows how cutting protozoa to pieces helps to explain how a fertilized egg gives rise to specialized tissues.

3. "Fertilization of the Egg" by Alberto Monroy, *Scientific American*, December 1950. Also not easy reading, but very interesting.

4. *Life and Growth* by Alice V. Keliher, Appleton-Century, 1938. Gives more information about human reproduction.

5. *Methods and Materials for Teaching Biological Sciences* by D. F. Miller and G. W. Blaydes, McGraw-Hill, 1938. Useful in many experiments.

Unit Eight

Heredity and environment

CHAPTER 27
Why offspring resemble their parents

CHAPTER 28
Why offspring differ from their parents

CHAPTER 29
How characters are changed

CHAPTER 30
Improving plants and animals

CHAPTER 31
Human heredity

Have you ever seen the blueprints an architect makes of the house he intends to build, or blueprints that are the plans for a piece of furniture? Much measuring and calculating goes into them. The man who makes them labors long before his work is complete; he often has sheet after sheet of plans.

But how about living things which are so much more complex than any building could ever be? Look at the many different young people opposite. Were they made according to a plan? Yes, all of these young people, all living things, are made according to a blueprint, a blueprint quite invisible to the naked eye. The plan was completed when the egg and sperm united. The "drawings" were in these two cells. But the "drawings" were in the form of complex chemical substances. These substances determined many characteristics — whether the hair would be red or black or blond, whether the nose would be long or short or broad, whether the right or left hand would be used, and so on.

Can parents, who produce the chemical substances for the plans, predict what the plans will be like? Are the plans ever the same for two different people? Are the plans ever changed after they are made? Can the "building" be changed while it is being built? You will find answers to these and many other questions in the chapters which follow.

Chapter 27

Why offspring resemble their parents

27.1 The baby hippopotamus developed from a hippo egg and sperm. What do these cells contain to make it possible for them to produce a baby hippo that looks so much like its parents? Read the text carefully. *National Zoological Park*

The baby hippopotamus. Look at Figure 27.1. Why does the baby hippopotamus look so much like its mother? How did it get to be a hippo and not a rabbit? You would answer, no doubt, that hippos develop from a hippo egg which had been fertilized by a hippo sperm. A biologist can give a fuller explanation than that, although he will be quick to add that a really complete explanation can still not be given. He will tell you that it seems to be largely because of the nucleus of the sperm and the nucleus of the egg that an offspring resembles its parents and further that it is largely because of the chromatin of those nuclei. For many years it was suspected that chromatin was important in causing the similarity between parents and offspring. Since the early part of this century biologists have proved this and have developed a theory about the nature of chromatin which is generally accepted. It is called the theory of the **gene**. The evidence for this theory has been collected by thousands of biologists in many countries.

The gene theory. The gene theory was first stated in 1910 by T. H. Morgan, Figure 27.2. According to this theory, chromatin is composed of tiny parts called genes. It is the genes that cause the various characteristics to appear in an organism. And the science which attempts to explain why all organisms both resemble and differ from their parents is called **genetics** (jen-ett′icks). It is believed that the genes are complex molecules of living matter which are able to form more of their own kind of substance. It is not certain that anyone has ever seen a gene, although possibly genes have been seen recently by the use of the electron microscope.

One thing that led scientists to suspect the presence of genes was that chro-

27.2 Thomas Hunt Morgan, a leader in the field of genetics. *Keystone View Company*

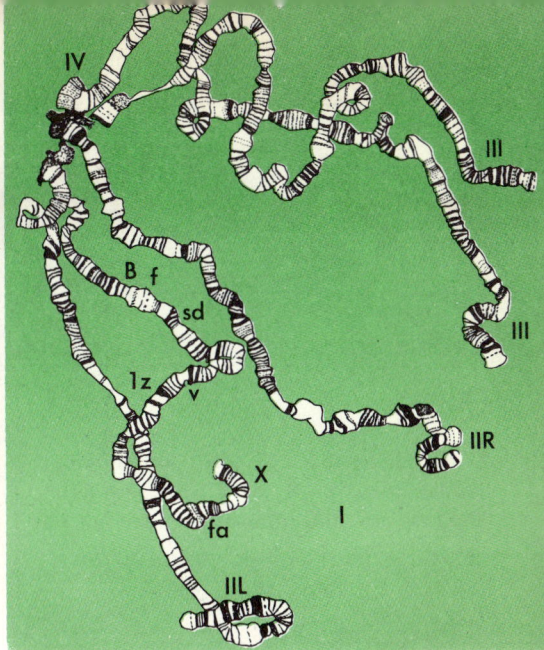

27.3 A drawing of the giant chromosomes in the salivary gland cells of the larvae of the fruit fly. The lines, of course, are not genes. Genes cannot be seen. The letters mark the location of some genes. *T. S. Painter*

matin behaves in a most complicated and regular way each time a cell divides. Let us examine nuclear division.

How chromatin behaves. Let's study the behavior of the chromatin in some simple plant cells first. Figure 27.4 shows stained chromatin clearly. Later we can study chromatin in fertilized egg cells. Before the cell divides the chromatin is strung out in threads throughout the nucleus. It is in several spirals, looking somewhat like loosely coiled springs. As the cell begins to divide, the chromatin threads become shorter and thicker. These short pieces of chromatin are like rods — some straight, some bent. They are called **chromosomes** (crow'mo-somes). The chromosomes are jellylike in composition, yet so firm that they can be pushed around with a micro-needle. The chromosomes are not all alike in shape and size; but there are always (with one important exception) two chromosomes of a kind: that is, two that are alike in shape and size. There is evidence that the genes are arranged in a single row within the chromosomes like a string of beads, and that there are thousands of genes in a chromosome. See Figure 27.3.

Chromosomes in cell division. While chromosomes are forming, the nuclear membrane disappears and the rest of the nuclear material becomes mixed with the cytoplasm. The chromosomes then move to the center of the cell.

By the time this has happened, the genes of the chromosome have doubled so that a new chromosome lies next to the old one. There are now twice as many chromosomes as were there originally, and twice as many genes. Now the new and the old chromosomes move apart until they are at opposite ends of the cell. In this way each daughter cell gets the same number and kind of chromosomes as the original

A   B   C   D   E

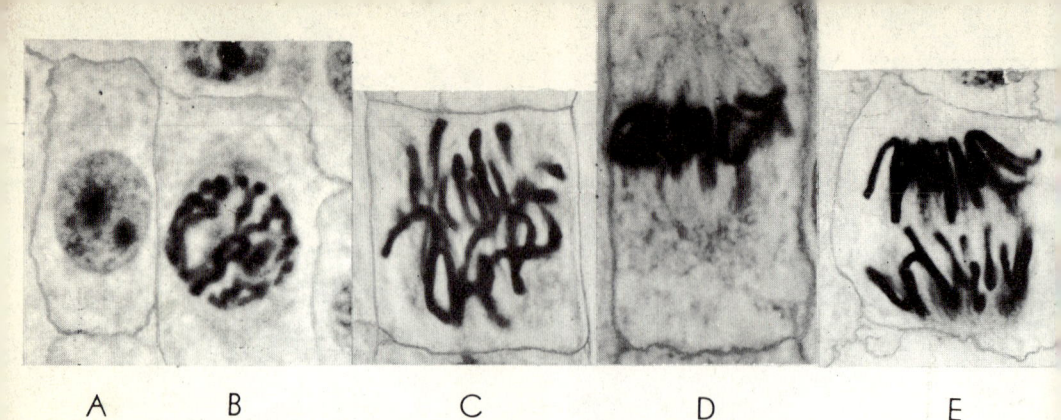

27.4 Onion skin cells dividing. Chromatin threads show in **A**. In **B** you see distinct chromosomes. In **C** chromosomes are lined up and duplicating themselves. What is happening in **D** and in **E**? A and B, *Kline;* C, D, E, F— *General Biological Supply House*

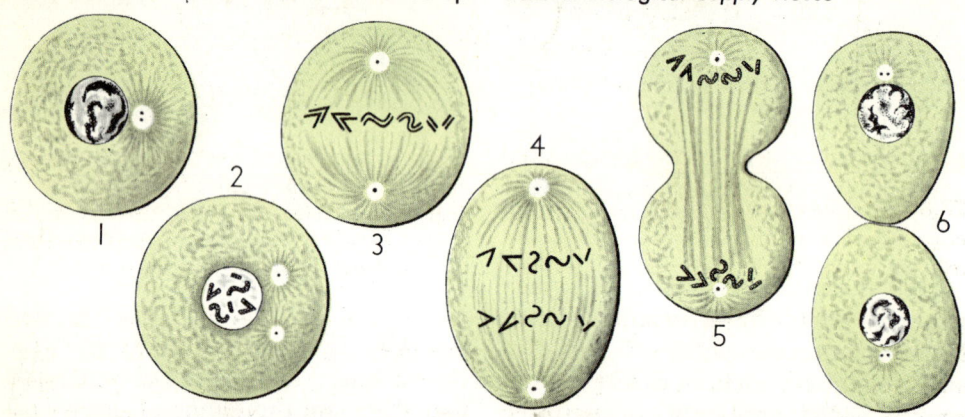

27.5 A diagram of mitosis in an animal cell. No. **1** shows chromatin in spirals. What does **2** show? In **3** each chromosome has reproduced. What happens to chromosomes in **4** and **5**? This diagram shows the spindle and centrosomes too.

cell had. This means that the genes of the two cells are alike.

A membrane then forms around each group of chromosomes. In the meantime, the chromosomes change back into the coiled form. Thus two new nuclei are formed, each like the nucleus from which it came. Each is exactly like the nucleus from which it came because it contains a set of chromosomes and a set of genes which came from the exact lengthwise doubling of the original chromosome. Now the cytoplasm splits. Two daughter cells take the place of the original cell. And each, as you read, has the same kinds of chromosomes and the same kinds of genes as the original cell. The whole process in some organisms takes no more than half an hour. This complicated division of the nucleus in which each daughter cell receives a new, complete set of chromosomes is known as **mitosis** (mit-toe′sis). See Figure 27.4 again.

Now suppose the cell that divides is a fertilized egg cell. The same thing happens. And when each daughter cell divides *its* nucleus divides by mitosis. In fact, in every cell division thereafter the nucleus divides by mitosis. There is only one normal exception to this;

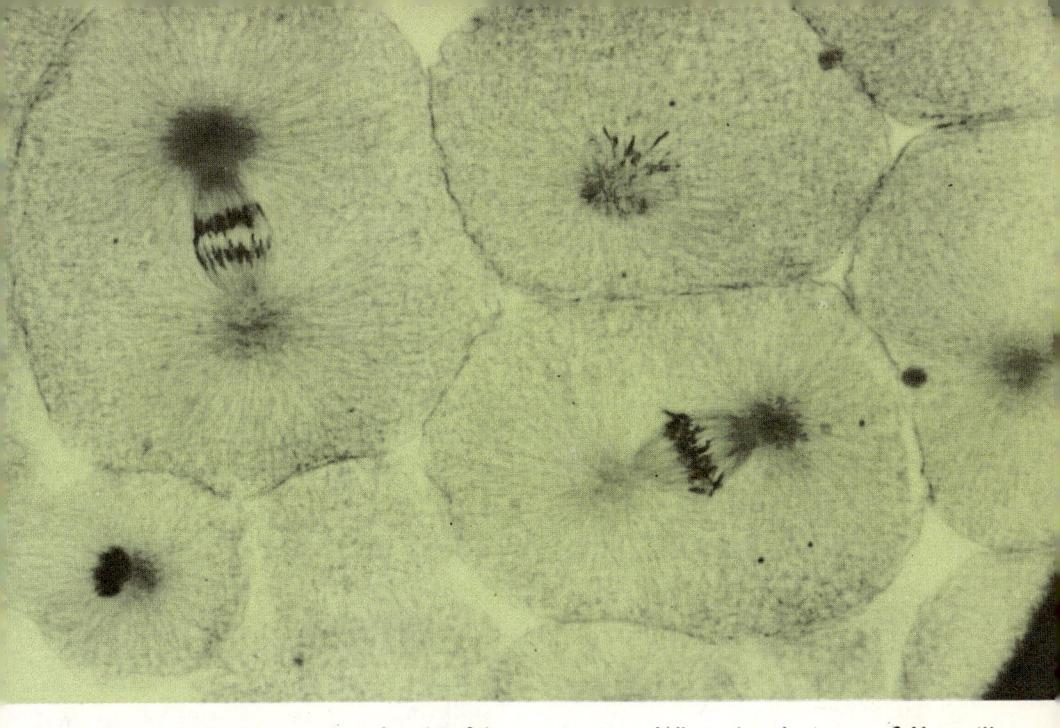

27.6 This photomicrograph of whitefish eggs shows chromosomes in the center of one cell, and in another cell the chromosomes are separating. What else do you see? You will read about the other structures shown. *General Biological Supply House*

you will read of the exception later. Mitosis, or some modified form of it, occurs in the cell division of the simplest animals and plants as well as in the most complex organisms. See Figure 27.6, which is a photograph of mitosis in fertilized egg cells of the whitefish.

Other structures in mitosis. You have noted the important part of mitosis, the exact doubling of each chromosome and the separating of the two parts of each doubled chromosome. But there are always some other interesting structures present in dividing cells which show best when the cells are stained. See Figures 27.4 and 27.5. Do you see thin, curved threads extending from one end of the cell to the other? These threads form what is called a **spindle**. You can also see spindles clearly in two of the cells in Figure 27.6. The threads seem to support the chromosomes. You can see that the chromosomes line up in the middle of the spindle. After that they move away from one another along the spindle threads. Near the end of division you see the new groups of chromosomes at opposite ends of the spindle, known as the poles of the spindle.

Mitosis in plant and animal cells is the same except that animal cells have a structure (called a **centrosome**) which is lacking in plant cells. It shows best in Figure 27.5 at each pole of the spindle. But the important thing for you to remember about mitosis is that when the nucleus divides the genes reproduce. Each daughter cell has exactly the same kind of genes as its sister cell; and each has exactly the same kind as the mother cell had.

What chromosomes do. Since we know about genes in chromosomes and

CHAPTER TWENTY-SEVEN — WHY OFFSPRING RESEMBLE THEIR PARENTS

how the same kinds of chromosomes get into every cell of the embryo, it is less surprising that the fertilized egg develops into an organism like its parents. But isn't there something else that you do find surprising?

What is surprising is that the chromosomes and genes, which are the same in all the cells, should be able to form an eye in one part of the body and a leg in another part. But this is exactly what happens. Biologists, by clever experiments, have discovered that the position of cells in the early embryo determines what tissues and organs they will form. It is probable that some genes in the chromosomes act to produce certain characteristics in one part of the embryo, while other genes act in different ways in other parts.

Chromosome numbers. Since in every mitotic division the number of chromosomes remains the same, a certain number of chromosomes gets to be characteristic of each kind of animal. For instance, a cottontail rabbit has twenty-two chromosomes in its fertilized egg cell and in its body cells. Twenty-two is the chromosome number of the rabbit. Forty-eight is the chromosome number of man; that is, all men (and women) have forty-eight chromosomes in their body cells. Below are listed some chromosome numbers.

Keeping chromosome numbers constant. Isn't it strange that the species number of chromosomes should stay the same, generation after generation, even though two cells unite in fertilization when each new generation is formed? Why does not the fertilized egg have a double set of chromosomes and thus have twice as many chromosomes as its parents? Evidently something happens that keeps the number of chromosomes from being doubled each time fertilization occurs. This "something" occurs before fertilization. It occurs during the formation of eggs and sperms in the parents. Let us see how eggs and sperms are formed.

Formation of gametes. As the young animal develops, cells differentiate into tissues; and the various organs form. The sex organs, spermary and ovary, begin to form at this time, too. Connective tissue and some other kinds of tissue form in them, but the organs do not complete their development. Some of the cells remain unchanged or undifferentiated for quite some time. But they do divide, thus increasing in number. We call these undifferentiated cells **primary sex cells.** In time the primary sex cells in the male change into sperms and in the female into eggs. This process is called **maturation.** We say the animal now becomes sexually mature; it is ready for reproduction.

And now let's look more closely at the primary sex cells changing into sperms or eggs during maturation, for it is at this time that something occurs that keeps the number of chromosomes

TABLE 20
CHROMOSOME NUMBERS

Organism	Chromosomes
Man	48
Monkey	48
Frog (*leopard frog*)	26
Maize (*corn*)	20
Evening primrose	14
Pea (*garden pea*)	14
Rabbit (*cottontail*)	22
Onion	16
Housefly	12
Fruit fly	8
Chicken	18
Starfish	18
Mosquito (*Anopheles*)	6

UNIT EIGHT — HEREDITY AND ENVIRONMENT

from being doubled in fertilization. At this time there is always a different kind of nuclear division, called **reduction division.** It is quite different from mitosis. In reduction division the number of chromosomes is reduced by one half.

It happens this way: as a primary sex cell starts to go into reduction division the two members of each pair of chromosomes come close together. They may even twist about one another. Then the members of each pair move away from each other to opposite ends of the cell. Thus from a primary sex cell are formed two daughter cells each of which has only the half number of chromosomes. We call this the **haploid** number. The full number we call the **diploid** number. See Figure 27.7. This shows you that when the chromosomes separate it is not a haphazard separating. Do you see that one of each pair goes into each daughter cell?

After a few more changes, the daughter cell becomes a gamete. In the male it changes its shape and forms a sperm; in the female an egg. In males the daughter cells undergo a number of mitotic divisions, producing a large number of cells with the half number of chromosomes.* In the female the cytoplasm of the primary sex cell divides unequally, making one large egg cell and a tiny cell which dies. The important thing to remember about gamete formation is that one only of each pair of chromosomes goes into each gamete.

What have you learned? Let's begin with what you learned last. In the male animal, whether human, rabbit,

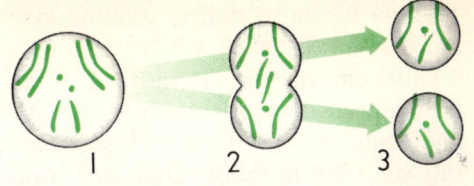

---
* In some animals these mitotic divisions occur in the primary sex cells before reduction division takes place, instead of after it. The result is the same.

27.7 A simplified diagram showing formation of gametes. Primary sex cell (1), reduction division (2), two gametes (3). How many chromosomes in the primary sex cell? How many in each gamete? If a primary sex cell had ten pairs of chromosomes, how many single chromosomes would there be in each gamete?

or hippo, mature sperm cells form. It happens in this way: the undifferentiated cells of the spermary, called primary sex cells, divide. But the nucleus does not divide by mitosis this time; it divides by reduction division. That means that each sperm cell gets the half (haploid) number of chromosomes and genes. In the female the same thing happens. Primary sex cells in the ovary also divide by reduction division. Each egg gets half of the chromatin material; it too gets the half (haploid) number of chromosomes and genes.

When the egg and sperm unite in fertilization the fertilized egg gets the full (diploid) number of chromosomes characteristic of the species. It gets one haploid set from the sperm, another from the egg. So its chromosomes are in pairs. Then the fertilized egg divides again and again, forming the embryo and later the young animal. Each time, its nucleus divides by mitosis. Because of mitosis, the nucleus of every cell formed in division has the same number of chromosomes that the fertilized egg had. And the nucleus of every cell gets the same kind of chromatin material that was in the fertilized egg. Differentiation of cells occurs.

CHAPTER TWENTY-SEVEN — WHY OFFSPRING RESEMBLE THEIR PARENTS

Tissue cells (also called somatic cells) are made. They all contain the same kind of chromatin material. And thus the hippo's babies become hippos, and thus the rabbit's babies become rabbits. But in those rabbit and hippo babies certain cells will again remain undifferentiated for a long time, as they did in the parents. These are the cells which in time form the gametes that some day make the next generation.

USEFUL WORDS IN BIOLOGY

gene	spindle	maturation
genetics	centrosome	reduction
chromosome	primary	division
chromatin	sex cell	haploid
mitosis	diploid	

TEST YOURSELF

1. Tell briefly in your own words why the hippopotamus baby is always a hippopotamus.
2. (a) Describe the gene theory. (b) By whom was it first stated? (c) What led scientists to believe that a connection exists between chromosomes and heredity?
3. (a) What is mitosis? (b) Draw and label a series of at least five or six diagrams showing clearly what happens during mitosis.
4. (a) In what respects is mitosis in plant cells like mitosis in animal cells? (b) How is it different?
5. What is meant by chromosome numbers? Give five or six examples.
6. Using the terms "primary sex cell" and "reduction division," tell in your own words how gametes are formed in the male; in the female.
7. Explain why, generation after generation, the chromosome number of a species remains the same.

DO IT YOURSELF

1. **Study of mitosis.** The rapidly dividing cells of growing onion root tips show nuclear division (mitosis) clearly. Stained slides will enable you to see all stages, if you use the high power of the microscope. By moving the slide around and looking at many different cells in one root tip you should find cells in all stages of mitotic division. Draw and label several cells to show the steps in the process.

2. **Get a head start.** Start Drosophila (fruit fly) cultures now. There is a good account of the procedures in an article by Andreas A. Paloumpis in *The American Biology Teacher*, December 1953. It is called "The Use of Drosophila melanogaster in High School Genetics." The General Biological Supply House, Chicago 37, Illinois, should be able to help you, too, with a Turtox leaflet. You can also consult *Methods and Materials for Teaching Biological Sciences* by D. F. Miller and G. W. Blaydes, McGraw-Hill, 1938.

ADVENTURES IN READING

1. *The New You and Heredity* by Amram Scheinfeld, Lippincott, 1950. Has many clear explanations of facts in heredity and many good diagrams. You will find it particularly useful in the later chapters of this Unit, but look into it now to see what is coming.
2. "Nuclear Division" by George W. Shaw, *The American Biology Teacher*, March 1954. For those who are interested in going more deeply into the subject of mitosis as explained in recent years. Or consult some very recent standard college text in genetics. You will find references in the next chapter.
3. "Chemical Heredity Carrier," *Science News Letter*, April 15, 1950.

Chapter 28
Why offspring differ from their parents

Whom do you resemble? Do you look like both your parents, or either, or neither? You may have blue eyes although both your parents are brown-eyed. You may look more like a grandparent than like one of your own parents. Perhaps you resemble more closely some aunt or uncle. Do you? You may have blond hair and blue eyes; your brother may have dark hair and brown eyes, or dark hair and blue eyes, or blond hair and brown eyes. Yet you have the same parents!

Differences such as these between parents and offspring have been observed and studied in experiments with plants and animals; the similarities have also been observed and studied. Look at the cats in Figure 28.1.

The last chapter made clear why offspring often resemble their parents. Now you will read of equally good reasons why offspring must differ from parents. It is interesting that the gene theory explains the differences between parents and offspring just as well as their similarities. You have learned that this part of biology is called genetics and that genetics explains how offspring inherit from their parents. What we know about heredity has been learned by experiments with both plants and animals.

Mendel's first experiments. Gregor Mendel (1822–1884) was a monk who lived in Austria about a century ago, long before anything was known

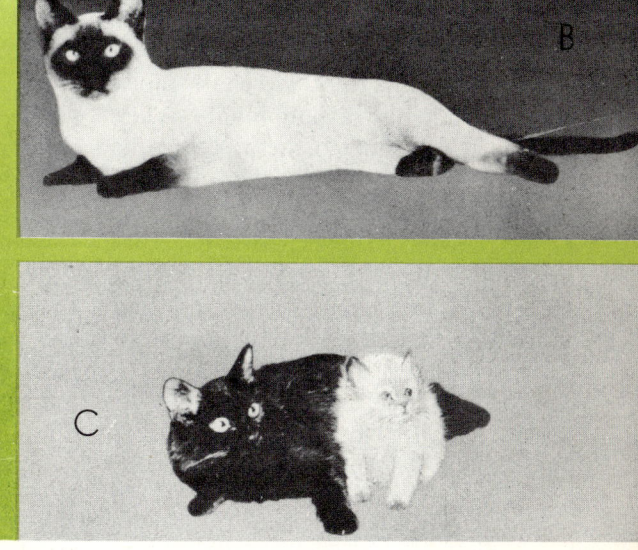

28.1 The Persian cat, **A**, and Siamese cat, **B**, are the parents of the black, long-haired daughter in **C**. What do you notice about her ears? The light-colored kitten in **C** is the grandchild of the cats in **A** and **B**. Note the spots on its face and toes. Do organisms resemble or differ from their parents? *Journal of Heredity*

CHAPTER TWENTY-EIGHT — WHY OFFSPRING DIFFER FROM THEIR PARENTS 411

28.2 The method used to prevent accidental pollination in an experiment with onion plants. What kind of experiment might this be? *U.S. Department of Agriculture*

about genes or even chromosomes. Mendel was a good scientist, and a great deal was learned about heredity from his experiments. He was an accurate observer, a clear thinker, and a careful worker who kept most accurate records of all he did. Mendel experimented with garden peas. He had one strain of pea plants that were tall, six to seven feet high. He had other pea plants that were all short, about a foot and a half high. When Mendel self-pollinated these pea plants for several generations, the offspring always showed the same character as the parents in regard to size. That is, the tall plants always had tall offspring and the short plants all had short offspring; there were no exceptions. Mendel, therefore, said the plants "bred true."

Having tall plants and short plants that bred true, Mendel began his experiments. He crossed or mated the tall plants with the short plants. You may be interested to know how a breeder crosses plants. He puts pollen by hand from a flower of the tall plant, for example, on the pistil of a flower on the short plant. Or he can do the reverse. He can put pollen from a flower of the short plant on the pistil of a flower on the tall plant. Then to make sure there is no accidental self-pollination he cuts away the stamens of the pollinated flower. With certain kinds of flowers he must cover the flowers with paper bags after he has pollinated by hand so that other pollen will not settle on the pistil, Figure 28.2. In the case of pea plants this is not necessary. After pollination, fertilization occurs; the flowers wither, and the fruits and seeds develop. Careful records are kept so that the experimenter knows the parents of every seed. The seeds are planted the next season and grow into new plants.

Now when Mendel crossed the tall and short plants, all the offspring to his surprise were six to seven feet tall; they were as tall as the tall parent! See Figure 28.3. Mendel said that the character tallness is **dominant** over shortness. The character shortness did not show at all in the offspring; he spoke of this character as **recessive**. Then he crossed pea plants producing green seeds with plants which bore yellow seeds. Again one character (in this case yellowness) was dominant over the other (greenness). All the offspring had yellow seeds.

Mendel's law of dominance. Mendel experimented with still more contrasting characters, for example, smoothness and wrinkledness of seed coat, and four other contrasting characters and always found that one character completely dominated the other. Therefore, he formulated his "law of dominance." *When two organisms which differ in a character are crossed, one character, the dominant, dominates or hides the other, the recessive.*

Since Mendel's time, we have found that the law of dominance does not

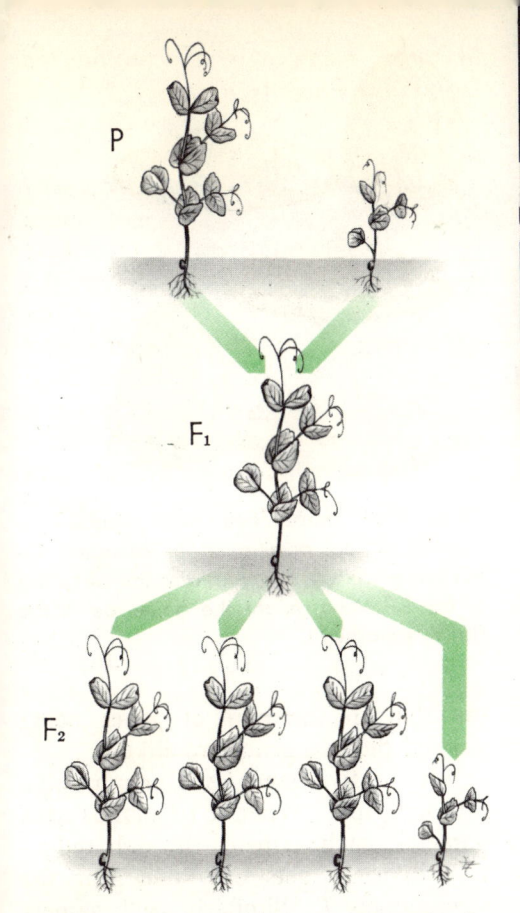

28.3 One of Mendel's experiments. The hybrids (F₁) are like only one parent. Three fourths of the offspring of the hybrids (F₂) are like one grandparent; one fourth are like the other grandparent. This illustrates the law of segregation.

28.4 The blossom of the four-o'clock. Some four-o'clock plants have red flowers; some, white; and some, pink. How does incomplete dominance explain the pink flowers? *Gehr*

always hold. Let us examine a plant in which one character does not dominate a contrasting character.

Figure 28.4 shows the flowers of the four-o'clock plant. Some plants have white flowers, other plants have red flowers. When these are crossed, the offspring have pink flowers. There is **incomplete dominance** or **blending inheritance**. It is clear that we cannot speak of a "law" of dominance even though dominance occurs frequently. Another example of blending inheritance or incomplete dominance is shown in Figure 28.5.

Mendel's second law. Mendel continued his experiment. He worked with the tall offspring he had got by crossing tall and short. These plants, although they were as tall as their tall parents, were hiding the character of shortness. They were **hybrids.** Mendel crossed these hybrid tall plants, and found that among the offspring there were always some short plants. Surprised? See Figure 28.3. In this picture three generations are shown: P (parents); F₁ (first generation of offspring); F₂ (second generation). F stands for filial, or offspring. Because of the results obtained in this second part of the experiment Mendel formulated a second law which he called the "law of segregation." This states that *when hybrids are mated with each other, or self-pollinated, the recessive character separates, or segregates, out again in some of the offspring.* In fact, Mendel said, if there is a large number of offspring, about one-fourth of the

CHAPTER TWENTY-EIGHT — WHY OFFSPRING DIFFER FROM THEIR PARENTS · 413

28.5 The body feathers of this breed of Andalusian fowl are called "blue"; they are slate gray, a blending of black from the one parent and white from the other parent. Are these slate gray fowl hybrid or pure? *Snyder, The Principles of Heredity*

28.6 Fruit shape has been studied in squash. Is this dominance or blending inheritance? Which law explains the offspring in the F_2? What might the genes be in the flat F_2 squash?

offspring of matings between hybrids show the recessive character. Mendel's law of segregation is truly a law, for it holds for all of the plants and animals studied. Figures 28.6 and 28.7 show examples of segregation in squash and rats.

Pure and hybrid. You, who know about chromosomes and genes, can explain why some of Mendel's plants bred true and why some of his plants were hybrid. You know that chromosomes contain the genes that determine the characters of an organism. And you know that chromosomes and their genes are present in pairs in the fertilized egg and in every other cell, except the gametes. In Mendel's pure bred plants, with which he started the experiment, the character of tallness is determined by a pair of genes. For convenience let's use symbols for genes — *T* for tallness. And since in this experiment we are interested in no other character and no other genes, we can call this plant *TT*. Similarly, the short plant that always bred true can be called *ss*. We use small letters, of course, to show that the gene is recessive. Such *TT* and *ss* plants are called **pure**, meaning that in the pair of genes being studied the two genes are alike.

But the two genes of a pair may be different, too. When a *TT* plant forms gametes, each gamete, through reduction division, gets only one gene for size, namely *T*. Similarly, each gamete of the short plant (*ss*) will have one gene for size, namely *s*. When a *T* gamete meets an *s* gamete and fertilization occurs, the new plant will, of course, be *Ts*. That is, every cell will have a pair of genes for size — a pair of different genes — a *T* and an *s*. The *Ts* plant is clearly not pure; it is a hybrid. In a hybrid the two genes of a pair are different. Figure 28.3 showed you how these hybrids looked.

Segregation explained. Let's diagram the results of Mendel's experiments with tall and short pea plants. See Figure 28.8. The crossing of pure tall (*TT*) and pure short (*ss*) plants can result in nothing but hybrid (*Ts*) offspring. Now when the hybrid off-

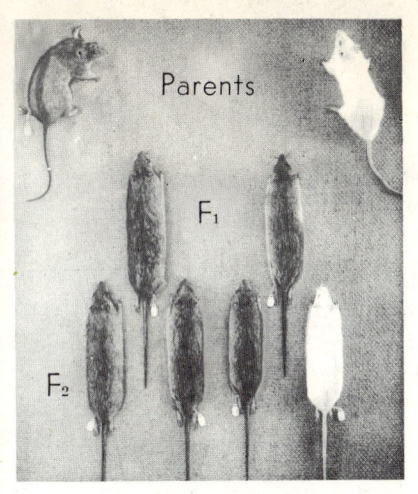

28.7 Mendelian inheritance in rats. Which coat color is dominant? Which law explains the offspring in the F₁? Where does segregation show? *American Museum of Natural History*

spring produce gametes, through reduction division, they form two kinds of gametes, *T* gametes and *s* gametes, and in equal numbers. If you look at diagram 28.8 again you will see that now there are four kinds of fertilizations possible. But these four fertilizations result in only three kinds of offspring — *Ts* offspring (or *sT*, which is the same thing), or *TT* offspring, or *ss* offspring. Which kind of sperm cell meets which kind of egg cell is a matter of chance. If for some reason there are only a few fertilizations those few might all be of the kind that produces *Ts* or they might all be of the kind that produces *TT* or *ss*. But if hundreds or thousands of seeds are formed we would have about 25% *TT* plants, 50% *Ts* plants and 25% *ss* plants. In fractions, this is $\frac{1}{4}$ *TT* plants, $\frac{1}{2}$ *Ts* plants, and $\frac{1}{4}$ *ss* plants. We sometimes say that the tall plants are found in a ratio of three to one, or that the pure tall, the hybrid tall, and the short plants are found in the ratio of 1 pure tall : 2 hybrid tall : 1 short.

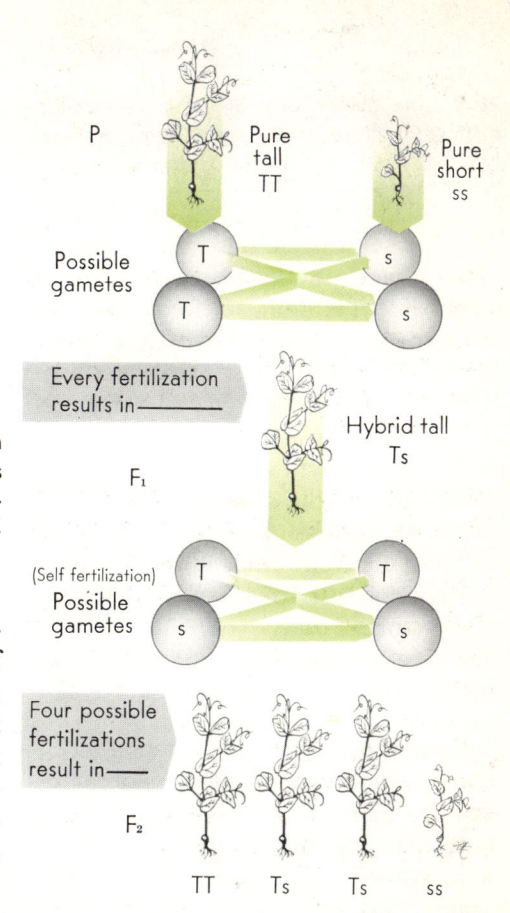

28.8 Three generations of Mendel's peas showing dominance and segregation. What is the ratio of tall peas to short peas in the F₂ generation? Read and you will discover why.

If few offspring are produced there might be several generations before two recessive genes happened to come together, thus producing a short, *ss*, plant. An organism that appears in this way after several generations is sometimes called a **throwback**. Mendel's law of segregation is illustrated in the guinea pigs of Figure 28.9.

Mendel's law of unit characters. Mendel was able to make sense out of

28.9 The guinea pigs at the left were the parents of those at the right. If the parents had both been pure black (BB), how would the offspring have looked? *Castle's Genetics and Eugenics*

the difficult problem of inheritance because he studied the inheritance of one character at a time. This made it possible for him to formulate his laws of dominance and segregation. But then he asked himself this question: If a tall plant with yellow seeds is crossed with a short plant that has green seeds, will the tall offspring always have yellow seeds? Must the character tallness always remain with the character yellowness of seed? Look at Figure 28.10 to see what happens when a plant that is pure for tallness and pure for yellowness is crossed with one that is pure for shortness and for greenness of seed. All the F_1 plants are tall and have yellow seeds. Of course, they are hybrids for both characters; we call such a plant a **dihybrid** (die′hy-brid).

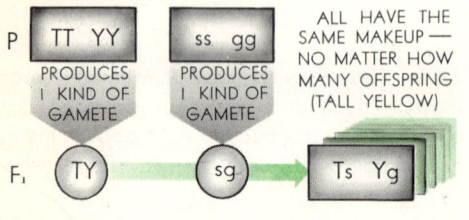

28.10 The rectangles represent garden pea parents pure in two characters. How many types of gametes can each, therefore, produce? Is the F_1 pure or hybrid for size? For seed color? How does it look?

But then Mendel continued his experiment to the next generation; he crossed the dihybrids. Figure 28.11 shows you that the dihybrids, through reduction division, form four different kinds of gametes. This happens because the two pairs of genes are in two different pairs of chromosomes. Each pair of chromosomes segregates independently.

Now look at Figure 28.11 again to see the many possibilities in fertilization when there are four different kinds of gametes in each parent. Try making one of these checkerboards. It is easy and fun to do. You can see that among these different kinds of offspring there are some in which tallness and yellowness do not remain together; some are tall and green and some are short and yellow. Mendel, therefore, formulated the "law of unit characters." This law states that *every character is inherited independently of every other.* Since Mendel's day this law, too, has been found to have many exceptions. It is a "law" only when the genes being considered are in separate chromosomes. Now we speak of **independent assortment of genes** rather than inheritance of unit characters.

Endless variations. We just saw that genes assort independently of each other. This leads to many variations among the offspring of every cross. When you looked at the checkerboard, you saw that there were nine kinds of offspring with different genetic make-ups. And here you were tracing the inheritance of only two different characters. Remember, too, that in each generation, unless there is self-fertilization, genes from two different individuals are brought together in fertilization. There is a constant reshuffling of genes,

UNIT EIGHT — HEREDITY AND ENVIRONMENT

	F₁ cross	Ts Yg		Ts Yg	
		Male gametes			
		TY	Tg	sY	sg
Female gametes	TY	TT YY tall yellow	TT Yg tall yellow	Ts YY tall yellow	Ts Yg tall yellow
	Tg	TT Yg tall yellow	TT gg tall green	Ts Yg tall yellow	Ts gg tall green
	sY	Ts YY tall yellow	Ts Yg tall yellow	ss YY short yellow	ss Yg short yellow
	sg	Ts Yg tall yellow	Ts gg tall green	ss Yg short yellow	ss gg short green

28.11 Crossing two dihybrid garden peas. The parents were hybrids for both size and seed color. See also Figure 28.10. How many of the sixteen kinds of crossings result in tall yellow plants? In short yellow? In tall green? In short green? What ratio does this give when you are dealing with large numbers? How many different kinds of gene combinations are obtained in this 9 : 3 : 3 : 1 ratio?

and new combinations are constantly being made in each generation. For this reason there are endless variations due to gene make-up among the individuals of the same species.

Inheritance in other organisms. Inheritance has been studied in very many animals and plants. Among the more familiar ones are tobacco, corn, squash, rats, rabbits, cattle, chickens, and many others including man himself. In recent years a simple mold, *Neurospora* (newr-oss'pora), has become famous in the study of genetics. It is being used especially to discover how genes make it possible for certain characteristics to appear. But the organism that has probably taught us most about heredity is the famous fruit fly, DROSOPHILA MELANOGASTER.

The fruit fly is a tiny fly frequently found near ripe fruit. You have seen it without knowing how famous it is. Its heredity has been studied in laboratories all over the world because it is particularly suitable for such work. It is small, needs little food, and is easy to raise. (Figure 28.12.) Its life cycle takes only about two weeks, making it possible to study 25 generations in one year. Each mating produces about 400 offspring; these large numbers give us reliable ratios. Then, too, it has a relatively small number of chromosomes, only four pairs, each pair differing from the others in size and shape. Biologists probably know more about the heredity of the fruit fly than of any other animal or plant. Professor Morgan and his students and fellow workers succeeded in de-

28.12 Half-pint milk bottles make inexpensive homes for families of fruit flies. In a laboratory where fruit flies are studied, you would see row after row of such bottles. Each contains flies with some character or group of characters to be followed in experiments. *Professor H. Charipper*

veloping a map of its chromosomes, showing at which point each kind of gene must lie.

When fruit flies are crossed, most of the characters show dominance and recessiveness. See Figure 28.13: A few show blending inheritance. The law of segregation, of course, holds here as it does in all organisms.

Genes may be linked. In the fruit fly, as in other organisms, however, some characters do not assort independently. Figure 28.13 showed you one striking character which has been studied: short (**vestigial**) wing, as opposed to the normal long wing. Body color is another character that has been studied — black body versus gray body. Now when flies with short wings and black body are crossed with flies that have long wings and gray body, the characters of short wing and black body always tend to be inherited together; they do not assort independently. And for a very simple reason: the gene for black body lies in the same chromosome as the gene for short wing. When reduction division occurs, these two genes normally remain together and go into the same gamete. They are said to be **linked**. Figure 28.14 shows this. Since there are genes for many different characters in each pair of chromosomes, there are many cases of linkage. It just so happened that Mendel studied only characters whose genes were in different pairs of chromosomes and for this reason he came to the conclusion that every character is inherited independently of the others.

Sometimes, the members of a pair of chromosomes break and exchange parts while they are twisted together during reduction division. This is called **crossing over.** When this happens, genes normally linked may be separated and appear in different chromosomes. Since crossing over occurs in only a small percentage of cases, only a small percentage of the offspring have a new combination of characters. Figure 28.15 shows gametes produced when chromosomes cross over.

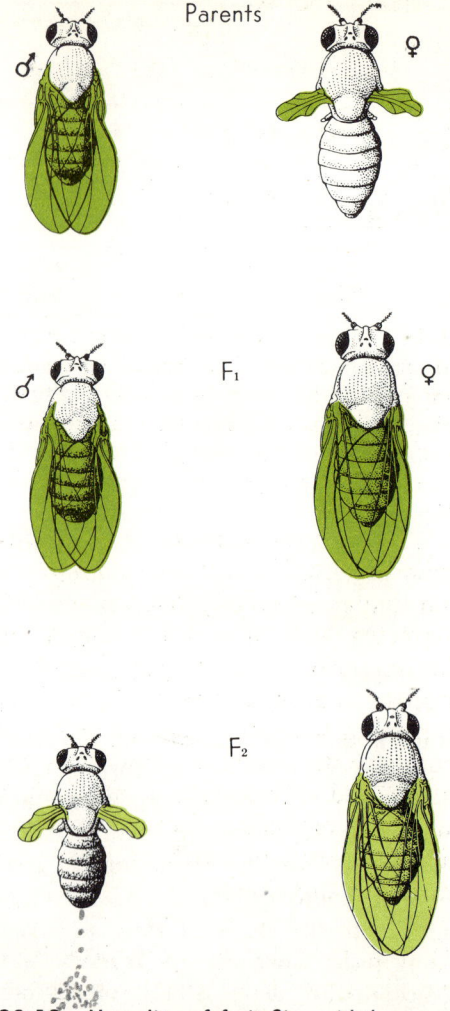

28.13 Heredity of fruit flies with long and with short (vestigial) wings. Which character is dominant? How do you know? In what ratio will long and vestigial wings appear in the F₂ if large numbers of flies are produced?

UNIT EIGHT — HEREDITY AND ENVIRONMENT

A
Primary sex cell

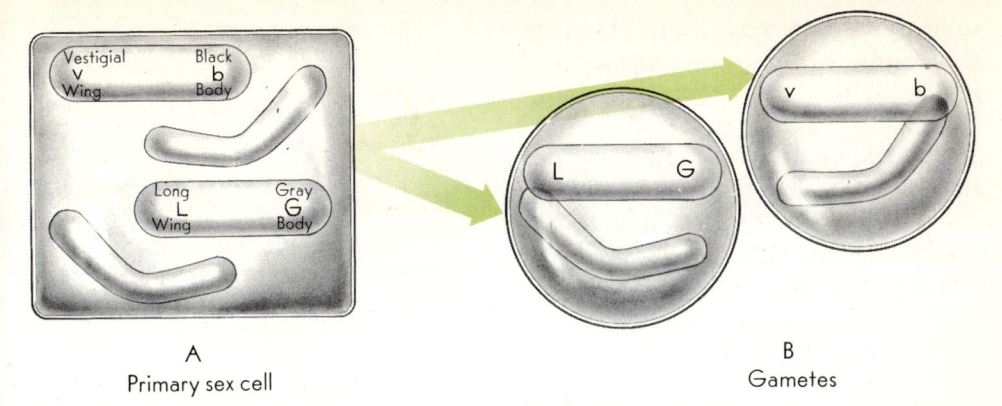

B
Gametes

28.14 This shows you two chromosomes of a primary sex cell of a dihybrid fruit fly; one that is hybrid for both size of wing and body color. Note that the genes we are interested in, those for length of wing and those for body color, lie in one pair of chromosomes. In reduction division a sex cell will receive either v and b (vestigial and black) or L and G (long and gray).

What have you learned? You already knew that chromosomes contain genes, and that genes largely determine which characters will or will not appear in the organism. And you had learned, too, that chromosomes and genes are in pairs in the zygote (one of each pair from the mother, the other from the father) and therefore in pairs in every cell of the organism. This information helped to explain much of what you learned in this chapter.

(1) If all the cells of an organism have two like genes for a character, we say it is pure for that character. If the genes of a pair are unlike, the organism is hybrid in that character. An organism that is hybrid in two characters is called a dihybrid.

(2) Unless bred for a long time in a laboratory, no animal is pure in all or even in most of its characters. It is easier to get plants that are pure by resorting to self-pollination.

(3) In the four o'clock, when a gene for redness and a gene for whiteness come together in fertilization, they produce a character which shows blending or incomplete dominance. But for most characters in most organisms one of the two genes of a pair dominates the other, which is then called recessive.

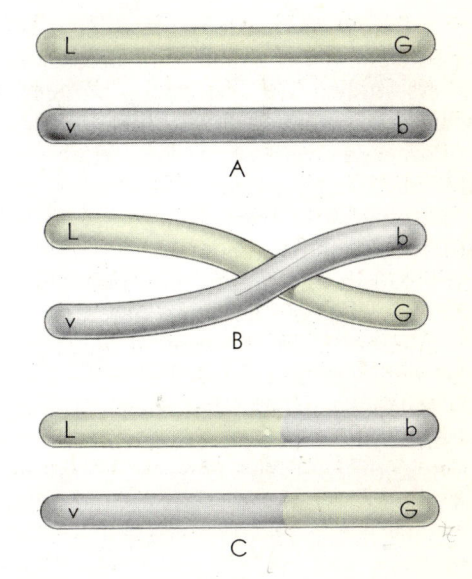

28.15 B shows crossing over between the members of a pair of chromosomes in the fruit fly. C shows the two new chromosomes formed. This shows how linkage is broken when *crossing over* takes place during reduction division. What new combinations of genes have been formed?

CHAPTER TWENTY-EIGHT — WHY OFFSPRING DIFFER FROM THEIR PARENTS

To have a recessive gene show its effects, there must be a "double dose" of that gene. Do you remember how "throwbacks" are explained?

(4) Gregor Mendel, by studying the inheritance of one character at a time, was able to give us the "law of dominance" and "the law of segregation." Can you state these laws? There are so many exceptions to dominance that we can no longer speak of it as a law.

(5) In studying the inheritance of two or more characters at a time, Mendel formulated his third law, the "law of unit characters." This also has exceptions and therefore is no longer called a law. Can you state and explain it? Exceptions to the law of unit characters occur when the two characters studied are determined by genes which lie in the same chromosome, in other words, when the genes are linked. Independent assortment of genes, therefore, occurs only sometimes.

(6) If you have understood all that you read in this chapter you know why the offspring of the same parents can be different from one another and from the parents: reduction division, with its independent assortment of chromosomes followed by chance fertilizations, constantly results in new combinations of genes.

TEST YOURSELF

1. What does the gene theory explain besides resemblances between parents and offspring?
2. (a) Tell what you know about Mendel's life. (b) What characters of a good scientist did he possess?
3. Mendel started his experiments with pea plants that "bred true" in regard to size. (a) What is meant by plants breeding true, and how did Mendel obtain such plants? (b) What was the result of crossing such plants? (c) State what Mendel called his "law of dominance."
4. Give at least one clear example of a cross which shows incomplete dominance or blending inheritance.
5. In your own words, state the law of segregation.
6. Using the garden pea as an illustration, explain the difference between the terms "pure" and "hybrid."
7. Using the symbol T for the gene for tallness and s for the gene for shortness, draw and label a diagram of three generations of peas—P, F_1, and F_2. Start with pure tall and pure short garden pea plants.
8. In your own words, explain Mendel's law of unit characters. Why do we now call it the law of independent assortment?
9. Name some of the organisms that are used in experiments in genetics and state which organism has been used most.
10. Explain linkage by using an illustration from the genetics of Drosophila.

USEFUL WORDS IN BIOLOGY

dominant
recessive
"law of dominance"
incomplete dominance
blending inheritance
filial (F)

hybrid
pure
breed true
segregation
throwback
Drosophila
ratio (in genetics)
dihybrid

law of unit characters
independent assortment
linkage
crossing over
vestigial

PROBLEMS TO THINK ABOUT

1. Using symbols for the genes in Drosophila (N for normal wing, v for vestigial, or short, wing; G for gray body and b for black body), show the cross from P to F_2 of flies pure for normal wing and gray body, with flies pure for

vestigial wing and black body. Assume that linkage is complete.

2. A really difficult problem is to assume that 2% crossing-over takes place in the cross you worked out in (1) above, and then to show the types of offspring and the percentages of each type.

DO IT YOURSELF

1. A genetics squad. If your school does not yet have a genetics squad this is the time to start one. If you are interested in this subject and are willing to give up considerable time to this work, you should join the squad. You will learn how to raise and breed fruit flies, rats, and other experimental animals. And gradually many different techniques will be required. Some members of the squad will also make charts and models.

2. Demonstrate that a hybrid cross results in a 1:2:1 ratio. Convince yourself that when you deal with large numbers in crossing hybrids a 1:2:1 ratio is obtained. For this study in statistics you will use red and white beans, each of which represents a gene. You will handle these "genes." Start with the P generation. Fill a large bowl with hundreds of red beans and another with hundreds of white beans. Now make a cross by putting one red bean with one white bean and dropping the pair into an empty bowl. When you have made some hundreds of crosses in this way and filled two large bowls, these two bowls represent a generation of hybrids (F_1). Now go into the next generation of the experiment. Blindfolded, pick one bean at random from each of the two F_1 bowls and hold them next to each other to represent a fertilization. Let someone record the result at once (whether RR, RW, or WW). Return each bean to the bowl from which you took it. Keep the beans well stirred in each F_1 bowl, and repeat again and again. These instructions must be followed exactly or your statistics will be of no value. The longer you keep this up the more closely will your ratio approach the 1:2:1 ratio Mendel found. What ratio do you actually get in the F_2?

3. Inheritance in fruit flies. If you learn to breed fruit flies you will find experiments in fruit-fly inheritance rewarding because they reproduce so fast. Follow the inheritance of one simple trait. Buy fruit flies from the nearest biological supply house or collect the wild fruit flies which gather about fruit. The techniques you will need are described in "Drosophila Experiments for High School Biology" by Allan B. Burdick, *The American Biology Teacher*, May 1955. Or consult *Methods and Materials for Teaching Biological Sciences* by Miller and Blaydes, McGraw-Hill, 1938.

4. A study of ratios in F_2 plants. Write to a biological supply house or your nearest university to inquire whether you can obtain seeds of the F_2 of a cross between red-stemmed and green-stemmed sorghum plants. Or inquire about ears of corn with kernels of two different colors. When the sorghum seedlings reach a size of several inches count both red- and green-stemmed plants. In what ratio? Count the kernels of corn of each color on as many ears as possible. What is the ratio? Which color seems to be dominant?

5. Inheritance in plants. This can be done only by those of you who have a garden and by those who are ready to begin an experiment lasting over several years. Of course, you must use plants that bloom and form seed at the end of the first year. Cross the flowers of two plants which differ in some striking character, such as flower color for example. If you cross-pollinate by hand remember to cover your flowers with a bag after pollination. Keep very detailed and accurate notes. This experiment might be the beginning of a life-long hobby or even a career.

ADVENTURES IN READING

1. *Genetics Is Easy*, 2nd Ed. by Philip Goldstein, Lantern Press, 257 Fourth Ave., New York 10, N.Y., 1955. Easy and helpful.
2. *The New You and Heredity* by Amram Scheinfeld, Lippincott, 1950. Fascinating!
3. *Experiments in Plant Hybridization* by Gregor Mendel, Harvard University Press, 1924. Mendel's report translated.

CHAPTER TWENTY-EIGHT — WHY OFFSPRING DIFFER FROM THEIR PARENTS

Chapter 29
How characters are changed

CHANGES THAT CAN BE INHERITED

A new inherited character. In 1910, in a laboratory in Columbia University, a fruit fly with white eyes appeared; normally fruit flies have red eyes. That seems like a rather unimportant event. But the scientists in Professor Morgan's laboratory did not feel that way about it. A white-eyed fruit fly was a new kind of fly; white eye was a really new character. Could it be inherited? When the fly was crossed with a normal red-eyed fly the F_1 were red-eyed as usual. But in the next generation, in the F_2, there were some flies with white eyes. That showed two things about this new character: first it could be inherited, meaning there had been a gene change; and secondly, the gene that produced white eye was recessive to the original gene causing red eye. See plate, page 450.

Thousands of such changes that can be inherited have been noted in plants and animals; and they have been seen in human beings, too. In the fruit fly alone, more than 500 such changes have been discovered. You can see some in Figure 29.1.

The new hereditary characters that appear in the fruit fly are interesting to students of genetics. But sometimes such new hereditary characters appear suddenly in cattle or chickens or other farm animals or in crop plants or in flowers raised for the market. Occasionally the new character is one that improves the animal or plant. You can see that it then becomes of great practical importance. Hornless (polled) cattle appeared several times as the offspring of cattle with horns, and this new character was inherited. Hornless cattle are desirable because they are easier to handle.

Mutations. A change in a gene is known as a **mutation** (mew-tay′shun). A mutation can occur at various times in the development of an organism. It may occur in a primary sex cell or in the egg or sperm produced by primary sex cells; or after fertilization has taken place, a mutation may occur within the fertilized egg cell; or it may occur during the early development of the embryo while the germ layers are forming in the animal.

A mutation is believed to be a chemical change in the gene; but since no one knows the chemical make-up of a gene, of course, the exact change that takes place is also unknown. But whatever the change is, and however it may happen, the change is sudden and complete, and the change is inherited. The animal or plant that shows the result of a mutation is called a **mutant**.

The mutation may produce a large or small change in the organism; it may be very noticeable or scarcely visible. The change to white eye in the fruit fly was very noticeable, as was the change to vestigial wing. See Figure 29.1. Usually mutations produce harmful effects in the organism. Short (vestigial) wings are clearly harmful to the fruit fly. By far the greater number of mutations that have been discovered are so harmful that the

422

UNIT EIGHT — HEREDITY AND ENVIRONMENT

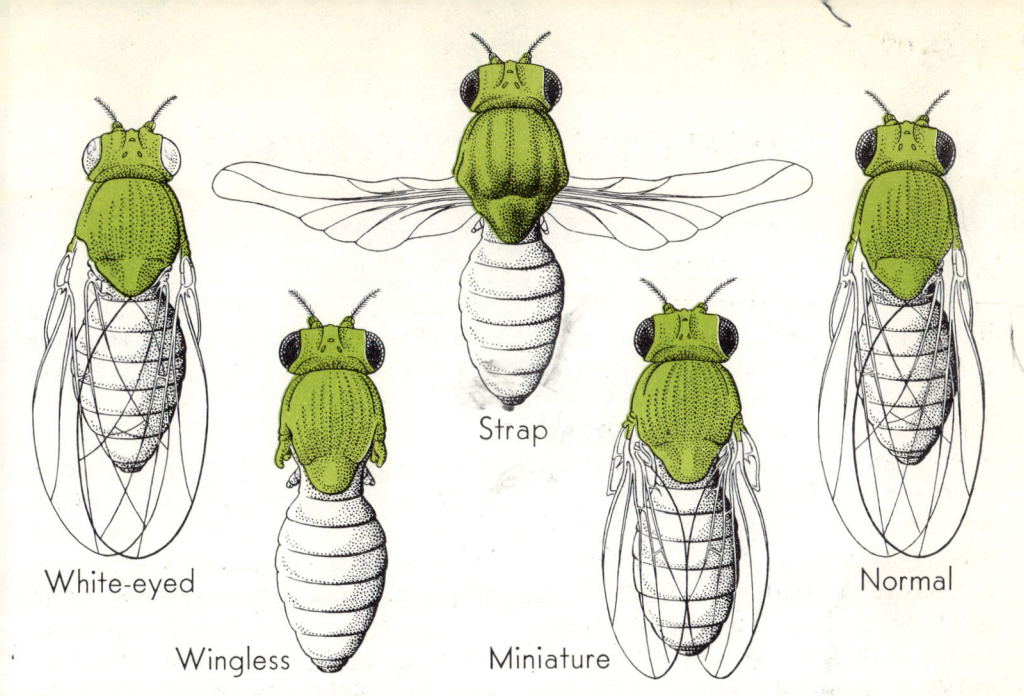

29.1 The fruit fly on the right is normal. The others show four inheritable changes that have occurred. What are they? What do the words strap and miniature refer to? What other wing character have you read about? Which of these flies are mutants?

organism dies; or they make the animal or plant scarcely fit to live. Only a few mutations that have been discovered are of advantage to the organism.

You remember, of course, that chromosomes and genes exist in pairs in all cells except the sperm and egg; and that a character is normally determined by a pair of genes (or even several pairs), not by a single gene. Now suppose a mutation occurs in one gene of a pair in a fertilized egg. The other member of the pair remains as it was. If the changed gene is dominant to the unchanged gene, a new character will appear in the organism in which the gene changed. The organism will be a hybrid in that character, of course. Most changed genes, however, seem to be not dominant, but recessive. If the changed gene is recessive the character will not show until a later generation when an organism is formed that is pure for the new recessive. You know that recessive genes sometimes don't show up for several generations, not until an organism gets a double dose of the recessive.

Somatic mutations. Gene changes, and in fact, any of the changes in chromosomes, may occur at any time and in any tissue, as you might expect. These changes which occur in any of the tissues except reproductive cells are called **somatic mutations.** Somatic mutations are not inherited in animals, except in a few of the lower animals, like *Hydra*, which can reproduce by budding; normally, the change is lost when the animal dies. In plants, however, somatic mutations are frequently inherited. The mutation may be in any of the plant parts which produce new individuals through vegetative reproduction. And a mutation may

CHAPTER TWENTY-NINE — HOW CHARACTERS ARE CHANGED

29.2 A bud mutation in delphinium. A mutation of the flower color gene occurred in a cell which gave rise to the branch at left. These flowers are purple; the others are lavender. *Demerec, Journal of Heredity*

29.3 Professor Herman J. Muller in his laboratory x-raying flies. In 1946 he was awarded a Nobel prize for his discoveries. What mutations might occur when flies are x-rayed? *Life*

appear in a bud that grows into a branch which eventually produces flowers. The seeds which form from these flowers will have the changed gene. See Figure 29.2.

X-rays and mutations. Figure 29.3 is a picture of Professor Muller, a biologist at the University of Indiana. Here he is shown doing an interesting experiment. He is bombarding fruit flies with x-rays. He found, as he had hoped to find, that x-rays reached the reproductive cells and speeded up enormously the rate at which mutations occur. Some of them were mutations that had occurred naturally in the laboratory, such as white eye; others were mutations that had never been seen before. It seemed as though any one of the countless genes affecting all parts of the body might mutate. X-rays had indeed bombarded the genes! Plants, too, have been exposed to x-rays and the rate at which mutations occur has been greatly increased. See Figure 29.4.

Other forms of radiation, such as radium emanations, produce similar results. So do extreme temperatures. And a variety of substances, for example, the poisonous mustard gas, will do it too.

The radiation that comes from the explosion of an atomic bomb or a hydrogen bomb may also cause mutations in plants and animals. See Figure 29.5. Organisms exposed to these radiations have an increased rate of mutation. The only safety lies in great distance. In war the effects of such explosions on the genes of the reproductive cells of human beings would be likely to cause hereditary changes for generations, even though the people near the explosion showed no immediate sign of injury.

29.4 Mutant (left) in barley produced by x-ray treatment. How does it differ from the normal plant at the right? Is this a useful or a harmful mutation? *Stadler*

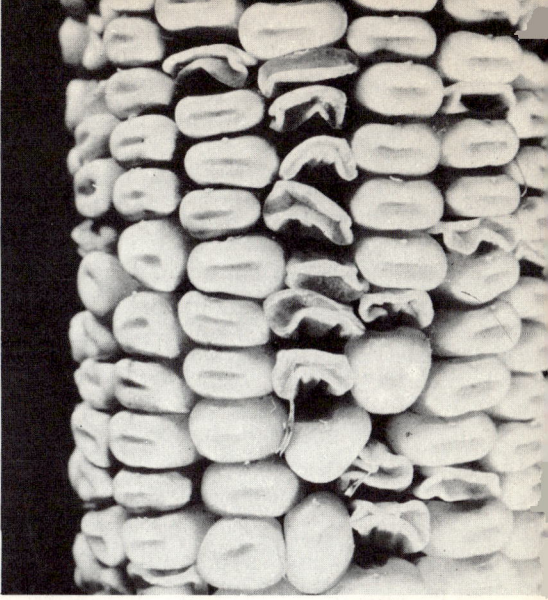

29.5 Effect of atomic bomb radiation on corn. Corn grains were exposed to the radiation, then planted together. This is part of one of the ears that grew. *California Institute of Technology*

Other changes in chromosomes. There are other changes in the chromosomes besides gene changes; and these, too, change the characters of an organism. Sometimes the number of chromosomes is increased or decreased. This happens fairly often. If something goes wrong in mitosis or reduction division, a gamete might get an extra chromosome or lose one or more. If a plant or animal has only one gene or has three or four for a character instead of the normal two, it is reasonable to expect a character to be changed. Changes in chromosome number can be brought about by radiations; some chemicals cause changes, too. **Colchicine** (kole′chi-seen), for instance, is a chemical that prevents the division of the cytoplasm but does not prevent the division of the nucleus. For this reason, the cells affected by colchicine will have double the number of chromosomes. See Figure 29.6.

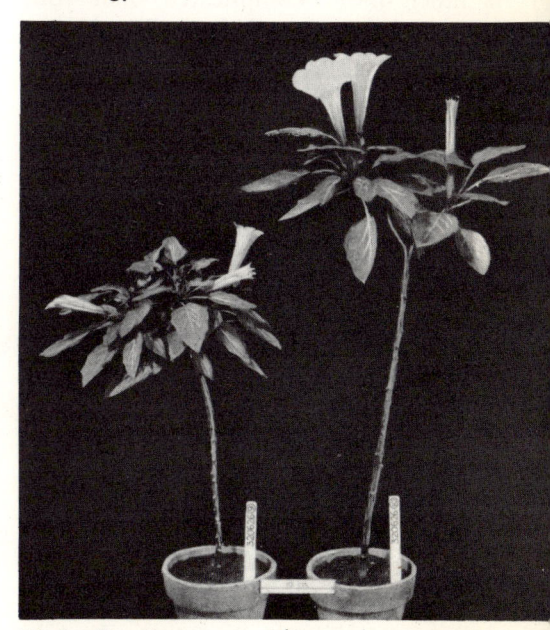

29.6 The Jimson weed (Datura) on the left has the half (haploid) number of chromosomes in its cells; the one on the right has the normal (diploid) number. What differences do you note besides height of the plants? *Blakeslee, American Genetics Association*

CHAPTER TWENTY-NINE — HOW CHARACTERS ARE CHANGED

Other changes in chromosomes include almost everything you could imagine that might happen to a chromosome. Sometimes a piece breaks off one chromosome of a pair and sticks to the other member of the pair. Sometimes a short length of a chromosome gets completely turned around so that the genes are in a different order. All these changes and others that happen may produce new characters. And the organism that results from any of these chromosomal changes is called a mutant, too. That is, a mutant is not always an organism showing a gene mutation. People observed mutants many years ago, though they had no idea what caused the mutant to appear. They called them **sports**, a name that is still used by breeders.

Gene action. The action of genes is much more complicated than you may imagine it to be. Sometimes it takes several pairs of genes working together to produce a character. And often a pair of genes has an effect not only on one character but on many different characters. For example, the white-eye mutation in the fruit fly makes changes in several other characters at the same time. You can see, therefore, that a tiny change, such as a change in one gene even, may produce the most unexpected results. Small changes in the genes may make a very different animal or plant. And changes in one whole chromosome or in the number of chromosomes may produce even greater changes in the animal or plant.

Gene action and the environment. Have you ever noticed that potatoes, sprouting in the dark, form white stems and leaves? Of course, the shoots have genes for the production of chlorophyll. But unless the plant is in the light these genes do not act. The gene must have the proper environment internally, in the fertilized egg and in the many millions of cells of the animal or plant body, and externally, in the world outside the organism. If the environment is not suitable, the gene does not result in the formation of a character. Figure 29.7 illustrates this. A gene for producing red kernels in this corn can act only in the presence of light.

Some fruit flies, as you know, have a gene for shortened (vestigial) wings. If some of the eggs containing this gene are raised at room temperature and others are raised in an incubator where the temperature is high, a strange thing happens. The incubator flies develop with a vestigial wing that is almost as long as the wing of a normal fly. Temperature, evidently, has a profound effect on the action of this gene.

Among Chinese primroses there is one variety that has genes for white flowers; another variety has genes for red flowers. And the white and the red flowers of these varieties develop on each kind of plant under all experimental conditions. But there is a third variety that produces red flowers when growing at low temperatures and white flowers at high temperatures. That does not mean that the temperature changes the genes. The genes remain the same and have remained unchanged for many generations. But evidently these genes have different effects in different environments.

CHANGES THAT ARE NOT INHERITED

Changes caused by the environment. Surely you have heard that formerly in some Chinese families the feet of every girl baby were tightly bound

29.7 This corn contains genes for the production of red kernels. But the red kernels are produced only when light reaches them. Professor R. A. Emerson cut away part of the husks in the second and fourth ears. How did the word SUN appear? *Brooklyn Botanic Garden*

29.8 Sentinel Pine, Yosemite National Park. Its one-sided growth is caused by steady winds which dry the tips of the twigs on the right so that they cannot grow. If seeds from this tree were planted in a sheltered valley, how would the new trees look? *U.S. Department of Interior*

soon after birth to keep them fashionably small. After this had been done for many, many generations, were Chinese girls in these families born with smaller feet? Of course not. This is an example of a variation caused by the environment; such variations are not inherited.

Changes caused by the environment occur constantly in plants and animals. A striking variation caused by the environment is shown in Figure 29.8. In fact, the environment affects every plant and animal to such an extent that no two organisms, even those with the same genetic make-up, are ever exactly the same. No two leaves on one tree are identical in every respect. It would be interesting for you to collect leaves from one tree and compare them, to see in how many respects they vary.

Measuring variations. Wilhelm L. Johannsen, a Danish biologist, made an interesting study of variations. He began by developing pure lines of beans, that is, beans that were alike in their genetic make-up. Then he removed the ripe beans from their pods and measured the beans to see how the environment had affected them. Of course, even the beans in one pod do not have exactly the same environment; they are placed differently in the pod. He measured more than 3,000 beans and found that they varied in length from 9 millimeters to 18 millimeters. (A millimeter is about one thirty-second of an inch.) Look at Figure 29.9. On the right are shown the variations in length of beans and the number of beans of each length. When these figures are made into a diagram called a graph or curve they

CHAPTER TWENTY–NINE — HOW CHARACTERS ARE CHANGED

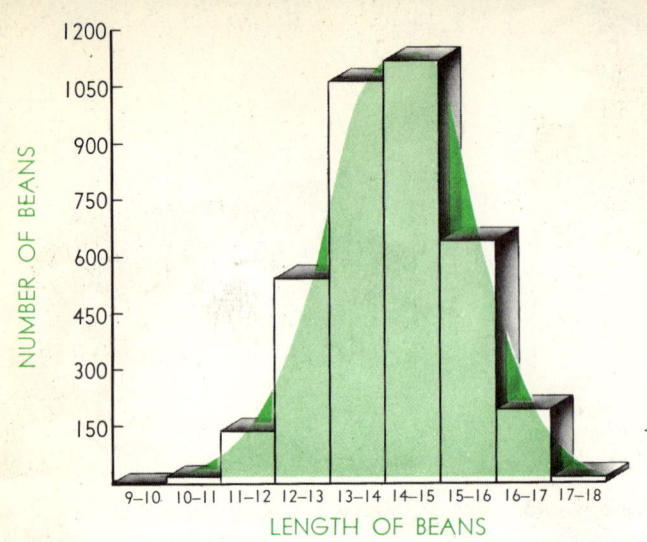

LENGTH OF BEANS MILLIMETERS	NUMBER OF BEANS IN EACH GROUP
9–10	2
10–11	20
11–12	136
12–13	540
13–14	1068
14–15	1125
15–16	636
16–17	180
17–18	18
TOTAL	3725

29.9 The results of measuring large numbers of beans are given in the table. These results were used in making the graph at the left. Variations of bean size arranged in a graph give a bell-shaped curve.

are much more interesting. Look again at Figure 29.9 to see how a graph or curve is constructed. When you measure variations caused by the environment among enough specimens, the figures always arrange themselves in this kind of regular bell-shaped curve.

Johannsen found that the variations shown in his beans were not inherited. Whether the largest or the smallest of the beans was planted the offspring in the next generation showed the same range of variation, from very small to very large.

Acquired characters are not inherited. New characters caused by the environment are called acquired characters. See Figure 29.10. They are caused by changes in the cells of the body and not by gene changes in reproductive cells. There is much experimental evidence that acquired characters are not inherited. The following controlled experiment on the inheritance of acquired characters was performed by two American scientists. They removed the ovaries from a pure black (*BB*) guinea pig. Naturally every egg produced by this guinea pig had a gene for blackness. They transplanted these ovaries to the body of a white (*ww*) guinea pig in place of its own ovaries. After a while this white female was mated with a white male (*ww*). Normally you would expect two white guinea pigs to produce white offspring. But what were the results? All the offspring were black! It is clear that the genes for blackness in the transplanted ovaries were not affected by the body of the *ww* female. Of course, this is only a tiny fraction of the evidence collected in many, many experiments.

Figure 29.11 should make clear why in the experiment with guinea pigs the eggs in the transplanted ovary were not affected by the body of the white parent and why the Chinese girls you read about above were never born with smaller feet. In other words, the

UNIT EIGHT — HEREDITY AND ENVIRONMENT

29.10 These hogs are of the same age and of the same breed. The one on the left was raised on clean ground; the other was raised on ground infested by parasitic worms. Their size, therefore, was an acquired character. If the offspring of the large hog were raised on ground infested by worms, what might you expect? *U.S. Department of Agriculture*

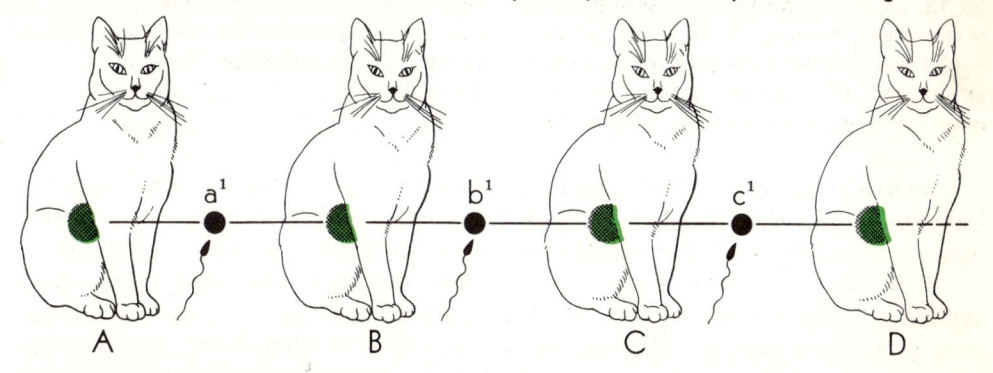

29.11 Female cats of four generations. The primary sex cells are shown as the green portion in each cat, and the eggs and sperms are shown in black. A sperm cell is shown about to fertilize an egg at a^1. When fertilized, this egg forms an embryo. Some of the cells of this embryo change into primary sex cells. The rest of the cells make the body of cat **B**. You can see, therefore, that changes in genes of any cells except reproductive cells will not be passed on to another generation. Can you explain how the reproductive cells and the bodies of cat **C** and cat **D** are formed? Do you see from this diagram how the reproductive cells (germ plasm) continue directly from generation to generation?

figure shows why you would not expect to have acquired characters inherited. Examine the drawing and read the legend under the picture carefully. You will see why, in cats as in all the higher animals, changes in the body cells occurring during the animal's lifetime do not cause changes in the reproductive cells. It is clear that the reproductive cells are not made by the body cells. This sharp distinction between reproductive and body cells, however, does not hold for all living things. It is not true of some lower animals and of plants. But even in these organisms there is no evidence that acquired characters are handed on to the offspring.

CHAPTER TWENTY-NINE — HOW CHARACTERS ARE CHANGED

29.12 A country home. Wide spaces, cows, horses, trees, tractors, trucks, crops, gardens —all these and more are part of the nearby environment of a country person. Would a person who grew up here be different and think differently from one who grew up in one of the apartment houses in the picture at the right? Why? *Black Star* and *H. Armstrong Roberts*

Lamarck's theory. Jean Baptiste Lamarck (1744–1829), a French biologist, believed firmly in the inheritance of acquired characters and at the beginning of the 19th century his beliefs were generally accepted. But this was long before anything was known about chromosomes, genes, and heredity. And, of course, Lamarck had no experimental evidence for his views.

The inheritance of acquired characters seems such a reasonable idea that until you know about the experiments of biologists and until you know how genes are passed on you might easily believe in it, too. In fact, many people without this knowledge still seem to think that acquired characters can sometimes be inherited, at least to a slight degree. Some think, for example, that the man who develops his muscles, his eyesight, and his coordination in playing baseball sometimes passes on some of this to his son.

It is true that such a son often becomes a good baseball player, but for two very different reasons. First, it is likely that the father had genes which made him the kind of man well fitted for sports of some kind; and second, the boy was raised in a home in which everything connected with baseball assumed great importance. But there is no evidence that the skills acquired by the father during his lifetime are inherited.

Modern views. It is probable that there are no biologists in the western world today who believe that acquired characters are inherited as Lamarck thought they were. Some biologists, however, are studying the chemistry of the cytoplasm to find out whether it can influence the chromosomes of the nucleus. There is some evidence that in some cases this is possible. It might also be that a substance from outside the cells directly affects the cytoplasm and the genes at the same time. These discoveries, however, do not mean that we can now believe in inheritance of acquired characters.

How the environment affects us. Think of yourself and what your environment can do to you. First there is your physical environment, your food, the air you breathe, the amount of sunlight you get, the playground you have, the house you live in. But there are many, many other factors in your environment: your friends, your family, your school, the movies you attend, and the television shows that you watch. They all cause changes in you. Your own behavior causes changes in you: practicing the violin causes changes in your muscle, nerve, and brain cells; playing baseball and all your other activities do the same. The more complex the organism, the greater the number of factors affecting it, and the more capable it is of being changed by the environment. See Figure 29.12.

Even if there were no variations due to gene make-up and to the occasional chromosome changes you read of earlier in this chapter, there would still be great variation among us because of differences in environment.

There used to be arguments about which was more important in determining the characters of an individual, heredity or environment. Some believed that the only way to improve the human race was by **eugenics** (you-gen'ics), or getting "good" genes. Others believed in **euthenics,** or improving the race through a better environment. You don't hear many such discussions among scientists today. It is clear to us now that both the heredity and the proper environment are necessary for the development of

CHAPTER TWENTY-NINE — HOW CHARACTERS ARE CHANGED

an organism. Which influences a character more depends on the character and the situation.

What have you learned?

1) From time to time a single gene changes, perhaps in a primary sex cell, a gamete, or even in the zygote. This is called a mutation. This mutated gene may change at least one character of the organism, often several characters. And the new character is inherited.

2) There can be other kinds of changes in the chromosomes; in some cases the number of chromosomes is changed, or something goes wrong with a chromosome. The new character produced is inherited.

3) It is important to remember that genes, in order to act, must have the proper environment. Can you illustrate by giving an example?

4) But there are other changes in organisms besides those caused by changes in the chromosomes and genes. There are changes in the body brought about by the environment. These result in endless variations in animals and plants of every species. But such changes, sometimes called acquired characters, are not inherited. Lamarck, who lived long before chromosomes and genes were discovered, believed that acquired characters could be passed on to the offspring. Can you give any evidence that acquired characters are not inherited?

5) Recent studies of the possible effect of the cytoplasm on the chromosomes may eventually change our understanding of gene action.

USEFUL WORDS IN BIOLOGY

mutation   somatic mutation   acquired
mutant   colchicine   character
sport   variation

TEST YOURSELF

1. Give examples of inherited changes that have been discovered in animals and explain how one was of economic importance.
2. Define the terms "mutation" and "mutant."
3. Show that you know the meaning of mutation by stating at least three important facts about a mutation.
4. Explain what is meant by somatic mutations and why they are more important in plants than in animals.
5. Name four environmental factors that have been shown to increase the rate of mutation.
6. What is the genetic danger of hydrogen and atomic bombs?
7. Describe the various changes in chromosomes, other than mutations, that can lead to changes in the characteristics of organisms.
8. (a) How does it happen that a change in a gene may produce a very different animal or plant? (b) In general, how much of an effect would you expect a change in a chromosome to have?
9. Using at least two illustrations, show how the environment influences the action of genes.
10. By telling about the study made of the lengths of beans, show that the environment can produce changes in a character without any gene change.
11. What did Johannsen discover when he planted the largest and smallest of his beans?
12. Describe an important experiment that shows that acquired characters are not inherited.
13. (a) In the beginning of the nineteenth

century what was very generally believed about inheritance of acquired characters? (b) Give the name of a famous biologist associated with this belief.

14. By showing how body cells and reproductive cells develop in a vertebrate, explain why we think that acquired characters cannot be inherited in these animals.

15. Under what circumstances might a gene be changed by the environment?

16. In your own words tell how your environment can affect you.

PROBLEMS TO THINK ABOUT

1. If you study carefully a handful of bean or sunflower seeds and list all the characters in which they vary you will see that no two seeds are exactly alike. Try it. There are three possible reasons for the variations. What are they?

2. Ask your parents and other adults for examples of what they consider cases of inheritance of acquired characters. Analyze these with your classmates.

DO IT YOURSELF

1. Measure variations and arrange them in a graph. Measure the length, or the width, of the leaves of a single willow tree, in centimeters and millimeters. Or if you are in a large high school get from the health education teachers the height of all boys or girls of a given age. Or study the variations in any character of any organism that can be measured. When you have a large number of figures arrange them in a graph as Johannsen did. Do you get a similar curve?

2. Acquired characters produced by variations in light. Try the effect of differences in hours of daylight on young plants. Plant 20 to 30 oat seeds in each of three flower pots or cheese boxes. When the seedlings are about three inches high place the pots next to each other at a window. Leave one pot uncovered. Give the second pot half as many hours of light by covering it at noon each day and uncovering it at night. Cover the third pot and keep it covered except when watering the plants and measuring them. Do your measuring every day or two, but regularly. Keep a careful record of the results and report them to the class for discussion.

3. Acquired characters produced by variations in water. Set up an experiment similar to the one in (2) above but vary the amount of water. You must measure the amount of water given each plant carefully and be sure that all other factors of the environment are as nearly alike as you can make them.

ADVENTURES IN READING

1. *General Genetics* by Adrian M. Srb and Ray D. Owen, Freeman, 1952. A college text so clearly written that you will enjoy large parts of it if you wish to read up further on a subject.

2. "Heredity and Environment" by A. M. Winchester, *The American Biology Teacher*, February 1955. Shows how in various organisms the expression of the genes is changed by the environment.

3. *Outposts of Science* by Benjamin Jaffe, Simon and Schuster, 1935. Contains interesting information about Muller and Morgan.

4. *The Principles of Heredity*, 5th Ed., by L. H. Snyder and P. David, Heath, 1957. A college text which you may want to consult.

5. The Yearbooks of the Department of Agriculture for 1936 and 1937. You can read here of many useful mutations which have occurred in cultivated plants and domestic animals.

CHAPTER TWENTY-NINE — HOW CHARACTERS ARE CHANGED

Chapter 30

Improving plants and animals

30.1 How does the wild horse from Asia differ from the thoroughbred? What other breeds of horses have you seen that are quite different from the thoroughbred? Do you know how new breeds of animals are developed? *U.S. Bureau of Animal Industry*

Raising animals and plants. The oldest civilization we know of had domesticated animals and cultivated plants. Wheat, barley, oats, corn, dogs, horses, sheep, and cattle are among the many kinds that date so far back that no one knows exactly when men began to raise them and keep them. For thousands of years man has been trying to produce special kinds of cultivated plants and domesticated animals to meet his special needs. The wild horse and the thoroughbred shown in Figure 30.1 are vastly different animals; the thoroughbred was developed because men were looking for fast running horses.

A look through the Department of Agriculture Yearbooks of 1936 and 1937 will give you some idea of the variety and the great number of different types of animals and plants that have been produced, particularly within recent years. Would you believe it possible that 75 different varieties of apples are grown commercially in the United States, and 200 other varieties are grown for private use! Three principal methods are used for producing new and better types. Let us examine each.

Selection of new types. Selection is the oldest method of producing new and better types of plants and animals. Until recently it was the method generally used. Farmers have long saved the best of their crops for next year's seed and the best animals for a new generation. Nowadays, however, selection is often practiced more scientifically. Suppose you are raising soybeans, and you want to improve your beans. Suppose you want beans that contain more oil. You may begin

434 UNIT EIGHT — HEREDITY AND ENVIRONMENT

30.2 This once was an experimental field of strawberry plants. We have no way of telling which character the breeder was trying to develop. But note how few plants he selected and how many he must have discarded. *U.S. Bureau of Plant Industry*

by analyzing seeds from different plants in the laboratory. When you have discovered which plants produce beans with the most oil, you keep their seeds for planting. You *select* them and discard the seeds from all the other plants. You will discard large numbers. Figure 30.2 is a picture of a field of strawberry plants after selection had been done.

The crop produced from the seeds you have selected will probably have a higher average oil content than last year's crop because the plants whose seeds had little oil were not used as parents; they were discarded. But you are still not satisfied. You analyze seeds of the new crop and again select the best and discard the worst. You repeat this for several seasons until you discover that the percentage of oil in the seed is no longer increasing. From this time on all you can do is to prevent cross-pollination from soybean plants that have a lower oil content.

Why selection stops. Now that we know about genes we know why selection can increase the oil content up to a certain point only. Each time you selected, you chose those plants that had the best gene combination for oil production. These "good" gene combinations tended to be inherited when these plants were used as parents. By consistently discarding plants with "poor" gene combinations for producing oil, you have after a while only plants with good combinations. But unless a chromosome change of the right kind should occur, you couldn't expect to get offspring that were better than the "good" parents. It is then that selection stops. When working with plants, usually only a few years are necessary to find the best gene combinations, for plants can be self-pollinated. If the "good" genes are recessive, we can often find them in one year.

Improving animals by selection. Race horses are a good example of the way selection has produced improved types of animals and then stopped working

CHAPTER THIRTY — IMPROVING PLANTS AND ANIMALS

30.3 At the left is a Brahman bull imported from India. It does well in hot climates. Note its physical characteristics. It was mated with a Hereford cow. At the right is the F_1 of this cross. Which of the physical characteristics of the father were not inherited? But the offspring did inherit from its father its ability to stand hot climates. Experiments like this have produced new breeds of beef cattle. *Nabours, Kansas Agricultural College*

when the "best" gene combinations had been reached. There have been few improvements in racing records for some years. Some records of thirty or forty years ago are better than those made today by famous horses.

Selection has been practiced successfully on many animals. The best Holstein-Friesian cow in 1880 produced 18,004 pounds of milk during one year. By 1942 this breed had been improved so much that one cow produced 41,943 pounds of milk in one year. But the animal breeder faces one extra difficulty. Animals cannot be self-fertilized, of course. The best the breeder can do is to mate close relatives, such as brother and sister cattle. This helps because the genetic make-up of close relatives is usually similar. Mating close relatives is called **inbreeding**. Improved breeds of animals are usually kept up by inbreeding.

The second method — hybridization. When selection has finally reached its end, does the breeder give up? Not at all. He uses another method of improving his animals or plants. For example, Hereford cattle produce good meat and plenty of it. But they cannot do well in the heat of our Southwestern cattle ranges. There is a breed of cattle in India, however, that does well in the heat but is a poor meat producer. The breeder imports some cattle of this breed and **hybridizes;** that is, he mates individuals of the two breeds. He hopes that the offspring, the hybrids, will combine the good qualities of both breeds. See Figure 30.3.

After the first hybridizing there must be constant selection and continued hybridizing. Often the undesirable characters of the two parents are combined in the offspring; these offspring cannot be used for breeding. You can see that it takes luck and much time and money to hybridize, especially when one works with expensive and slow-breeding animals like cattle. But by this method the breeder can actually make new types of animals and plants to order. See Figure 30.4. The United States Department of Agriculture, various state departments of agriculture, and experiment stations have done most of this kind of work. But much has been done also by independent workers.

Crosses are sometimes made even between different species, not only

30.4 The Jersey cow (left) and the Brahman bull (right) are the parents of the calf between them. The cow is a good milk producer in cool climates but does not produce well in warm climates such as our southern states have. The bull thrives in warm climates but cows of this breed are not good milk producers. What characters are the breeders trying to combine in a new type? *U.S. Department of Agriculture*

between different varieties, or breeds. When different species are crossed, however, the offspring often turns out to be sterile (cannot reproduce). Hybridization between the horse and donkey is not new. The highly desirable mule results. American breeders have crossed the bison (buffalo) with domestic cattle and produced the **cattalo.**

Pedigreed animals. Animal breeders and progressive farmers keep careful records, so that the exact ancestry, or **pedigree,** of every animal is known. They make much use of this information. For example, a study of pedigrees showed that bulls can transmit to their daughters the characteristics of producing much or little milk. Figure 30.5 shows a pedigreed bull that carries genes for the production of milk rich in butter fat. He is used as the male parent, the **sire,** for further breeding. From the registries of the cattle breeders associations one can learn which animals have desirable gene combinations for a certain character and which have produced the best offspring. Such animals are worth a great deal of money. A pedigreed Hereford bull was recently sold for $20,100. Thus, by carefully choosing one or both parents, stock is kept up to standard and is improved.

Inbreeding and outbreeding. When once plant and animal breeders obtain a desirable variety or breed, they

CHAPTER THIRTY — IMPROVING PLANTS AND ANIMALS 437

30.5 This purebred bull is valuable because he carries genes for the production of milk rich in butter fat. His daughters are known to produce particularly rich milk. Such an animal is worth many thousands of dollars. *U.S. Bureau of Animal Industry*

inbreed these organisms, as you read; that is the only way in which they can keep the same desirable gene combinations. Inbreeding, however, has disadvantages. It may lead to offspring that are defective in one way or another. This is what may happen: organisms usually carry some recessive genes and close relatives are likely to have the same recessive genes. In fertilization, two like recessive genes may come together, producing a character that was possessed by neither of the parents. If the recessive gene is undesirable, and many recessives are undesirable, the inbreeding results in poor offspring.

In **outbreeding**, or **crossbreeding**, two organisms are crossed that belong to the same species or even the same variety but have no family connection. After outbreeding, the offspring sometimes shows **hybrid vigor**. Hybrid corn, as you may know, is larger and more vigorous than either of the two pure lines which are crossed to produce the hybrid. See Figure 30.6. Of course, the seeds of this hybrid corn are not kept for planting; hybrids do not "breed true." Less desirable characters again appear.

On western ranches a brood flock of ewes (females) are bred to rams of another breed in order to get hybrid vigor in the lambs. The lambs grow faster and are more desirable in other ways. The same procedure is used to get increased vigor in hogs.

Hybridization in plants. Some years ago Dutch breeders in Java produced a new variety of sugar cane to order by hybridization. The sugar cane that grows wild in Java contains almost

UNIT EIGHT — HEREDITY AND ENVIRONMENT

HYBRID CORN

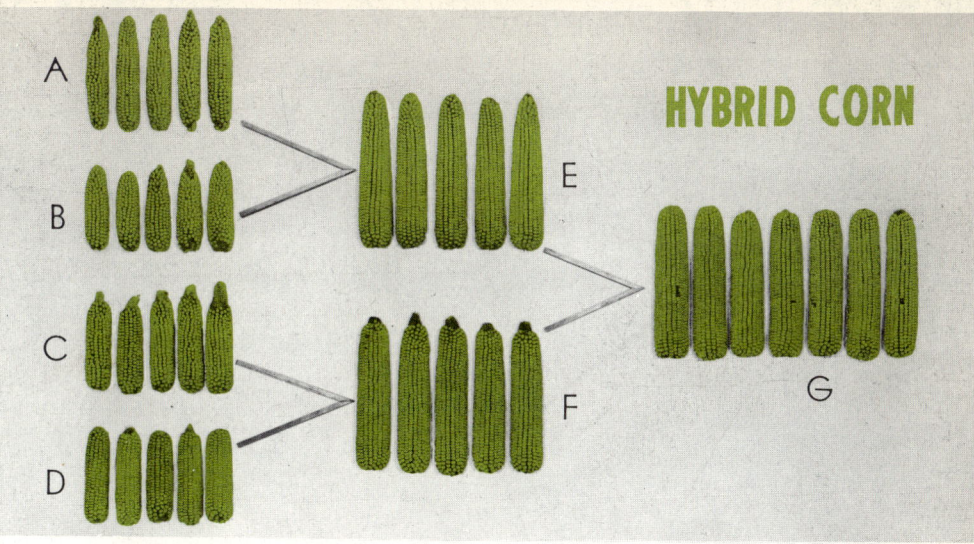

30.6 Ears of hybrid corn. Note that the pure line ears, **A, B, C,** and **D,** are much smaller than the single-cross hybrids, **E** and **F.** The increase in size when pure lines are crossed is called hybrid vigor. Hybrid vigor is retained in the double-cross hybrid.

no sugar but it is highly resistant to disease and to insect enemies. The cultivated cane is rich in sugar but is particularly susceptible to disease. The breeders wanted to put together in one variety of sugar cane this desirable combination of genes. They did it within three years. A new and much better variety of sugar cane was thus made to order.

There are many well-known instances of planned hybridization producing a desired result. The red wheat of Kansas, known as Kanred, famous for its resistance to rust, was developed by hybridizing native wheats with a variety imported from the Crimea.

Even unscientific breeders, like Luther Burbank, have had well-known successes. Burbank wanted a cultivated daisy that would be hardy and have large, showy blossoms. His first step was to cross the sturdy but modest-appearing American wild daisy with the less sturdy but large-blossomed English daisy. After hybridizing these two forms and selecting for several generations, he got the desired combination of genes. Then he crossed this new plant with a Japanese daisy noted for the whiteness of its flower. In this way another desirable gene was introduced, and the result was the "Shasta" daisy, named after California's giant snow-capped peak. This daisy now grows in many gardens. Blueberries, too, have been successfully made to order — combining size with good flavor. Figure 30.7 shows a plant with large berries. This plant was hybridized with another whose berries were small but rich in flavor.

Producing new varieties that combine more than two desirable characters is common practice. The Conqueror watermelon combines at least five desirable characters: it is disease resistant, is covered with a rind which is thin but tough enough to stand shipping, has flesh of the right quality, and is full of juice.

Sometimes, in trying to hybridize, experiments fail because a desirable gene is linked with an undesirable one; to get one, you must take the other. In oats, for example, the desirable

CHAPTER THIRTY — IMPROVING PLANTS AND ANIMALS

30.7 These blueberries are a little more than one inch across, but they lack flavor. This plant has been hybridized with a plant known for its flavor. Selection was practiced. One bush was obtained whose berries combined large size and flavor. If seeds of the hybridized berry were planted, what kinds of plants would they produce? Is it necessary to raise the desirable plants from seed? See page 442. *U.S. Department of Agriculture*

characteristic of many seeds on a stem is produced by a gene which is linked with an undesirable gene. This happens among animals, too. Then the breeder is in trouble.

The third method — using mutations. A short-legged lamb was born on a New England farm in the latter part of the eighteenth century. The shrewd farmer kept this lamb for breeding in the hope of establishing a new breed of sheep that would be too short-legged to jump fences. He was fortunate. The sheep was apparently a mutant; the new character was passed on to the offspring. Thus he was successful in starting the Ancon breed shown in Figure 30.8. This proved to be a desirable breed until fence building became easier and other qualities were wanted in sheep; then the Ancon breed was permitted to die out.

Another desirable mutation that has occurred on several occasions in different parts of the world is hornlessness in cattle which you read about in the last chapter. The polled (hornless) condition is desirable because such cattle are easier to handle. You may have seen polled Angus cattle (black) or polled Herefords in many parts of the country. Hornlessness is produced by a dominant gene.

A mutation from the common red fox to the black or silver fox has occurred in the wild fox population occasionally. Trappers are fortunate if they catch a silver fox. Two wild silver foxes, one

30.8 An Ancon sheep used in breeding experiments. What new character did this sheep possess? This mutation occurred a second time in a Norwegian farmer's flock many years later. *Storrs Agricultural Experiment Station*

30.9 This mink has an unusual combination of white hair and jet black hairs scattered in a pattern. The normal mink is brown. This color combination is a dominant mutation and can thus be inherited. *Ward's Natural Science Establishment*

from Alaska and another from eastern Canada, were caught alive. These mutants were bred on fox farms and proved to be of considerable economic importance, since silver foxes are now raised in large numbers. Figure 30.9 shows you a striking change in mink.

The plant breeder has a better chance of finding gene or chromosomal changes than the animal breeder because plants, as a rule, have so many more offspring. Many examples of plant mutants could be cited. Figure 30.10 shows you the result of one very profitable chromosomal change in the tobacco plant. In another instance, many years ago in Brazil, a seedless orange appeared on an ordinary orange tree. Many of the oranges we eat now are seedless. Naturally, this particular mutation could become established only through vegetative propagation.

30.10 Mammoth tobacco. It had 112 leaves when photographed. It arose as a mutation from parents like those at the left in the photograph. *Yearbook of Agriculture, 1936*

Side   **Tongue**   **Cleft**   **Bud**

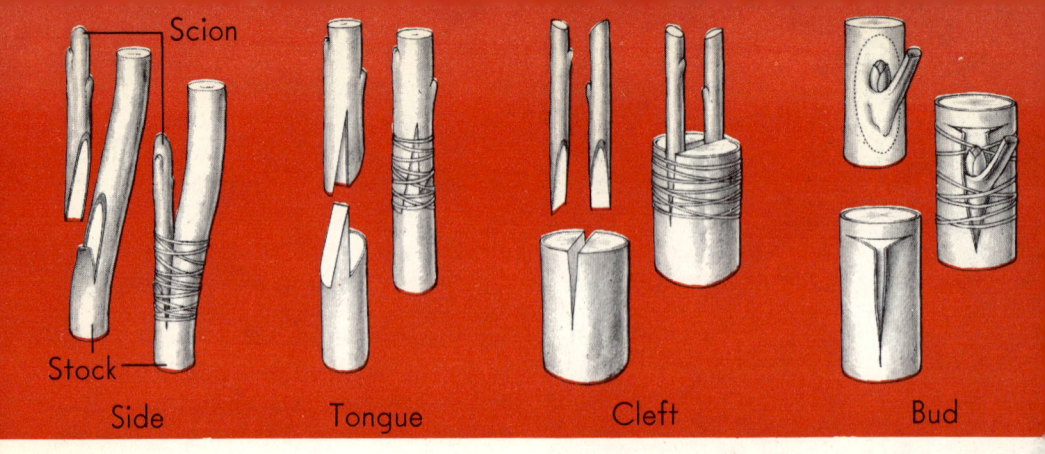

30.11 There are many ways of grafting the scion to the stock. What tissues of scion and stock must be placed in contact? If you have any woody plants in your garden, you would find it fun to try to make a number of these grafts.

But nowadays we don't just wait for mutations to occur by chance. As you may know, many kinds of oats are particularly susceptible to a serious plant disease known as oat rust. In the Brookhaven Laboratory, oat seeds of a variety that is very susceptible to rust were exposed to neutrons for eight hours. In a carefully controlled experiment, some of the plants of the second generation that grew from these seeds were inoculated with the spores of the fungus that causes this destructive rust. The infection began to spread, showing that each plant had been successfully inoculated, but the fungus did no really serious damage to these plants. They had evidently, through a mutation, acquired resistance to the disease.

These are but a very few examples of gene and other chromosomal changes that are known to have occurred; some changes are useful to the breeder, some are of little or no importance.

You can see that the alert breeder must be constantly on the lookout for desirable mutants, even when he does not try to bring them about. And at the same time he practices selection and hybridization. These are his three methods of getting new and better varieties of plants and animals: selecting (with inbreeding), hybridization, and looking for useful chromosomal changes.

The plant breeder's advantages. Plant breeding is easier than animal breeding for many reasons. Plants are cheap and easy to raise. Many can be self-fertilized. You just read that the large number of offspring increases the chance of finding desirable mutants. These mutants are often hybrids for the desirable character; therefore, of course, they won't breed true. The animal breeder must do much crossing and selecting before he gets an animal that is pure for the desirable character. But the plant breeder can raise more of these desirable hybrid mutants by vegetative propagation, by slips, or bulbs, or tubers, or other plant structures. The offspring then will have exactly the same gene combination as the parent and will show exactly the same characters; no new genes are introduced.

Grafting. Besides the methods of vegetative propagation mentioned above, plant breeders use a method

30.12 A pecan stock has been grafted with pecan scions of a better variety. How many scions were grafted? The grafts were made on August 10; the lower branches (not grafted) were removed on September 1. Why were the lower branches not removed when the grafting was done? Why were the lower branches ever removed? *U.S. Department of Agriculture*

called grafting. Grafting consists of attaching a small twig, the **scion** (sy'on), to a branch of a growing plant, the **stock**. The scion is placed against or in the stem of the stock in such a way that the growing layer (cambium) of one is in direct contact with the growing layer of the other. This can be done in a number of ways as shown in Figure 30.11. To prevent infection and too much loss of water the two parts are bound tightly together and covered with wax. After a short time the scion grows onto the stock, forming a part of the rooted plant. But the genes of the scion and the genes of the stock remain unchanged. They do not mingle or affect one another. When the cells of the scion divide and the scion grows, it will keep the genes it had before it was grafted. Thus you see that grafting is not a method of hybridizing. It is a convenient way of obtaining more of a certain type of plant, for the grafted scion grows larger every season. See Figure 30.12. If a breeder has a plant with a particularly desirable combination of characters, perhaps a hybrid, he can graft many such scions onto healthy stock. He is sure that the desirable characters will continue to appear in every scion. All commercial varieties of fruit trees can be propagated by grafting. And grafting is the only method by which seedless fruits of woody plants are obtained. When the first scion from a seedless orange tree was grafted on an ordinary orange tree, the scion grew and branched; twigs were again cut off and grafted. Soon there were whole orchards of trees bearing seedless fruits.

Good environments. Have you ever visited a model dairy farm? Look at Figure 30.13. The barns are clean. Sunlight pours in. The cows have been inoculated against diseases. They are fed a diet containing the right proportions of food substances. Thus the cattle grow to a larger size and produce more milk. On modern farms crops are raised in fields that have been carefully tilled, and the crops are protected from damage by insects and fungi. By such methods the yields per acre of wheat, corn, and of other food plants have been much increased; and further increases are possible. In a good environment animals and plants are given an opportunity to grow big and strong. If the

30.13 The cows on this dairy farm were bred and selected for ability to produce a large quantity of high-quality milk. Only when they are kept healthy and fed correctly, however, do they produce as much milk as they are able. *Great Northern Railway*

breeder has plants with desirable mutations or good gene combinations, they are able thus to thrive. But the characteristics dependent on the environment are acquired characters. They are not passed on to the offspring. Although a good environment does not produce new types, it is a factor which must not be neglected.

What have you learned? Three methods of breeding better varieties of animals and plants are used: (1) By selecting in each generation the organisms that show to the highest degree the character you wish to develop. These, and only these, are used as parents of the next generation. After a while you can go no further with this method; you have probably selected the plants with as good gene combination as you could find among these plants. Example: selection of soybeans. (2) By hybridizing or making a new kind of plant or animal to order. Parents of different types, each with a desirable character, are crossed. Among the offspring in the F_1 or F_2 some may contain a combination of genes for the two desired characters.

Can you give examples in both animal and plant hybridization? (3) By finding and raising mutants that show a desirable new character. Many examples among both animals and plants are known. What are some?

Do you know the advantages and disadvantages of inbreeding and of outbreeding? Do you know the advantages of grafting and other methods of vegetative propagation to the plant breeder? Are you able to name several other advantages that a plant breeder has over an animal breeder?

In all his work the breeder gives the best possible environment to the plants and animals he is raising, knowing full well, however, that the characters developed because of the good environment will never be passed on to the offspring.

USEFUL WORDS IN BIOLOGY

selection
inbreeding
hybridization
pedigree
stock
sire
outbreeding
hybrid vigor
polled
disease resistance
scion

TEST YOURSELF

1. If your object were to improve the oil content of soybeans explain how you would go about it.
2. Give an example of how breeders improve cattle by the method of hybridization.
3. Explain (a) what is meant by a pedigreed animal and (b) why a pedigreed bull will bring a price of $20,000.
4. When is inbreeding advantageous and when is it undesirable?
5. "Outbreeding often results in hybrid vigor."
Explain this statement, giving an example of it.
6. How was a new variety of sugar cane "made to order" by Dutch breeders?
7. (a) Give two or three examples, besides sugar cane, of plants made to order. (b) Explain why hybridization of the oat plant failed in at least one instance to produce better plants.
8. Besides by selection and hybridization, we may get more desirable varieties by a third method. (a) What is it? (b) Give at least four examples among animals and plants.
9. Giving a specific example, explain how mutations can be brought about.
10. Of what importance is grafting to the man who attempts to improve plants?

PROBLEMS TO THINK ABOUT

1. Between 1880 and 1942 the record milk production advanced from 18,004 to 41,943 pounds per year, largely through careful selection. Would you expect record production to continue to improve at this rate if only selection were used? Give a reason for your answer.
2. Let your imagination create some plant or animal type that would be desirable. Can you explain how you might get it?
3. A breeder has two varieties of apple trees. One bears sweet green apples and the other sour red ones. He discovers that he would have a market for sweet red apples. What could he do about it? Would he be sure of success?

DO IT YOURSELF

1. **Learning at first hand.** Visit an agricultural school or agricultural experiment station. After reading these last chapters you will have many questions to ask about mutants, hybridization, and the effects of the environment.
2. **Breeding new varieties of flowering plants.** Have you a garden? And have you the patience

to wait for results? Decide on what kind of plant you want to get through hybridization. See Chapter 28, "Do it yourself" No. 5, where suggestions for learning the facts of heredity were given. Making a new plant to order is a practical application of what you learn. Careful records are all-important.

3. A report on hybridization. Look through the 1936 and 1937 Yearbooks of the Department of Agriculture. Then write a report on some plant or animal that interests you particularly. Some of the most interesting and profitable work in plant breeding has been done with hybrid corn. The *Scientific American*, August 1951, has a good article on that subject.

4. A chart to show recent plant improvements. Get seed catalogues from your friends or directly from seed growers. Find pictures of the most striking improvements in flowering plants and garden vegetables. Mount pictures of the original and the improved plants to make attractive posters. On these tell how the improvements were made if you can find out.

ADVENTURES IN READING

1. *Plant Breeding for Everyone* by John Y. Beaty, Branford, 1954. This well-illustrated book tells in simple language how to select, breed, and propagate new plant varieties.
2. "Those Homemade Apple Trees" by Frank L. Taylor, *Saturday Evening Post*, Feb. 27, 1954. Easy to read.
3. 1936 and 1937 Yearbooks of the Department of Agriculture.
4. "Opportunities for Employment in Biological Sciences" by Hilmer C. Nelson, *The American Biology Teacher*, November 1953. Discusses opportunities for the horticulturist.

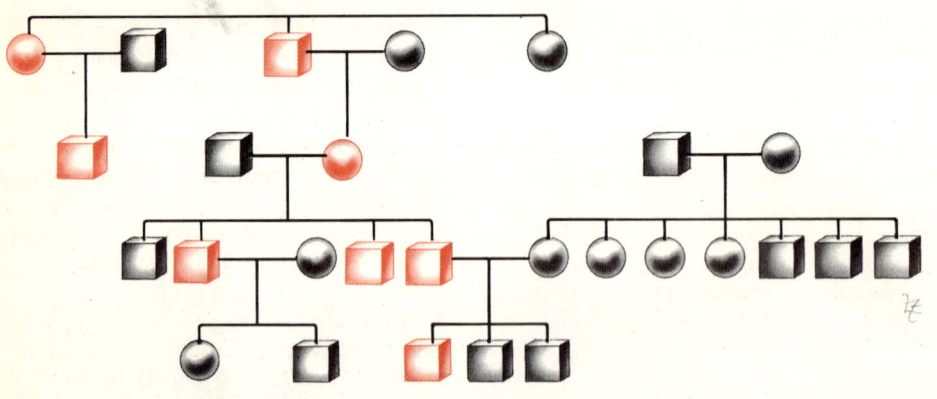

31.1 This pedigree shows the inheritance of an abnormal skin condition in which the slightest friction causes blisters to form. Remember that the red symbols stand for individuals who have this condition. Squares stand for males, circles for females.

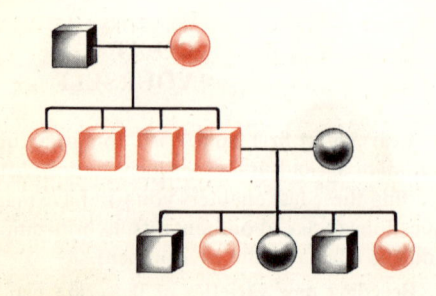

31.2 A pedigree showing the inheritance of one type of extreme shortsightedness. Are the shortsighted individuals (red symbols) in the F_2 pure or hybrid? *Snyder*

Chapter 31

Human heredity

What we all want to know. By this time probably a dozen questions have come to your mind that you would like answered: can we inherit curly hair? Are the children of deaf parents always deaf? How is the Rh factor inherited? Do you belong to the same blood group as either of your parents? Why do some families have all girls, or all boys? Does having twins run in families? Do you know why laws are sometimes passed to forbid close relatives to marry? Do bright parents have bright children? Which is more important, heredity or environment? And so on. You will find some answers to these questions in this chapter.

Difficulties. Mendel's discoveries about the garden pea, the discoveries about inheritance in fruit flies, squashes, and rabbits being made by Muller and the many other present-day geneticists, all teach us about your heredity and mine. The principles underlying our heredity are the same. We have chromosomes (twenty-four pairs of them!), genes, reduction division, segregation of genes, independent assortment of characters, linkage, mutations, and other chromosomal changes. But we know much less about the inheritance of definite characters in ourselves than in fruit flies or in corn. Our knowledge is growing, however, but it grows slowly for several reasons. First of all, experimental matings are not possible in our civilization. Another reason is that the time from one generation to another in human beings averages twenty years. A student of human heredity can observe only two, or at most three, generations with his own eyes. He must, therefore, depend partly on hearsay and unverified records. Another difficulty is the small number of children in a family; we never know what characters might have appeared if the number of offspring had been larger. And, lastly, many human characters are the result of the action of several pairs of genes. In fact, the characters that interest us most seem to result from the action of several or even many pairs of genes.

Despite these difficulties, it has been possible to learn many important facts about human heredity.

How we study human heredity. One method is to trace a character through several generations by using pedigrees. Just as we keep pedigrees for cattle, so we can keep them for human beings. In showing these pedigrees, males are usually represented as squares and females as circles. Solid black symbols represent individuals having the character being traced. If you study Figures 31.1 and 31.2, you will see how pedigrees are shown; and you will see how two different characters are inherited. There may be some character, such as red hair, in your family for which you yourself can construct a pedigree.

Another method is to study the inheritance of a certain character in hundreds of families by personal observation. The inheritance of eye color has been studied in this way. Eyes are of so many shades that biologists

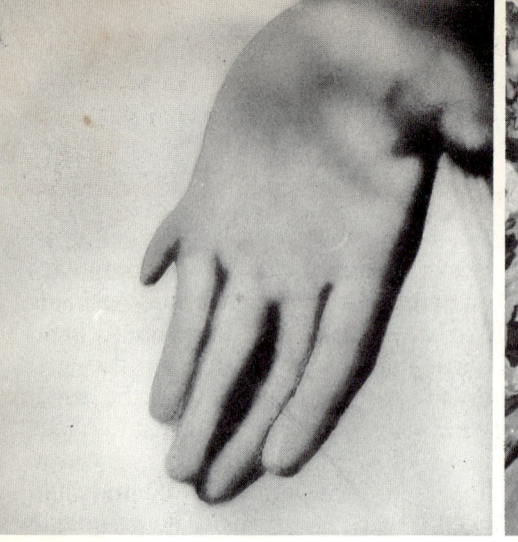

31.3 Hand of a six-fingered man. This is a case of polydactyly. Six-fingeredness is a hereditary trait caused, apparently, by a dominant gene. Not infrequently one sees cats with six toes. Have you ever seen one?

31.4 An albino child. Do you know why he keeps his eyelids half shut when he is in strong sunlight? How does this character act in heredity? Was either parent necessarily an albino? *Acme*

must use a complicated machine that enables them to match eye colors. It has been learned that one special type of blue eyes seems to be recessive to a certain type of brown eyes. When dealing with large numbers of cases in which it is known that the parents are hybrid brown there is the typical Mendelian ratio of 3 brown to 1 blue in the offspring. But many other eye colors seem to be produced by several pairs of genes, giving us the characters of green and gray and hazel and so on; the inheritance of these characters is much more complicated. Skin color, too, is a character determined by several pairs of genes.

Simple cases of heredity. Six-fingeredness (polydactyly) and short-fingeredness (brachydactyly, in which fingers commonly have only two bones) are two characters that are easily traced from generation to generation. They are striking and they are not affected by the environment. Each condition is

TABLE 21

SIMPLE INHERITANCE IN HUMAN CHARACTERS

Dominant	Recessive
Shortened eyeball (farsightedness)	Normal eyeball
Normal eyeball	Elongated eyeball (nearsightedness)
Normal free ear lobes	Attached ear lobes
White forelock	Normal hair color
Woolly hair (mutation in whites)	Curly or straight hair

But the genes for curly hair (C) and straight hair (S) in white-skinned people show incomplete dominance. The offspring of CC and SS is a hybrid wavy-haired person, CS. (However, in yellow-skinned or black-skinned people the inheritance of straight and curly hair is more complicated.)

caused by a single gene which is dominant to the gene causing normal fingers. Most of the hereditary abnormalities of human beings that have been studied are caused by a dominant gene. Such genes arise by mutation. See Figure 31.3.

Figure 31.4 is a picture of an **albino** boy. **Albinism** (al'bin-ism) is another character that is easy to trace. You have all seen albino rabbits or mice, even if you have never seen albino people. Albinos lack pigment or coloring matter in the skin, hair, and eyes. The eyes, therefore, are pink since they have no pigment to hide the color of the blood. Albinism in people has appeared again and again as a mutation; it is the result of a recessive gene. Matings between albino parents can produce only albino children, for albinos have no gene for pigmentation. Two normal-looking parents, if they both carry this same recessive gene, may also have albino children. This is an illustration of what may happen when close relatives marry. The relatives may be carrying the same recessive gene; they are certainly more likely to be carrying the same recessive than two parents who are unrelated. Their children, therefore, may get a "double dose" of that recessive.

Deafness sometimes results from infection or injury. But sometimes the inner or middle ear does not develop perfectly (or these parts degenerate in later life). This kind of deafness is due to a recessive gene and is, therefore, hereditary. Two distinct mutations in different chromosomes have appeared. A "double dose" of either one of these mutated genes will produce this type of deafness.

Complex characters. When we turn from abnormalities and try to trace the inheritance of ordinary characters such as size, we run into difficulties. You may think of tallness or shortness as a simple character. It is very complex indeed. It depends on the length of the head, the neck, the torso (trunk), the upper leg, the lower leg, even of the arch of the foot. You can see that a great many genes are likely to determine how tall or short you will be and that heredity in this case can be exceedingly complicated. Besides this, the genes, of course, must have the correct environment in order to act. What is true of size is true of weight, shape of head, and most of our characters. Even such a simple character as hair color and skin color, and in most cases, eye color, is determined by more than one pair of genes.

Blood types. A person of blood type A apparently has at least one dominant gene (A) responsible for the production of agglutinogen A (the substance in the corpuscles that makes them agglutinate, or clump, in the presence of type B serum). The type B person has at least one gene (B) for producing agglutinogen B. Persons of group AB have both genes (AB). Persons of type O have genes recessive to the genes that produce groups A, B, and AB; they could be called oo. Thus a person may have these gene combinations for determining blood type: AA, Ao, BB, Bo, AB, or oo.

Rh factor. You have read about the Rh factor and the possible damage to the unborn child if it is Rh positive and the mother is Rh negative. The heredity is simple. Let us see how the child could be Rh positive although the mother is Rh negative. The gene for giving the blood the Rh factor (which makes the person Rh positive) is a dominant gene. We can use the symbol R for that gene. The gene responsible for a lack of the Rh factor is recessive. Let's write it *r*. If the father is Rh positive, he will therefore be either pure, *RR*, or hybrid, *Rr*. If the mother is Rh negative she must have a double dose of *r*; she is *rr*. In a mating between an Rh positive father and an Rh negative mother there are two possibilities. If the father is *RR*, the child is sure to be *Rr* — that is, Rh positive. If the father is hybrid, *Rr*, the chances of any of his children being Rh positive are one to one. Parents should know whether they are Rh positive or Rh negative.

The heredity of sex. About 1900 it was discovered that the chromosomes of males and females of most animal species are not all alike. In man, for example, 23 pairs of chromosomes are the same in both males and females.* But the two chromosomes of the 24th "pair" are like each other in women and unlike each other in men. We call the unlike ones X and Y chromosomes. The 24th pair in women is made up of two X chromosomes. The X and Y chromosomes are therefore called **sex** chromosomes. Since the gametes have only one of each pair of chromosomes, the eggs produced by the female are all alike; each has an X chromosome. But the male produces two kinds of sperms; one kind has an X chromosome and the other a Y. If the egg is fertilized by a sperm which carries an X chromosome the child is XX, a girl. If the egg is fertilized by a sperm with a Y it is XY, a boy. Thus, the father determines the sex of his child.

Sex-linked characters. Now X chromosomes are larger than Y chromo-

---
* Recent investigation suggests that man may have only 46 chromosomes, of which 22 pairs are alike in male and female.

somes and carry more genes. The characters determined by genes in the sex chromosomes are therefore inherited in an unusual way, as you will see. We say such characters are **sex-linked**. Color blindness for red and green is one of these sex-linked characters.

Among the various kinds of color blindness the most common type is red-green color blindness. Let's see how this is inherited. The gene for color blindness lies in the X chromosome. It is a recessive gene. Let's use X̲ for the chromosome carrying the recessive gene for color blindness, and X for the chromosome which carries the gene for normal sight. A woman with sex chromosomes XX̲, therefore, would not be color-blind because the gene for color blindness is recessive; but she is carrying this recessive gene. On the other hand, a man with chromosomes X̲Y is color-blind because he has no normal gene in the Y chromosome to dominate the recessive gene. If a color-blind man marries a woman who is not color-blind (Fig. 31.5) and who does not carry the gene for color blindness (that is, she is XX) none of their children will be color-blind. But if a normal man marries a woman who is not herself color-blind but who carries a gene for color blindness (XX̲), none of their daughters will be color-blind; but the likelihood of having color-blind sons is one to one, as Figure 31.6 shows.

All the sons of a color-blind female (X̲X̲) and a normal male (XY) will be color-blind; but the daughters will not be color-blind. You can see why this is true by examining Figures 31.5 and 31.6.

Another sex-linked character is **hemophilia** (the trait of being a bleeder). This, too, is caused by a recessive gene. The heredity is just like that for red-green color blindness.

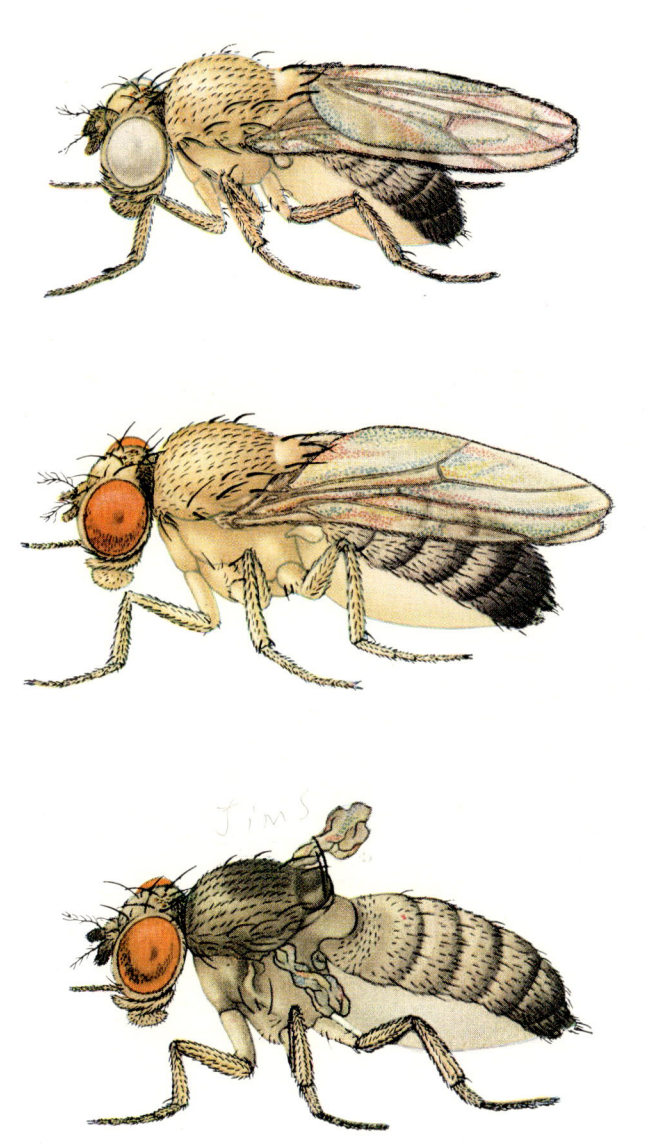

Fruit flies. Top, white-eyed, long-winged, gray-bodied, male Drosophila. Middle, red-eyed, long-winged, gray-bodied, female Drosophila. Bottom, red-eyed, vestigial-winged, black-bodied, female Drosophila. *Snyder and David, The Principles of Heredity, 5th ed., D. C. Heath and Company.*

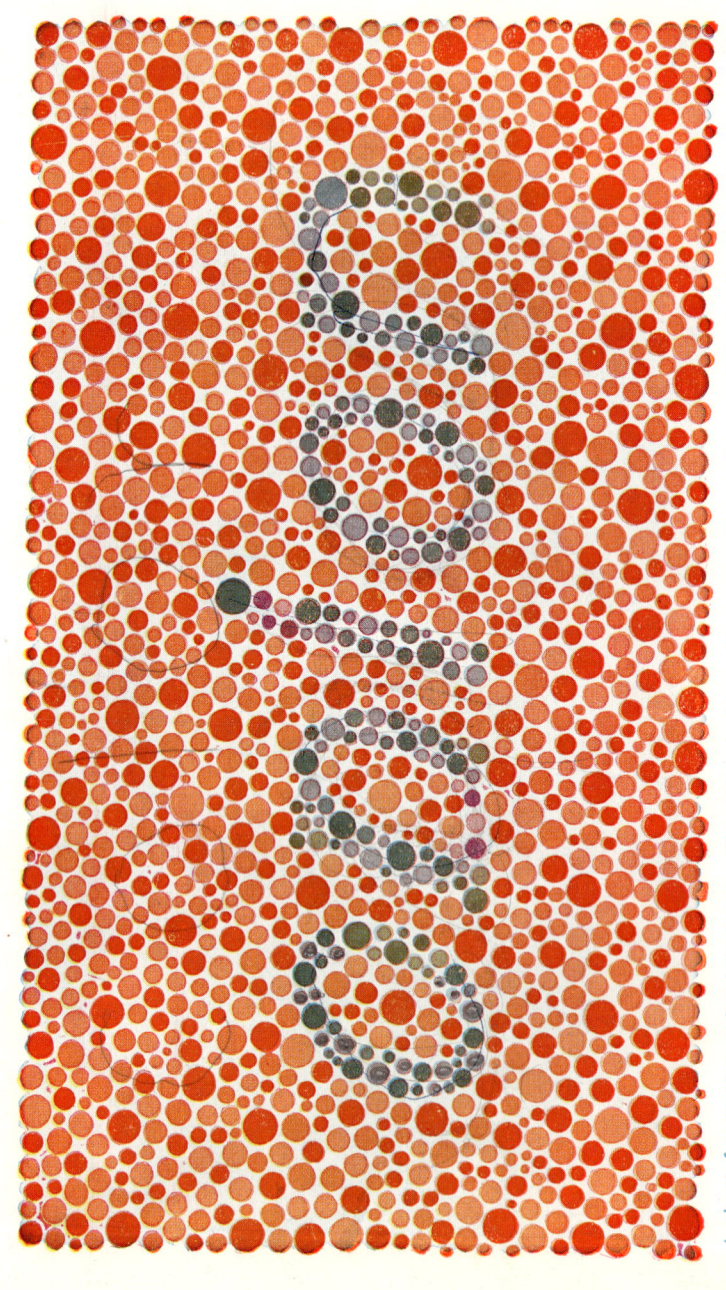

A chart for testing color blindness. The normal-visioned person will see the word "onion." The red-green color-blind individual will see the word "color." The pastel-shade color-blind person will not be able to make out any word. (This is an original chart based on the Ishihara method of determining color blindness.)

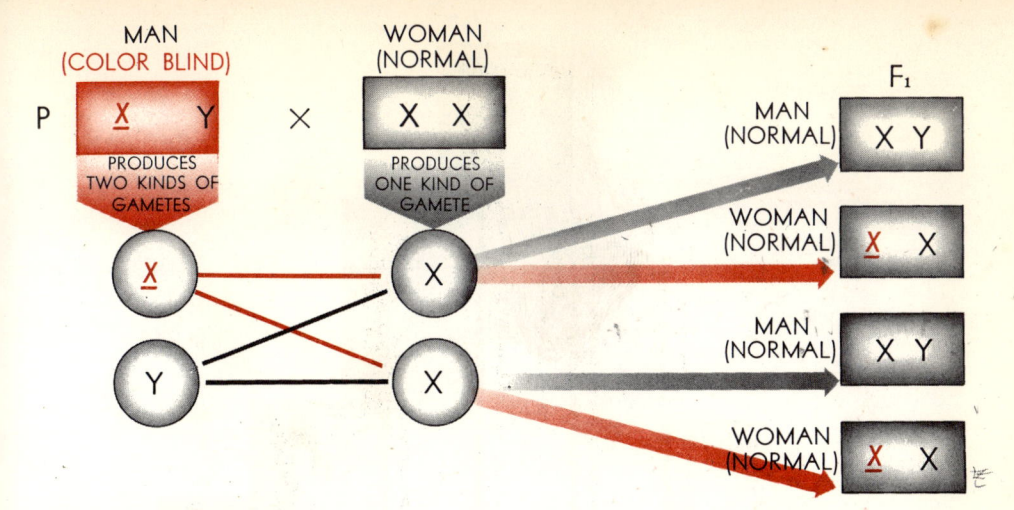

31.5 Inheritance of color blindness in man. Only the sex chromosomes are shown. Is the male parent normal or color-blind? How about the female parent? Now look carefully at the four possible kinds of fertilizations which produce the F_1. The women are not color-blind. Why? The men are not color-blind. Why?

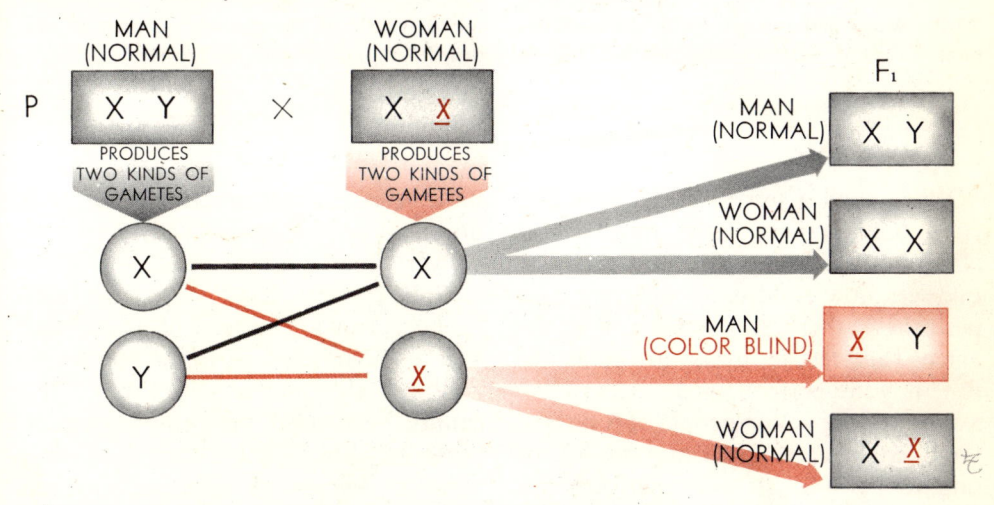

31.6 One of the women in the F_1 shown in Figure 31.5 marries a man without red-green color blindness. What are the chances that the sons will be color-blind? Will any of the daughters of this marriage be color-blind? Color blindness is only one of several sex-linked characteristics of man. Do you know of others?

Mental traits. Strictly speaking mental traits are also physical; they seem to depend on the structure of the nervous system and on the ductless glands. But for convenience we call intelligence, personality, and behavior traits "mental." But what is intelligence? It is quite different from knowledge. It is the ability to obtain knowledge and to use it in solving problems. It is often "measured," as you know, by intelligence tests. You have no doubt taken one or more of these.

CHAPTER THIRTY–ONE — HUMAN HEREDITY

451

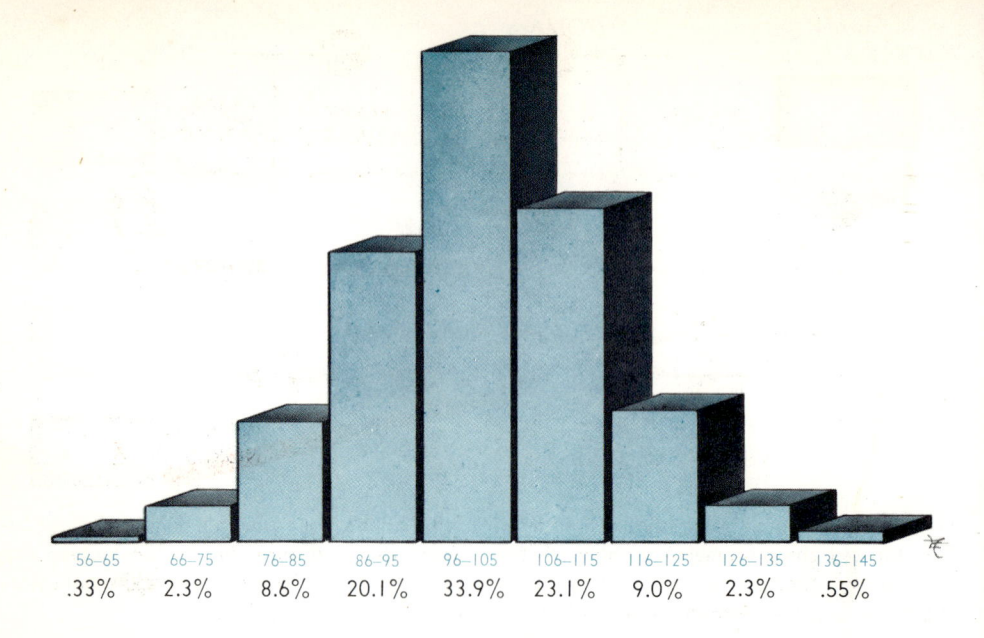

56–65	66–75	76–85	86–95	96–105	106–115	116–125	126–135	136–145
.33%	2.3%	8.6%	20.1%	33.9%	23.1%	9.0%	2.3%	.55%

31.7 A graph showing the Intelligence Quotient (I.Q.) of 905 children. What I.Q. is characteristic of the greater number of children? *Adapted from L. M. Terman*

When such a test is made, it is first tried out on very large numbers of children of different ages. In this way one sees how children of different ages perform on this test. When you, at the age of fourteen, let us say are given the test, if your performance is up to the average of the young people of fourteen, your **intelligence quotient,** or IQ, is said to be 100. If your performance is up to the 16-year-old average, your IQ is found by dividing 16 by your age; this makes it 114+. Figure 31.7 shows the graph, or curve, obtained when the IQ's of many children are tabulated.

Group intelligence tests often do not accurately show the "intelligence" of the person tested. Schools continue to use the tests but are careful not to depend on them completely. If such factors as knowledge of the English language, environment, and emotional difficulties do not interfere, the tests do show up the people with very high or very low intelligence.

Some people have very low intelligence; they are spoken of as morons. The feeble-minded person is one whose intelligence score is still lower. He cannot even meet the ordinary conditions of life. There are not only various degrees of feeble-mindedness but there are apparently several causes about which little is known. The scores of the lower grades of feeble-minded children are not even shown in the graph in Figure 31.7. Such children generally do not go to school; they are usually cared for in institutions.

Are mental traits inherited? Certain mental traits seem to run in families, but actually we know little about their inheritance. Figure 31.8 is the pedigree of the famous biologist Charles Darwin

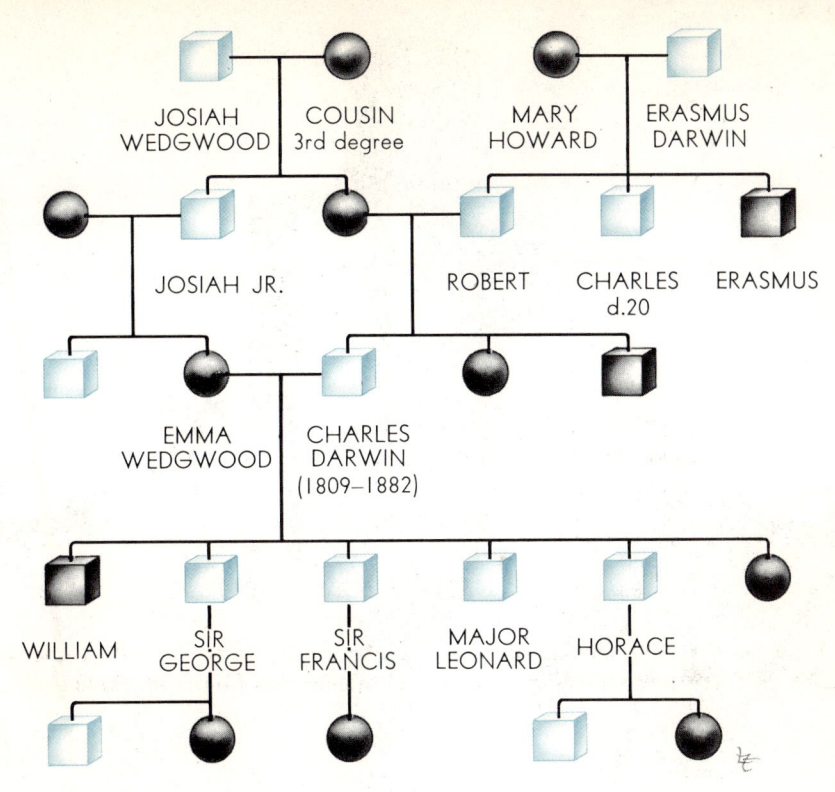

31.8 A part of the pedigree of five generations of an illustrious family. Blue symbols indicate illustrious individuals. Note the cousin marriages. Is there more than one way to explain the large number of illustrious men in this family?

and his children. Did so many of the members of the family become distinguished because of their inheritance, their environment, or both?

There are pedigrees, too, of the opposite kind. You may have read of the so-called "Jukes" family, that is said to have produced large numbers of shiftless and generally undesirable people, and of the "Kallikaks," many of whom in one branch of the family were said to be feeble-minded. The "facts" one reads about these families must be critically examined. We have little reliable information about them; we cannot, therefore, safely draw conclusions about the inheritance of the undesirable traits described in generation after generation. We have every reason for believing that in the case of these two families environment played a large part in determining the outcome.

A person's environment is of great importance, of greater importance even than it is in the case of any other animal. We humans have not only the physical environment to affect us; many other factors have an effect on us:

CHAPTER THIRTY-ONE — HUMAN HEREDITY

31.9 These identical twins have the same gene make-up. What striking similarities and what differences do you find? Can you explain? *Monkmeyer*

the kind of family, the home, the neighborhood we live in, the school, the church, the library, the theater, radio, movies; one could go on indefinitely listing them. Scientists have given us some clear evidence of the importance of the environment in determining what kind of person you will be. Let's see how they got this evidence.

Identical twins. Are there any identical twins in your school, twins who look so much alike that you can hardly tell them apart? Such twins develop from the same fertilized egg. In the many-celled stage two groups of cells separate. Each group grows into a baby attached to the same placenta. Since the two babies came from the same zygote they have the same chromosomes and genes. Of course, they are always of the same sex. Figure 31.9 shows a pair of identical twins. There are also fraternal twins; they develop from two separate egg cells fertilized by different sperms. Naturally, they are as different as any two children born to the same parents.

Some years ago a scientist succeeded in locating and following up 19 pairs of identical twins who, for one reason or another, had been separated shortly after birth. In this study biologists came as close as they can ever come to a controlled experiment in human heredity. Two people with identical genes were raised in different environments. Did they turn out to be identical? In physical traits the twins brought up in different environments showed comparatively slight differences. But in IQ, and in personality, several pairs showed very great differences. Evidently, the environment definitely affects "intelligence" and the ability to succeed in school.

Conservation of intelligence and talent. All of us owe much to the men and women of great intelligence and talent who have provided us with great scientific discoveries, great inventions, and great works of art. In fact, if these people had not lived or were not living now, we would not have the kind of civilization in which we live. Our clothes, houses, means of transportation, telephones, lighting, medicine, weapons of war — everything you can think of is the product of the work of gifted men and women. One of our greatest responsibilities, therefore, is to make sure that intelligence and talents are conserved, that wherever we find them we provide for their being developed instead of wasted.

We try to do that today, of course, by giving free schooling to everyone, building and equipping libraries, museums, theaters, concert halls, and so on. But to conserve our greatest natural resources — the abilities of our people — we must make sure that the physical environment is as good as we can make it. We want for all people the very best possible housing, nutrition, and medical care, as well as the best possible schools and other educational institutions.

Science and man. Our debt to artists, musicians, architects, authors, and religious leaders is very great. These and other professional people have throughout history contributed to the betterment of mankind. It is to scientists, however, that we must give the basic credit for most of the changes that give us better health and make life easier. And it is to scientists, too, that we must give credit for greater security. They have banished many of our fears; they have taught us to conquer superstition.

All this has been made possible within recent times by the use of scientific methods. But what are the methods used by scientists? How do scientists solve problems? They see clearly the problem they want to solve; they seek out all the facts, particularly by observation and, in many cases, by observation in controlled experiments; they face these facts squarely, facing the facts that seem to disprove, as well as those that seem to prove, their hypothesis or guess; they reason accurately; they suspend judgment while weighing the facts; they report truthfully; and when new information becomes available, they are ready to change their conclusions. While using these methods, they must learn how to work with others, for progress is greatest when men work together, sharing information freely. It is thus that problems are solved. And it is thus, by using the methods of science, that we can best solve many of our own problems in everyday living.

What have you learned? Progress in the study of human heredity is slow for these reasons: no experiments possible; small families; the length of time it takes for one generation; the characters which interest us particularly seem to be caused by several pairs of genes; and it is difficult to know how much of most characters is due to heredity and how much to environment.

Relatively easy to explain are: the inheritance of a good many defects, blood type, the presence of the Rh factor in your blood, and sex. The sex chromosomes are called X chromosomes. Women have a pair of sex chromosomes, XX. Men have, instead, an X and a Y chromosome. Red-green color blindness and hemophilia are caused by genes which lie in the sex chromosomes and are therefore sex-linked. If you understand sex inheritance you understand how these characters are inherited.

We know relatively little about the inheritance of mental traits because our intelligence and our character are determined to so large a degree by the many factors of our complex environment. Can you explain what makes our environment so complex? And can you explain how study of identical twins helps us understand the relative importance of the environment in affecting mental traits?

Much of man's progress depends on our conserving intelligence and talent in human beings. And it depends in a large measure, also, on our applying the scientific method to our problems. Are you sure you know the elements of the scientific method?

USEFUL WORDS IN BIOLOGY

albinism
polydactyly
sex chromosome
fraternal twins
sex-linked hemophilia
intelligence quotient (IQ)
identical twins

TEST YOURSELF

1. Give four reasons why we know relatively less about human heredity than we do about heredity in some other organisms.
2. Describe two methods used in the study of human inheritance.
3. Most of our characters are due to the action of several pairs of genes. But some are due to the action of a single pair of genes. Name some due to a single dominant gene and some due to a double dose of a recessive gene.
4. Give the various gene combinations that determine the four blood types, A, B, AB, and O.
5. Copy the following into your notes, making each statement correct: (a) Both men and women have —— pairs of chromosomes. (b) One of these pairs in a woman is the pair of sex chromosomes which are represented as ——. (c) A man has sex chromosomes shown as ——. (d) Therefore the eggs are (all alike) (of two kinds). (e) The sperms are (all alike) (of two kinds). (f) The sex of a child is therefore determined by the gamete supplied by the (father) (mother).
6. Name two characters caused by recessive sex-linked genes.
7. Explain: (a) how intelligence tests are made; (b) how a person's IQ is measured.
8. How are identical twins produced, and how are fraternal twins produced?
9. What has bringing up identical twins in different environments shown us about the effects of heredity and environment?

10. Name at least a dozen of the factors of your environment which have had an effect on you.

PROBLEMS TO THINK ABOUT

1. The child of an Rh positive father and an Rh negative mother may or may not be Rh positive. Can you show by diagram how this is possible? If the child of an Rh negative father and an Rh positive mother is Rh positive is there any danger to the child? Explain.
2. Show by diagram which is more likely to produce a larger proportion of children with hemophilia: (a) a cross between a normal father and a mother who carries a sex-linked gene for hemophilia, or (b) a cross between a father who has hemophilia and a normal mother.

DO IT YOURSELF

1. **Making your own pedigree.** Can your parents tell you about their parents and grandparents? And do you have aunts and uncles and cousins? Then if there is any rather striking characteristic in your family such as unusual hair color, crooked fingers, or attached ear lobes, or any special talent, make a pedigree like those shown in Figures 31.1 and 31.2. You will enjoy doing it and your pedigree might even be of interest to your classmates.
2. **Inheritance of the taste for PTC.** (PTC are the initials for a chemical called phenylthiocarbamide). PTC tastes bitter to about 7 out of 10 people, but to others it has no taste; a very few report it as sweet or salty. And this taste is inherited. Try it out on all your family and show the results in a diagram. You can get the materials for the PTC taste test from the American Genetics Association, 1507 M St., Washington 5, D.C.
3. **Red-green color blindness pedigrees.** Test yourself and other members of your family with the text color-blindness chart. If you find color blindness in your family, make a pedigree to show the inheritance of this character. If you do not find color blindness in your own family, perhaps you will find it in the family of one of your friends.
4. **The percentage of color-blind girls and boys in your school.** Make arrangements to test several classes of students in your school. Calculate percentages among girls and among boys. If you can, find out about color blindness in the parents of each student who is color-blind.
5. **Improving your environment.** Your environment is of great importance. It affects your thinking and your health. Consider the possibility of organizing class committees to study the ways in which the environment provided by your community could be improved. This would, of course, be a long-range activity.

ADVENTURES IN READING

1. *The New You and Heredity* by Amram Scheinfeld, Lippincott, 1950, will be of great help to you again in this chapter.
2. *Principles of Human Genetics* by Curt Stern, Freeman, 1949. Written for college students but so well written that those who want to go into this subject more deeply will wish to consult it.
3. *The Journal of Heredity*, and for those of you who want easier reading, the *Science News Letter* are sure to contain interesting articles.
4. "Man's Genetic Future" by Curt Stern, *Scientific American*, February 1952. It contains good pictures to show the many possibilities.

Unit Nine

The history of living things

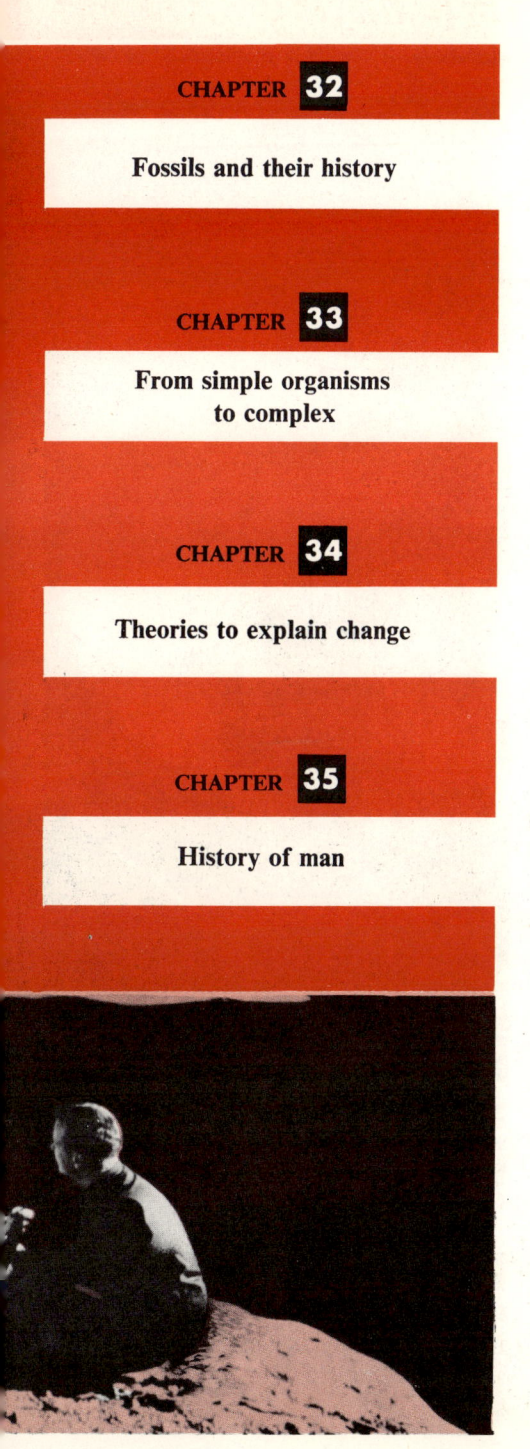

CHAPTER 32

Fossils and their history

CHAPTER 33

From simple organisms to complex

CHAPTER 34

Theories to explain change

CHAPTER 35

History of man

Try to imagine how our continent looked 500 years ago, when the early explorers came. Then, if you can, imagine how it may have looked 1000 years ago, 10,000, a million, a billion, and three billion years ago! Yes, our earth was in existence then; you will read how scientists estimate its age. But things were very different three billion years ago. Perhaps even the continent of North America had not been formed.

And yet we know surprisingly much about the earth long, long ago. We know that some 400 million years ago fish were already swimming in the vast oceans; and that about 60 or 70 million years ago dinosaurs roamed over the land. How do we know? In this unit you will learn some of the ways in which scientists have learned about the history of the earth. Slowly the rocks have been giving up the secrets that they have held for so many years. Scientists have found other good evidence that seems to indicate that plants and animals have changed during the ages of earth history, new and more complex species appearing as time went on. You will learn that this gradual change in living things through the ages is called "evolution."

Most people today agree that there is no conflict between the theory of evolution and religious teachings. Many believe also that the theory of evolution leads to a clearer understanding of a divine plan for the earth and its creatures. As you read the chapter on the history of man, you will find that the theory of evolution helps us to understand certain common physical characteristics which man shares with other forms of life. It does not deal with the spiritual qualities which set man apart from lower forms of animal life.

459

Chapter 32

Fossils and their history

A few billion years ago. Two billion years ago — some scientists now say even four billion years ago — the earth was made up principally of molten rock which was cooling and hardening. When the earth cooled it hardened into **igneous** (ig'nee-us) **rock,** like granite. After a time water appeared and oceans formed. The rocks that rose above the seas were bare. There were no living things.

We learn these things from **geologists** (jee-ol'o-jists), scientists who study the earth. Geologists use several methods to study the age of earth materials. The most widely used method is to analyze rocks that contain uranium. Uranium slowly changes to one kind of lead, always at the same rate. Thus, from the percentages of uranium and lead, the age of a rock that contains uranium can be calculated. The oldest rocks found by this method are at least two billion years old. Another method used seems to show that some rocks are three billion years old. We think that before the earth was solid it was liquid, and before that it was possibly gas. Changes take place slowly; perhaps two billion years were required to change the gaseous earth to a solid one.

Erosion. Even after it became solid, the earth continued to change. When it rained, water dashed down the steep slopes. Pebbles and boulders (large rocks) were broken loose by the rushing waters and the changing temperatures; slowly the rock was ground up. There was **erosion.** You can see the results of erosion in Figure 32.1. At the same time chemical changes were occurring in many of the rocks; the surfaces were softened and changed to fine clay and sand. Where rocks were level, this

32.1 Rivers of ice, known as glaciers, still wear away the land, breaking up hard rock. Note the broken rock below the glacier. *Geological Survey of Canada*

32.2 At one time these strata of rock must have been sand, or mud, or limestone shells of animals, or plants under water. How do you know? *Geological Survey of Canada*

soil remained on the rocks, becoming deeper as more soil formed. On slopes the soil was washed away by rain and blown by wind — more erosion. Minerals, once part of the solid rocks, dissolved in the rain water and were carried to lakes and seas. But some of the minerals remained in the soil, dissolved in the soil water.

Eventually, perhaps after a billion years, much of the level part of the earth was covered with soil and the lower portions of the earth were covered with water. Rivers flowed into lakes and seas. The first living things appeared. Probably they were plants of a sort. No one knows just what or how or when.

More erosion and new land. For billions of years erosion has changed the face of the earth. And it still goes on. Erosion of soil has become one of our greatest problems. You have seen erosion during a heavy rain, perhaps even on your own school grounds. Where the soil is bare, it is eroded much faster.

But the rock and soil that crumbles and is washed or blown away from one place collects elsewhere. Most of it is carried by streams to oceans and lakes or left by flooded streams along their banks. At the mouth of a river much of the sand and silt (fine particles of earth) settles. This sediment piles up, even above sea level, forming mud flats. Seeds fall on the mud and plants grow. Their roots bind the soil. As the plants die, their decaying bodies make the soil richer. Other types of small plants appear, finally shrubs and trees. Thus deltas form; new land is made.

New rock forms. Very, very slowly, throughout millions of years, the sediment that settled turned to rock, **sedimentary rock.** Minerals that were dissolved in the water cemented the particles of sand or silt together. Thus sandstone was made from sand, and a rock called shale was made from silt. The sediment turns to rock even faster if the land sinks under an ocean or lake. Then the great weight of the water helps to press it into rock. Thus sedimentary rocks are still being formed.

CHAPTER THIRTY-TWO — FOSSILS AND THEIR HISTORY

32.3 These are sedimentary rocks. They were made from materials deposited under water, and therefore, must have been in horizontal beds at one time. You would enjoy reading in a geology book how the strata have been turned on edge. See suggested books on page 470. *Geological Survey of Canada*

And in large bodies of water a different kind of sedimentary rock forms. Do you remember reading of the countless microscopic animals and plants and larger organisms, too, which form limy shells around themselves? As these organisms die they settle and decay. But their shells are left on the ocean floor and are pressed into rock, called limestone. As you probably know, there are vast beds of limestone, as well as of sandstone and of shale.

Sedimentary rocks — sandstone, limestone, and shale — occur in layers or **strata** (stray′ta) because the materials deposited by the waters change from time to time. You can see such strata clearly in the cliffs shown in Figure 32.2.

Sometimes in the long history of the earth the strata of sedimentary rock were lifted up and turned on end. Imagine the upheaval that must have taken place to bring about what you see in Figure 32.3! And the terrific pressure of the earth and the heat which is generated have crushed and twisted many of the rocks until their structure is completely changed. These changed rocks, whether they started as igneous or sedimentary rocks, are called **metamorphic rocks**. In this way granite, an igneous rock, is changed to gneiss (nice); shale is made into slate; and limestone becomes marble.

Fossils. As erosion took place and sediment was deposited, organisms, even quite large organisms, died and sank into the sediment. When conditions were favorable, the soft parts decayed and the hard parts remained. See Figure 32.4. As the sediment changed to rock, the bones or shells of animals and the harder woody portions of plants were sometimes changed to rock, for mineral matter gradually replaced the parts which once were living. Thus one type of **fossil** was

32.4 Fossil fish. Note that the upper fish, from rocks in Kansas, had swallowed another fish just before it died. The hard parts of both fish were then fossilized. Above: American Museum of Natural History. Below: U.S. Geological Survey

formed. The replacing of living matter by mineral matter is called **petrification.** Figure 32.5 shows you a petrified plant. Petrification goes on now, too. But it goes on very slowly.

32.5 Part of a petrified tree from Petrified Forest of Arizona. Grant, U.S. Department of Interior

CHAPTER THIRTY-TWO — FOSSILS AND THEIR HISTORY   463

32.6 Dinosaur footprints hardened in stone. If your home is in New Jersey, you can think of dinosaurs once roaming the land where you now live. These rocks were found in a quarry in West Orange, New Jersey. *American Museum of Natural History*

Sometimes living things left only an imprint in the sand or mud. By chance the imprint may have remained as the mud hardened into rock. See Figure 32.6. These imprints, too, are called fossils. Even delicate organisms like jellyfish and tiny delicate water plants have left their imprints in the mud which later hardened into rock.

Figure 32.7 shows you some common imprints. Perhaps you have found some in coal. You probably know that coal was formed in past ages from forests of ancient plants growing in swamps. The land was slowly sinking in these regions. As parts of the trees died and fell to the ground they were kept covered with water in the swamps; this kept them from decaying. Then came more rapid sinking. The plants were covered deeply with water and finally with sediments. Gradually the pressure and heat brought about many changes. Most of the other elements were removed but the carbon was left. This, almost pure carbon, is our coal and in it are many imprints and other remains of the buried plants or plant parts.

32.7 Various kinds of ferns left imprints on soft sediments which hardened into rock. Can you recognize the animal that left its imprint? These fossils were found in Pennsylvania. *Ward's Natural Science Establishment*

Sometimes it isn't water but sand, dust, or volcanic ash that covers a dead animal or plant. As these materials harden into rock around the plant or animal, a fossil is formed.

UNIT NINE — THE HISTORY OF LIVING THINGS

32.8 This painting by Charles R. Knight shows three ground sloths, animals no longer in existence, caught in a tar pit. A sabertooth tiger, also now extinct, is shown on the left. It appears ready to step into the pit. This is one way in which fossils were formed occasionally. *American Museum of Natural History*

A fossil defined. A fossil is any remains of a living thing from bygone ages, preserved in any form whatever. Petrifications and imprints are very common but other types of fossils were sometimes formed in strange ways. They give us an interesting glimpse into the past. In Los Angeles there are pools of tar or asphalt. In past ages animals sometimes sank into these pools and were caught. The tar preserved the skeletons; thus fossils were formed. Figure 32.8 shows you how scientists believe animals were trapped in the tar pits.

In somewhat the same way live insects were often trapped ages ago in the sticky resin that oozed from the trunks of evergreens. In time, this resin hardened into amber with the insect preserved in the center of the mass. Along the Baltic Sea where amber is commonly found, such insect fossils are plentiful.

Some mammoths, a type of woolly elephant no longer in existence today, were found some years ago frozen whole in the icy bogs of northern Siberia. Their flesh, when thawed, could still be eaten. The men who discovered them caught an actual glimpse of the earth of many thousands of years ago. One animal still had in its mouth the grass it was chewing when it fell into a crack in the ice.

Fossil hunting. In many parts of the country any boy or girl may discover fossils and see what kinds of animals and plants lived in the past. Hunting fossils is an exciting adventure; some scientists devote their lives to it. The men and women who study the earth's inhabitants of former ages are called **paleontologists** (pay-lee-on-tol′o-jists). Look at Figure 32.9, and you will see how fossils that are buried deep in the earth may be found. Here walls of rocks to a depth of thousands of feet are laid bare.

Sometimes, too, through the uplifting of a mountain chain and the later slow erosion of the slopes, fossils are brought to the surface. You can see in Figure 32.10 how fossils in the shale and in the deeper gray sandstone are

CHAPTER THIRTY-TWO — FOSSILS AND THEIR HISTORY

32.9 The Grand Canyon of the Colorado. Many, many millions of years of earth history are shown in this picture. Ages ago strata of sediments were laid down, one on top of the other. Animals and plants died and were petrified in each layer of sediment as it turned to rock. Then, through some upheaval, the strata were raised forming a plateau. Through long ages the Colorado River gradually cut an ever deeper channel through these rocks. Fossils buried in the earliest rocks that are way at the bottom of the canyon are thus exposed. *Aeronautical Chamber of Commerce of America*

brought to the top. No digging is necessary.

In Wyoming and in the Gobi Desert in Asia are some of the richest fossil beds. Here huge dinosaurs once roamed. Their bones were buried, turned to stone, and later brought close to the surface. Large expeditions of scientists have explored these regions. When they are lucky, they find the bones of one huge dinosaur all together; more often, through the shifting of the rocks, the bones are widely scattered. Many bones are much broken or completely lost. See Figures 32.11 and 32.12.

32.10 Ages ago a mountain was pushed up, **A** (dotted line), and later worn down to **B**. Before the mountain rose, the fossils in the gray sandstone were deeply buried. Now as you climb mountain **B**, you find them on the surface. Had the mountain been pushed still higher the red sandstone would display its fossils. *American Museum of Natural History*

Reading the history of the earth. To geologists the rock strata make an enormous book in which the history of the earth can be read. It could be called the Book of the Rocks. Lay your book down for a moment with its front cover against the table; the

466 UNIT NINE — THE HISTORY OF LIVING THINGS

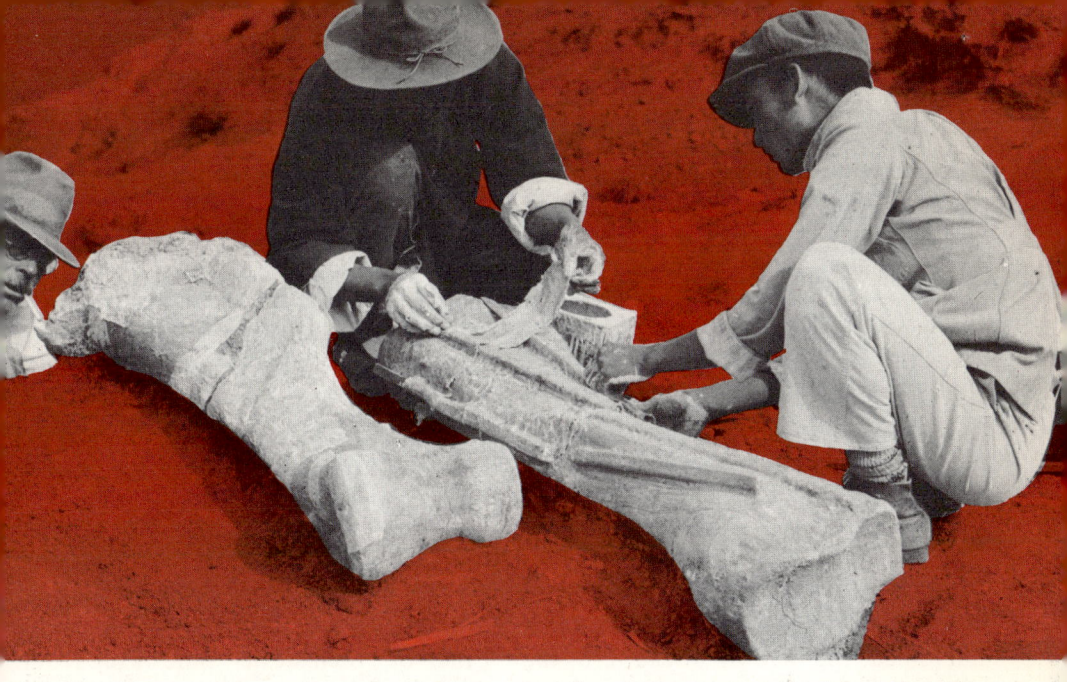

32.11 These men are wrapping large fragile bones found in the Gobi Desert. Burlap and flour paste protect the bones for shipment. *American Museum of Natural History*

32.12 This huge "picture puzzle" occupies the paleontologists at home. Only experts can identify and piece together the fossil fragments. *American Museum of Natural History*

CHAPTER THIRTY–TWO — FOSSILS AND THEIR HISTORY 467

TABLE 22
BOOK OF THE ROCKS

TABLE OF CONTENTS

6th — Era of recent life	(Cenozoic)	Began about 70 million years ago
5th — Era of middle life	(Mesozoic)	Began about 200 million years ago
4th — Era of old life	(Paleozoic)	Began about 500 million years ago
3rd — Era of first or simple life	(Proterozoic)	Began more than 1 billion years ago
2nd — Era of most ancient life	(Archeozoic)	Began about 2 billion years ago
1st — Era of no life	(Azoic)	Began about 3 billion years ago

first chapter is then at the bottom. The last chapter is on top. So in the Book of the Rocks the rocks laid down first — the oldest rocks — are at the bottom; the most recently formed rocks lie on top. In many of these strata are fossils of animals and plants; and since the lowest rocks are the oldest, they contain fossils of the plants and animals that lived in very early days. Just above them lie the remains of slightly more recent organisms. In the uppermost strata lie the remains of the most recent plants and animals. These resemble most closely the animals and plants alive today.

To be sure, the rock strata are harder to "read" than the pages of a printed book; in places they are broken and twisted. Pieces of the lowest or oldest strata therefore may, here and there, lie near the surface of the earth or even sometimes on top of younger rocks. The book has been mutilated; at times it would be difficult for you and me to know which are the earliest chapters. Geologists, however, have learned to "read" the book quite accurately.

They tell us from all they have "read" that the earth has been in existence for perhaps three billion years, and it has been inhabited by plants and animals for two or more billion years. Now historic time (since man has been keeping records) can be divided into periods according to what men did.

You will remember such periods as the Middle Ages and the Renaissance. Both of these periods were part of the Christian era. In much the same way prehistoric time is divided into **periods** and **eras** according to what happened to the earth and the living things on it. Eras of prehistoric time are from many millions to a billion years long. They are divided into periods just as eras of historic time are divided into periods. Some periods are further divided into epochs.

Geologists and paleontologists have learned much about different eras and periods of the earth's history. And so we shall find the following six eras listed in the "Table of Contents" of the Book of the Rocks. But we must remember to begin with the first era; we must read from the bottom up. Let's see how these six eras differed from each other.

What have you learned? One word, "change," sums up this chapter — three or more billion years of change. The earth has changed and is changing still, and with it, of course, its inhabitants have changed. How do we know this? Geologists explain how sediment piles up and hardens into sedimentary rock, forming layer on top of layer (strata) of rock. Paleontologists tell us how organisms buried in the sediment become petrified, forming fossils.

(Do you remember in what other ways fossils are formed?) Thus the history of the earth can be read in its rocks. The rocks are found like chapters in a book, the first or oldest "chapter" at the bottom of the pile, except in those regions where pushing up and twisting of the rocks has occurred. The time it took for all these happenings is divided into eras — stretches of millions or billions of years. Thus in describing or recording, geologists speak of six eras. The earlier eras, those about which they know least, are the longest eras.

formed; (b) what is meant by strata; (c) how metamorphic rock is formed.

6. Many fossils are formed by petrification. Explain this process fully.

7. In defining a fossil, state three ways in which fossils may be formed other than by petrification.

8. From looking at the figures and reading the text, give some idea of the work of a paleontologist.

9. (a) Where would you look for the first "chapter" in the Book of the Rocks? (b) How many chapters are there? (c) What name is given to any chapter of some millions of years? (d) In which chapter would you read about fossils of plants and animals that lived first on this earth?

USEFUL WORDS IN BIOLOGY

geologist
igneous rock
sedimentary rock
metamorphic rock
erosion
period
strata

shale
fossil
petrification
paleontologist
era
tar pit
mammoth

DO IT YOURSELF

1. **A fossil collection.** Start a fossil collection for yourself or for your school. Fossils are common in many parts of the country, in limestones, shales, and sandstones. If you visit or write to the geology or biology department of a nearby college, you will find out just where to look. Consult *Introduction to the Study of Fossils* by Hervey W. Shiner, Macmillan, 1952. To be most interesting and helpful the label on each specimen should give the name, where the specimen was found, the age of the rock, and how you found it. You can also buy fossils from biological supply companies. Ward's Natural Science Establishment, 3000 Ridge Road East, Rochester 9, New York, has a good collection.

2. **Learning to know common rocks.** What you find depends, of course, on the region where you live. You may well find granite (igneous rock), sandstone, shale, or limestone, and metamorphic rocks like slate or marble. Use *Rocks and Minerals* edited by Roger Tory Peterson, Houghton-Mifflin, 1953. Perhaps you will begin to make a rock collection that would be part of an "indoor museum" at home or at school. Knowing rocks will certainly help you in your search for fossils.

TEST YOURSELF

1. (a) What was our earth like three to five billion years ago? (b) What is one method of estimating the age of the earth?

2. What do you understand by erosion?

3. What, besides erosion, helped to build up soil on the earth?

4. Describe the steps in the formation of new land at the mouth of a river.

5. Sandstone, limestone, and shale are all sedimentary rock. Explain: (a) how each is

CHAPTER THIRTY-TWO — FOSSILS AND THEIR HISTORY

3. Demonstrate how imprints are formed. Use plaster of Paris, a powder that quickly "sets" hard after it has been moistened with water. Prints of any hard object can be made by pressing the object into the moist plaster of Paris. Cover the object with Vaseline before making the imprint. Try shells such as scallops and clams; try woody twigs or beetles or a real fossil. By experimenting you can learn to make a "mold" of plaster of Paris and with it make replicas of interesting or rare fossils.

4. Building up the class library. Write to the American Museum of Natural History, New York 24, to the Chicago Natural History Museum, and to the Denver Museum, Denver, Colorado, for lists of publications on fossils and the history of the earth. Most of these are well illustrated.

ADVENTURES IN READING

1. *Our Amazing Earth* by Carroll Lane Fenton, Doubleday, 1941. A book you will enjoy reading.
2. *Rocks and Their Stories* by Carroll Lane Fenton, Doubleday, 1951.
3. *Stories in Rocks* by Henry Lionel Williams, Holt, 1949. Very simply told and interesting.
4. *The Earth for Sam* by W. M. Reed, Harcourt, Brace, 1929. Once you begin this you won't want to put it down.

Chapter 33
From simple organisms to complex

A glance at the early eras. Rocks of all the six eras have been examined, and many thousands of kinds of fossil plants and animals have been described. Much more of this kind of work remains to be done, but enough rocks have been examined to make it possible for us to know what the earth must have been like during much of its history. Imagine that, like "Alley Oop," you could be sent by a "time machine" for a visit to the earth in each era. To be sure you know where you are going, look at Figure 33.1.

On your trip to the first era you would see only rock and water, no living things. In the second era you still can see no living things; they are too small. Scientists tell us that some rocks of this era seem to give evidence that life did exist. They find graphite in the rocks, and graphite is a form of carbon. Carbon in the rocks means that living matter — perhaps a very simple form like single-celled plants — must have been present. On your third trip you see the earth during its third era (Proterozoic). You see simple seaweeds and a few kinds of simple invertebrates in the waters about you. Erosion is building soil from the rocks, but you see no plants or animals on the land.

You have looked at the earth in the first three eras — perhaps the first 2 or 3 billion years of its existence. The earth changed a great deal during this long time, but it was still quite bare, and the only living things were those that lived in water. Next you visit the earth during its fourth era, the Paleozoic. Suppose you visit it twice — at the beginning, about half a billion years ago, and again near the end. You will note great changes during the Paleozoic. Paleontologists have divided the Paleozoic and later eras into periods and epochs, as you may note from Figure 33.1. Let the "time machine" take you to visit some of these periods.

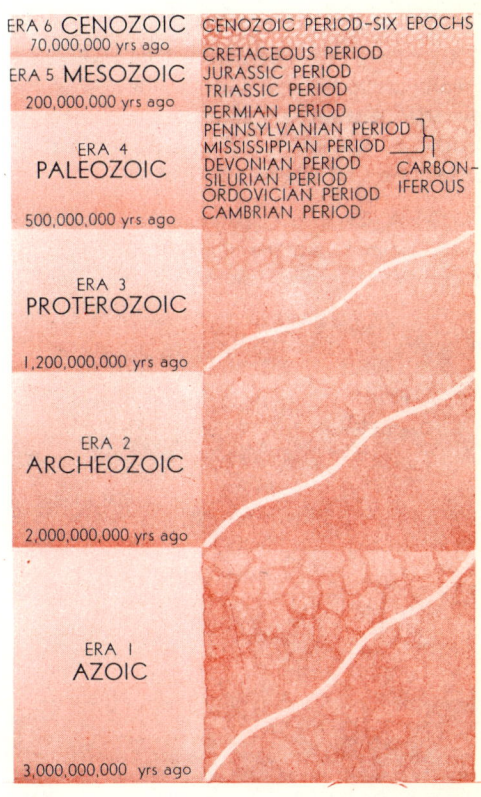

ERA 6 CENOZOIC
70,000,000 yrs ago
CENOZOIC PERIOD–SIX EPOCHS
CRETACEOUS PERIOD
ERA 5 MESOZOIC
200,000,000 yrs ago
JURASSIC PERIOD
TRIASSIC PERIOD
PERMIAN PERIOD
PENNSYLVANIAN PERIOD
ERA 4 PALEOZOIC
MISSISSIPPIAN PERIOD } CARBONIFEROUS
DEVONIAN PERIOD
SILURIAN PERIOD
ORDOVICIAN PERIOD
500,000,000 yrs ago
CAMBRIAN PERIOD

ERA 3 PROTEROZOIC
1,200,000,000 yrs ago

ERA 2 ARCHEOZOIC
2,000,000,000 yrs ago

ERA 1 AZOIC
3,000,000,000 yrs ago

33.1 A diagram of the 6 eras of time. Read from the bottom up. The rocks of the first era were the first to be laid down and are generally deepest down in the earth.

CHAPTER THIRTY-THREE — FROM SIMPLE ORGANISMS TO COMPLEX

33.2 Long years of study of the rocks lead geologists to believe that what is now North America was largely under water during an early period of the Paleozoic era. How about the spot where you live?

33.3 A Cambrian underwater scene. The large animal near the center is a giant trilobite. What others can you recognize? To which subkingdom of animals do all these strange organisms belong? *Smithsonian Scientific Series, Inc.*

THE PALEOZOIC ERA

The Cambrian period. You visit North America early in the Paleozoic era. Figure 33.2 is a map to guide you. Most of the continent was under water. You look about, but you see no land-living forms. No fossils of land-living plants or animals have been found. But in the oceans you see much life as Figure 33.3 shows. The large animal near the center is a **trilobite** (try′lo-bite), a very common animal in those days but now extinct. See Figure 33.4. You might guess that it was a relative of the present-day lobster. Trilobites varied in size from two inches to two feet or more. Some of the animals and plants shown in Figure 33.3 are related to forms you may have seen living in the oceans of today. Which can you recognize? Did you notice that all the animals living in the early part of this era belonged to the group of invertebrates?

The carboniferous periods. You now visit late in the Paleozoic era. Two periods here are called **carboniferous** because many of the plants of this time became coal: they were carbonized. Land plants are everywhere. You see huge swamps. The trees, as Figure 33.5 shows, are tree ferns, which have disappeared in all but a few spots in the world of today. On the tree at the left is shown a cockroach, three to four inches long. As you wander through the carboniferous swamps you see other insects, too, such as dragonflies with a wingspread of a foot! Amphibia, like our newts and salamanders, crawl over the moist land. And some reptiles live in these forests, but the variety is small. Fish in large numbers live in the oceans.

33.4 Trilobite fossils in limestone of the early part of the fourth era. This gives you some idea of how crowded with trilobites the seas must have been in this era. *U.S. National Museum*

33.5 A photograph of a reconstruction of a forest in the late Paleozoic era. Ferns varied from small plants to huge trees. Do you recognize the animal on the tree at the left of the illustration? *Field Museum of Natural History*

CHAPTER THIRTY–THREE — FROM SIMPLE ORGANISMS TO COMPLEX

33.6 Imprint of a strange birdlike animal (Archaeornis) which lived in the Mesozoic era. *Smithsonian Institution*

THE MESOZOIC ERA

The Age of Reptiles. You will find it worth while to visit several times during the Age of Reptiles. Reptiles of many species live on the land, in the sea, and in the air. The tree ferns are nearly gone. Huge evergreens have replaced them. You can see the fossil remains of these evergreens in the Petrified Forest of Arizona. Some strange, birdlike animals with teeth, shown in Figure 33.6, have appeared; and a few kinds of small mammals live on the land. The waters are still crowded with fishes and the many kinds of invertebrates so numerous in the Paleozoic era.

Toward the close of the Mesozoic era you would see the **dinosaurs,** dragonlike reptiles. Some species of dinosaurs were small, others gigantic. The "Thunder Lizard" (*Brontosaurus*) was sixty-six feet long, the size of five elephants end to end. It seems to have waded about in swamps, eating perhaps 300 pounds of plants a day. Scientists have estimated that its body must have weighed more than 70,000 pounds, its brain not much more than one pound! This might be reason enough for its becoming extinct when it was obliged to compete with more intelligent animals, but no doubt its size was not the only cause. We do know that dinosaurs, after flourishing for a few million years, died out completely before the next era began. It seems as though they became extinct very suddenly; actually it may have taken thousands upon thousands of years.

You would see the "King Tyrant" reptile (*Tyrannosaurus rex*). With a monstrous body and enormous mouth armed with great teeth, this dinosaur was no doubt a flesh eater and a powerful fighter. Dinosaur fossils give evidence of many bone fractures which must have occurred while the animals were alive.

THE CENOZOIC ERA

The Age of Mammals. Now you visit in the Age of Mammals, and both the plants and animals are more familiar. You see no dinosaurs, but there are still many other kinds of reptiles. There are many species of amphibians, thousands of species of fish, and many thousands of species of invertebrates. Birds are common. Of course, the mammals are not new on the earth. You saw primitive mammals in the Mesozoic era. But now you see more mammals than any other kind of animal, and they belong to

33.7 How one artist pictures a landscape during a late period in the age of reptiles. Tyrannosaurus rex and the three-horned dinosaur, Triceratops horridus, are shown. Notice the vegetation of this era. *American Museum of Natural History*

33.8 A scene in an early period in the age of mammals. In this era mammals became plentiful; but, of course, there were still representatives of all the other vertebrate classes and invertebrate phyla. Which reptiles do you recognize? How did the vegetation differ from that of earlier eras? *Royal Ontario Museum, Toronto*

CHAPTER THIRTY-THREE — FROM SIMPLE ORGANISMS TO COMPLEX

33.9 What is now western Nebraska looked very different during the age of mammals. In those days horses, somewhat like the present (modern) horse, roamed the plains. Later these died out. What other mammals lived here? *American Museum of Natural History*

33.10 How far south did the ice sheets extend? Glaciers are still to be seen in our western mountain ranges. The greater part of Greenland is still covered with ice.

many different species. A large number of these have died out. Besides the mosses and ferns, flowering plants are abundant: trees, shrubs, herbs, monocotyledons and dicotyledons, in great variety.

During this era the Alps and the Himalayas were thrust up as mountain ranges; the Rocky Mountains were still rising. There seems to have been a broad land connection between North America and northern Asia and between North America and northern Europe. North and South America, on the other hand, seem to have been separated during most of the era. The world was very different in the era known as the Age of Mammals.

About a million years ago the temperature dropped. Glaciers formed on the mountainsides. Sheets of ice, miles deep, accumulated in northern Europe and eastern Canada and spread in all directions. Figure 33.10 shows how far south the ice sheets reached. Many plants were killed; animals retreated before the wall of ice. The woolly mammoth was driven from its northern home to south of what we now call the Ohio River, and the walrus of the Arctic seas lived off the shores of what is now New Jersey. After a time the climate changed again. Now ice sheets by melting retreated northward. Plants and animals followed them. It seems to have been comparatively warm on the earth. Lions and hippopotamuses roamed among palm trees in the British Isles. These changes from warm to extreme cold happened four times during the Age of Mammals. The last of the ice sheets melted away from North America not more than 25,000 years ago. In the meantime manlike creatures had appeared.

UNIT NINE — THE HISTORY OF LIVING THINGS

Years of duration

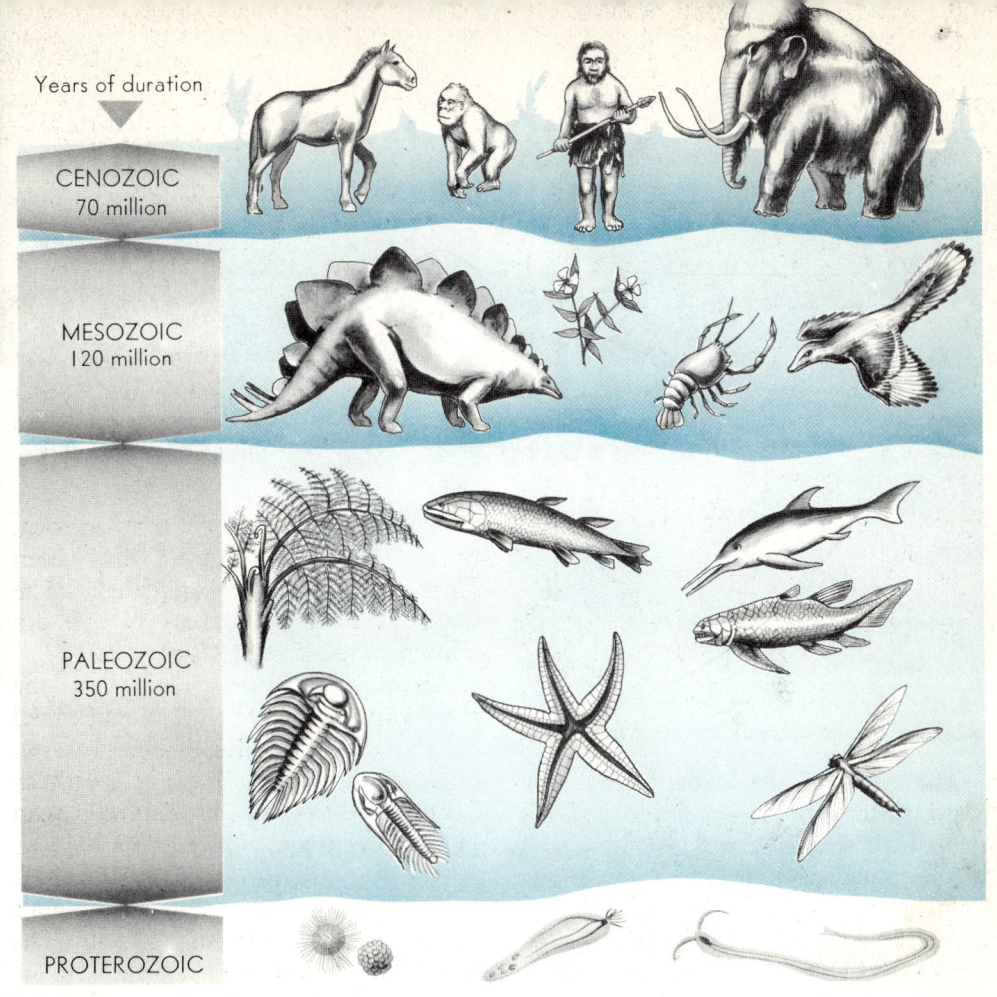

CENOZOIC
70 million

MESOZOIC
120 million

PALEOZOIC
350 million

PROTEROZOIC

33.11 This shows a few of the kinds of animals and plants common in each era.

Simple life to complex. Let us review what we have just read in the Book of the Rocks and begin at the bottom with the older eras. You may have noticed that the lower (older) rocks contain fossils of only the simplest animals and plants. In the strata lying just above, we find the same kinds of fossils as below; but fossils of new and different organisms are also found. There are fossils of more complex invertebrates, such as lobster-like forms, and insects, and fossils of some lower vertebrates — fish and amphibia. In still more recent rocks, fossils of reptiles are the most common, and fossil remains of primitive mammals appear for the first time. But of course, in these rocks fossils of the lower vertebrates and the invertebrates are present, too, although the species are not identical with those found in the earlier rocks.

What is true of animal life is just as true of plant life. Judging from the fossils, there seems to have been a progression from simple life to complex. Of course, these changes in living things occurred very, very slowly; all this took a long, long time — two thousand million years. Figure 33.11 shows all this.

CHAPTER THIRTY-THREE — FROM SIMPLE ORGANISMS TO COMPLEX

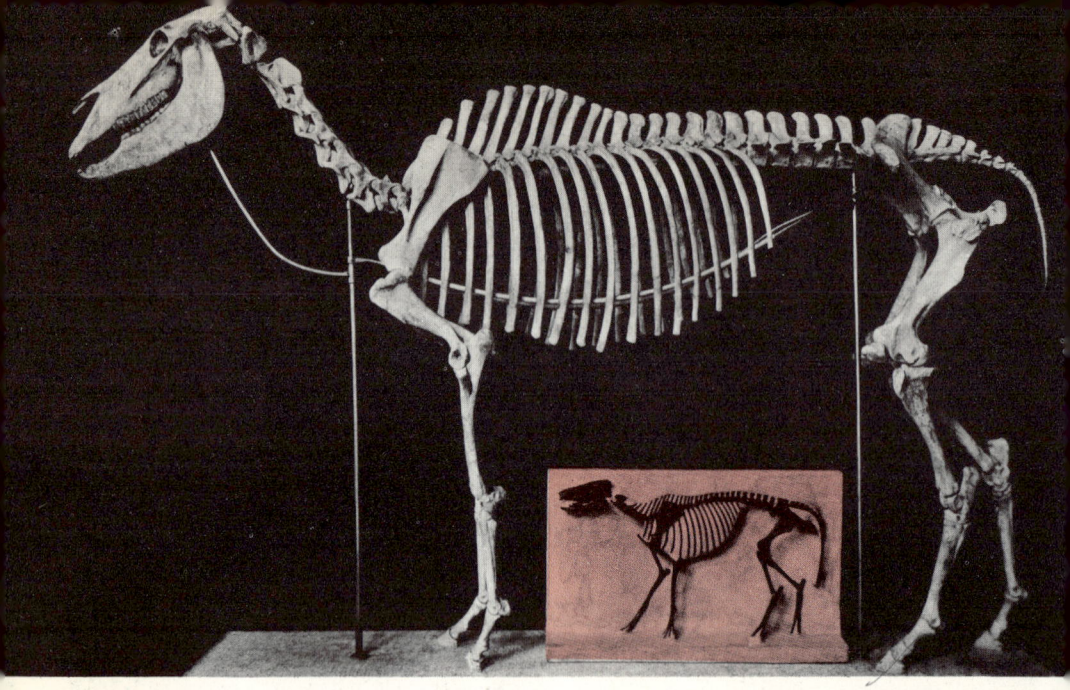

33.12 Skeletons of the modern horse and Eohippus to show comparative sizes. What resemblances and differences can you see? *American Museum of Natural History*

The origin of the horse. When the fossil history of some single type of animal or plant is studied in detail it shows us more clearly that simple living things must have changed into complex. It shows us many of the steps by which one animal or plant changed into another more complex form. For example, horses were not always as they are today — long-legged creatures, walking on the tip of a much lengthened single toe, somewhat like a ballet dancer. And there was a time when they did not have complex grinding teeth. How do we know?

The rich fossil beds of Wyoming and Montana have given us an answer to the question. The horse's pedigree has been traced back sixty million years to an ancestor not much larger than a cat. This ancestor has been called *Eohippus* (ee-oh-hip′pus). Its front legs were four-toed; its hind legs had three toes. It had simple teeth that lacked cement. Look at a reconstruction of the skeleton of *Eohippus* in Figure 33.12 standing between the fore and hind legs of a modern horse. But many, many other horselike fossils have been found in many strata. When these fossils are arranged according to the strata in which they were found, from the older to the more recent, they show horselike animals leading in a series from *Eohippus* to the modern horse. In other words, many intermediate forms have been found between *Eohippus* and the modern horse. See Figure 33.13.

Other fossil series. Similar fossil series have been found tracing the development of other animals, for example, the camel, the pig, and the elephant. The early elephant was not impressive like the modern elephant. It was only three feet tall, and had no tusks or trunk. In Figure 33.14 you see a particularly complete series of fossils of snails.

478   UNIT NINE — THE HISTORY OF LIVING THINGS

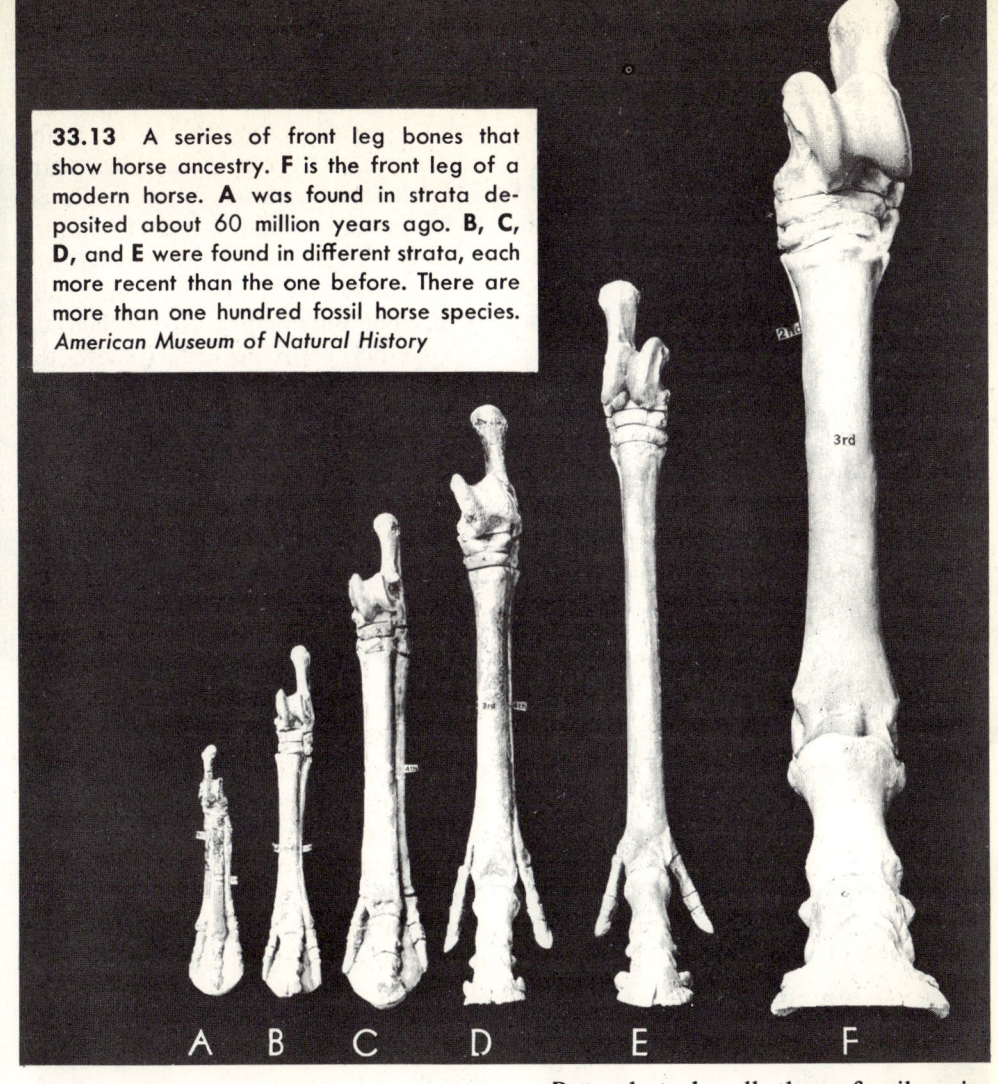

33.13 A series of front leg bones that show horse ancestry. **F** is the front leg of a modern horse. **A** was found in strata deposited about 60 million years ago. **B, C, D,** and **E** were found in different strata, each more recent than the one before. There are more than one hundred fossil horse species.
American Museum of Natural History

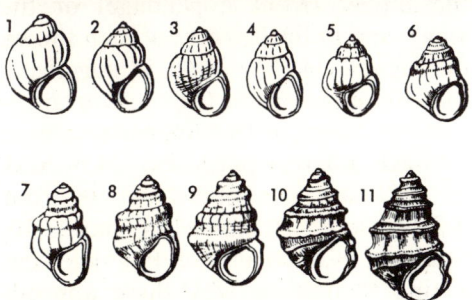

A   B   C   D   E   F

33.14 As all other living things changed throughout the ages, step by step, so did the snail. Numbers **1** and **11** are very different. What do you learn about their relationship when you look from each shell to the next?

But what do all these fossil series show? What do we mean when we say that the horse came from an early ancestor called *Eohippus?* We mean that *Eohippus* must have given rise to an organism that was slightly different from itself. After many centuries this form again gave rise to offspring that were slightly different. This happened again and again over a long period of time — 60 million years. But would it be possible for organisms to change in the ways described? Let's turn our attention from fossil beds to biological laboratories.

CHAPTER THIRTY-THREE — FROM SIMPLE ORGANISMS TO COMPLEX

In the laboratory. Right before our eyes in the laboratory the most striking changes sometimes occur in plants or animals. They are caused by mutations or other chromosomal changes. In just the same way, early horses could well have left offspring with slightly longer leg bones, with legs in which the toes on either side did not increase in length and thus were left behind, so to speak. Suppose a similar change occurred once every few thousand years or more; it has been found that mutations, when they once occur, are likely to repeat themselves. And each time the mutation is inherited. In 60 million years an accumulation of relatively slight changes could add up to great changes.

Think back for a moment to what you read about plant and animal breeding. Man has succeeded in producing new types of living things in a few centuries, or even in a few years. The breeder's methods are not different from processes that go on in nature. Changes from one type of organism to another take place without man's help; man only helps to speed them up.

Together with the fossil record this seems to be good evidence that plants and animals have changed during the ages of earth history, new and more complex species appearing as time went on. We speak of this as **evolution.**

A SOLUTION TO MANY BIOLOGICAL PUZZLES

The first puzzle solved. Some biologists devote themselves to a study of animal or plant structure. This part of biology is called **anatomy.** In comparing the anatomy of different vertebrates, these scientists many years ago were puzzled by this: Why should animals that are so different show such great similarity in their structure, both in their skeletons and in their internal organs? Look closely at the bones in the flipper (front appendage) of the whale and in the forearm of man shown in Figure 33.15. Isn't it surprising that there should be the same arrangement of bones in two appendages used for such different purposes? Now look at the row of appendages of four different animals, shown in Figure 33.16. Students of comparative anatomy kept asking themselves why these appendages should be so much alike. And when they studied the other organs of different vertebrates they always found great similarities. Look, for example, at the brains shown in Figure 33.17.

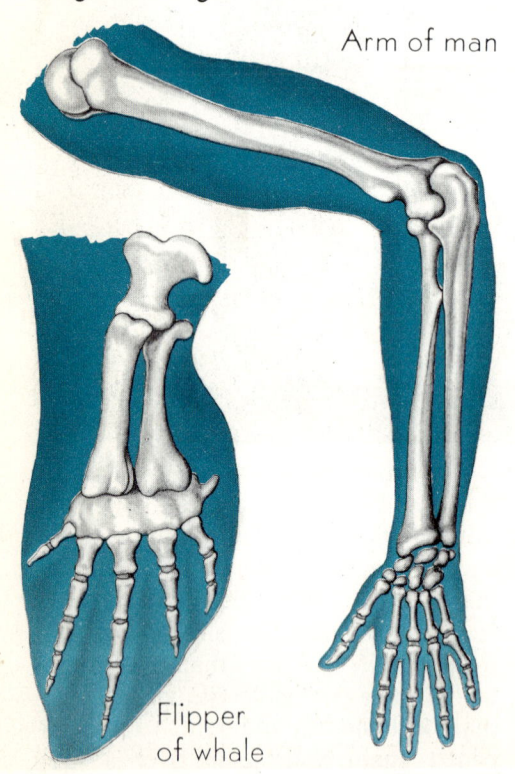

33.15 You would think a whale does not have much in common with a man other than that both are mammals. But compare the bones of a whale's flipper with the bones of a man's arm. What resemblances do you find?

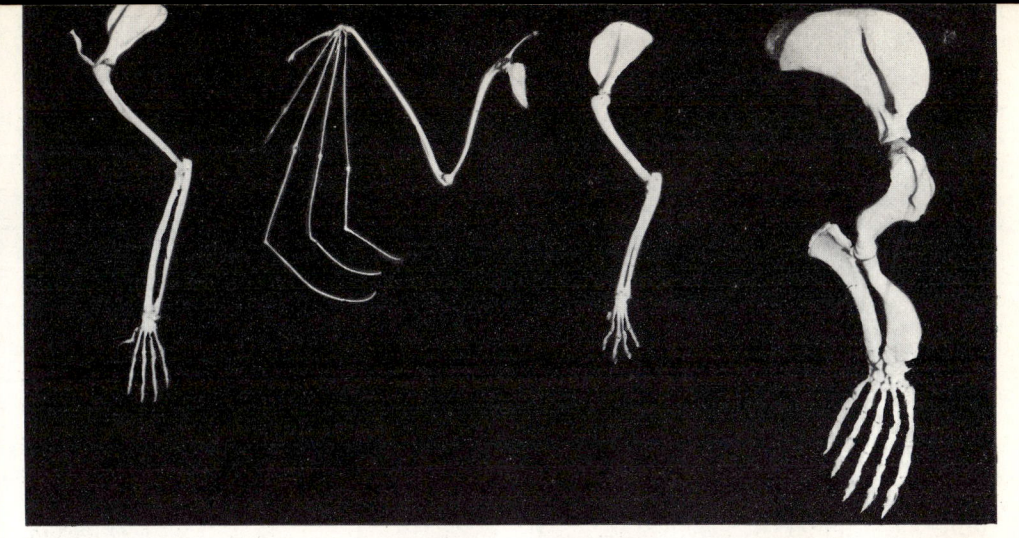

33.16 This shows (left to right) the front appendages of monkey, bat, cat, and seal. The appendages are used in very different ways. What similarities do you note? In what region do you note the greatest difference? *Ward's Natural Science Establishment*

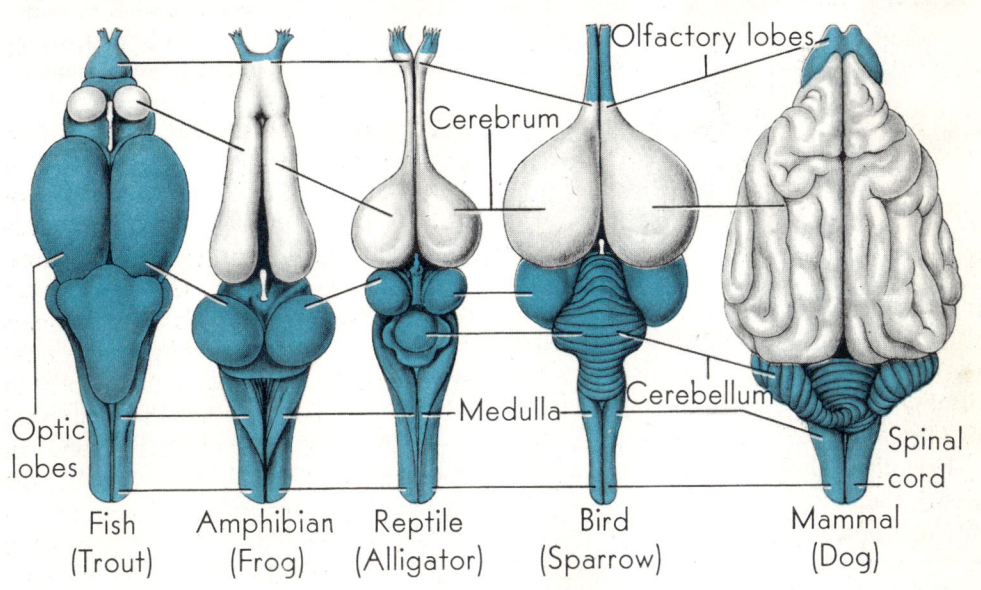

Fish (Trout) Amphibian (Frog) Reptile (Alligator) Bird (Sparrow) Mammal (Dog)

33.17 Which parts do you find in all five brains? Optic lobes are hidden in the dog's brain. What other similarities do you find?

At first glance the brains of these different animals may look very different to you, but a closer study shows striking resemblances.

When paleontologists had learned enough about fossils to write a fossil history of some animals, they provided a clue to the questions asked by the students of anatomy. Fossils showed that vertebrates changed through the ages. The most reasonable explanation for new forms is that they were descended from the older ones. That means that they were all related to each other, some more closely, some more distantly. If they are related,

CHAPTER THIRTY-THREE — FROM SIMPLE ORGANISMS TO COMPLEX

Fish Frog Turtle Chick Pig Man

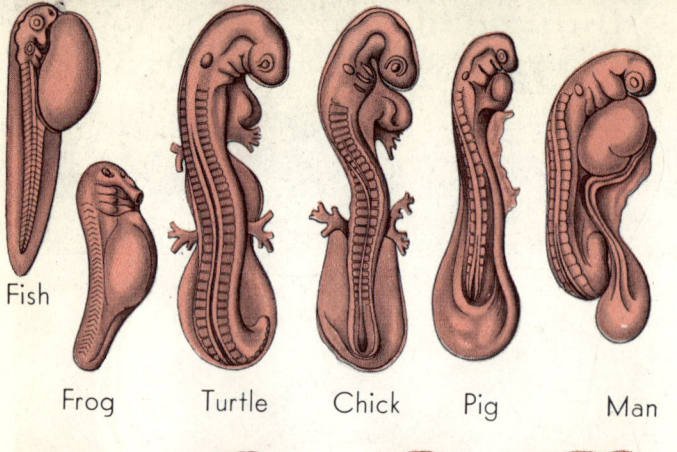

33.18 In what ways are these early embryos alike? As embryos grow older, there is more and more differentiation. Thus, each begins to look less like the other embryos and more like the adult into which it grows.

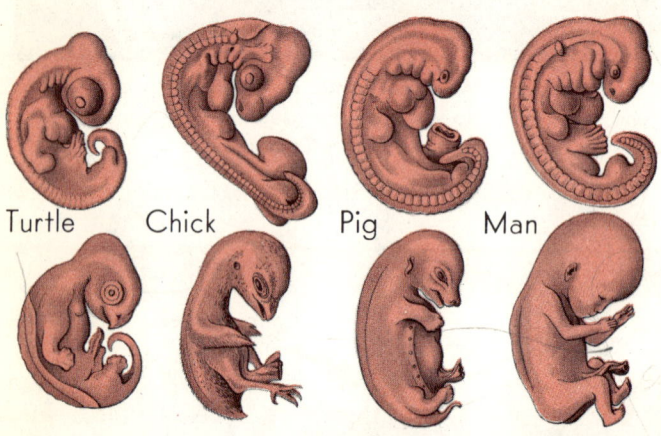

Turtle Chick Pig Man

33.19 In the top row there is still great resemblance between embryos of reptiles, birds, and mammals. In what respects are they similar? At a still later stage, which embryo looks more like the human embryo, the turtle or the pig?

it is not surprising that they should show similarities. And what is believed to be true of vertebrates is also, no doubt, true of all other animals and of all plants.

Paleontologists also have the answer to another question that arises as one studies animal structure: why should a fish resemble a frog more closely in its structure than it resembles a cat? Fossil history shows that frogs appeared on the earth soon after the first fish. Cats, however, appeared on the earth long after fish and after frogs. That would account for the greater resemblance between fish and frog than between fish and cat. This is really another way of saying that fish seem to be more closely related to frogs than they are to cats.

A second puzzle is solved. Now look at Figure 33.18 to see what puzzled the students of embryology. Why should the embryos of fish, frog, turtle, chick, bird, and man show such basic similarities? And when you look at the late stages of embryos of reptiles, birds, and mammals they are still very similar, as shown in Figure 33.19. Why this similarity?

An answer to these questions can, again, be found in the discoveries made by paleontologists. Fossils show that all vertebrates seem to have come one from another; they are all related, some more closely, some more distantly. Naturally organisms that are related show resemblances. The closer the relationship the greater is the resemblance.

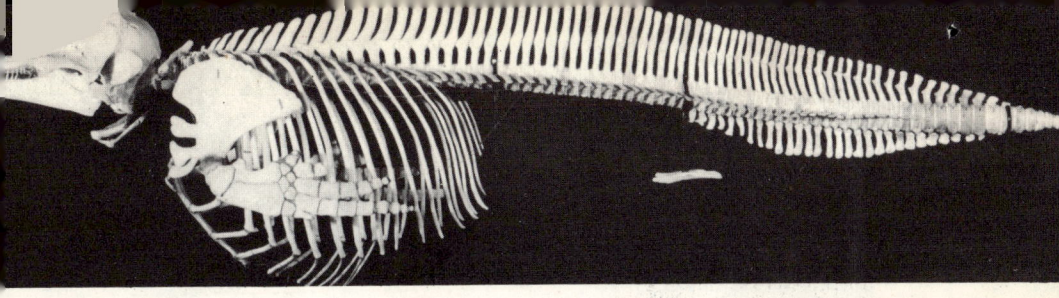

33.20 Skeleton of a porpoise, relative of the whale, which never leaves the water. What vestigial structure do you see? *Ward's Natural Science Establishment*

A third puzzle is solved. Why should all mammals be so similar in their chemical make-up? The pancreas of the pig can supply insulin which serves the same purpose as our own insulin. The thyroid gland of the sheep was long used for supplying thyroxin for our use. The hormones seem to be identical. And why are the digestive enzymes of mammals, in many cases, chemically the same? The answer can again be given by paleontologists. Fossils seem to show that mammals are descended from a common ancestor; they are closely related to each other.

A fourth puzzle is solved. Man has an appendix which seems to be of no use and may do harm. Some people have scalp and ear muscles which they can contract, but to no purpose. You have small fused bones at the lower end of your spinal column that form a short tail. The whale has no hind legs, but it has a number of small bones on each side of the spinal column in that region where you would expect hind legs to be attached. See Figure 33.20. If you believe that the different types of animals are related — that they are all descended from some common ancestor or ancestors — you can explain why these useless structures are present. You can consider them as "remnants" of structures that once were useful to the ancestor. We call these structures that no longer serve a useful purpose **vestigial** (ves-tij'ee-al) **structures.**

For example, we believe the whale has some small bones (vestigial structures) on each side of the spinal column because it is descended from animals that used their legs and needed hipbones in that region. And so all other vestigial organs can be explained.

A fifth puzzle is solved. You will remember how our system of classification works. A kingdom is divided into phyla, these into classes, these into orders; orders are subdivided into families; then come genera, species, and often a final subdivision into varieties or breeds. Scientists wondered for a long time why animals and plants could be fitted so neatly into this scheme of classification. There is an explanation if you remember what fossils and the facts of genetics seem to show — that animals and plants changed step by step throughout the ages.

Look at the table on the next page. The cat and lynx have so many characters in common that Linnaeus could fit them into the same genus. They seem to be closely related; they probably came from a common ancestor.

Linnaeus found that the tiger has not enough characters in common with the cat and lynx to put them in the same genus, but they all do have much

CHAPTER THIRTY-THREE — FROM SIMPLE ORGANISMS TO COMPLEX   483

TABLE 23

SPECIES	GENUS	FAMILY	ORDER	CLASS	PHYLUM	KINGDOM
cat	cat	cat	cat	cat	cat	cat
	lynx	lynx	lynx	lynx	lynx	lynx
		tiger	tiger	tiger	tiger	tiger
			dog	dog	dog	dog
				rabbit	rabbit	rabbit
				horse	horse	horse
				man	man	man
					bird	bird
					snake	snake
					frog	frog
					fish	fish
						insect
						oyster
						starfish
						worm
						jellyfish
						sponge
						protozoan

in common. He found the tiger, lynx, and cat enough alike to put them into one family. We believe the tiger is related to cat and lynx, but less closely; it, the cat, and the lynx probably had a common ancestor at an earlier time.

The dog has canine teeth like the cat, lynx, and tiger; and yet it is different from them in many other respects. It seems to be related to all the other three, but more distantly. That is why Linnaeus could fit it into the same order as the cat, lynx, and tiger.

Look at the table again. The animals of each larger group — class, phylum, and kingdom — have fewer and fewer characteristics in common. However, we can explain their common characteristics by assuming that all of any one group arose from a common ancestor.

A sixth puzzle is solved. Biologists have long been puzzled over the distribution of plants and animals. In general, animals and plants tend to spread far and wide over the earth to areas which are suitable in climate, provide the right food in sufficient amounts, and have not already been occupied by enemies. They spread until they meet barriers. The barriers may be mountain ranges, great bodies of water, or large deserts.

Long ago some puzzling facts were noted about the distribution of animals and plants. Why should almost all native mammals in Australia and nearby islands be pouched mammals? There are many kinds of pouched mammals in Australia besides the kangaroo; and they are all more primitive or simpler in structure than the mammals of other continents. Figure 33.21 shows one of these simpler mammals that carries its young, when first born, in a pouch. Why should pouched mammals not exist all over the world? The opossums of North and South America are the only other pouched mammals. This strange distribution puzzled biologists for a long time. It can be explained, however, if we assume that more complex animals develop from simpler forms throughout the ages, as fossil history seems to show. But to understand the explanation you must know the history of the continent of Australia. Geologists say that Australia very long ago, in the era

UNIT NINE — THE HISTORY OF LIVING THINGS

33.21 An Australian koala, one of the many kinds of pouched mammals found in Australia. When it was born, the youngster was put into the mother's pouch. It has graduated to this method of transportation. *Nature Magazine*

when mammals first appeared, was connected with Asia, and Asia was connected with Europe. Then there came a time when Australia was cut off from the rest of the world and became an island. Now it is believed that the first mammals to appear were pouched forms. They, no doubt, spread all over Australia, Asia, and Europe since there were land connections. Later Australia was cut off by ocean barriers. After it had been cut off a new type of mammal, without a pouch, developed in Asia or Europe. This new type was better fitted to get along, and the pouched mammals died off. But these newer kinds of mammals could not spread to Australia. And the same kind of change did not happen to occur in Australia. Naturally, the pouched mammals (since they had no competition) throve in Australia and gave rise to more and more different kinds of pouched mammals.

What is true of pouched mammals is also true of many of the plants in Australia. Many are different and more primitive than those of the rest of the world.

Almost always where we find that the animals and plants of a certain region are peculiar, we find that this region has been cut off from neighboring regions for a very long time by natural barriers. This is true of many of the remote islands of the earth.

What have you learned? You can separate what you have learned into two parts.

(1) In the rocks of the earliest era no fossils have been found. Fossils of the simplest kinds of plants and animals are found in the rocks of the second era, and more and more complex fossils in succeeding eras. Fossils of the highest forms of animals, the vertebrates, and of the highest forms of plants, the flowering plants, appear only in the more recent rocks. This seems to show that animals and plants changed throughout the ages, simple forms producing more complex. The complex forms, then, are descended from the simpler forms; and all are related, some more, and others less closely. That is what is meant by the evolution of living things, or organic evolution. Fossils even show the evolution of a special kind of organism, such as the horse. Large numbers of intermediate fossil forms have been discovered between the modern horse and its ancestor *Eohippus*, which lived millions of years earlier. The history of fossils is clear evidence of organic evolution.

As fossils show that changes took place in animals and plants throughout the ages, experiments with living animals in the laboratory show that changes are still taking place, producing

CHAPTER THIRTY-THREE — FROM SIMPLE ORGANISMS TO COMPLEX

new kinds of organisms. Can you give examples of this?

(2) Using the idea of organic evolution, it is easy to account for the puzzling facts which troubled scientists for many, many years. Evolution explains quite naturally each of the following: the similarities in structure of some organisms; the similarities in development of embryos; the chemical similarities; the presence of vestigial structures; the reason that all plants and animals fall into the classification devised by Linnaeus; and the seemingly strange distribution of some of the plants and animals on the earth.

The idea that organic evolution occurred is evidently a tremendously important idea since it can explain so much about the living things of this earth. The idea grew slowly among scientists over a period of centuries.

USEFUL WORDS IN BIOLOGY

Paleozoic era
Cambrian period
Carboniferous period
trilobite
Mesozoic era
Cenozoic era
dinosaur
Eohippus
anatomy
vestigial organ

TEST YOURSELF

1. Describe the earth as it must have looked in each of the first three eras.
2. (a) What kinds of living things would you have found if you had visited the earth early in the Paleozoic era? (b) What was North America like at that time?
3. What name is given to (a) the early period in the Paleozoic in which trilobites were so common? (b) To the period at the end of the era?
4. In the 150 million years which elapsed between the early and the late periods of the Paleozoic, what changes occurred in living things?
5. Describe the Mesozoic era in its early periods and toward its end.
6. The "era of recent life" is interesting because of (a) the changes in the earth, (b) the changes in the climate of the earth, (c) the plants and animals inhabiting the earth. Describe all of these.
7. Think of the six eras from the oldest to the most recent and consider the plants and animals which flourished in each era. In general, how do the animals and plants of the later eras differ from those of earlier eras?
8. State in detail what is known about the fossil history of the horse.
9. Of what other animals do we have similar fossil series? What do all these series seem to show?
10. State in your own words, as though explaining to a friend, what is meant by the phrase "organic evolution."
11. You read in the last unit how plants and animals are seen to change in the laboratory and on the farm. Explain how plants and animals could change through the ages.
12. Vertebrate animals are much alike in their anatomy. How can this similarity be explained?
13. How do scientists explain the fact that embryos of all vertebrates are much alike?
14. (a) What is meant by a vestigial organ? (b) Give several examples of vestigial organs.
15. Copy these sentences, and supply the missing words. *Do not write in this book*. (a) Cats and lynxes have many characteristics in common; Linnaeus placed them in the same ——. (b) Cats and dogs have fewer similar characteristics. Linnaeus placed them in the same ——. (c) Animals as different as cats, dogs, horses, and men have even fewer characteristics in common. These are placed in the same ——.
16. (a) Note the animals named below. Which are placed in the same genus? (b) Which fit into the same order? (c) Which fit into the same class? (d) Which fit into the same subphylum? *cats men dogs horses lynxes birds frogs snakes*

17. (a) Explain how barriers affect distribution. (b) Give an example of how a barrier that was in existence very early in the era of recent life affected the distribution of pouched mammals.

18. What are some of the similarities in the chemical make-up of mammals? How do scientists account for these similarities?

DO IT YOURSELF

1. **Collecting pictures of early eras.** You can't go back in time to visit the earth in its early eras but you can build up a collection of pictures. Use pictures such as those from "The World We Live In," *Life*, September 7, October 19, November 30, 1953. Visit or write to the nearest natural history museum to find out what pictures are available.

2. **Bringing the early animals and plants to life.** Those of you who have artistic ability could form a committee to make two things for the class: (1) A mural around the room showing the characteristic animals and plants in each of the eras or important periods, like those shown in Figures 33.3 and 33.5. Perhaps those students who cannot help with the drawing or painting could help with the research. This is a large project. (2) Models of prehistoric animals; soap, Plasticine, or clay might be used.

3. **A tree of life.** Another committee might make a large wall chart, showing the eras and important periods by means of parallel lines. The names of the animals and plants living in each era could be shown by drawings and neat printing. You will find that *Man and the Animal World* by B. R. Weimer, Wiley, 1951, has a good diagram on page 496. A "tree of life" diagram could be drawn on a large chart. Many college zoology, botany, and biology textbooks show animal and plant relationships by means of a "tree" diagram.

ADVENTURES IN READING

1. *Dinosaur Book* by Edwin H. Colbert, McGraw-Hill, 1951. This can also be obtained from the American Museum of Natural History, New York 24. This is a "must" for those interested in dinosaurs. The pictures alone give you much information.

2. Leaflets and booklets published by the Chicago Natural History Museum, Chicago, Illinois, and the American Museum of Natural History, New York 24.

3. *The Book of Prehistoric Animals* by R. L. Ditmars and H. Carter, Lippincott, 1935. Although out of print you might find it in a library. Much information given by an expert.

4. *Life of the Past* by George Gaylord Simpson, Yale University, 1953. Recommended to the somewhat more ambitious students.

Chapter 34
Theories to explain change

An important theory. The idea that living things arose from living things that preceded them was not a new idea in 1859 when Charles R. Darwin (1809–1882), an English scientist, wrote *On the Origin of Species by Means of Natural Selection*. Scientists had been thinking about it for centuries. But Darwin had given so many years of study and thought to the subject and he was able to give so many facts as evidence for his beliefs that the book created a tremendous stir. A great intellectual battle was waged before biologists and other people accepted Darwin's theory of how new species originate. *On the Origin of Species* is not an easy book to read; it is crowded with facts.

As a young man Charles Darwin was invited to join a surveying expedition around the world. They set sail in 1831 on the *Beagle*. Darwin, as the naturalist, was supposed to collect plants and animals in oceans and on land. For five years he collected and observed. He collected living specimens and some fossils, too. He observed where and how plants and animals lived, and he kept the fullest kinds of notes. By the time he returned to England he believed, as the result of all his observations, that plants and animals had changed throughout the ages. You had much of this evidence reviewed for you in the last chapter but Darwin lived before most of the fossil evidence had been discovered. But in spite of this, the longer he studied the more firmly did he believe in organic evolution. Then he formulated a theory to explain how evolution could occur. He called it the theory of **natural selection.**

Darwin and Wallace. When Darwin was about to publish his book on the origin of species, he received a report from another scientist, Alfred Russell Wallace, who had been studying animals in the East Indies. In this report Wallace presented the very ideas that Darwin had been turning over in his mind for almost thirty years: first, that the different species of plants and animals arise by evolution; and second, that evolution takes place by the method which Darwin spoke of as natural selection.

With characteristic fairness and generosity, Darwin was at first inclined to publish Wallace's report and say nothing of his own conclusions. Finally, he was persuaded not to do this and both men agreed to present their conclusions at the same time. Wallace, very generously, always gave Darwin credit for the theory because Darwin had studied the problem so much more thoroughly.

Natural selection. Darwin suggested five steps to explain how organisms changed throughout the ages, producing new species. These are the steps.
(1) *Overproduction.* If a microscopic one-celled animal like *Paramecium* divided twice a day for only a few months it would produce a ball of paramecia as big as the earth. A fish like the cod lays about 8,000,000 eggs every year. The descendants of

that cod, in a few years, would fill the oceans from shore to shore with codfish. And so with all other kinds of animals and plants. See Figure 34.1. Each kind of animal and plant produces offspring at so fast a rate that if all lived and reproduced there would not be standing room on the earth for the individuals of even one species!

(2) *Struggle for existence.* Evidently there is not food enough or room enough for all the offspring of plants and animals. Most of them must die before growing up. If the number of codfish in the ocean remains about the same, it means that only two of the 8,000,000 eggs result in mature codfish and 7,999,998 of that family die before they can reproduce. Darwin believed that overproduction leads to a **struggle for existence** among plants and animals. Under ordinary circumstances, the more offspring produced, the keener is the struggle. It is a struggle that goes on steadily between members of the same species and between members of different species.

(3) *Variation.* Which of these many organisms will survive? Darwin answered this question by pointing out that all the members of a species are different in many small ways. You know that this is true; you even know the causes of such variations. They may be caused by the environment or by constant recombinations of genes or by gene and chromosomal changes that are passed on to the next generation. But remember that Darwin knew nothing about chromosomes or genes. But he did know that no two individuals are exactly alike. See Figure 34.2.

(4) *Survival of the fittest.* Since there are always variations among the members of a species, Darwin argued, some will be more fit to meet existing conditions, some less fit. In general, those organisms that are more fit will survive

34.1 A puffball is related to the mushrooms. It cracks open and discharges its spores. It has been calculated that a large puffball may contain 6,000,000,000 spores. *Clarke*

and the others will die. It is clear that the word **fittest** does not mean the strongest; it means the organism that fits into the whole environment best at that particular time.

(5) *Inheritance of variations.* Evidently, if a new species is to arise, the variation which happens to make one organism more fit than its competitors must be passed on to its offspring. The horse could not have evolved from *Eohippus* through natural selection unless there had been inheritance of variations.

Now Darwin lived too early to know that there are very different kinds of variations — that some kinds could, and other kinds could not, be

34.2 Countless thousands of daisy seeds fell in this field. Many thousands of these grew into daisy plants, as you can see. In which ways may these have been better fitted for survival than those that failed to grow? *American Museum of Natural History*

inherited. He assumed that the variations with which he was so familiar could be inherited. This was a weakness in his theory; he, himself, was aware of this weakness.

De Vries. The theory of how evolution can occur was improved by Hugo De Vries (1848–1935), a Dutch biologist. In 1901 De Vries published a book on evolution telling the results of experiments with the evening primrose (*Oenothera Lamarckiana*). In breeding evening primroses, De Vries had observed that new types occasionally appeared. These new types seemed not to be caused by the environment. See Figure 34.3. And when he crossed these plants, the new characters appeared in the offspring. He called these sudden changes in character "mutations." This was the first use of the word, used several years before anything was known about genes.

De Vries believed that his discovery of what he called mutations made it possible to accept the theory of natural selection. He could now explain how new species could arise. De Vries' theory came to be known as the **Mutation Theory of Evolution.** It includes these steps: overproduction, struggle for existence, mutation, survival of the fittest, inheritance of mutations. See Figures 34.4 and 34.5.

Most biologists today accept the theory of natural selection as modified by De Vries. There are still many unsolved problems, however, about many of the details of natural selection and even about the importance of the various factors that Darwin listed.

Lamarck. Darwin was not the first to propose the idea that new species came from preceding species by descent. In 1809, some sixty years before Darwin presented his theory, Lamarck published a book in which he suggested that new species arose from earlier forms, and he stated how he believed this might happen. His theory is known as the theory of **Use and Disuse.** People who have not studied biology often accept this theory because it seems so simple and natural.

Lamarck pointed out that when an organ is used it tends to grow larger or stronger or more efficient. When an organ is not used, it tends to grow smaller or weaker or less efficient. Then, said Lamarck, when this organ-

490 UNIT NINE — THE HISTORY OF LIVING THINGS

34.3 The evening primrose (left) and one of its mutants. What do you notice about the flowers and the leaves of the mutant? *B. M. Davis*

34.4 The okapi (a relative of the giraffe) eats the leaves on the lower branches of trees in the forest. Note its short neck. *American Museum of Natural History*

34.5 The giraffe eats leaves from higher branches of trees. How might De Vries have explained the origin of the giraffe's long neck? *American Museum of Natural History*

CHAPTER THIRTY-FOUR — THEORIES TO EXPLAIN CHANGE 491

34.6 Spruce grouse on the ground. Of what advantage are the mottled brown markings? *American Museum of Natural History*

34.8 This insect is called the walking stick. Why? Can you see how its structure helps it to hide from its enemies? *Schneider and Schwartz*

34.7 Find the geometrid moth caterpillar in the photograph. It is the color of a twig. It holds itself at this angle all day. It moves and feeds at night. Of what advantage is this to the caterpillar? *American Museum of Natural History*

ism produces offspring, there would be a tendency for a similar slight change to be inherited. If this continued in each generation, he argued, the changes would, in time, produce an animal or plant quite different from the original form. Thus new types of animals and plants would arise.

Now the only difficulty with this theory is that it assumes that acquired characters — those that are caused by changes in the environment and through use and disuse of an organ — are inherited. As you have learned there is no clear evidence that acquired characters can be inherited. For this reason biologists, in general, believe that Lamarck's theory cannot explain how new species of living things can arise.

Adaptations. The most difficult fact that any theory of evolution must explain is the astonishing adaptations that some organisms show. Examples of three remarkable adaptations which make the animal difficult to see in its natural surroundings are shown in Figures 34.6, 34.7, and 34.8. We speak of such adaptations as cases of **protective resemblance.** Other animals have special structures which fit them to their environment in different ways.

34.9 An ichneumon fly deposited eggs in the body of this caterpillar. The young fed on the caterpillar and now they have formed these white cocoons. Many insects have remarkable adaptations. *American Museum of Natural History*

The ichneumon fly can place its eggs in the body of a caterpillar buried an inch deep in wood because it has a long and very strong ovipositor or egg-laying organ. How did this ovipositor happen to develop? There are countless remarkable adaptations in the animal world.

Many plants, likewise, have adaptations useful to them. Cactus plants living in the desert have a thick epidermis and a thick cuticle that help prevent loss of water. Mistletoe has a rootlike structure that grows through the bark of trees, enabling it to get water and minerals. Most lichens are adapted to remain alive, even though they may become so dry they can be crushed to a powder.

The best explanation that the mutation theory can offer of these and a host of other remarkable adaptations is that chance mutations occurred which made the mutants especially well fitted to get along in their environment.

What have you learned? You have learned that the various kinds of living things seem to be related to one another through common ancestors, starting far back in geologic time. This means that new species of animals and plants arose from preceding species. We know of much evidence that this has been happening ever since animals and plants first existed on the earth, and it is still happening.

Biologists are not in complete agreement about how evolution could occur. Darwin's theory of how species originate was modified by De Vries; in that form it is rather generally accepted. Can you give the five steps of this theory? And can you explain the possible origin of some particular animal or plant species by means of these five steps?

USEFUL WORDS IN BIOLOGY

natural selection
overproduction
struggle for existence
survival of the fittest
adaptation
protective resemblance
mimicry

TEST YOURSELF

1. Charles Darwin is a name you have heard before. (a) What is the name of his most famous book? (b) About when was it written? (c) What ideas did he present in this book?

CHAPTER THIRTY-FOUR — THEORIES TO EXPLAIN CHANGE

(d) How was he prepared for writing it?
2. What name did Darwin give to his theory of how change could occur?
3. Tell briefly the story of Darwin and Wallace.
4. Name the five steps in Darwin's theory of natural selection.
5. To show that you understand the meaning of each of Darwin's steps explain how the modern horse could have developed from Eohippus, or how a giraffe could have developed from a short-necked animal like an okapi.
6. (a) What discovery by De Vries strengthened Darwin's theory? (b) Name the five steps in the theory as modified by De Vries.
7. Explain Lamarck's theory of how new species could arise.
8. In view of what biologists have learned since Lamarck's time, state the objections to Lamarck's theory.
9. Describe examples of protective resemblance in animals and some other adaptations.

DO IT YOURSELF

1. **A study of overproduction in plants.** Do some calculating on your own of the rate at which living things overproduce. If daisies are available (wild or cultivated) count the number of seeds produced by a single flower head. Assume that each seed could produce a plant with one flower head having as many seeds as just counted. Assume the process would be repeated for five years. How many daisy plants would you have? Of course each plant bears many flower heads; your estimate, therefore, is far too small. Now look again at the picture of the daisy field in the text. Can you imagine the number of daisy plants produced after five years from this field of daisies! If daisies are not available, use some other flower for your calculations, perhaps a dandelion, a hawkweed, or any other. You will enjoy looking into *Seed Time and Harvest* by Sir Edward Salisbury, pages 300–304, to read his calculations.

2. **Overproduction in animals.** You can use frogs for this study or better still buy roe in the fish market. Roe is the mass of eggs enclosed in the membrane of the ovary. Find out whether the roe you buy is the eggs in one ovary or in both. In order to count, divide the egg mass in half and continue subdividing each into two parts until you have $\frac{1}{16}$ or $\frac{1}{32}$ or $\frac{1}{64}$ of the entire mass. If you have scales you can subdivide by weight. Then actually count the eggs in one small portion, such as $\frac{1}{64}$, and multiply that number by 64 to arrive at a total. Calculate the number of fish of this species that there would be in five generations if every egg developed and if each *pair* of fish reproduced just once. In connection with overproduction you will be interested in reading in the *World Almanac* or *Information Please Almanac* how many herring are caught each year by man alone.

3. **How can you see the results of change in organisms?** Look at your *Field Book of Wild Flowers* and count the species of violets in the genus Viola. Then go out to find some of these many species, and describe the differences. Can you explain how these differences may have arisen?

ADVENTURES IN READING

1. *Charles Darwin* by Ruth Moore, Knopf, 1955. Tells about much of Darwin's scientific work. Very readable and interesting.
2. *Charles Darwin, and the voyage of the Beagle* (unpublished letters and notebooks edited by Lady Barlow, Darwin's granddaughter), Philosophical Library, 1949. Gives you a good idea both of the man and the voyage from which he learned so much.
3. "Evolution Observed" by Francis J. Ryan, *Scientific American*, October 1953. Yes, the author observed evolution with his own eyes! A simple organism has more generations in two years than man has in a million years.
4. "The Land of the Sun" by Lincoln Barnett, *Life*, April 5, 1954. Would you like to read more about adaptations?
5. "Mimicry and Other Protective Devices" by Alfred Russell Wallace in *The Book of Naturalists* edited by William Beebe, Knopf, 1948. The title speaks for itself.

Chapter 35

History of man

Man's beginnings. Biologists think of present-day man (HOMO SAPIENS) as a newcomer on this earth. Evidence from fossils has led them to this conclusion. Primitive men existed perhaps a million years earlier. Scientists disagree about the exact length of time. Some would put the first prehistoric men as far back as two million years; others believe that he appeared less than a million years ago. Let us think of the time as about one million years. In that case man himself, *Homo sapiens*, in all probability appeared sometime between 50,000 and 35,000 years ago. Look at the clock in Figure 35.1. This shows how recent, relatively speaking, was our arrival. If the first prehistoric men appeared when the hour hand stood at noon, modern man arrived when the hour hand was almost at 12 midnight — at about twenty-six minutes before midnight. And all our written history, which seems so long in the history books, is crowded into the last three or four minutes. All the peoples of the earliest civilizations of which we have written records, such people as the Sumerians and Egyptians, were members of the species *Homo sapiens*, the species of which you and I are examples.

Learning about prehistoric men. How can we learn about prehistoric men who lived long before written records were kept? By fossils, of course. Unfortunately, only a few fossils of the very earliest men have been found. But enough teeth, bones of the jaw and of the top of the skull, leg bones,

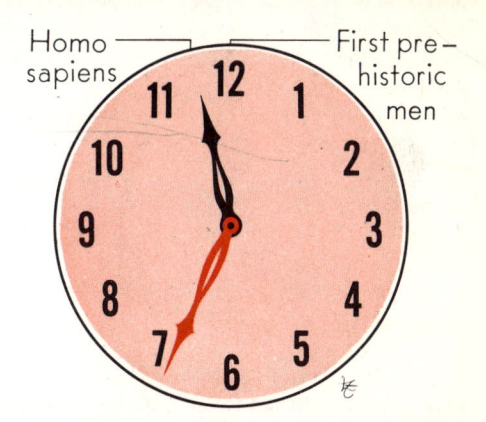

35.1 The hour hand is shown in black. If the first prehistoric man appeared at 12 noon on this clock (1,000,000 years ago), exactly when did *Homo sapiens* arrive?

and occasional other bones have been found to give us an idea of how some prehistoric men must have looked. We know about how tall they were, about how they must have held themselves and walked, and in a general way what their faces looked like.

A great deal has been learned about prehistoric men, also, from the tools and other articles they left behind them. All such tools and implements are called **artifacts.** Figure 35.2 shows some artifacts from different ages. Sometimes the fossil bones and the artifacts are found together. Then we can get a fairly complete picture of how these men must have lived. In some places, especially in caves, the bones of other animals have been found together with the fossils and the artifacts of primitive men. Thus we can make a good guess at what these men ate. Furthermore, if charcoal or charred bones are found, we may

CHAPTER THIRTY-FIVE — THE HISTORY OF MAN

Old Stone Age
Paleolithic

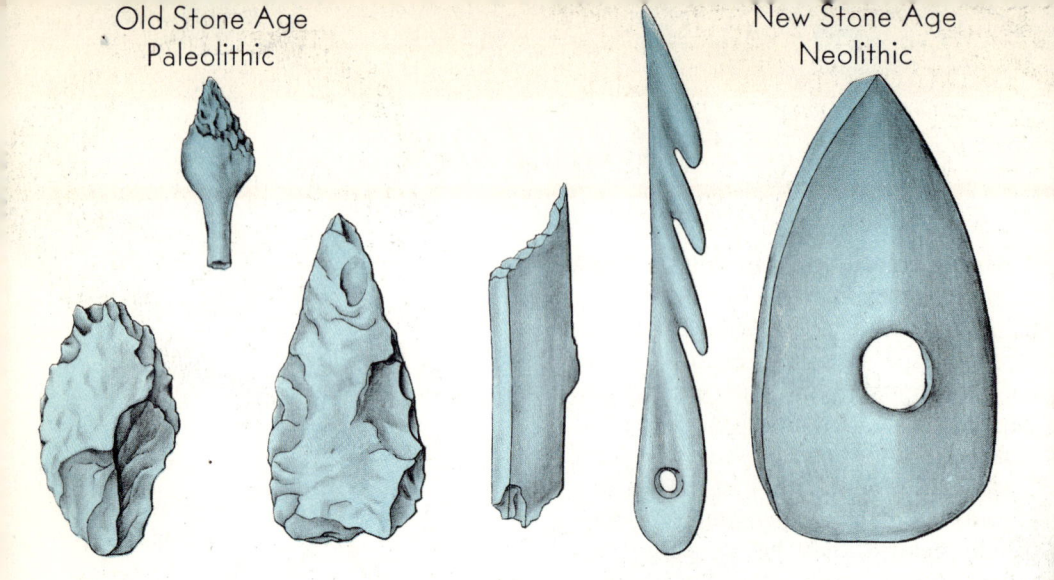

New Stone Age
Neolithic

35.2 Some artifacts found with fossil bones. How do the tools and weapons on the left differ from those on the right? Which were made by men of the greater skill?

assume that these men knew the use of fire.

The date, or "how long ago," is of much importance in a study of human fossils and artifacts. During the last few years thousands of fossils and artifacts have been dated by analyzing the percentage of carbon 14 (C_{14}) in them. C_{14} changes to C_{12} (ordinary carbon) at a regular rate, so that the older an object is, the less C_{14} it contains. Obviously, the method can be used only on materials that contain carbon — wood, bone, shells, etc. It is useful only in dating objects less than fifty thousand years old.

Careful detective work like this helps us to get an idea of the **culture** of primitive and prehistoric men who have long since disappeared from the earth. By the word "culture," applied to a group of men, we mean how they live, what they do, and how they think. Studying the cultures of early men is as interesting and as important as the study of their bones. The scientists who study man and his culture are called **anthropologists** (an-throw-poll'-o-jists).

Early prehistoric man. One of the earliest prehistoric men that we know about has been called the Java man (PITHECANTHROPUS ERECTUS — pith-e-can-throw'pus). The fossil bones, found on the island of Java, indicate that these early men lived at least half a million years ago. According to some estimates it may have been a million years ago. Parts of the bones of several individuals have been found and studied. They seem to show that the Java man was about five and a half feet tall. He was named *erectus* because it is believed that he walked upright. The pieces of skull bone show that his brain was smaller than our brain. Since no artifacts have been found with the bones, we know nothing of his culture.

Peking man (SINANTHROPUS PEKINENSIS — sin-an-throw'pus) is another

496   UNIT NINE — THE HISTORY OF LIVING THINGS

35.3 Excavating for Peking man near Peiping (Peking), China. Why are the squares drawn on the side? *Rockefeller Foundation*

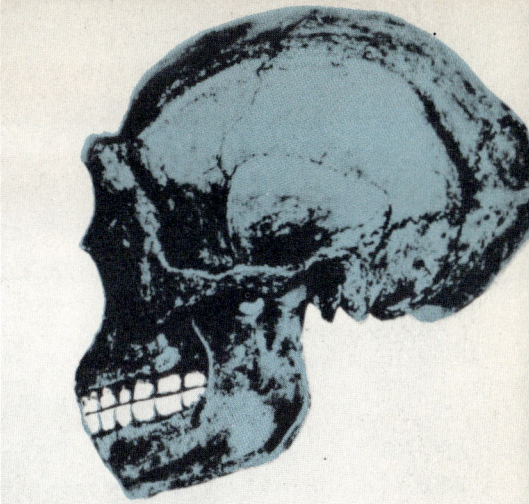

35.4 Skull of Peking man. Note the heavy eye ridges and lack of chin. *Rockefeller Foundation*

prehistoric man supposed to have lived about half a million years ago. In caves near Peiping (Peking), China, anthropologists have found hundreds of fossils of Peking man, including bones from at least forty different individuals. Figure 35.3 shows an expedition digging for fossils of Peking man and Figure 35.4 shows one of the skulls that was found. The fossils indicate that in many ways Peking man was like Java man; he certainly walked upright, but he was somewhat shorter than Java man and had a larger brain. Judging from the structure of the inside of the skull, the part of the brain used in speech was well developed; anthropologists reason that Peking man could speak some kind of language. The culture of Peking man was surprisingly advanced. Near the bones in the floors of caves heavy tools and smaller scraping tools of stone have been found. The tools are crude, but they are undoubtedly tools that were made to be used for a special purpose. Some evidence leads us to believe that Peking men were cannibals and that they knew the use of fire. We have reason to believe that Peking men existed over a long period of time and that the fossils and artifacts just described belonged to men well along in their development. It may well be that the ancestors of Peking men were among the earliest of primitive men, earlier even than Java man.

Neandertal man. Neandertal (Nee-an'der-tall) men came much later than the primitive Java ape men and Peking men. Neandertal men lived as recently as 150,000 years ago. See Figure 35.5, and notice that Neandertal men came after Java and Peking men are believed to have died out. Neandertal is classified in our own genus *Homo* (HOMO NEANDERTALENSIS). So many, many skulls, other bones, even complete skeletons, have been found that we

CHAPTER THIRTY-FIVE — THE HISTORY OF MAN 497

JAVA MAN

PEKING MAN

NEANDERTAL MAN

MODERN MAN

1,000,000 YEARS AGO   500,000 YEARS AGO   TODAY

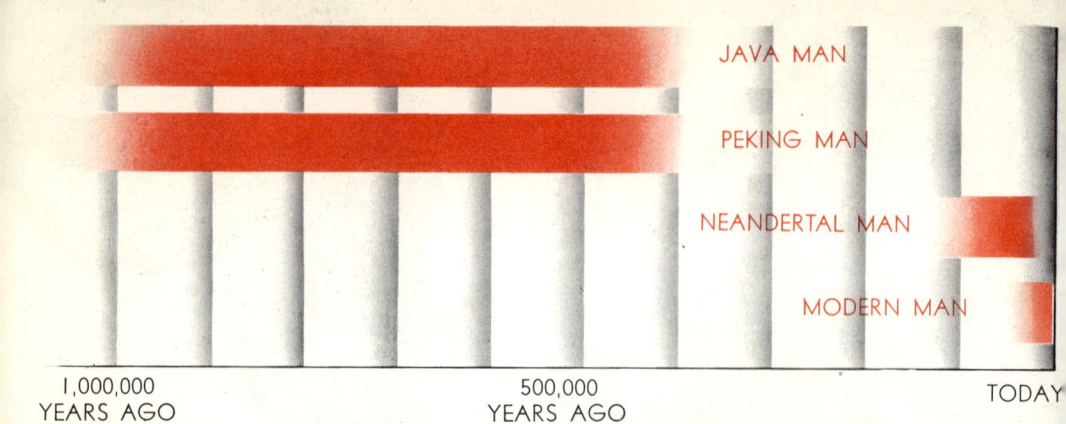

35.5 The graph shows when anthropologists think some prehistoric men lived and when modern man began. The dates are very uncertain. Do you know why?

know a great deal about the structure of Neandertal men. See Figure 35.6 which shows a model of his head beside the model of the Java man's head. These men rarely reached a stature of more than five and a half feet. They had broad frames with large muscles, big heads, and short arms and legs. Their knees were bent a little, so that it is believed they must have walked with a shuffling gait, and they evidently stooped at the shoulders. Their faces were quite different from those of modern men. They had low foreheads, projecting eye ridges, heavy jaws, and large noses separating deeply sunk eyes. Their brains were large in proportion to their size, somewhat larger than our brains. But the small frontal lobe makes us think they were less intelligent than modern men.

Neandertal men lived in Europe and Western Asia for 75,000 or 100,000 years. Fossils have been found in many parts of the world — in Germany, Belgium, France, Russia, Yugoslavia, Palestine, and other places. The varying locations show that there were times when these men roamed about, perhaps during the warm period between the third and fourth ice ages. Figure 35.7 shows these men in action. No doubt, when the most recent ice age began, they must have lived in caves. They survived this difficult environment and developed a rather advanced culture. They were able to fashion a variety of flint tools. When they chipped flint, they used the flakes, making them into small tools that could be used for cutting, drilling, boring, and scraping. They not only used fire but they probably had learned to make fire. And what seem to be burial places have been found in their

35.6 Prof. J. H. McGregor painstakingly modeled these heads of Java and Neandertal man, by studying available bones. What differences do you note in these skulls? Which looks more like modern man? *American Museum of Natural History*

35.7 Some scientists believe that toward the end of Neandertal man's development he used spears tipped with flint. He was perhaps not so well formed or equipped as this artist has shown him. How long ago did Neandertal man live? *Logan Museum, Beloit College*

caves, showing probably a remarkable advance over earlier prehistoric men. These burial places indicate that the Neandertals may have had some special beliefs or thoughts about death.

Neandertal men seem to have disappeared from the earth about 25,000 years ago. It is not known whether they became extinct at this time or whether they were at least partly absorbed by modern man, *Homo sapiens*, who appeared in Europe somewhat earlier.

Modern man — HOMO SAPIENS. How do we decide that a fossil man is a member of our own species and not one of the primitive men we have just described? By comparing the fossil bones with the bones of men of today. Chiefly the structure of the head is used in comparisons. The skull of *Homo sapiens* differs from that of all other species in having much thinner walls and a much more rounded, or vaulted, form. The bones of the face show that the features are far more delicate.

The large eye ridges of more primitive men are absent in the skulls of *Homo sapiens* and the chin is better developed. The body is held upright and straight.

Most anthropologists think that modern man, our own species, originated in Asia, although many fossils of modern man have been found in many parts of the world. They believe that over a period of years, thousands perhaps, modern men gradually replaced Neandertal men. Thus, eventually, there remained only one species of man, *Homo sapiens*. The various races that we know today developed from that one species.

There were many types of *Homo sapiens* at the time he replaced Neandertal but the type that has attracted most attention was Cro-Magnon man, who lived in caves in what is now southern France and Spain during the last ice age, about 25,000 years ago. These men were tall, almost six feet tall, with well-proportioned bodies and regular features, as you can see in Figure 35.8. This figure also shows Cro-

CHAPTER THIRTY-FIVE — THE HISTORY OF MAN   499

35.8 Using available facts, an artist made this painting of Cro-Magnon life in a cave. One man is sculpturing on a wall. *Logan Museum, Beloit College*

Magnon man decorating the walls with paintings or sculptures of animals. It is because of these paintings that Cro-Magnon man is well known.

Life 25,000 years ago. A great deal has been learned about Cro-Magnon and the other early modern men from the large number of artifacts and from the bones of animals found with the human fossils. It is clear that these men lived in groups, either occasionally or regularly. In one spot in southern Europe the remains of 100,000 horses and 35,000 flint implements were found. In Moravia in the Balkan peninsula, the site of an ancient village was uncovered. Here were found the remains of living quarters of about 25,000 years ago — fireplaces in front of what must once have been houses of some sort. There was a large workshop and huge refuse pits containing the bones of mammoths, horses, and reindeer. Countless artifacts were unearthed, including household utensils such as spoons and two-pronged forks.

There is evidence that as the glaciers began to retreat and the summers became warmer these modern men lived in the open, hunting and moving about. They apparently went back to the caves in the winter. The earliest remains of modern men are associated with fossils of the woolly rhinoceros and mammoth, animals that existed when Neandertal men lived in these regions. Then in higher levels the remains of horses, bison, and deerlike animals are found. But there is no evidence that the horse was tamed.

These early modern men apparently knew how to handle fire and use it for light. Pots have been found, and hollows in the floors of caves suggest that these men knew how to cook by dropping hot stones into water, as some American Indians did. Not only did Cro-Magnon men make weapons and tools of chipped flint but they worked with new materials, bone and ivory. About twenty-five thousand years ago these ancestors of ours could fashion darts and pointed instruments,

UNIT NINE — THE HISTORY OF LIVING THINGS

like awls and large sewing needles. We believe that they sewed skins and made substantial clothing. They were obviously expert hunters and fishermen, so that they must have been able to get plenty of food even when the weather was cold.

A plentiful supply of food produced leisure; with this came artistic activities of various kinds. You read above of the paintings made by Cro-Magnon man. They were done in beautiful colors, still visible, and they were drawn so well that the species of animals are easily recognizable, as you can see in Figure 35.9. Among the artifacts have been found beads and other personal adornments of ivory and bone. Of course, we do not know whether all this was done for purely artistic reasons or to satisfy a belief in magic.

It is clear that even as long as 25,000 years ago modern men had developed many skills and had moved far in the direction of controlling their environment.

The history of civilization. Scientists have divided the history of civilization into a few great periods. The first of these is called the **Old Stone Age (Paleolithic Age** — pay-lee-oh-lith′ik). It lasted a long time, almost a million years, ending about 10,000 years ago. The cultures of Java, Peking, Neandertal, and even early modern men belong in what we now call the Old Stone Age. In the Old Stone Age, tools and other implements of chipped flint were used. They were crude at first, for even chipping off flakes of flint requires great skill. People lived largely in caves and there was little, if any, cultivation of plants and domestication of animals. The dog seems to have been the first animal domesticated, perhaps toward the close of this age.

35.9 Drawing found in a cave in Spain. What does this show about the culture of Cro-Magnon men? *American Museum of Natural History*

The **New Stone Age (Neolithic Age** — nee-oh-lith′ik), is the period in which stone implements were produced by grinding. With such improved tools, wooden shelters, crude boats, and farming implements were made. In this age plants were very generally cultivated and animals domesticated. With agriculture came a settled community life. There are indications, too, that in this age people definitely held religious beliefs. The New Stone Age began after the end of the latest glacial period.

Then about 6000 years ago men learned how to get copper from its ores and to cast it into tools. At about the same time came similar discoveries for tin. And about a thousand years later came the discovery that copper and tin could be combined to make a much harder metal, bronze. And so we have the **Age of Bronze,** with the beginnings of a new and much more advanced culture.

The next step, the one that led directly to our own age, came about 3500 years ago when men learned how to smelt iron. This was the beginning of the **Iron Age,** which led in time to the **Age of Steam,** then the **Age of Electricity,** and now, of course, the **Atomic Age.** Most peoples have traveled far in these 3500 years. But, of

CHAPTER THIRTY-FIVE — THE HISTORY OF MAN

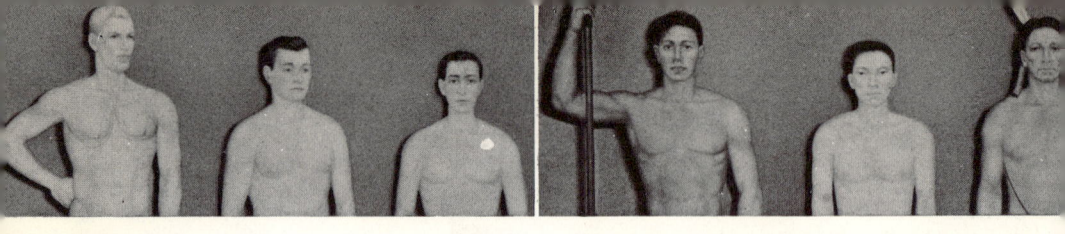

35.10 By making use of thousands of measurements, Dr. H. L. Shapiro has been able to construct figures illustrating some of the races of the three great stocks of mankind. At the left is the Caucasoid stock with three of its races: the Nordic, Alpine, and Mediterranean. The Mongoloid stock is next, showing the Polynesian, Mongolian, and American Indian. At the right is the Negroid stock: the African Forest Negro, the Bushman

course, around the world peoples live in cultures at various levels, some as low as the Neolithic.

The races of men. All of us belong to the species of *Homo sapiens*, but we don't all belong to the same race. There are many races; in fact, there are so many that anthropologists classify human beings into three large groups, or stocks. Then these stocks are further subdivided into the races of which we commonly hear. Not all anthropologists use the same classification, but the one given in the table is one that is frequently accepted. The table gives the three main stocks, the "white," the "yellow," and the "black," and the major races into which each is divided. Note carefully the physical characteristics on which the classification is based.

But in examining this table with its many races there is one very important fact that must not be forgotten. These many races belong to the same species, *Homo sapiens*. We all belong to one species; we are basically alike. This similarity is deep-seated. It goes beyond outward appearance. Our in-

RACIAL CLASSIFICATION OF MAN*

Stocks and Races†	Texture of Hair on Head	Head	Stature
Caucasoid ("White")			
Nordic	Wavy	Narrow	Tall
Alpine	Wavy	Broad	Above average
Mediterranean	Wavy	Narrow	Medium
Hindu	Wavy	Narrow	Above average
Mongoloid ("Yellow")			
Mongolian	Straight	Broad	Below average
Malaysian	Straight	Broad	Below average
American Indian	Straight	Variable	Tall to medium
Negroid ("Black")			
Negro	Woolly	Narrow	Tall
Melanesian	Woolly	Narrow	Medium
Pygmy Black	Woolly	Broadish	Very short
Bushman	Peppercorn	Narrow	Very short
Of Doubtful Classification			
Polynesian	Wavy	Variable	Tall
Australoid	Wavy	Narrow	Medium

* A few minor races of doubtful classification have been omitted.
† Adapted from Kroeber's *Anthropology*, Harcourt, Brace and Company (1948).

502 UNIT NINE — THE HISTORY OF LIVING THINGS

(Black), and the Australian. Note that this anthropologist makes slightly different subdivisions of the Mongoloid and Negroid stocks from those given in the table. *Shapiro, American Museum of Natural History*

ternal organs are the same; our blood is the same, down to the very blood groups of which you have learned. The percentages of the various blood groups among different peoples vary somewhat; but a Group A Mongolian can give blood to a Group A Nordic as safely as he can give blood to another Group A Mongolian or to a person of any other race.

Variations within a race. Figure 35.10 shows what the major races look like in general. But, of course, not all people of one race are alike in all their characteristics. In Figure 35.10 the average or typical individual is shown. The anthropologist who made the picture has purposely chosen as a representative of the Nordic race, for example, a man who shows most strikingly all the Nordic characteristics, a man who is tall and broad with blond hair and blue eyes and who has many of the other traits characteristic of a Nordic. But remember that to be classified as a Nordic a man need not have all the characteristics of a Nordic, but only a majority of them. Nordics vary all the way from tall to short; some are smaller than some Alpines and others are darker than some Alpines. Yet in the majority of their characteristics they are Nordic.

Of course, some of the variability of men, perhaps much of it, is the result of intermarriage among peoples. This has gone on for thousands of years all over the world. It has increased variability in physical characteristics and made it difficult for anthropologists to classify races.

Common errors about race. Some people speak of the "white race" when they really mean the Caucasoid stock. There are four white races, as the table shows. Some people also speak of the "Italian race" or the "Aryan race" or the "Jewish race." The Italians are not a race; they are a national group composed of many races. The people who belong to the Italian nation may have white or black skins and straight or wavy hair. This is true of all national groups. It is true that in some nations the majority of the people are of one racial group. Most Swedes, for instance, are Nordics. But, although in Sweden the proportion of Nordics to people of other races happens to be large, by no means all Swedes are Nordics. In China, too, most of the people, but not all, are clearly of the Mongoloid stock.

When people speak of the "Jewish race," however, they are confusing religious groups or cultural groups with races. Remember that races are classified by the anthropologist for scientific convenience on the basis of such traits as shape of head, stature, texture of hair, and so on.

And there is, of course, no Aryan race. Aryan refers to a group of languages — the group to which, among others, English and German belong. All people whose native tongue is English or German are, therefore, Aryans.

Race superiority. Stocks and races differ. However, we have no evidence that one stock or race is superior

CHAPTER THIRTY-FIVE — THE HISTORY OF MAN

or inferior to another. Each race or stock is more primitive — like ancient man — than some other race or stock in one characteristic and less primitive in some other characteristic. Among cultures, however, some are far more advanced than others. Cultures differ from each other more widely than races do. If, then, a race is associated with a culture, the race may seem to be inferior or superior. Actually, a great deal of evidence shows that races with less advanced cultures quickly learn the knowledges and skills of more advanced cultures when the opportunity arises. Naturally, a person of one culture is at a great disadvantage, at first, when placed in a foreign culture. This would give a false impression that he is inferior. One of the great advantages of differences among cultures and races is that each race can make its own important contributions to the advancement of civilization.

What have you learned? We have hurried through a long story of the development of man from the earliest prehistoric men to the races of men who live on our earth today. You learned first about Java and Peking men who lived at least a half million, possibly a million, years ago. So many fossils have been found of Peking man that scientists have a rather clear idea of how he must have looked. And the artifacts found with the bones give some idea of his culture, or how he lived.

Then came Neandertal men, men so much like modern men that they can be put into the genus *Homo*, although they belong to a different species within this genus. Their fossils have been found in many parts of the earth, showing that they had spread far. Neandertal men lived for about 100,000 years, into the fourth, or last, ice age, disappearing about 25,000 years ago.

All these men lived in what we call the Old Stone Age. Probably a short time before Neandertal men disappeared, *Homo sapiens* appeared. Of this species, Cro-Magnon man, who lived in southern France and Spain, is the one you hear most about. The first of these modern men may still have belonged to the Old Stone Age, but gradually they were making better tools. Crude dwellings and boats were built. This was the beginning of the New Stone Age in which civilization advanced rapidly. In quick succession, starting about six thousand years ago, came the age of metal: Bronze and Iron. This brings us to modern times.

Today we have a world that has grown small because of modern transportation and communication. It is inhabited by three great stocks of peoples, the Caucasoid, the Mongoloid, and the Negroid. These stocks include the varied races of men. Though differing in certain physical characteristics which are easily observed, the men of these many races are basically alike. All the races include the same blood types, for example, making safe transfusions between people of different stocks. But the cultures developed by the different races differ. Each of the varied races, therefore, has abilities and talents useful for the advancement of mankind.

USEFUL WORDS IN BIOLOGY

Homo sapiens	Neandertal man	Caucasoid
artifacts	Cro-Magnon man	Mongoloid
culture		Negroid
anthropologist	race	Nordic
Java ape man	Old Stone Age	Alpine
Peking man	New Stone Age	

TEST YOURSELF

1. (a) About how long ago did manlike forms appear? (b) About how long ago did modern man, *Homo sapiens*, appear?
2. Explain what anthropologists mean by culture and how they learn about the culture of prehistoric man.
3. Tell all you know about two early manlike forms: the Java ape man and Peking man.
4. Tell about Neandertal man: (a) his scientific name, (b) how he probably looked, (c) when he lived, (d) where he lived, (e) what changes were occurring on the earth at the time he lived, (f) what is known of his culture.
5. *Homo sapiens* is thought to have replaced Neandertal man 25,000 years ago. Describe what we believe life was like at that time.
6. Explain what skills enabled man to move from the Old Stone Age into the New Stone Age and then into the Age of Bronze.
7. Describe the advances that were made possible by the fashioning of better tools.
8. Anthropologists often classify man into three main stocks. (a) What are they? (b) What are the races within each stock?
9. For convenience, men are classified on the basis of what physical characteristics?
10. Copy into your notes those of the following statements that are true; omit those that are not true. (a) Not all people of one race are alike in all their characteristics. (b) Some Alpines are taller than some Nordics. (c) The people who belong to the Aryan race are tall and blond. (d) Some cultures of the present day are more advanced than others. (e) Races with less advanced cultures are known to be inferior, or less intelligent.

DO IT YOURSELF

1. **A visit to a museum.** If you live near a museum turn into an anthropologist for a while. You will find it a fascinating study. Inquire for exhibits of skulls and other bones of prehistoric men, and for artifacts found with these bones. Look at exhibits of people of different races. Observe very closely and take full notes. Find out whether the museum has any pamphlets on any of these subjects.
2. **Getting acquainted with races and nationalities.** It would be interesting to make a study of the pupils in your school to see which races and which nationalities are represented. Of what advantage is it to you to have representatives of many different nationalities and races in your school?

ADVENTURES IN READING

1. *Meet Your Ancestors* by Roy C. Andrews, Viking, 1953. Gives you much interesting information on the prehistoric men you read about and others not mentioned in the text.
2. "Search for Early Man" by G. H. Von Koenigswald, *Natural History Magazine* (published by American Museum of Natural History), January 1947. Tells a fascinating story of the author's discoveries in Java.
3. *Everyday Life in Prehistoric Times* by Marjorie and C. H. B. Quennell, Batsford, 1952. Describes life in the Old and New Stone Ages.
4. *Back of History* by William W. Howells, Doubleday, 1954. Don't miss this!
5. *The Races of Mankind* by Ruth Benedict and G. Weltfish, Public Affairs Pamphlet No. 85. Public Affairs Committee, 30 Rockefeller Plaza, New York 20. Short and packed with information.
6. "How the Races of Man Developed," *Life*, May 18, 1953.
7. *Today's Science and You* by Lynn Poole, McGraw-Hill, 1952. This contains a chapter, "Key to the Past," for those who want to look further into the subject of dating living things of past ages.
8. *Man, Time, and Fossils* by Ruth Moore, Knopf, 1953. Chapter XVIII on Libby and carbon dating is made as easy as this difficult subject can be made.

CHAPTER THIRTY-FIVE — THE HISTORY OF MAN

Unit Ten

Conservation

CHAPTER 36

Materials used and re-used by living things

CHAPTER 37

The tangled web of life

CHAPTER 38

A bountiful future

Many hillsides, like the one in this picture, once forested have lost their trees. The trees were cut by men who, like the man in the fable, "killed the goose that laid the golden eggs." Water then rushed down the bare slopes and caused floods. In these floods precious water, which is becoming ever scarcer, was lost to us as it flowed into the sea. Good soil was washed away; most plants disappeared. Insects are gone. Why? No food. Birds have left — there are no insects or plants to feed on. Where are the mice, squirrels, and deer? Gone, too. They can't hunt nor can they graze. Man took what he needed and then moved on to unspoiled grazing or forest land.

When populations could be counted in the millions this waste was unimportant. Now billions of people must be fed and housed and clothed; and every year the number grows. The land must produce more and more. Will there be food for all of us? "Yes" is the answer of most scientists. But only if we practice conservation. We must learn how to keep the soil and water and the living things of this earth. We must learn how to keep them even while we are using them. This is conservation. If we, you and I and all of us, learn to do this we can look into the future with confidence. If not, man cannot survive.

Chapter 36

Materials used and re-used by living things

The future. We are animals, and like all other animals we depend on air, soil with its minerals, water, and on all other living things. These make up our environment. We often speak of these as **our natural resources** as though they had been made for us. And yet, although we claim them as our property, we often fail to protect and conserve them. We have been using up these resources faster than they can be replaced. Looking to the future is our responsibility — yours and mine, no matter where we live, whether on the farm or in the city. **Conservation** concerns us all.

The dictionary tells us conservation means "preserving, protecting, guarding." To the conservationist it means more than that. It means using resources and at the same time preserving them — using them and yet keeping them as nearly as possible at their present level. This is wise use of natural resources; and to use resources wisely, we need answers to a good many questions, questions such as these: How do plants and animals get their food? How do living things change the air? How is soil made? How do green plants and nongreen plants change the soil? How do *we* change the earth through our activities? What about the supply of water in the ground? Do our activities affect our supply? Why is it that for billions of years plants and animals have been getting what they need from the earth and its atmosphere and yet have not used it all? You already know answers to some of these questions. You will know others by the time you have finished this unit of the book. In this chapter you will learn why some of the materials of the earth and its atmosphere do not get used up.

Food chains. All organisms, except the green plants, eat, or at least get their food from, some other organism. You are no exception. Let's see how this works. Floating in the surface waters of the ocean are countless numbers of single-celled plants called diatoms. Hardly visible water fleas dart through these same waters and feed on diatoms. Water fleas are eaten by shrimp or small fish. And these, in turn, are eaten by herring or mackerel. We eat the herring and mackerel. Another food chain is illustrated in Figure 36.1.

In the orange groves of California are countless tiny scale insects that suck the contents from cells in orange trees. Ladybugs eat the scale insects; kingbirds eat ladybugs; hawks eat kingbirds. But in or on the hawk there may be parasites, much smaller animals or plants. They steal their food from the hawk and perhaps kill the hawk, thus cutting off their food supply and killing themselves. These intimate relationships of parasite and host are far more common than you would suspect. Many food chains seem to end with the parasite. But the host that is killed serves as food for other organisms. The chain goes on.

Thousands of food chains exist all over the world, in the water and on land. But no matter what the links

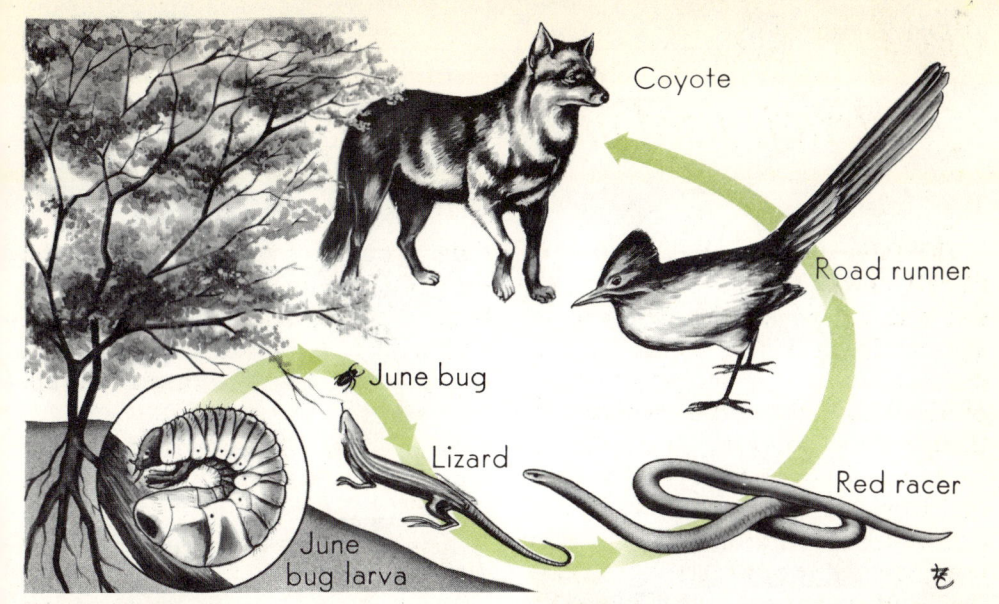

36.1 Each organism in turn serves as food for the next. Which organism is at the beginning of this long chain? What can this organism do that the others cannot do?

are in the chain, no matter whether the food chain is long or short, with rare exceptions the first link is a green plant.

Green plants will continue. Look again at Figure 36.1 above. In time all die. However, the coyote, the road runner, the snake, and the toad may die a natural death. While they are alive, these animals leave wastes containing compounds of nitrogen. These wastes and the bodies of the animals after death lie on the ground. But the bodies don't lie there long; you seldom find dead animals in the woods when you go for a hike. Why is this? Birds that are scavengers (animals that eat dead flesh) quickly spot the dead animals and feed on them. Flies are attracted and lay their eggs in the animal remains; the eggs hatch and the maggots begin their feast. Carrion beetles may even bury the animal. Worms and pill bugs soon arrive. Many kinds of organisms make use of the dead remains.

36.2 Plants, too, have their parasites. A goldenrod plant is host to the dodder wound around its stem. Both of them may be a link in some longer food chain. *Blakiston*

CHAPTER THIRTY-SIX — MATERIALS USED AND RE-USED BY LIVING THINGS

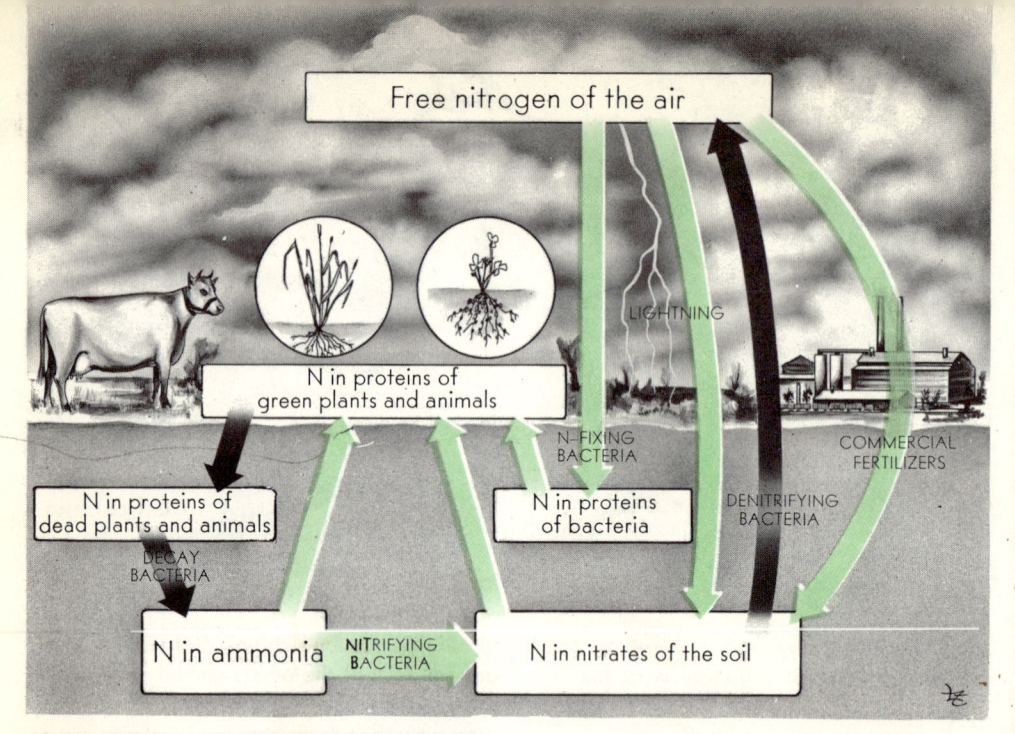

36.3 Nitrogen cycle. Every colored line means that a smaller molecule is being built up into a more complex molecule. Black lines mean that compounds are being broken down. Name the various kinds of bacteria that break down compounds.

Bacteria of decay and spores of various fungi have settled from the air on the dead or waste substances. The bacteria and larger fungi digest the proteins and use the digested products as their food. Decay has set in. In decay large molecules are broken down into smaller ones. Protoplasm is broken down into the substances from which it was formed. Carbohydrates are oxidized into carbon dioxide and water. Simpler protein compounds are formed, then amino acids, and then far simpler, inorganic, compounds — carbon dioxide, water, nitrates, and compounds containing sulfur and phosphorus. The gases become part of the atmosphere; the solids become part of the soil. They are the same kinds of compounds as those out of which the green plants originally made their food. All this goes on in oceans, too.

The farmer, whose interest lies not in starting long food chains but in raising crops for himself and his stock, often spreads manure on his land or puts fertilizer in his pond. Thus he provides for restoring nitrates and other compounds so that his green plants can grow.

You have seen that dead organisms as well as living ones form a link in food chains. As these links are added to the chain, a cycle or wheel is formed. You read about green plants as the first link in a chain and now you have come back to green plants again. Thus food chains can continue and green plants can grow, generation after generation.

The nitrogen cycle. As the organisms of decay use and break down the proteins of animal and plant remains,

510   UNIT TEN — CONSERVATION

ammonia is formed. If you have been on a farm, surely you have noticed the smell of ammonia around the manure heap or compost pile. This is one part of the nitrogen cycle, Figure 36.3. Some ammonia is used directly by green plants. Most of it is used by microscopic organisms in the soil, **nitrifying** (nigh′tri-fy-ing) bacteria. Nitrifying bacteria change ammonia into nitrates, which are used by green plants to make plant proteins.

But there are many, many kinds of soil bacteria besides the nitrifying bacteria you have just read about. Some of these break down the nitrates into free nitrogen. These are called **denitrifying** bacteria. The nitrogen gas they make cannot be used by the green plant, as you know. Still other kinds of soil bacteria use the nitrogen; they combine it with other elements and compounds and make their own proteins. Look at Figure 36.4. It is a picture of one of the legumes, the peanut plant. Do you see the little swellings or **nodules** on its roots? These nodules contain **nitrogen-fixing** bacteria, which build up nitrogen into their proteins. Some of the protein they make is used by the plant on whose roots they grow. Such root nodules are normally found on the roots of all the other legumes, too — the clovers, alfalfa, soybeans, vetch, and many others. If these plants are plowed into the ground or left to die where they grow, their proteins decay and nitrogen compounds are put back into the soil. A few kinds of nitrogen-fixing bacteria live free in the soil.

Lightning makes nitrates, too. During thunderstorms, some of the nitrogen in the air is combined with oxygen. The compound is washed by rain into the soil. There it unites with potassium or some other element. The result is nitrates that can be used by green plants.

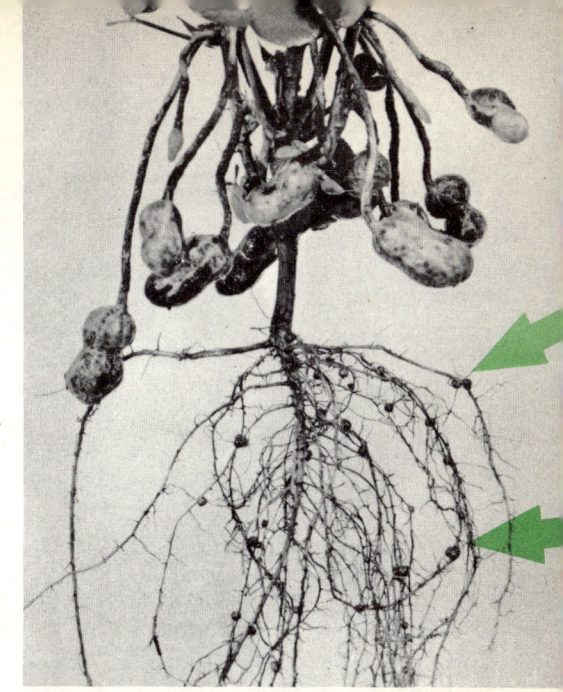

36.4 Roots and base of peanut plant. Nitrogen-fixing bacteria live in the nodules. How are legumes such as the peanut related to the nitrogen cycle? *Brooklyn Botanic Garden*

The carbon cycle. If you want a very little of something to go a long way, you use it over and over again, once in one form, then in another. And if it is something that never wears out, a limited supply of it can last forever. That is why nitrates have lasted so long and that is why carbon, also, will not give out.

Green plants get their supply of carbon from carbon dioxide in the air. The carbon is made into sugars; the sugars may be changed into starches, fats, cellulose, and other carbon compounds. Many of them are built up into proteins and protoplasm. Almost 20 per cent of protoplasm is carbon. When animals eat plants, some of the carbon becomes a part of the animal's body; some is oxidized. When oxidation takes place in the plant or in the animal, carbon dioxide is released and

PHOTOSYNTHESIS — Used by green plants

CO_2 (carbon dioxide) and H_2O (water)

O_2 (oxygen) and $C_6H_{12}O_6$ (sugar)

OXIDATION — Used by all living things

36.5 The three elements **oxygen**, **hydrogen** (in the form of water), and **carbon** (in the form of carbon dioxide) are used over and over again by living things. What two activities of organisms keep these elements in circulation? The amounts of oxygen, water, and carbon dioxide on the earth are affected by many other processes in which living things play no part. What are they?

returned to the air. This is a very simple cycle. See Figure 36.5.

Most plants, however, are not eaten by animals; nor do animals oxidize all the carbon compounds that they eat. But as you read, eventually all animals and plants die, and most of them decay. During decay, carbon is oxidized into carbon dioxide, and this carbon can be used again.

Of course, some carbon was taken out of circulation millions of years ago. The trunks, leaves, and roots of many plants were changed to coal, petroleum, and natural gas; but when these substances are used as fuel, this carbon, too, is put back into circulation again.

You have read that in the oceans and fresh-water lakes, millions upon millions of organisms, both plants and animals, form shells of carbon compounds. As the organisms die, these shells pile up. Throughout the ages this has been going on, and thus thick beds of limestone or other rock have been formed. Some carbon has been taken out of circulation in this way, too.

Oxygen and hydrogen cycles. All of us, animals and plants, constantly join oxygen to carbon atoms in oxidation. Thus we take oxygen out of circulation. Yet the per cent of oxygen in the air is not growing less. And you already know why not. In making carbohydrates, green plants separate carbon dioxide into carbon and oxygen. They keep the carbon and release the oxygen. And so the oxygen cycle goes on and on, as long as plants live in the oceans and on land.

Hydrogen, too, is used over and over, not as an element but in its compounds. In photosynthesis, water (H_2O) is used in making carbohydrates. The carbohydrates may be changed into fats or proteins. Whether these compounds stay in the plant or are eaten by animals, they will, in time, be oxidized in the living organism or after death. In oxidation, water is produced, and so hydrogen is used over and over.

What have you learned? You learned that both in the oceans and on land living things in the world are all linked up with other living things in food chains. The green plant is the first link in every chain. Each animal forms some link in some chain; it may be near the beginning or near the end, depending on whether it feeds on some green plant or on some other animal. And it in turn, either dead or alive, is fed on by some other organism. The chain becomes a wheel, a cycle, with the last organisms in the chain, the soil bacteria, making compounds that can be used by new green plants. We can now understand why green plants have been growing for at least two billion years and why we can expect them to continue indefinitely.

Then you traced four of the important elements in protoplasm: nitrogen, carbon, hydrogen, and oxygen; and you saw why each element does not grow less. Dead protoplasm, fed on by bacteria of decay, is broken down into simpler and simpler nitrogen compounds and finally into ammonia, which may be absorbed again from the soil by green plants.

But you also learned that many different kinds of bacteria live in most soil.

Some bacteria (nitrifying) build up ammonia compounds into nitrates.

Some bacteria (denitrifying) break down nitrates into free nitrogen.

Some bacteria (nitrogen-fixing) build free nitrogen into proteins. Most of these live in swellings on the roots of legumes.

Back and forth these changes go. Activity of soil bacteria never ceases as long as there is decaying material in the soil. And so the nitrogen in protoplasm can be used over and over again.

The carbon, hydrogen, and oxygen in protoplasm are also used again and again as long as chlorophyll continues to exist. You traced the carbon, oxygen, and hydrogen in the compounds CO_2 and H_2O. Carbon dioxide and water are made into carbohydrates and other foods. But these foods in time are oxidized and thus release carbon dioxide and water, which can be used again.

USEFUL WORDS IN BIOLOGY

environment
natural
  resources
conservation
food chains
nitrogen cycle
nitrifying
denitrifying
nitrogen-fixing
nodules
compost
legume
carbon cycle
oxygen cycle

TEST YOURSELF

1. How is an understanding of biology necessary to planning wise use of our natural resources?
2. What does conservation mean to the biologist?
3. (a) By giving an example of a long food chain, show that you know the meaning of the term. (b) What part do plants play in all food chains?
4. Why have the elements used by plants in food manufacture not become exhausted during the millions of years of the earth's history?
5. Explain the nitrogen cycle with the use of a diagram, naming the different kinds of bacteria involved in it.
6. (a) What special role do legumes play in the nitrogen cycle? (b) Give four examples of common legumes.
7. Show how carbon is kept in circulation by telling of the processes that remove carbon dioxide from the air and those that return it to the air.

8. Explain fully why plants and animals do not use up all the oxygen in the air.
9. Explain the hydrogen cycle.

DO IT YOURSELF

1. Finding your own food chains. Select some wild animal you are interested in. Consult references to learn what the animal eats and which animals eat it. Continue your investigations until you can construct a food chain, showing all the plants and animals involved. E. Laurence Palmer's *Fieldbook of Natural History* will be helpful.

2. Survey of death in woods and fields. On one of your trips make a survey of all the plant and animal remains you find. Take notes on all you see. Dig into the soil to look for the larger soil dwellers that may be feeding on dead organisms. You may have to take these home to identify them and to learn about their habits. Of course, you won't see the smaller "helpers." You have read what they do, and for further information consult a good college text such as *Textbook of Botany* by Transeau, Sampson and Tiffany, Harper, 1953.

3. A study of legumes. List all the legumes you find around your home or school and in neighboring fields. Star those being used for soil improvement in agriculture and gardening. Dig up some legumes and look for the nodules. Describe them.

4. Observing interdependence of organisms on a small scale. If you have not already started an aquarium, start several small ones now. You will find full directions in *Methods and Materials for Teaching Biological Sciences* by Miller and Blaydes, McGraw-Hill, 1938. When your aquaria have shown successful interdependence of organisms for some time, add a number of individuals of some species to one aquarium. Add animals of other species to another. To a third add a large number of plants. Observe closely for several days or weeks. Describe and explain what happens.

5. Making charts for your school. Make charts for classroom use showing the nitrogen cycle. Illustrate the cycle by using specific plants and animals.

ADVENTURES IN READING

1. "Discoveries in Nitrogen Fixation" by Martin D. Kamen, *Scientific American*, March 1953. Is not easy reading but has interesting illustrations.

2. "Legumes for Erosion Control and Wildlife" by Edward H. Graham, 1941 Yearbook of Department of Agriculture. Good illustrations of many useful legumes.

3. *Fieldbook of Natural History* by E. Laurence Palmer, Whittlesley House, 1949.

UNIT TEN — CONSERVATION

Chapter 37

The tangled web of life

Ecology. Earlier in the year you went to the fields and the woods; you looked into ponds and streams and you learned about a few of the many plants and animals of this earth. Then you learned how plants and animals (mostly you yourself) perform the many activities that keep you alive. You fixed your attention for the most part on one organism at a time. But plants and animals do not live alone. Each individual is affected in one way or another by other plants or animals. And each individual is affected by its nonliving environment, too. Biologists have come to realize the importance of studying living things in their natural habitats. They see the need for understanding relationships between organisms and their living and nonliving environment. This study is a science called **ecology** (ih-coll′o-jee).

Ecologists study relationships in fields, gardens, yards, forests, jungles, swamps, ponds, on high mountaintops — everywhere. They use every field of science to help them discover and understand the relationships. Geology, chemistry, physics, or meteorology (the study of the weather) — all are used. It is clear that if we are to make wise use of living things, we must have some knowledge of ecology and apply this knowledge to our biological problems.

The plant's environment. What are the needs of plants? You will say they must have air, water, minerals in the soil, light, and a suitable temperature. But that doesn't tell us enough. Let's look more closely at some of the factors of the plant's environment.

First, there is soil. It contains mineral compounds; some are used by all species of plants, some by only certain species. Some plants need an alkaline soil, others an acid soil. But there are many other differences in soil. The soil may be largely ground-up rock, sandy soil through which water runs quickly. If the soil is clay the particles are fine and packed together very closely. Clay soil holds much water, sometimes too much. In a forest, soil is usually not deep, but the top layers contain much decaying plant material called **humus**; it will have many bacteria, molds, the young of insects, and other animals. Such soil is loose and its top layers of decaying plant materials hold water a long time. Usually soils that develop in a prairie (grassland) are very deep and full of humus. As long as the land is covered with living grasses such soil also holds water well. You can see that the amount of water that a plant can draw on could be affected by several factors: the amount of rainfall, how and when the rain falls, and the kind of soil that receives and retains the rain.

Altitude, too, is an important factor in the lives of living things. A few kinds of green plants are fitted for living half a mile down in the sea; that is as far as light reaches. Some smaller kinds of plants can grow three miles above sea level, though the "tree line," where trees stop growing on a mountainside, is always lower

37.1 The Field and Forest Wildlife Conservation Club, Senior High School, University City, Missouri. This club of boys found that good conservation practices must be based on a sound knowledge of ecology. This picture shows one of their projects. *Rex Conyers*

down. The soil is poor on mountaintops, the temperature is low at night, the strong winds dry up plants; and the strong ultraviolet rays of light at high altitudes may help to stunt the growth of plants. An old alpine willow tree grows like a shrub and may be only six or eight inches tall. The growing season is very short on mountaintops. Only species that can produce flowers and seed in a short season survive. See Figure 37.2.

The length of day makes a difference, too. Some plants blossom and produce seeds best when the days are short. This is true of chrysanthemums and fall asters. If you should want to hold back the blossoming of such plants, you must lengthen their day by exposing them to some extra hours of artificial light. That slows them up. On the other hand, those plants that normally bloom in the early spring respond in the opposite way to long daylight hours. You can force them to bloom sooner by giving them more light. Remember that as you go north the days grow longer in summer. For this reason wheat can be grown in the Arctic region; the long days make up for the shortness of the summer season.

Some kinds of plants need alternate seasons of warmth and cold in order to form flowers and seeds. The seeds of some oaks and certain other plants will not germinate unless the temperature has fallen below the freezing point for part of their resting time. Leaf buds, too, formed on plants that live where there is a winter season fail to grow unless they have been cold for a certain time. And the farmer knows that his potatoes store more food when cold nights alternate with warm days. Plants such as these cannot survive in climates that are warm the year round.

Ecologists know that all these physi-

UNIT TEN — CONSERVATION

37.2 Springtime view of a natural mountain meadow. In these meadows some plants may push their flowers through the snow. By early fall the cotton-grass you see here will be replaced by other, very colorful, flowers. What exceptional characteristics must plants have to live in this environment? *United States Forest Service*

cal factors and many more determine which plants can grow in a certain region: the kind of soil, the amount of water the soil can hold, rainfall, temperature, the length of the day, altitude with all the factors it includes, and seasonal changes. Then add to this the all-important factor of plant and animal neighbors. Ecologists are learning how complex the plant's environment is.

Communities. Evidently plants do not grow hit or miss, wherever a seed or a spore happens to fall. They can grow in a particular spot only if all the many factors of the environment are favorable for them. But an environment favorable for one plant is usually favorable for others of its kind. Usually, also, any one environment is favorable for several kinds of plants. These kinds will tend to live together unless one kind crowds another out. Large plants, for example, make shade. Some kinds of plants can't grow in this shade, although all the other factors of the environment are favorable in this spot. Other plants can. In this way definite kinds of plants become associated with one another. And these plants make an environment suitable for certain animals — animals that eat these plants or find shelter among them, insects of many kinds, and larger animals. Thus we find that plants and animals live in definite **communities.**

In every community, or group of plants and animals living together, one or several kinds are found in larger numbers than other kinds. Those that are found in the largest numbers are spoken of as the **dominant** species. Look at the lawn outside your school building. This is a relatively simple

CHAPTER THIRTY–SEVEN — THE TANGLED WEB OF LIFE   517

37.3 A balanced aquarium is a tiny community that you helped to establish. What kinds of animals do you see? What substances do they get from the plants? What microorganisms probably are living in this community? *Schneider*

community. The dominant species is some kind of grass. Mixed with the grass may be a few dandelions and some of the common weeds known as plantains. Earthworms are probably present, too, and ants. Molds and bacteria are plentiful in the soil. Many interrelationships exist between these organisms. A community you may have right in your classroom is the balanced aquarium. See Figure 37.3.

Succession. If much care is given to this lawn, if the weeds are uprooted as they appear, if the lawn is given enough water and fertilizer, this community may remain the same year after year. Otherwise this, like most communities, changes slowly. The growth of one plant affects the others. The dandelions may shade out the grass. Certain minerals may become exhausted. After some years the plantains may have become the dominant species. Now conditions have changed so much that seeds from neighboring plants find conditions suitable. These new plants move in, or **invade,** the old community. Then new kinds of insects appear. The meadow mouse or white-footed mouse may move in, too. Other organisms underground will change. A new community succeeds the old one. That is what we call **succession.** It happens all around us all the time, sometimes rapidly, but sometimes so slowly that we may not notice it. As you may know, a lawn community that receives no care can change within a year.

A community has a natural lifetime, just as you and I have natural lifetimes. Ecologists who have studied the special needs of certain kinds of plants and animals can predict how long some communities will live and in which order new communities will appear. See Figure 37.4.

Climax communities. Look at Figure 37.5. It took many thousands of years to make the soil where these vast forests grow. First, rock was broken down into a thin layer of soil

518

UNIT TEN — CONSERVATION

37.4 Water communities succeed each other, too. As pond lilies die and build up soil, cattails and bulrushes move into the lake. Soon the swampy ground you see will become more solid, and shrubs like alders and willows will take root. Do you know of a pond where this has happened? *New York State College of Agriculture*

37.5 This Ontario, Canada, forest stretching to the horizon was preceded by what plants? *Photographic Survey Corporation Ltd., Canada*

by lichens, which are the **pioneers** in soil formation. Mosses or other tiny plants can grow in the thin soil held by the lichens. The mosses gradually replace the lichens and help build and hold more soil. Now ferns and other larger plants can grow. Thus soil is made rich and deep enough to support grasses and even larger plants. Birds and larger animals of many kinds find food and cover here; they bring with them seeds of some trees and shrubs. Other tree seeds are carried by the wind. The trees that can grow where there is much light, such as cedars and poplars, are often the first to grow. An oak and hickory community may come next. The final, or **climax,** community may be a forest of beech and maple. This is one succession in the northeastern United States. Often the climax forest is a mixture of many kinds of trees. In the plains area the climax growth is grasses, not trees. And in desert lands or in the South successions will be different.

The climax community reproduces itself, sometimes for many centuries, though the relative numbers of some of its species change even from year

CHAPTER THIRTY-SEVEN — THE TANGLED WEB OF LIFE

37.6 The boll weevil lays its eggs in a cottonboll. The young destroy the cotton inside. *U.S. Bureau of Entomology*

to year. It can be wiped out by man, or fire, or wind, or flood. Then a new and pioneer community takes over.

Cycles within communities. Populations of a community constantly change. In some years the northern woods are crowded with rabbits. The lynx, which feeds on rabbits, increases. So many of the lynx offspring find food, survive, and reproduce that rabbits become scarce. The lynxes feel the pinch of hunger. They have fewer offspring; some die of starvation. Thus rabbits can again increase. The pendulum swings back, and in time the cycle is repeated.

But rabbits and lynxes are not the only members of this community. As rabbits become less plentiful the plants on which they feed may increase in numbers. They may crowd out other plants. This gives different kinds of insects a chance to increase in numbers. Mice, and perhaps birds, now find new kinds of insect food in this community. The community changes as these new kinds of plants and animals multiply. Then the lynx-rabbit pendulum swings back as we saw; many species of animals and plants are affected. Do you wonder that we speak of the tangled web of life?

Our part in the web of life. When it comes to food, we are like other animals; and thus we are part of many food chains — the last link. Thus we become part of the tangled web of life. But we are different, too, from other animals; because of our civilization we have many needs that other animals do not have, and we do things on a much larger scale. We cut down whole forests. We plow up whole prairies. We dam big streams, flooding large areas of land. In doing these things we create tremendous problems for ourselves. Let's see what some of these problems are.

In Mexico, cotton plants had been raised for many years in small patches here and there. The cotton boll weevil shown in Figure 37.6 lived on the cotton but did little damage; it was kept in check by its natural enemies. But then farmers in our southern states planted thousands of acres to cotton. When the boll weevil migrated north to these cotton fields, it found a banquet table laid for it. It ate its fill and multiplied enormously. It had no natural enemies here; their nesting places in forest and prairie had been destroyed. Each year more cotton was planted; each year the weevil pest grew worse. Our present problem is thus partly of our own making.

And so it goes with cotton, potatoes, corn, and most other crops. When Maine farmers began planting vast fields to potatoes, potato beetles (Figure 37.7) increased in the same ratio as the crop. They made life easy for the potato beetle by supplying it with acre after acre of food. And look at the European corn borer in Figure 37.8. The small moths of the European

37.7 The larva of the Colorado potato beetle is shown above, and the adult is shown below. Both are good feeders. How do they injure the potatoes underground? When the State of Maine planted vast fields of potatoes, this pest increased in the same ratio as the crop. Why? *U.S. Department of Agriculture*

corn borer lay their eggs on the leaves of the corn or on some neighboring weeds. After a few days the larvae enter the ear or the stalk. Here they spend the winter; then they spin a cocoon and shortly afterwards come out as adults. The more corn we plant, the more the borer multiplies unless all old stalks are destroyed.

Thus you can see we encourage insect pests by planting vast areas to a single crop. We create problems for ourselves.

Importing destructive organisms. Through all our means of communication we are now in close touch with all parts of the world. This has its dangers, as well as its advantages. In 1912 some special iris bulbs ordered from Japan arrived in New York. Hidden in the bulbs were small, white, wormlike grubs, the young of the Japanese beetle. Within a few years the beetle spread west to Ohio and

37.8 These larvae of the European corn borer feed in both ears and stalks, thus weakening the stalks. How do we help this insect to increase? *U.S. Bureau of Entomology*

CHAPTER THIRTY-SEVEN — THE TANGLED WEB OF LIFE

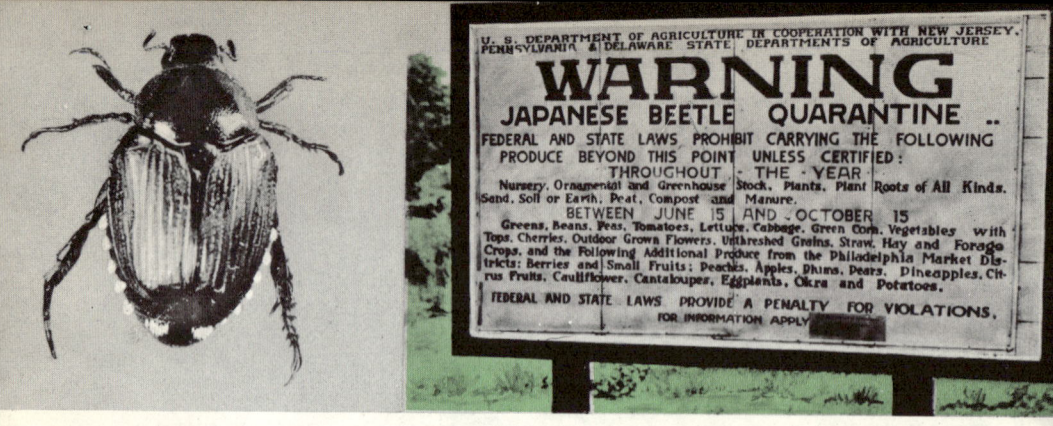

37.9 The brown and green adult of the Japanese beetle is about $\frac{1}{2}$ inch long. It destroys leaves and fruit. The grub injures roots. How does the Department of Agriculture try to stop its further spread? Read this sign. Quarantine is used to stop the spread of insect pests as well as disease germs. *U.S. Department of Agriculture*

south to Virginia, attacking 275 kinds of plants; it had no enemies in this country; the enemies had stayed in Japan. The Department of Agriculture has tried to introduce natural enemies but has been only partly successful. Read the sign in Figure 37.9, and take a good look at the Japanese beetle so that you will recognize it.

Some of our worst insect pests have been accidentally imported. Besides the corn borer and the Japanese beetle we have imported the Hessian fly which destroys wheat, the Mediterranean fruit fly, and the brown-tail moth which destroys shade trees.

Fungus diseases of plants have been imported accidentally, too. The Dutch elm disease is caused by a fungus which destroys the phloem tissues in the trunk and roots of elm trees. This fungus was discovered in Holland in 1919. No one knows how it got there. About ten years later it was found in our country. It is believed that the fungus and two species of bark beetle which carry the fungus from tree to tree entered on logs imported from France.

Sometimes importations of plants and animals have not been accidental, but planned. These often have just as serious results. In 1864 an Englishman landed in Australia, bringing with him thirteen rabbits, which he wanted to breed, since there were no native Australian rabbits. To protect the newly introduced species, a heavy fine was imposed if anyone was caught killing a rabbit. Within a few years rabbits overran farms and fields; they had no natural enemies. Crops were destroyed. Losses ran into millions of dollars. Communities organized rabbit drives, and thousands of rabbits were killed. A bounty, much larger than the original fine, was now offered for every rabbit killed! Still they multiplied. In 1887, New South Wales offered a reward of 25,000 pounds to the person who could suggest a method of exterminating them. Pasteur suggested the introduction of the germ of chicken cholera. His suggestion was not accepted because of the danger to domestic animals, but it is interesting that Pasteur's idea proved eventually to be the right one. It took another sixty years, however, before the virus

37.10 A few pairs of rabbits were introduced to Australia by early settlers. It was estimated that by 1950 there were one half billion rabbits in that country doing untold damage to crops and pasture lands. Can you account for this rapid increase? What method was used to get rid of them? What is the danger in this method? *Black Star*

of Myxomatosis, a serious rabbit disease, was injected into a number of rabbits that were then turned loose. This, at last, gives promise of saving the country from its rabbit plague. It is estimated that the 500 million rabbits have been reduced in three years to 50 or 100 million. Unfortunately, however, the disease has also spread through Western Europe where rabbits are much used as food.

The prickly-pear cactus was brought to Australia from America. After a few years it covered about 60,000,000 acres, crowding out most other vegetation and spoiling grazing lands. Much money was spent on spraying and other methods, but still it continued to spread. Finally insects were imported from the natural home of the prickly pear. Where these natural relations were established between plant and insect, the cactus was held in check.

These few examples show you that making one small change in a community may result in far-reaching and undesirable changes which may be difficult to stop or undo.

Under natural conditions when an organism destroys another and multiplies rapidly, it will eventually destroy itself. It will exhaust its food supply.

37.11 Blister rust on white pine. It spends part of its life in a second host, a gooseberry or currant bush. *U.S. Forest Service*

CHAPTER THIRTY–SEVEN — THE TANGLED WEB OF LIFE 523

37.12 The small "worm" bores into the fruit just beginning to develop. Inside it feeds and grows, boring its way out when ready to pupate. When should the trees be sprayed if you want sound apples? To what extent does spraying help? Note the heaps of sound and wormy apples below. *Hylson, U.S. Bureau of Entomology*

This is true, too, of plant parasites. Figure 37.11 shows a parasitic fungus, the white pine blister rust, which has destroyed many white pines in the northeastern states. As these fungi destroy the host, they destroy themselves, too. But we cannot wait for that; we need the crops fungi and insects feed on. These organisms are our competitors, doing away with food, clothing, lumber, and other products. For this reason we must constantly engage in destroying them. How is this done?

Destroying insects. The least expensive way for us to keep down the number of destructive insects or other animals and plants is to make use of their natural enemies. You can see how much we must rely on the help of ecologists for this. And even they often cannot give us the help we need. In the meantime, we use poisons, too. For this, the life history and eating habits of the insect must be known thoroughly. And the right kind of poison must be used. We use stomach poisons against insects with biting mouth parts. Surely you have at some time bitten into an apple and found a "worm." The "worm" is the larva of the codling moth which can be kept in check with stomach poisons, as Figure 37.12 shows. We use contact poisons against aphids and scale insects

524

UNIT TEN — CONSERVATION

37.13 The low- and slow-flying helicopter is ideal for dusting crop plants with DDT. Here the helicopter is used to dust tomato plants in order to destroy mites and hornworms which are ruining the crop. *New England Helicopter Service*

which puncture the stem or leaf and suck the juices of the plant. These poisons enter or clog up the insect's breathing pores (spiracles). The breathing pores connect with tiny air tubes which branch and run to all parts of the body. When the breathing pores are clogged, the insect dies from lack of oxygen.

The best known insect exterminator, DDT, enters the insect through any part of its body and travels to vital organs. You know that by use of DDT the malaria mosquito has been practically exterminated in several parts of the world. DDT was the first of many similar substances used against insects. See Figure 37.13.

But in large-scale spraying of DDT we run the risk of killing some of the helpful species of insects and disturbing natural relationships. There are many threads in the tangled web of life, and when we attempt to make a change, we often lack the wisdom to foresee how it will end.

What have you learned? There are many threads in this tangled web of life; ecologists are gradually learning to disentangle them. Ecology, the study of the relationships between organisms and their environment, is a recent science. It has taught us how complex is the plant's environment. It has taught us, too, how plants and animals live in definite communities — some simple communities like the lawn outside your school, others far more complex. It has taught us how communities change as new plants and then new animals invade the community. This succession may occur slowly or rapidly. Successions end in a climax community unless some stage is destroyed by some means. The climax may be a forest or grasses on the plains or desert plants in the Southwest.

Ecologists have taught us also that cycles occur within a community while it is changing. Now rabbits are on the increase in some community; then lynx multiply. They die off for lack of food, and rabbits again increase.

And lastly, we learned that we are a part of all communities. But we, because of our civilization, play a somewhat different part. By raising crops on a large scale, we encourage insect pests; we import organisms from other lands and upset natural relationships. Thus we create problems for ourselves which we must solve. In the next chapter you will read of more problems we have created for ourselves.

USEFUL WORDS IN BIOLOGY

ecology
tree line
humus
community
pioneers
dominant species
succession
invasion
climax community

TEST YOURSELF

1. (a) What is the meaning of the word "ecology"? (b) Explain how a knowledge of ecology must be applied if we are to make wise use of natural resources.
2. Soil is a complex mixture of substances. Explain some of the ways in which soils differ.
3. Name at least four factors which affect the growth of plants on mountaintops.
4. Make a list of the many factors of the environment that affect a plant.
5. (a) Define a community in nature. (b) What is meant by dominant species of plants and animals?
6. Give an example of invasion and succession in a natural community.
7. Give an example of a pendulumlike swing in the populations of a community.
8. Show, by giving examples, how man through his civilization and ways of living changes populations of plants and animals.
9. (a) Name some of the important plant and animal pests introduced accidentally into the United States. (b) Tell about some intentional introduction of organisms which resulted in troubles.
10. Which groups of organisms do the greatest damage to the plants and animals upon which we depend for food?
11. Describe several methods of controlling insect populations.

DO IT YOURSELF

1. **How soils differ.** Go out into the woods and fields. Collect samples (perhaps a quart of each) of different types of soil—sandy soil, clay, soil rich in humus. How do the soils differ in color, in texture, in dry weight? Devise experiments to answer the following questions. (a) Which sample has the greatest water-holding capacity? (Hint: Start with samples of dry soil of equal weight.) (b) Which soil is most acid? (Hint: Ask the chemistry teacher for litmus paper.) (c) What percentage, roughly, of the dry weight of each sample is organic matter; what percentage is inorganic or mineral matter? (Hint: Do you remember the test for mineral matter? Perhaps the chemistry teacher can help you.)

2. **Do the different samples of soil differ in bacterial content?** This is a job for a *really good* student. You can expect some interesting results. Look for some bacteria or molds that produce antibiotics.

3. **A study of communities.** Take pictures, if you can, or get pictures of different types of plant communities. Then prepare lists of animals which would be likely to be found in each one. This will require considerable research. Use the various field books recommended earlier. These pictures can be attractively mounted for classroom display.

4. **A study of invasion.** Find a field being invaded by trees and shrubs. Identify as many species as possible, particularly the pioneers. Use field books for identification. Make a large chart to illustrate what is happening. Or, study the invasion of a marsh by land plants.

5. A plant's environment. Make a chart which will illustrate the various factors of a plant's environment. This is a chance for you to show your originality.

ADVENTURES IN READING

1. "Day Length and Flowering" by H. A. Berthwick in the *Yearbook of the Department of Agriculture*, 1943–1947. You will find this a fascinating subject.
2. "The Eelgrass Catastrophe" by Lorus J. and Margery J. Milne, *Scientific American*, January 1951. A simple account of a catastrophe which shows the importance of a knowledge of ecology.
3. *The Web of Life* by John Storer, Devin Adair, 1953. A very small book containing a great deal of information.

Chapter 38

A bountiful future

The need for conservation. If you visit the Department of Commerce building in Washington, you see a light flash every twelve seconds, day and night; it never stops. Each flash means that one person was added to the population in the United States. A baby is born much oftener than that, of course. But in these figures the deaths as well as the births are counted, and so are the people who move in and out of the country. Every twelve seconds, every time you see the light flash, our land must support one more person. Our population has doubled in the last fifty years. By 1960 it is expected to be close to 170,000,000. Can our land support so large a population? Yes! You read and hear of the millions of pounds of butter, the bales of cotton, the bushels of wheat, and the other crops being stored and often going to waste. We won't be starving by then.

But what of the rest of the world? In many countries populations are growing much faster than in the United States. The food supply in these parts of the world is far from sufficient now. One third of the world's people live on near starvation or starvation diets. They, too, must be fed. And as we consider the world's food supply we must look ahead not to the years of your lifetime but to the next several hundred years. As you read further, you will learn that some of the materials we depend on for our existence are being used up and can never be replaced. Conservation is necessary. See Figure 38.1.

Our natural resources. We speak of the things on which life depends as our natural resources. These resources must be *used;* not merely kept. And so, as you have read before, conservation means the wise use and control of all our natural resources for the permanent good of all people.

We have two kinds of resources — **renewable** and **nonrenewable.** Forests, grasslands, and wildlife can often be replaced or brought back to their original state after the supply has decreased. Water, too, is replaceable, though it takes tremendous effort to replace it. And some chemical elements of our soil are replaceable; they can be added in the form of natural or commercial fertilizers.

But soil, for all practical purposes, is not replaceable or renewable because many centuries are required to make one inch of **topsoil,** the soil needed for growing crops. Time and weather must assist in the long slow process of soil building. The other resources that can't be renewed are inorganic substances, metals like silver, tin, copper, lead, and others, and the nonmetals — sulfur, rocks such as granite and marble, and ground-up rock or sand. Coal and oil, though they came from living things, also cannot be renewed.

Whose business is conservation? Conservation concerns you and me, all of us, no matter where we live, whether on the farm or in the city. A conservation program is needed for bettering the lives of human beings now and

LEGEND

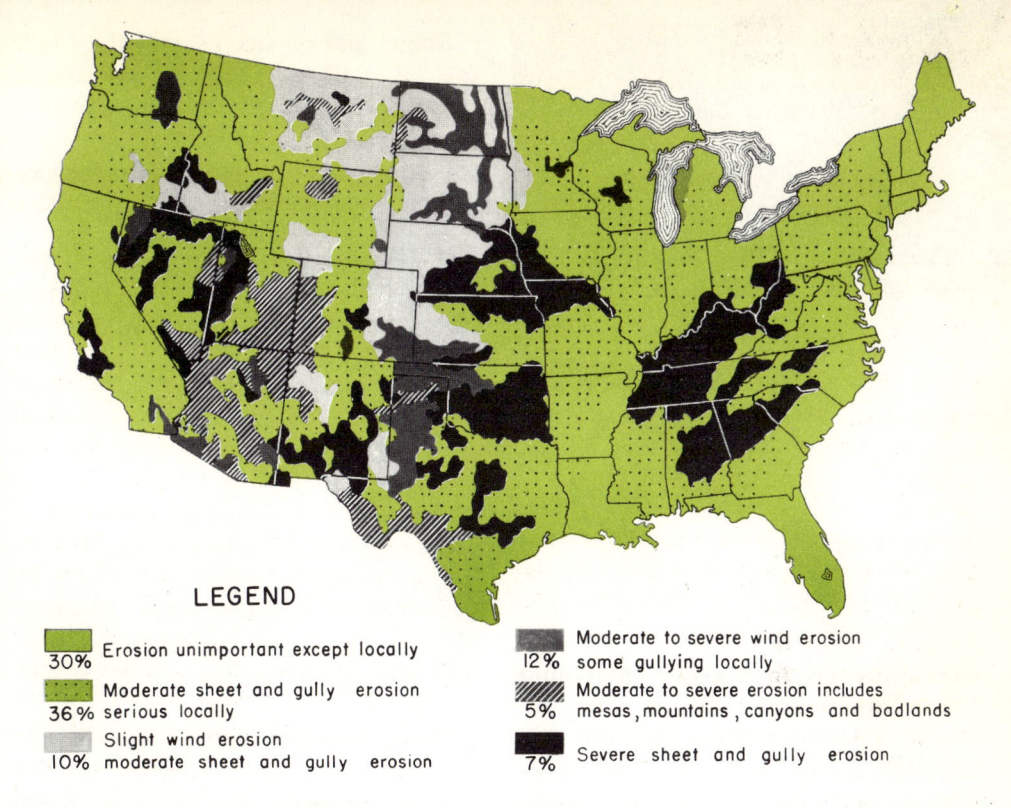

- **30%** Erosion unimportant except locally
- **36%** Moderate sheet and gully erosion serious locally
- **10%** Slight wind erosion moderate sheet and gully erosion
- **12%** Moderate to severe wind erosion some gullying locally
- **5%** Moderate to severe erosion includes mesas, mountains, canyons and badlands
- **7%** Severe sheet and gully erosion

38.1 An erosion map of the United States. Erosion removes the topsoil needed for crop production. When you study this map, you will agree that the problem is widespread. How severe is the erosion problem in the section where you live? What is being done about it? What can you do about it? *U.S. Soil Conservation Service*

for preserving our resources for the use of all people in the future.

President Theodore Roosevelt many years ago said, "When the soil is gone, man must go; and the process does not take long." In 1908 he appointed the National Conservation Commission. This group consisted of scientists, businessmen, and politicians. Later, departments were organized in the Federal Government for forests, for wildlife, and for National Parks. State governments also established Conservation Departments and Fish and Game and Forestry Commissions. Do you know who takes care of conservation in your state? There are many private organizations, too, that try to make people more conscious of the need for conservation. But let's see what has been done and what still needs to be done in the conservation of soil, water, forests, and wildlife.

THE CONSERVATION OF SOIL

Soil. The soil of the earth is a very thin layer, only two or three feet thick in most areas, although in old prairies it may be much thicker. It took thousands of years to make the soil. As you know, it was made by the erosion and chemical breaking down of the original rock and the gradual addition of plant and animal remains. This dead matter is decayed by micro-

CHAPTER THIRTY-EIGHT — A BOUNTIFUL FUTURE

38.2 The topsoil is often dark colored as shown here. About how deep is it? Why must we keep it from being washed away? *Geographic Review*

organisms and changed into compounds which can be used again. Only the top part of the soil contains the substances needed for raising good crops. This topsoil we believe was, on an average, about ten inches deep at the time America was settled by Europeans. But today we estimate the average depth to be only six to seven inches. Figure 38.2 shows the difference between the topsoil and the soil underneath. How did we lose so much topsoil? If we know or can find out, we can perhaps take the proper steps to prevent further losses.

Erosion. The splash of raindrops may start it all. On sloping land hundreds of tons of soil may be lost by erosion in a year or even in one bad storm. The amount of soil that is eroded or washed away depends on many things: the rainfall in that area; how steeply the land slopes; the nature of the soil; how dense the vegetation covering the soil is; the kinds of plants growing there; and the methods used to cultivate the land.

Sometimes on steep slopes the whole top layer of soil becomes so soaked by heavy rains that the water, instead of running off in furrows, floats the top layer of soil down with it in a sheet. This is **sheet erosion.** But more often the water collects in small channels which later start **gully erosion.** The gullies may cut up fields so badly that the fields must be abandoned. See Figure 38.3.

There may also be serious wind erosion which is shown in Figure 38.4; even flat fields are eroded by wind. To help prevent wind erosion, trees and shrubs can be planted along the edges of fields. We sometimes call these "living fences." Wider strips of trees extending in a north-south direction, because the prevailing winds are west-east, are called "shelter belts."

Improving the soil. Among the elements plants take from the soil are nitrogen, phosphorus, calcium, potassium, magnesium, iron, sulfur, and very small amounts of the "trace elements," such as manganese, copper, boron, and zinc. Soil often has too little of the first four mentioned — nitrogen, phosphorus, calcium, potassium — and some of the trace elements may be lacking. Minerals containing these elements may have become exhausted or they may have been washed, or **leached,** out of the soil. Good chemical fertilizers can supply all of these. Lime spread on the soil not only adds calcium but at the same time makes the soil more alkaline; this is what many field crops need. In addition to using chemical fertilizers, some farmers fertilize their fields with manure. They also plow into the ground the stalks of farm crops, such as corn, wheat, oats, and soybeans. Sometimes crops such as grasses and clovers are raised especially to be

38.3 Gully erosion has made this hillside useless. The topsoil is gone. Estimate the depth of the gullies. (See figure in front.) *Charles Phelps Cushing*

38.4 These drifts of good soil were blown from the neighboring fields. This is wind erosion. How can it be prevented? *U.S. Soil Conservation Service*

plowed under. These are called **green manure**. Adding manure and green manure benefits the soil in two ways. First, as you already know, decay bacteria and others change the proteins in these substances into nitrates. Second, the materials added improve drainage of clay soils and help hold water in sandy soils.

Soils that contain much humus usually are loose and porous and do not form a crust on top when they dry after a rain. Such soils are said to be in good "condition" or to have a good

CHAPTER THIRTY-EIGHT — A BOUNTIFUL FUTURE   531

38.5 Conservationists grade land so the farmer will know how to plant his crops. You will find the steeper slopes are given the higher numbers. *U.S. Soil Conservation Service*

structure. Several chemicals, such as Krilium, can be used instead of humus to improve the structure of the soil.

Which crops should be planted where? The county agent and the local soil conservationist advise farmers in the use of their land. In many regions land has been classified into eight classes. See Figure 38.5. Level bottom lands are called Class I lands; these require no special measures for erosion control. Steep land is graded from Class V to Class VIII according to which crops it is suited for. The classification has nothing to do with how "good" or how "bad" the soil is. Crops such as corn, cotton, or tobacco, which need cultivation, should not be planted on steeper slopes; cultivation of slopes increases water run-off and soil erosion.

Wheat, oats, and other grasses, however, may be planted on slopes; these plants grow close together, and their fine roots bind the soil.

Also, crops should be rotated in a field from season to season. Why? Different kinds of plants use the various minerals in different amounts. Rotating crops, therefore, helps to conserve the minerals. Besides, rotation helps to control plant diseases and insect pests. In some rotation schemes, every third or fourth year the land is planted to clover, alfalfa, or some other legume in order to add nitrates to the soil through the nodules on the roots.

Enormous areas of the United States have only enough rainfall for pasture grasses, not enough to produce grain crops. Overgrazing such land destroys the grasses, which are often replaced

38.6 Contour planting on slopes in Minnesota. The dark strips in the foreground are corn. How does contour planting help save soil? *U.S. Soil Conservation Service*

by worthless weeds. Great care must be taken if we are to conserve these valuable pasturelands.

Hillside planting. Look at Figure 38.6. On this sloping land erosion is being slowed by plowing and planting crosswise, not up and down the slope. This is called **contour planting.** In the foreground of this picture the crops are planted in strips. Strips of close-growing plants, such as grasses, which bind the soil, alternate with cultivated crops, such as corn or cotton or tobacco. The soil that washes from the strip above is then caught and held by the close-growing plants below. This is called **strip cropping.**

Terraces are often built to carry excess water to the edges of the field onto land covered with grass. Water on these grassed waterways is slowed up, and carries away little or no soil.

Soil conservation services. Since 1937, in many parts of the country, farmers have organized themselves for soil conservation. When a group forms a Soil Conservation District, the United States Soil Conservation Service furnishes an expert to help with farm planning; and specialists at agricultural colleges also give help. There are now soil conservation districts in every state. More than a million farmers have pledged themselves to farm so as to conserve soil. They find it possible sometimes to double their income from the sale of crops when they practice soil conservation. The Department of Agriculture in Washington administers the whole program.

Men and women trained in soil science and soil conservation work in the Department of Agriculture and in agricultural experiment stations and extension services in all parts of the country. They study the make-up of soils and classify them; they experiment with crop rotation in different regions; they measure soil erosion on plots planted to various crops; they investigate how much water various types of soil can hold; they experiment with fertilizers. There is much work to be done, and there are endless opportunities for young people trained for work of this kind.

CHAPTER THIRTY-EIGHT — A BOUNTIFUL FUTURE

38.7 Do you see the pipe which brings wastes into this stream? Such polluted water cannot support wildlife. *U.S. Soil Conservation Service*

WATER CONSERVATION

Use of water. Our problem is not that we have less water than we ever had before. Water is a renewable resource; it goes through a cycle. It evaporates constantly from all bodies of water, from the earth, and from plants (by transpiration); it is absorbed by the air as vapor; it condenses and returns to the earth in the form of rain or snow. Our problem is that we, in the United States, need much more water than formerly: in industry, for agriculture, even in our homes as our standard of living rises. Vast amounts of water are used for air conditioning, refrigeration, for the making of aluminum, steel, synthetic rubber, rayon, and many other products.

Twenty to thirty years ago we used 400 gallons per capita each day. Now we use two to three times as much. Our population is increasing rapidly. Where will we find the water we need ten years from now? Even now, in many large population centers, industrial growth is limited by water supply; and during years when the rainfall is less than normal, serious shortages occur.

The water table. Water seeps through the soil and through sand and gravel and rock until it has gone as far as it can go. The top level of this ground water is called the **water table**. In many places we are using the ground water much faster than it is being

38.8 Crop lands, machinery, and farm buildings were devastated by flood waters of the Kaw River in Kansas. What is being done here to hold the water back? What can be done to prevent such floods? *U.S. Department of Agriculture*

replaced by seepage down through the soil. We say that the water table or water level has fallen. It has dropped fifty or a hundred feet in many places. In California's Central Valley the ground-water level has fallen as much as two hundred feet because we have pumped water from the ground faster than it has been replaced. How can we conserve the ground water? In some places we can build dams to make marshes, ponds, or lakes from which water can seep into the ground. We can stop draining natural marshes; swamps are sometimes drained to get more farm land. But more important, we can take steps to slow up the run-off of water after rains. Whatever is done to slow up this flow of water off the soil not only saves water but saves soil as well.

You can see that the conservation of one resource is closely associated with the conservation of another. Conservation is a far more complex problem than was at first realized. Since this is true, large over-all planning for vast regions is desirable. Piecemeal conservation on individual farms will always be necessary but this alone will never be enough. Conservation requires the cooperation of governmental agencies and of all individuals, of the man who has a factory on a stream, of the farmer, the woodsman and the city dweller, of you, and of all of us. Everyone must cooperate.

How water supplies are lost. Much of the water we use is surface water from lakes, rivers, and smaller streams. This is easily polluted by sewage or industrial wastes. See Figure 38.7. In these cases it is usually lost to us. But water need not be polluted. Some industries help to conserve the water supply by cleaning the water they use so it can be used again. Others, such as the petroleum industry for example, have no wastes. You have already read about sewage disposal in connection with conserving human lives. Much surface water is still lost to us because of pollution by sewage. And polluted water is lost not only to us but to the many water-living organisms that are dependent on water that is free from all wastes.

Water supplies are lost to us, too, when floods occur. You have read how the misuse of land causes water to run off too rapidly, causing floods and much destruction of property.

CHAPTER THIRTY-EIGHT — A BOUNTIFUL FUTURE

38.9 The gates in the dam have been opened and the water allowed to drain from the reservoir behind this dam. The stream is now cutting a channel through silt, which through the years has been deposited on the bottom of the reservoir. Where did the silt come from? *U.S. Soil Conservation Service*

Damage by floods. Have you ever seen the results of a flood? Have you seen how the water cuts away land along the river banks? Much of this can be prevented by planting willows, locusts, or other fast growing trees along the banks. Sometimes the banks can be held by flat stones or concrete. See Figure 38.8.

As the water reaches level land it begins to flow more slowly. Then the soil that was worn away by the rushing water upstream is slowly deposited as **silt.** Silting in of streams and lakes makes the water unfit for use by us and by wildlife. Recreation areas are spoiled. Large reservoirs are sometimes so filled with silt they are no longer useful (Figure 38.9). Silt makes necessary the constant dredging of drainage ditches and harbors. More than 500 million tons of silt are deposited in the Gulf of Mexico by the Mississippi River every year.

Much of this silt is our precious topsoil. In the floods of 1948, each day for thirty days rich topsoil, enough to build up sixty farms of 80 acres each, was carried by the Columbia River into the Pacific Ocean.

Dams. Many floods can be prevented by soil conservation, but not all. Heavy rains or the melting of the snows in the spring may bring too much water. This extra water is sometimes led into reservoirs or storage basins. And dams are built to control rivers. The Tennessee Valley Authority has constructed a series of dams which have completely changed the whole valley fed by the Tennessee River and its tributaries.

But dams can do much more than control floods. First, water held back by dams can later be released as needed by towns. Parker Dam in the Colorado River stores water for Los Angeles, 241 miles distant. Second, with the construction of dams power is obtained. And third, dams can supply water to irrigate regions having insufficient rainfall. Water is carried to the crops either by a system of concrete-lined canals and ditches or by pipes. Figure 38.10 shows part of an irrigation system.

Water conservation agencies. Large water conservation projects can usually be handled only by Federal agencies.

Three vegetation zones determined principally by water supply are shown in this photograph of the Teton Mountains in Wyoming. In the foreground is the desert; behind it is a stand of pine; and in the background the bare rock of the mountains. *H. H. Holliger*

(Above) Contour-strip farming for soil conservation near Newton, Iowa. *Shostal*

(Below) Irrigated farm lands in Colorado. *G. Hunter*

38.10 An irrigated tomato field in Idaho. Acres of fertile soil would be going to waste without irrigation. Where is the water often obtained for such projects? Can you see how the water is brought to the field? *U.S. Soil Conservation Service*

Dams may be built by either the Bureau of Reclamation of the Department of the Interior or by the army engineers. The Soil Conservation Service in the Department of Agriculture does much to help conserve water resources on farms. This also helps control floods by slowing down the run-off of surface water into streams. Many states have water resources commissions, and all states have departments of public health concerned with the control of stream pollution. All cities and towns have staffs responsible for securing an adequate supply of usable water.

CONSERVATION OF FORESTS

Forest land. It is said that when America was discovered, a squirrel could start at the Atlantic coast and stay in the treetops until it reached the Mississippi River. By 1871 half of our trees had been lost either by cutting or by fire. Now there is left less than one fifth of the stand of trees we once had, and we are using our supply even faster than before. We are using trees faster than they are now growing. Forest conservation is a pressing problem even though forests are a renewable resource.

The early settlers, on the other hand, had a different problem: how to rid the land of trees. Land had to be cleared for building houses, raising crops, and making roads. They did not, and could not, think much about future generations.

Replacing forests. Forests that have never been lumbered are called first growth, or **virgin** forests. If you live in the far West you may well have seen virgin forests. In the East few such forests are left. **Second growth** forests are those that have grown up since the virgin forest was cut. Many second growth forests are found now on land that was cleared by the settlers and was farmed for a hundred years or more.

Trees grow slowly. In the South, pines can be used for lumber when they are between 30 and 40 years old. In the North it takes a tree from 75 to 150 years to grow to "saw-log" size. In the Rocky Mountain area trees become large enough to be called "saw timber" only after 180 years of growth.

After a forest has been burned or lumbered in such a way that erosion sets in, it takes a new forest many,

CHAPTER THIRTY-EIGHT — A BOUNTIFUL FUTURE

38.11 A virgin redwood forest in California. Stands of virgin forest are becoming scarce. What is the wisest use of such forests? *U.S. Forest Service*

many years to grow. The soil is built up slowly. First come the fast growing shrubs like raspberries and sumac. This community is succeeded by such trees as cherry and poplar. When these trees have grown up to provide enough shade, conifers, the softwoods, move in. These may be followed in some parts of our country by hardwoods. Yes, forests are renewable. But they are not being replaced fast enough to meet our needs.

Our need for wood. Trees are our largest crop. Four million conifers are cut and made into telephone poles each year! And think of all the railroads that stretch across the country, their tracks laid on wooden ties. So that some of you and your families may enjoy the Sunday newspaper, half a square mile of trees may have to be cut for one edition alone of a large paper. Each year we make more than 17 million tons of paper and cardboard from trees. Look about you. Even if you are in a stone building, the floors and woodwork, the furniture, your textbooks, your pads, pencils, all rayons, and many plastics all come from trees. Handles of shovels and rakes and parts of larger farm implements are made of tough hardwoods such as elm, ash, or hickory. Oak is used for heavy construction. We, in the United States, use 1700 pounds of wood per capita, each year; much wood is still being used for fuel. Our need for trees is great and unending.

UNIT TEN — CONSERVATION

38.12 Have you ever felt humus from a forest floor such as this? It is cool and moist for it holds much water. What enables it to hold water and give it up slowly? How does this help the man on a farm? *U.S. Forest Service*

Our need for forests. Forests help prevent both floods and droughts. Have you ever found shelter under a tree in the rain? It falls slowly here, dripping from leaf to leaf. When it reaches the ground, it soaks in. The **humus** (decaying plant and animal matter) of the forest floor is soft and spongy; it can hold large amounts of water. Thus brooks are fed slowly, and the larger streams don't overflow. See Figure 38.12. But when the forests are gone and the water is not held back on hillsides it rushes down rapidly after rains, washing away the good topsoil and causing floods. After the floods there is no water left on the bare hillsides to trickle down slowly into the valleys; droughts follow.

Forests, too, are important to us in supplying homes and food for wildlife. And they are used by thousands of us for recreation.

Maintaining our tree crop. It is not necessary for us to use up our forests faster than they can be replaced. Lumbermen can select carefully the trees to be cut, and harvest only those that have reached a certain size. Then they can remove the old, diseased, and crooked trees, those that may interfere with the new growth. As these young trees get more moisture and light they grow more rapidly. Through this **selective cutting** the owner can get one tree crop after another, year after year. This is called **sustained yield**. See Figure 38.13. In some places, instead of using selective cutting, it is better to cut the whole forest, leaving only some trees for reseeding.

Another way of increasing our crop of trees is by **reforestation** of cut-over land. Trees are raised by the thousands in nurseries (shown in Figure 38.14) to be used for this purpose. Or land can be reseeded by scattering seeds from airplanes. Then, too, further study of forest insects and fungus diseases will help maintain our tree crop.

38.13 Two lumbering methods in Oregon. Selective cutting (above) and clear cutting (below). Care must be taken to choose the best method for the particular forest to be cut. *U.S. Forest Service*

38.14 A forest tree seedling nursery in Mississippi. These are slash pine seedlings. *U.S. Forest Service*

UNIT TEN — CONSERVATION

38.15 These hillsides were once forest covered. The trees were destroyed by fire. What is lost besides trees? How is the farmer directly affected? *U.S. Forest Service*

38.16 Twelve million acres of forests are changed into this kind of waste every year. The standing trees are either dead or injured by fire. Further damage is caused by insects and fungi which attack the weakened trees. *U.S. Forest Service*

Forest fires. More than 12 million acres of trees, on an average, are lost to us every year through forest fires, Figure 38.15. Think what we lose in timber! But worse than that, the topsoil is burned out; soil erosion takes place; floods follow; wildlife grows less or completely disappears; the landscape is spoiled; recreational areas are lost. Figure 38.16 shows a common sight in forest regions. In a recent year there were more than

CHAPTER THIRTY–EIGHT — A BOUNTIFUL FUTURE

38.17 The forest ranger not only reports fires but helps direct the fighting of fires. Some rangers use airplanes and helicopters equipped with radio; others spend much of their time in lonely mountaintop fire towers. *Grundy* (left) and *U.S. Forest Service*

188,000 forest fires in the United States, and many of them could have been prevented; carelessness is usually the cause — man's carelessness in the burning of brush or using the forests in hunting, camping, or fishing. Occasionally fires are started by lightning or sparks from railroad trains.

To control a fire, it must be detected early. This requires a network of lookout points, airplanes, and some patrolling on the ground. Look at Figure 38.17. Informed by radio and telephone, the forest fire supervisor of the region mobilizes bulldozers, tank trucks, and tractor-drawn plows. "Smoke jumpers," using parachutes, get into action. Meanwhile scouting planes may take photographs which will show within fifteen minutes what help is needed. Plows are used to block fires; if there is nothing to burn, the fire dies. For the same reason, sometimes backfires are set to travel with the wind in the direction of the onward moving fire. See the next pictures.

Forest services. Today, the Forest Service of the United States Department of Agriculture is responsible for more than 160 million acres of forest land in forty-two states. The National Forests are set aside for controlled use; some cutting, grazing, and hunting are permitted here. At the head of the Forest Service is the Chief Forester. Under him are ten regional foresters, each with his staff.

All states have a forestry department, too, which cooperates with the United States Forest Service, with extension services, and with other agencies interested in forestry. They manage state-owned forests, help control fires, and

38.18 Study this and the two pictures on the next page to see modern methods of fighting forest fires. Which methods are illustrated? *U.S. Forest Service*

CHAPTER THIRTY-EIGHT — A BOUNTIFUL FUTURE

UNIT TEN — CONSERVATION

assist landowners in improving their forest lands.

Would you like to be a forester? If you are interested in forestry, you will find a large variety of jobs open to you. There are outdoor jobs and indoor jobs — teaching, research, and office jobs. Some foresters live in the forests as rangers; others survey and make maps; some study or control insect pests or plant diseases; some do research on forest products; some teach in colleges and agricultural schools; many are concerned with forest products commercially — lumber, paper, wood chemicals, plastics, and so on. The United States Forest Service and various state departments employ many men who have specialized in forestry. Railroads own and maintain forests and use foresters. Pulp and paper companies, and other wood-using industries, now employ more foresters than are employed by the government.

WILDLIFE CONSERVATION

Loss of wildlife. Our topsoil is being eroded, our inland waters are being silted in or polluted, our forests are being destroyed. Naturally, the animal inhabitants of grasslands, streams, and forests have been affected. Food shortages among many species have arisen, large numbers of animals have been driven out or killed. Food chains have been broken, cycles interrupted. In short, another of our resources is disappearing — our wildlife, the plants and animals which live and grow without the assistance of man. As civilization advances, some wildlife is bound to disappear. Railroads, roads, and growing cities all reduce our wildlife. But ignorance, thoughtlessness, and greed have also played their part. Unnecessary water pollution kills many water forms. Trapping and **market hunting** (hunting for purposes of selling) of wild mammals and birds for their skins and meat has led to much loss of wildlife in the past; now such practices are carefully controlled or prohibited.

Importance of wildlife. Wildlife, including fish and other sea foods, supplies a considerable amount of food. The commercial fishing and fur industries are sizable, giving work to many people. Fishing and hunting offer recreation to many thousands, as does observation of wildlife and nature photography. The appreciation and enjoyment of the out-of-doors has become an important national hobby for millions of people.

But there is another reason for preserving our wildlife resources. You will remember how closely all animals and plants are interrelated. We often harm ourselves when we change natural relationships.

Vanishing wildlife. Bison were seen by the first white men who landed in what is now Maryland. They lived where the White House stands today and roamed the prairies, far to the west, in vast herds. Elk once roamed our eastern woods. The California grizzly bear is gone. The year 1914 saw the end of the passenger pigeon, which at one time was widely used as food and could be bought for a penny a bird. As recently as 1932 the heath hen became extinct. The wild turkey, once plentiful, is now rare but thanks to wildlife conservationists is now increasing in numbers. The whooping crane, the ivory-billed woodpecker,

38.19 Elk protected in National Elk Range, Wyoming. *Fish and Wildlife Service*

the Florida key deer, and the California condor are very near extinction. The whooping cranes, which rear their young in Canada and return to Texas in the fall, are counted each time they start their northward migration and are anxiously counted as they return. Twenty-one of these birds returned in the fall of 1954.

Early conservation programs. In the early days of conservation programs mistakes were sometimes made. In an attempt to protect mule deer in certain regions, they were allowed to multiply so rapidly that they ran out of food and began to starve to death. Our protection of the white-tailed deer in other regions resulted in overrun gardens and destruction of vegetable crops.

At one time fishermen began a war on pelicans, large fish-eating birds. Only after many pelicans had been killed were the contents of the pelican's stomach studied. What was learned? Most of the fish eaten were kinds never used by us as food! Only then, but too late, fishermen learned that pelicans were not competing with them; they merely helped keep down the numbers of fish of no value to us.

There was a time, too, when the government paid bounties for animals believed to destroy useful birds or mammals. Bounty laws have sometimes proved to do more harm than good. For example, in Pennsylvania hawks and owls were raiding the farmers' chicken coops, stealing the young chicks. The farmers asked their legislature for help; a large bounty was offered for all hawks and owls. In a short time the raiding stopped; hawks and owls were pretty well killed off. But then the real trouble began for the farmer. It was learned, again too late, that it is mostly one hawk, the Cooper's hawk, that kills chickens. Other hawks eat mostly field mice, which in turn eat grain. The field mice increased enormously without their natural enemies. Millions of

38.20 Thousands of ducks in this California refuge. *Fish and Wildlife Service*

bushels of grain were lost to the farmers! Living things are so interdependent that we must be careful not to destroy a valuable resource in trying to control another form. Some states still offer bounties, even though their value is very doubtful.

Wildlife laws. Wildlife laws, usually called game laws, can be helpful, however. All states have game laws, which forbid killing certain mammals and birds, and regulate the time of year, even the time of day, when others may be hunted. Fishing is likewise regulated. For most species of game the season of "harvesting" (when hunting is permitted) is regulated so that the females are not killed while the young are dependent on them. The "season" limits and the "bag" limits (usually the number permitted to be taken in one day) vary according to the animal and the state. They are changed, too, from time to time as game becomes more or less plentiful and according to our better understanding of the game problem.

For animals like ducks and geese that cross state lines, the Federal Government helps to make and enforce conservation laws. And for those birds that travel from one country to another, there are migratory bird treaties, as for example, those between the United States and Canada or Mexico. For several years all hunters of ducks and geese in the United States have been required to purchase a Duck Stamp — a special tax on those who hunt these birds. By two recent Federal laws, hunting and fishing equipment are taxed. The money derived from such taxes, and money collected by states from sportsmen for hunting and fishing licenses, is used for restocking streams and for other conservation measures.

CHAPTER THIRTY-EIGHT — A BOUNTIFUL FUTURE

38.21 The mountain sheep was photographed on the Kofa Game Range in Arizona, the bear in Yellowstone National Park. Many of our wild animals would have vanished long ago except for protection in such refuges. *Fish and Wildlife Service*

Modern conservation programs. The conservation of wildlife is best accomplished by preserving or restoring the natural habitats of the animals and plants we wish to conserve. Nowadays, we think in terms of improving the living conditions of those species we want to encourage. Therefore, ecologists are needed to plan sound conservation programs. Let's see what is being done.

(1) More than a hundred National Parks and National Monuments have been established under the National Park Service. Some parks and monuments are small, some contain more than a million acres, but in all they include less than 1 per cent of the land area of our country. A National Park is established by act of Congress; a National Monument is set aside by the President. The primary object of the parks and monuments is to keep living things in their natural state. Fishing is permitted, but no hunting, no harvesting of timber, no mining, no grazing. The National Park Service is separate from the National Forest Service.

(2) Smaller tracts of land are used as **refuges.** See Figure 38.20. These are sometimes called **sanctuaries.** In some states — North Carolina, Massachusetts, New York, and others — whole towns have been declared bird sanctuaries. Refuges must be carefully selected and planned for. Lands that are not good enough for crops (called submarginal lands) are often used. However, the soil must be able to support the right kinds of plant food; there must be unpolluted water; there must be cover-places so that various animals can build homes and escape predators. This means grass, shrubs, or trees; it means holes in trees for squirrels, bears, raccoons, and owls. In short, the refuge must support a whole community if it is to give protection to any one kind of animal.

(3) In addition to refuges good habitats are sometimes provided on farms and woodlands, providing food and cover. Farm ponds are being built and stocked with sunfish, perch, and bass. And some swamps are kept for ducks, herons, and muskrats.

Raising birds and other animals on

38.22 Salmon are trapped on the Wind River, near Carson, Washington; and their eggs and milt (sperms) removed. Eggs are incubated at a fish hatchery. Waters are then stocked with the young fish. *Daniel H. Chapman, Fish and Wildlife Service*

game farms and releasing them later has been tried; in general, this is often not successful. The expense is great and the animals often do not survive when they are turned loose to get their own food. Wildlife managers prefer to improve natural conditions in forests and on the edges of fields where animals can breed naturally.

Have you ever visited a mink or chinchilla or silver fox "farm"? Then you will know that sometimes animals that normally make up part of our wildlife are raised on farms as an additional crop. These farms are encouraged as a conservation measure, especially if land is used that would not be useful for other crops.

Conservation of water life. Fish populations are decreasing for many reasons. Improved methods of canning and refrigeration mean there is much more demand for fish. Spawning (egg-laying) of fish like the shad and salmon and some others has been seriously interfered with by our use of traps and nets and by building dams that keep fish from reaching their breeding grounds. Then, too, commercial fishermen have overfished certain species, such as the lake whitefish. Pollution of streams by industrial wastes and sewage has killed many fish, especially the young. The oxygen normally dissolved in water is used up in the decomposition of sewage; plants fail to make food, and animals die. Poisonous substances in industrial wastes kill all kinds of living things. Silting in streams and bays smothers the eggs of both fish and shellfish. And then fish are often destroyed by droughts and floods and natural enemies other than man. A serious situation has arisen in the Great Lakes, where large numbers of economically important fish are being destroyed by the lamprey eel.

The Fish and Wildlife Service long ago built fish hatcheries; and state conservation departments or commissions raise game fish in hatcheries. When these young fish have reached a

CHAPTER THIRTY-EIGHT — A BOUNTIFUL FUTURE

certain size they are used for stocking streams, lakes, and farm ponds. But much research now goes into a study of how to prepare habitats for these young fish. If food and cover can be provided in lakes and streams by increasing plant growth through the use of fertilizers, the stocking of certain waters should not be necessary. Some stocking, however, of trout and other cold water species will probably still be required. See Figure 38.22. Certain methods of catching fish, such as by use of dynamite, have now been outlawed, and dams across streams used by fish on their way to spawning grounds must now be equipped with "fish ladders."

Conservation agencies and careers. Millions of dollars are being spent by the Federal Government and in your state capital for preserving and making the best use of our vanishing resources — soil, water, forests, and wildlife. Conservation is now the work of thousands of men and women. Whether your interest lies in ecology, chemistry, bacteriology, plant pathology, forestry, entomology, the out-of-doors, education, or engineering, you can find employment in State or Federal Government, or, if you prefer, in industry. Many wildlife specialists are needed to investigate the habits and the life histories of fish and game. Others are needed to establish and manage wildlife refuges, fish hatcheries, game farms, and hunting areas. Thousands of men are employed as game protectors and law enforcement officers. The Federal and State Governments and colleges employ college-trained biologists and wildlife specialists to conduct research, administer wildlife programs, and to teach. Many colleges now offer broad programs of training for careers in conservation.

Some private organizations, too, give much help in conservation and employ people trained as conservationists. Some of these are the National Audubon Society, the Izaak Walton League, the National Wildlife Institute, the Friends of the Land, the Soil Conservation Society, the American Forestry Association, and the National Parks Association.

What you can do. You have been reading about the need for conservation. You may have been wondering "What can I do to help?" Perhaps you can't build dams to prevent floods. Perhaps you live in a city; you can't farm, or make a farm pond, or establish a wildlife refuge. Perhaps you can't practice any conservation measures in a large way, but you **can** do some things right now. If your school is in a large city, you can feed birds on the window sills and you can take trips to city parks and to a water supply plant to learn about conservation at first hand.

If, however, you have school grounds or there is property nearby which can be used, you can undertake a number of satisfying and useful conservation projects. One problem almost always present on school grounds is to keep the ground covered with grass. Because of the heavy traffic, erosion on a small scale is likely to set in. You may be able to help your school by experimenting with various types of grasses to discover which is best suited to the school's needs. Or, perhaps, some shrubs can be planted where they will prevent short cuts or overuse of some parts of the grounds.

There may be room for some more trees. Select a species to provide shade but also to add color and serve as food and protection for birds. Perhaps the edges of your playing field are bare and

38.23 Wild flowers that need protection. Which do you recognize? What can you do to protect them? **A**, Trailing arbutus; **B**, Jack-in-the-pulpit; **C**, False Solomon's seal; **D**, Mountain laurel; **E**, Hepatica; **F**, Bird's-foot violet. **A, C, F**, *American Museum of Natural History;* **B**, *Brooklyn Botanic Garden;* **E, D**, *U.S. Department of Agriculture*

CHAPTER THIRTY–EIGHT — A BOUNTIFUL FUTURE

551

38.24 These Plymouth, New Hampshire, high school biology students are improving the appearance of their school lawn. They used fertilizer, grass seed, and hard work. Perhaps your school lawn needs improvement. *N.A.B.T. Conservation Handbook*

there are banks that need protection; berry-producing shrubs and vines can be used here. Bird houses and feeders can be placed about the school grounds. You may want to draw up a plan with the help of some parents and school officials for the improving of your school grounds. If possible, consult soil conservationists, nurserymen and landscape architects in order to be sure that you plant the right kinds of trees and shrubs.

If your grounds are large enough, you might start a wildflower garden for species needing protection. See Figure 38.23. Of if your school is fortunate enough to own or control a still larger area, you may want to establish a school garden or a school forest. Here you may grow some of the trees and shrubs needed in landscaping your school, and you can learn many gardening and forestry practices. See Figure 38.24.

Some of these things you may be able to do now, but there is something else of great importance that all of you can do now and at all times in the future.

Your representatives in State and Federal Governments are pledged to carry out the wishes of the people they represent. Even before you are old enough to vote, you can influence legislators through letters signed by all the members of your class. You may be surprised to learn how much influence you have. If you keep yourselves informed of pending legislation on matters of conservation, you can take an active part in the making of wise decisions.

The world of tomorrow. The world of tomorrow will be the kind of place we make it. We can waste our resources and change the earth into a barren globe. Or we can manage things so that as far as we can look into the future we will have plenty of food, clothing, and shelter. Throughout this last unit of study you have been learning of some of the steps necessary to insure a bountiful future. We know much about managing our soil so that it will not be lost faster than it is formed from the native rocks. We know much about managing our water supplies to insure enough water for both farming and industry. We know much about how the forests should be managed to provide a continuous supply of wood for all our needs. We know much about conserving human life and the wild animals and plants which are such an important part of our lives. We know that the conservation of human life and the conservation of soil, water, forests, and wildlife are all parts of one vast problem. All are interrelated.

Much is yet to be learned, of course, but if all that we now know were to be put into practice in all the inhabited parts of the globe, how much better our earth would be! Progress is being made, though slowly. Will you be one who helps or hinders it?

USEFUL WORDS IN BIOLOGY

fertilizer	contour	selective
topsoil	planting	cutting
inorganic	strip cropping	sustained
sheet erosion	sanctuary	yield
gully erosion	water table	reforestation
leaching	silt	market
green	virgin forest	hunting
manure	second growth	bounty
terracing	forest	refuge

TEST YOURSELF

Soil Conservation

1. Give some idea of the rate of increase in population in the United States at the present time. Find out from the *World Almanac* what the population is this year.
2. Explain why, when we consider the whole world, conservation is necessary.
3. (a) State in simple words what is meant by natural resources. (b) Name our natural resources and explain how we commonly classify them.
4. Give a short history of the conservation program down to the present time.
5. Explain fully how soil is formed. In doing this you will tell of what it is composed.
6. (a) Explain sheet erosion and gully erosion. (b) What can be done to help decrease wind erosion?
7. Name the mineral elements used by plants and tell which ones are most likely to disappear from many soils when the soil is cultivated.
8. (a) Explain the difference between fertilizer, manure, and green manure. (b) Show why each helps to restore fertility to the soil.
9. Soils often need improvement through the addition of minerals. In what other respects do they often need improvement?
10. On what basis are agricultural lands classified by the conservationist?
11. (a) How does crop rotation help conserve soil? (b) What is another advantage in crop rotation?
12. Describe agricultural practices which are especially useful in conserving soil on hillsides.
13. (a) Describe how soil conservation districts have been organized and explain why they have spread so rapidly to all the states. (b) Describe the work done by the United States Department of Agriculture, the agricultural experiment stations, and extension services.

Water Conservation

14. (a) What is the water table? (b) State three steps we can take to help maintain or raise the water table.
15. Describe several kinds of damage done by a flooded stream from source to mouth.
16. Explain (a) how soil conservation measures can help prevent floods and (b) how various kinds of dams are used in water and soil conservation.
17. In tabular form show which federal, state, and local agencies are concerned with water conservation.

Forest Conservation

18. (a) What proportion of our forest trees has been lost? (b) Comment on our need for trees now as compared to formerly.

CHAPTER THIRTY-EIGHT — A BOUNTIFUL FUTURE

19. (a) What is a virgin forest, a second-growth forest? (b) Give some idea of the length of time it takes trees to grow. (c) Explain the effect of burning or poor lumbering practice on forest replacement.

20. (a) Name some of the principal uses of wood. (b) Of what value are forests to us besides supplying us with wood?

21. What are the two principal methods used to maintain tree crops?

22. (a) State all the ways in which forest fires do harm. (b) Describe the methods used to help prevent forest fires and to control them.

23. Tell of the many openings for young men and women who study forestry.

Wildlife Conservation

24. Give examples of how man has affected wildlife populations.

25. Name some forms of vanishing or extinct wildlife.

26. Give some examples of how short-sightedness and ignorance of ecology in the past have led to disaster.

27. State some specific laws that help maintain wildlife.

28. Describe our modern conservation programs.

29. How can our water wildlife resources be increased?

30. Make a complete list of the opportunities for careers and employment in conservation work.

31. (a) Which of the suggestions offered under "What you can do" will *you* take? (b) What is the most important thing you can do to further conservation, no matter where you live?

DO IT YOURSELF

1. Studies at first hand. No matter where you live, on a farm or in a town, you can take some trips to see with your own eyes what you have been reading about. Here are suggestions of a few places to visit and study; think up others for yourself: a bird refuge or sanctuary, an agricultural school or experiment station, land being reforested, tree nurseries, a badly eroded hill, good or poor methods of hillside planting, a fire lookout, a fish hatchery, a fur farm, a city park or lot showing erosion, a place where erosion has been brought under control by some conservation method.

2. Inviting speakers to your school. No matter where you live, you will find organizations doing conservation work or work related to conservation. They will be glad to send speakers to tell you about their work. Even in a city, those in charge of parks and highway planting, an aquarium, or a zoo will help you. Make your own list of the possibilities now; and act promptly.

3. Telling your friends about wildlife conservation. Write to the National Wildlife Federation, Washington 12, D.C., for a price list of their wildlife stamps, notepaper, booklets, field guide series, and other materials. They are doing much to give conservation publicity but they need your help in spreading information and arousing people's interest. Interest your younger brothers and sisters in conservation now; the Federation will give you suggestions for gifts.

4. A study of population increases. Write a report after studying figures in the *World Almanac*, and reading *Limits of the Earth* by Fairfield Osborn, Little, Brown, 1953, or some other recent and reliable book on this subject.

5. Keeping the class up-to-date. Look through the price lists of the publications supplied by the Superintendent of Documents, Government Printing Office, Washington, D.C., for pamphlets that will interest the class. Send for some; the cost is nominal. You will find pamphlets such as this: "Youth can help conserve these resources, soil, water, woodland, wildlife, grass," 1951, 24 pp., 15¢.

6. A study of the soil in your region. By checking with your county agent and local soil conservationist list the soil types for your county and find out the average depth of the topsoil and the extent of erosion. If a soil auger is available, make some checks of your own on the depth of the topsoil in several locations. This can be made into an interesting report to the class.

7. Making a farm and crop survey. By interviewing some farmers and by observation, describe the crop rotation being used locally. Find out some of the reasons for this particular rotation.

8. Making a water survey. By checking with the county agent and some well drillers, try to learn the average depth of the water table in your area. Find out whether it has changed during the past 25 years and how much. Or if you live in a large city write a report on the city's water supply. Contact your bureau of water supply or your board of health for information.

9. Pollution chart. On a map spot the sources and location of various types of water pollution in your area. Find out from county, city, or state officials what is being done to decrease pollution. Make a sand table model to illustrate how water pollution could occur.

10. Organizing a fire-fighting patrol. Invite a local forester to exhibit his fire-fighting equipment at your school. This could lead to the organization of a fire-fighting patrol.

11. Making a survey of wildlife of your area. Compile a list of the game species of fish, birds, and mammals of your area. Determine the season and bag or creel limits for each. Write to your State Department of Conservation for help.

12. National Parks and Monuments. Where are your ten nearest national parks and monuments, and the nearest state and national forests and parks? The *World Almanac* and automobile maps will help you. Consult, too, one of the books on national parks and monuments.

ADVENTURES IN READING

1. *Our Plundered Planet* by Fairfield Osborn, Little, Brown, Boston, 1948. One of several books by this author who is much concerned about the future of mankind.
2. *Our Wildlife Legacy* by Durward L. Allen, Funk & Wagnalls, 1954. Makes good reading for those interested in wildlife.
3. *Water—or Your Life* by Arthur H. Carhart, Lippincott, 1951. The title shows that it is written in a popular style. Be sure to read it.
4. *Timber in Your Life* by Arthur H. Carhart, Lippincott, 1955. Written for the general reader; has a good chapter on forest fires.
5. *Exploring Our National Parks and Monuments* by Devereaux Butcher, Houghton Mifflin, 1949. Contains much needed information even for those of us who cannot go out to explore.
6. *Water, Land and People* by Bernard Frank and Anthony Netboy, Knopf, 1950. Gives you a good deal to think about.
7. *Man and the Soil* by Karl B. Mickey, International Harvester Co., 1945.
8. *Trees*, the 1949 Yearbook of the U.S. Department of Agriculture. Has chapters on so many different subjects; you are sure to find something here to interest you.
9. *Soils and Men*, 1938 Yearbook of the U.S. Department of Agriculture.
10. *The Sun, the Sea and Tomorrow* by G. Walton Smith and Henry Chapin, Scribner's, 1954. When we run short of food can we make better use of the sea? Be sure to read the chapters "Farming for Fishes" and "Ocean Pasturage."
11. *Food Resources of the Ocean* by P. Galtsoff, American Book, 1952.

"Algae as Food" by Harold W. Milner, *Scientific American*, October 1953. Discusses the possibilities of raising algae as food for man.

"The Tillamook Burn," *Scientific Monthly*, September 1952. An exciting article on a fire in the northwest.

A Primer on Conservation by Olin L. Kaupanger, Colwell, 1952.

A Conservation Handbook by Samuel H. Ordway, Jr., The Conservation Foundation, 1949. Will make an excellent small reference book for you.

CHAPTER THIRTY-EIGHT — A BOUNTIFUL FUTURE

Appendix

The structure of some animals other than man

Let's glance at half a dozen familiar animals, starting with the very simple and ending with some fairly complex vertebrate such as the frog. Let's see how each carries on its important activities — locomotion, digestion, circulation, breathing, excretion, reproduction, and nervous functions. Notice how the various animals resemble each other, and notice the differences which adapt each animal to its special habitat and mode of life. Notice, too, in how many ways the vertebrates, especially, resemble you. We'll study the hydra, the earthworm, the crayfish, the grasshopper, the fish, and the frog.

THE HYDRA

Phylum Coelenterata

You already know how the single-celled animals like ameba and paramecium live. Let's take a closer look at one of the simple many-celled animals, the hydra. It lives in fresh water; most of the time it remains attached to water weeds. You may see it attached to the glass sides of your aquarium. It secretes a sticky substance at its lower end by which it fastens itself; but it can detach itself and move in a jerky way, like a looping caterpillar.

Figure A.1 shows a hydra cut open. Its wall consists of two layers of cells surrounding a large cavity. Thus it resembles the early embryo (gastrula) of higher animals. The outside layer is

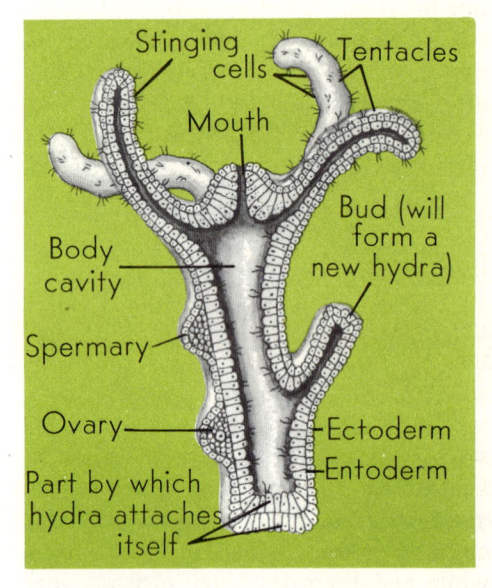

A.1 Hydra.

ectoderm; the inner is **endoderm.** The cavity opens to the outside on top through an opening called the **mouth.** This is at the top of a mound (**hypostome**) which is surrounded by 6 or 8 hollow **tentacles.** These have stinging cells. Both the endoderm and the ectoderm are made up of four kinds of cells: (1) **interstitial cells,** which originate buds, sex cells, and others; (2) **gland cells,** which secrete mucus and digestive enzymes; (3) **muscular cells,** which change the shape of the hydra and move it; and (4) **sensory cells.** Hydra, you can see, has some slight differentiation of cells, but it does not have the variety of tissues higher animals have.

How does hydra live? Currents created by the flagella draw smaller animals and small plants into the mouth. Then the pseudopods of the endoderm cells engulf some of this food, which is digested within the cell. Some of the food is digested by enzymes secreted into the cavity and is later absorbed. The digested food is changed into protoplasm. The undigested parts are expelled through the mouth. Hydra does not breathe. Oxygen, dissolved in the water, diffuses into all the cells. Oxidation takes place. Carbon dioxide diffuses out. Hydra has no sense organs, nerves, or brain. But its protoplasm, of course, has the property of irritability, and some sort of communication takes place between its cells, for they behave as a unit.

Hydra reproduces asexually by forming buds which break off and live as new hydras. It also forms, to the outside on the ectoderm, a **spermary** with sperm cells and, lower down on the same side, an **ovary** with egg cells. Fertilization and development into a young embryo occur in the ovary. The embryo, after it is set free, rests for a while and then develops into an adult hydra.

THE EARTHWORM

(Lumbricus) Phylum Annelida

Let's take a close look at the outside of an earthworm, or "night crawler," before we cut it open. It has normally about 80 or more rings, or segments (**somites**). Those at the posterior (rear) end are of less importance; but if you cut a worm in two in the middle, the posterior end will regenerate an anterior (front) end, and the anterior end will regenerate a posterior end. Examine the ventral (lower) side of each segment with the aid of a lens. You will see four pairs of tiny bristles, or **setae** (see′tee). The setae serve as "feet." The worm crawls by contracting one segment after another from head to rear. Along the middle line of the dorsal (back) side, you can see tiny dorsal pores which go through the body wall and open into the body cavity, or **coelom**. Now let's pin the earthworm to a sheet of cork and slit open its ventral side.

Digestion. The earthworm has a digestive tube open at the anterior and posterior ends, like ours. It runs through the long coelom. The coelom

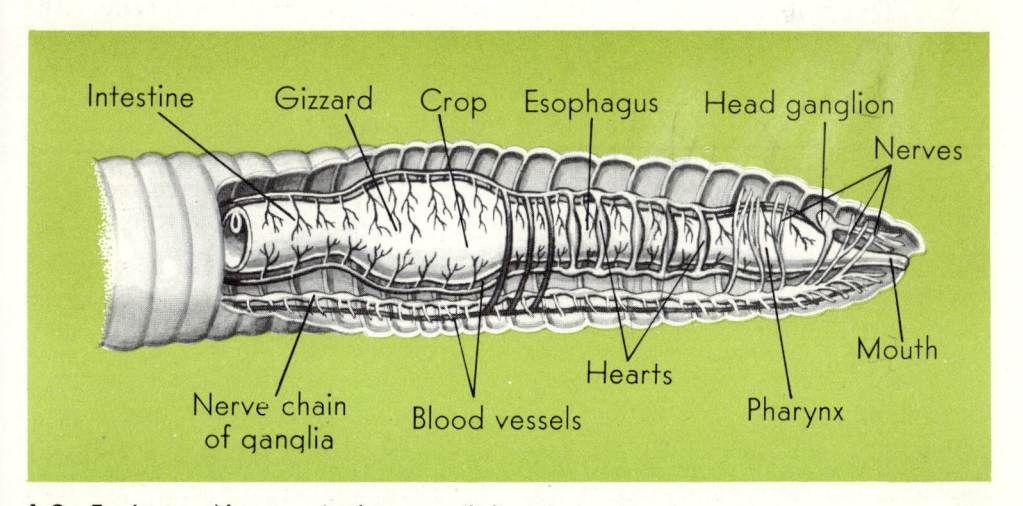

A.2 Earthworm. Nervous, circulatory, and digestive systems.

APPENDIX — THE STRUCTURE OF SOME ANIMALS

557

is filled with a fluid containing colorless blood corpuscles. Look at Figure A.2. Notice that the mouth opens into the **pharynx.** This leads into a long **esophagus,** which is followed by a much wider, thin-walled **crop.** Then comes the wide and thick-walled **gizzard,** and then the long **intestine.** All these parts make up the **alimentary canal.** It is lined with epithelial cells. Some of these secrete enzymes; others are concerned with absorption. The earthworm's digestive system is simple compared to ours; it has none of the large digestive glands outside the canal. You will remember that the worm eats its way through the soil, passing large quantities of decaying plant material and minerals through its body. It digests a part of all it eats and leaves the rest behind as **castings.**

Circulation. Three long blood vessels run the length of the body. Even from the outside of the living worm you can see blood in the long dorsal vessel shining through the skin. Figure A.2 shows two **ventral blood vessels,** one just under the alimentary canal and the other below it, close to the ventral body covering. Of course, all these blood vessels have branches which end in microscopic blood vessels in the various tissues. There is no heart; but you do see five hoops which connect the dorsal with the ventral vessels in the region of the esophagus. There are other hoops, but less conspicuous ones. Those around the esophagus beat rhythmically and are often called hearts. The walls of all the principal vessels have muscle tissue. By contraction of the vessel walls, blood is pushed forward through the dorsal vessel and backward through the ventral vessels. The earthworm's blood is red, but its hemoglobin is dissolved in the liquid part of the blood; the corpuscles are colorless.

Breathing and excretion. Because the main blood vessels run the length of the body just under the thin, moist skin, oxygen can enter the blood directly from the air and carbon dioxide can leave it. The worm does not have separate breathing organs. The organs of excretion, called **nephridia** (nef-frid'ee-a) are slender, looped tubes. They open into the coelom by means of a sort of funnel which has beating cilia. There is one pair of these nephridia in each segment except the very first and last segments. At its farther end the looped tube opens to the outside on the ventral surface of each segment. Look on the outside of the ventral surface for these paired excretory openings called **nephridiopores.**

The nervous system. The worm has no organs of sight or of hearing. Special cells around the region of the mouth seem in some way to enable the worm to distinguish between different kinds of food. Although it has no eyes, it is sensitive to bright light, as you can easily discover for yourself. Perhaps the light acts directly on the nervous system. The nervous system, shown in Figure A.2, is simple. The **brain** is a large, double, **dorsal ganglion** in the head. This is connected by a nerve ring around the esophagus to a **double chain of smaller ganglia.** There is a pair of ganglia on the ventral side in each segment. Nerves leave all the ganglia, which, like our ganglia, contain neurons.

Reproduction. In its reproduction the earthworm differs from almost all other animals. It has two pairs of small flattened **spermaries** in the 10th and 11th segments and a pair of small pear-shaped **ovaries** in the 13th segment.

Can you find them? Every earthworm has both male and female organs; because of this it is said to be a **hermaphrodite** (her-maf'row-dite). You saw that a hydra has both spermaries and ovaries in the same animal but the interesting thing about the earthworm is that, although it is a hermaphrodite, its sperm cells can never fertilize its own eggs. Sperm cells leave through a duct which opens on the 13th segment. But they leave only when two earthworms **copulate.** Two earthworms become attached by their ventral surfaces, heads in opposite directions. The sperm cells of each then come to the surface, where, as you will see, they can reach the egg cells of the other worm. Each worm has a pair of sacs (**egg receptacles**) opening to the exterior, where its own eggs are held. And it has two pairs of sacs (**seminal receptacles**) where sperm cells of the other worm can be held. Look at the outside of a worm again. Do you see that the worm has a region between segments 31 and 37 which looks swollen? This band is the **clitellum** (cli-tell'um). When the worms copulate, the clitellum and some special glands on the surface secrete a sticky substance, which forms a tube around the worm from the clitellum to the head. Sperms travel in this tube to the seminal receptacles. After the worms separate, eggs are fertilized and gathered into cocoons containing several eggs. The tube and cocoon is then slipped off as a ring is slipped off a finger, and the cocoon is left in the earth. In it, embryos develop into complete tiny earthworms.

THE CRAYFISH

(Astacus) Class Crustacea
Phylum Arthropoda

The crayfish that is common in rivers, lakes, and small streams is really a smaller edition of the lobster. (The shrimp is a very similar species but smaller than the crayfish, and Daphnia is much the same but still smaller than the shrimp. With all the crabs they belong to the Class CRUSTACEA of the Phylum ARTHROPODA — the phylum with an outside skeleton and jointed legs.)

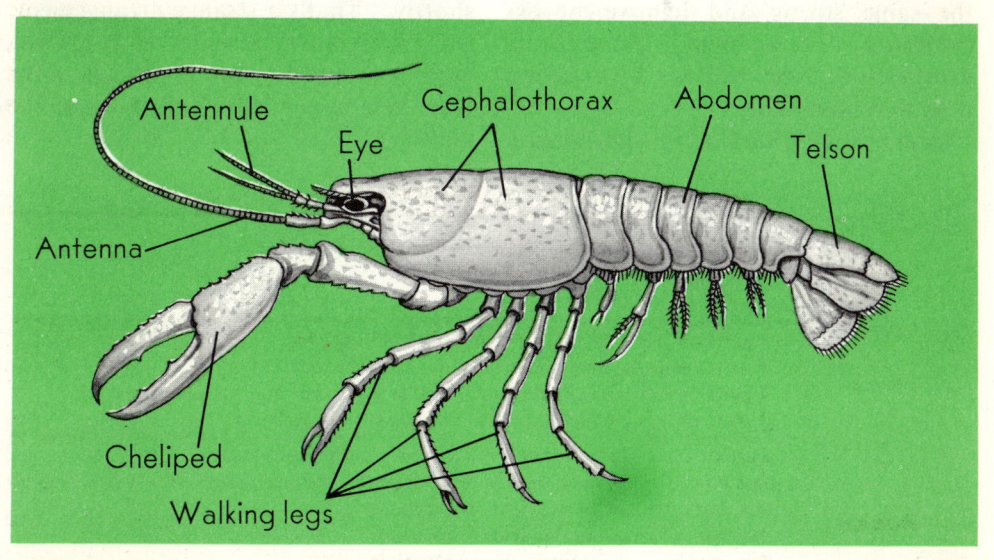

A.3 Crayfish.

APPENDIX — THE STRUCTURE OF SOME ANIMALS

Body parts and appendages. Look at the crayfish from the outside (Fig. A.3). You will see a pair of long, segmented **antennae,** which can point backward or forward, and a pair of shorter **antennules** (an-ten'youls). You will see, too, a pair of compound eyes as in insects; but these eyes are on stalks. The body is dark, and the whole animal is covered with an **exoskeleton.** The exoskeleton is made up largely of a substance called **chitin,** made still stronger by the lime deposited in it. It is both strong and extremely light — far lighter than bones in vertebrates.

You will see two body regions: the **cephalothorax** (sef'el-oh-thor'ax) and the **abdomen.** The cephalothorax includes the head and the region which, in insects, is called the thorax. The abdomen has seven segments. The last segment is triangular and flat; it is called the **telson.** The cephalothorax is covered with extra heavy armor plate, called the **carapace** (ka'ra-pace). In front it ends in a point between the antennae; this point is the **rostrum.** The legs and claws are covered with the same strong and lightweight exoskeleton. Try to break a piece of the exoskeleton; you will see how strong it is, and how light.

And now let's look at the **appendages.**

You have already noticed the large antennae. In front of them is a pair of small **antennules.** Each of these ends in two long many-jointed flagella. At the base of each antennule is a small sac which holds a few grains of sand. This is the **statocyst,** used in balancing. Looking at the crayfish from underneath you can see the jaws, or **mandibles** (man'di-bles), and two pairs of smaller jaws, or **maxillae** (max-il'lee). Both mandibles and maxillae work from side to side. All of these are head appendages.

Attached to the thorax (made up of eight fused segments) you will find eight pairs of jointed appendages. The first three pairs are called **maxillipeds** (max-il'li-peds) which means jaw feet. That's just what they are — small legs which hold the food and thus help in eating. Then comes a pair of huge pincers, called **chelipeds** (keel'i-peds), used in defense and in getting prey. Behind them are two pairs of legs with small pincers and then two more pairs of legs which end in a claw. Attached to all these eight pairs of appendages are the gills, which you will examine shortly. That's a strange arrangement, isn't it, to have the gills or breathing organs attached to the legs? The table lists these appendages and those of the abdomen.

APPENDAGES OF THE CRAYFISH

Head	antennae antennules mandibles maxillae	
Thorax	3 pairs maxillipeds, or "jaw feet" 1 pair chelipeds, huge pincers 2 pairs of legs with small pincers 2 pairs of legs ending in a claw	hold the food help get prey help get prey and for walking mostly for walking
Abdomen	1st pair 2nd pair 3rd pair 4th pair 5th pair 6th pair	in both male and female used in reproduction in male used in reproduction; in female used like 3rd, 4th, and 5th swimming feet, or **pleopods** swimming feet, or **pleopods** swimming feet, or **pleopods** double plates spread out beside the telson

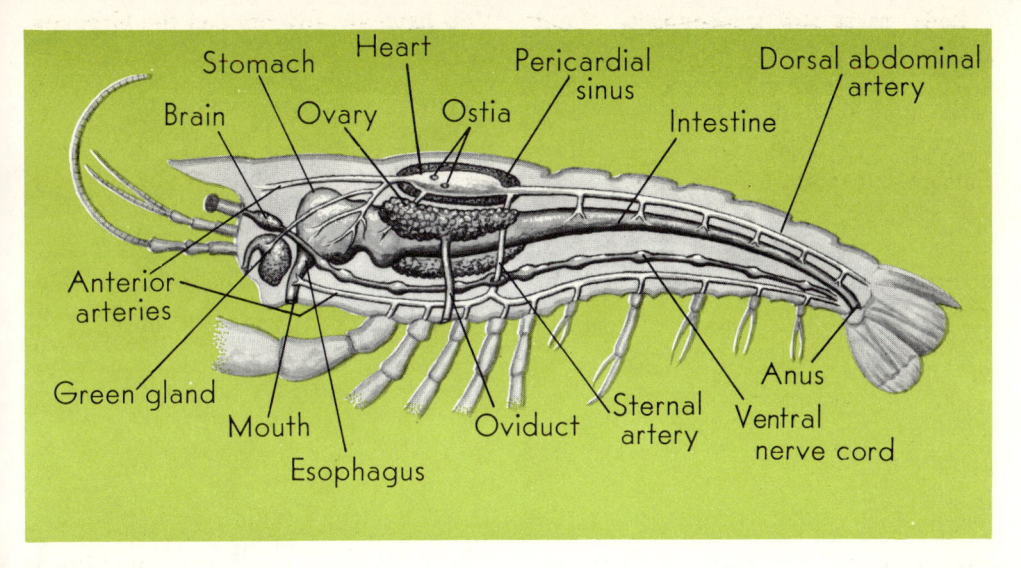

A.4 Female crayfish. Nervous, circulatory, digestive, and reproductive systems.

Nervous system. In the abdomen, especially, there is a system of very large and complex muscles, and of course, all these muscles are controlled by nerves. The small **brain** is in the head on the dorsal side. It is nothing more than two ganglia side by side. These connect with the sense organs. A nerve runs from each ganglion around the esophagus to **two fused ganglia** on the ventral side. These are the first of a double chain of **ventral ganglia** connected by a thickened **nerve cord.** Some of the ventral head ganglia and the first thoracic ganglia are fused to form a very large **ventral ganglion.** You can see much of this in Figure A.4.

Digestion. The digestive tract consists of (1) a **mouth,** (2) a short **esophagus,** (3) a **stomach,** (4) a very short **small intestine** lying far forward in the cephalothorax, and (5) a wider, **large intestine.** This ends in the anus on the ventral side of the telson. The stomach is interesting both because it lies in the head and because it does not help in digestion. Its anterior part (called **cardiac** because it is near the heart) has a thickened and hard lining. This is the **gastric mill,** which bears teeth. The mill grinds up the live animal food, such as snails, tadpoles, and small fish. Behind the cardiac portion is the **pyloric** division of the stomach. This is used for straining the food. Digestion takes place in the small intestine. Juices enter here from a pair of digestive glands which lie on either side of the stomach and small intestine.

Circulation, respiration, and excretion. A tubelike, muscular **heart** lies in the dorsal region of the thorax. As it contracts it sends blood forward into five **arteries** which supply the organs of the head and the stomach and the digestive glands. From the posterior end of the heart, blood is pumped into the **dorsal abdominal artery.** This passes above the intestine, sending branches into it. Blood is also pumped from the posterior end of the heart into the **sternal artery.** The sternal artery turns downward and then branches forward and back just beneath the nerve cord. Can you find it? It sends off branches

APPENDIX — THE STRUCTURE OF SOME ANIMALS

to legs, gills, and jaws. All the arteries branch and end in capillaries which are quite different from ours. They are not closed tubes; they open into spaces among the tissue cells, called **sinuses.** The heart itself lies in a **pericardial sinus** which connects with the other sinuses. Blood enters the heart from this sinus through three pairs of special openings called **ostia.** The ostia are closed by valves each time the heart pumps.

Water is constantly passing over the feathery gills. The blood in the gills picks up oxygen from the water and loses carbon dioxide to the water. This blood then passes to the pericardial sinus and thus reaches the heart.

Excretion of the other wastes of oxidation is performed by a pair of large, round bodies called **green glands.** They lie in the ventral part of the head, in front of the esophagus. Take a look at Figure A.4. Find the duct from one of these glands opening at the base of the antenna.

Reproduction. The male crayfish has a **spermary,** or **testis,** paired in front and unpaired behind. It connects with a pair of **sperm ducts,** which open on the upper segment of the last pair of legs. The female has a single three-lobed **ovary** in the same position as the spermary. This connects with a pair of **oviducts** opening on each third walking leg. The female has a **seminal receptacle** into which the male deposits sperms. When the eggs are laid, they are fastened to the swimming feet (pleopods) by a sticky secretion. They are fertilized immediately by sperms previously deposited. The embryo develops in the usual way. It remains stuck to the swimming legs of the mother. Even after hatching, the young crayfish remains attached for a while.

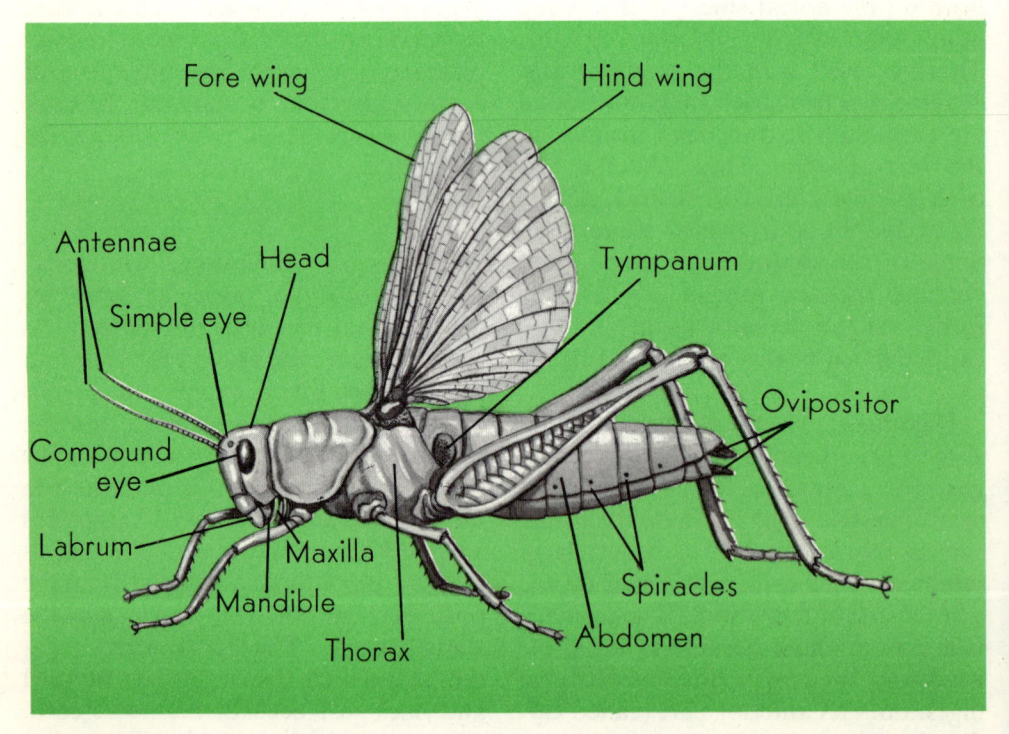

A.5 Grasshopper.

THE GRASSHOPPER

Order Orthoptera, Class Insecta
Phylum Arthropoda

Grasshoppers may be found in any part of the United States. There are many species, differing from each other in color, size, habits, and so on. A large one is easier to study. Like all insects the body is covered with an **exoskeleton** of **chitin** and is divided into three regions: **head, thorax,** and **abdomen.** The head appendages are a pair of **antennae,** a pair of **compound eyes,** three **simple eyes,** and three pairs of **mouth parts.** (See Fig. A.5.) Chewing is done by a pair of **mandibles** and a pair of **maxillae,** which work sidewise. There is an upper lip, the **labrum,** and a lower lip, the **labium.** (See Fig. A.6.)

The thorax consists of three separate segments, and attached to each is one pair of legs. The posterior pair is much the largest and strongest and is used in jumping. Also attached to the thorax are two pairs of wings. Notice that the **fore wings** are leathery and cover the **hind wings** when the grasshopper is at rest. The abdomen is made up of eleven segments. On the first segment find on each side a round **tympanum,** used in hearing. On each side of the next eight segments is a small hole, the **spiracle,** which is the outside opening of a branched tube, the **trachea.** The grasshopper breathes by pumping air through the tracheae (tray′key-ee), which branch throughout the body. The last two segments are used in reproduction.

Digestion, excretion, circulation, and nervous system. See Figure A.7. As in

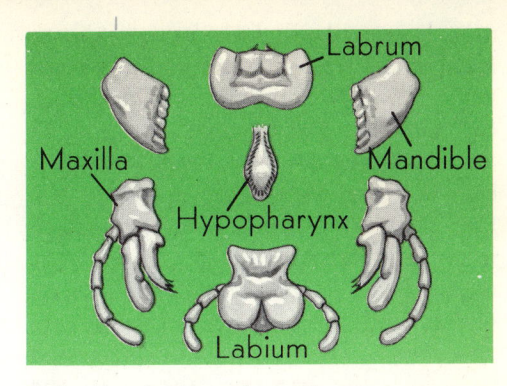

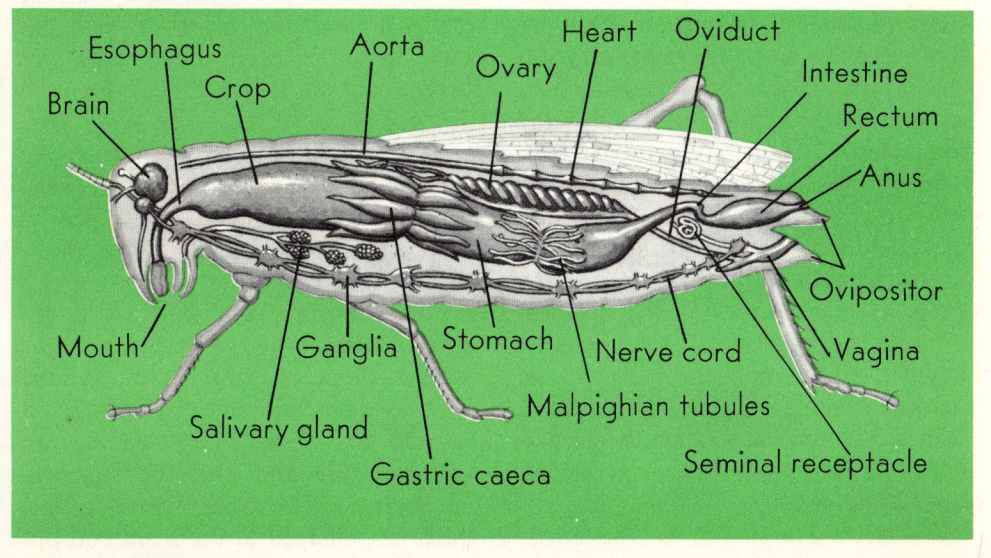

A.6 Mouth parts of grasshopper.

A.7 Grasshopper. Nervous, digestive, circulatory, excretory, and reproductive systems.

APPENDIX — THE STRUCTURE OF SOME ANIMALS

most insects, the digestive tube has three main parts: **fore-gut, mid-gut,** and **hind-gut.** Food is lubricated in the mouth by **salivary glands,** passes through the **esophagus** into the **crop,** and then into the **gizzard.** These parts are the fore-gut. Food passes from the gizzard into the **stomach** (mid-gut), where it is digested by juices secreted by gastric glands and the digested portions are absorbed. The portions not digested pass into the **intestine,** then into the **rectum,** and are egested through the **anus.** Threadlike **Malpighian tubules** remove wastes from the blood and excrete them into the intestine. The blood is colorless. It is pumped by a slender tube-shaped **heart** in the abdomen forward to the head through the **aorta.** There are no veins or capillaries; from the head the blood enters the body cavity and returns through the cavity to the heart. The nervous system consists of a **pair of ganglia** (the **brain**) **above the esophagus, a pair of ganglia below the esophagus, three pairs in the thorax,** and **five pairs in the abdomen.** Nerves connect all the ganglia and extend, also, to all parts of the body.

Reproduction. The male grasshopper produces sperms in the **testes** and deposits them inside the female, where they are retained in a vessel called the **spermatheca.** The female produces eggs in the **ovaries.** They are fertilized by sperms as they are laid. Eggs are laid through the **ovipositor** in tunnels in the ground in the fall; they hatch in the spring. The young are called **nymphs,** tiny wingless copies of their parents. They eat, grow, and then **molt,** that is, lose their outer covering. After several molts wings develop and the grasshopper is an adult. This is **incomplete metamorphosis.**

All insects are similar to the grasshopper in many respects: three-parted body; tubelike heart; breathe through tracheae; three-parted digestive tube; simple nervous system. But, of course, there are many variations. You can think of examples: some have no wings, some one pair; some have sucking or lapping mouth parts; some have **complete metamorphosis.**

FISH

Class Osteichthyes
Subphylum Vertebrata
Phylum Chordata

Most species of fish have one or more **dorsal fins,** a **tail fin,** an **anal fin,** paired **pelvic fins,** and farther front a pair of **pectoral fins.** The paired fins are used mostly for balancing; locomotion is accomplished by the muscular tail. The body covering of most fishes consists of scales covered with mucus; that's what makes them so slippery. At the back of the head on each side is the **operculum,** which covers the bright red gills.

Food getting and digestion. Most fish can open their mouths wide enough to take in a large animal or a mass of smaller animals and plants. The small **teeth** on upper and lower jaws are curved backward and cannot be used for chewing. If you look way back into the mouth of a fresh perch, at the entrance to the pharynx, on both sides, you will see five vertical slits fringed by bony projections. These make excellent strainers. The projections are a part of the gills; they are called **gill rakers.** Water gulped by the fish passes through these openings and over the gills. Food is strained out and left in the pharynx. From here it passes into a short gullet and into the **stomach.** The stomach opens into the **intestine,** which is U-shaped at the front end but pretty straight toward the back. It

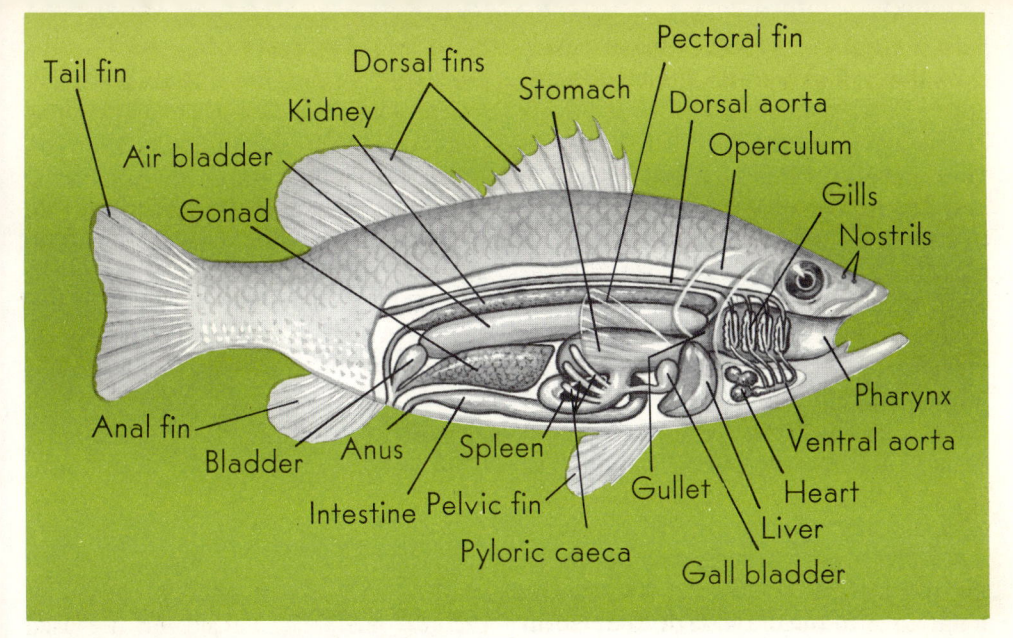

A.8 Fish. Digestive, circulatory, excretory, and reproductive systems.

ends in the **anus.** Do you see a large number, about forty, little sacs opening into the first part of the intestine (only a few shown in Figure A.8)? They are digestive glands, called **pyloric caeca** (pie-lor'ic see'ka). In this same region lies the **liver** which has two parts; like our liver it secretes bile which is stored in a large **gall bladder.** The fish usually has no pancreas but, in general, you can see that its digestive system is much like ours.

Breathing, circulation, and excretion. If you watch a living fish you will see it constantly opening and closing its mouth. Water thus constantly goes from the mouth through the strainers along the sides of the head. Here, on each side, it enters a **gill chamber** in which lie the gills. The gill arch and gill rakers are bony, but the **gill filaments** are soft. Feel them. Each has a thin membrane on the outside and large numbers of capillaries on the inside; thus gases can easily diffuse between the water and the blood. And the water is constantly being changed over the filaments, as the fish opens and closes its mouth. Gills can take in oxygen only when it is dissolved in water. But the gills have the same adaptations as our air-breathing lungs — a large amount of surface and a thin membrane covering large numbers of capillaries.

The **heart** lies under the gullet. It consists of three parts: a **sinus venosus,** in front of that an **auricle,** and then in front of that the thick-walled **ventricle.** Valves between these chambers keep the blood flowing forward. Contraction of the ventricle forces blood through a large, thick-walled, elastic blood vessel, called the **ventral aorta,** which sends branches to the gills. In the gills the arteries divide into capillaries. From the capillaries in the gills the blood flows into the **dorsal aorta** which distributes it to all parts of the body. Blood returns to the sinus venosus through veins. The two long **kidneys** on the dorsal side extract

APPENDIX — THE STRUCTURE OF SOME ANIMALS

wastes from the blood. These wastes flow through tubes into the **bladder.**

The nervous system. The fish is a vertebrate. It has a **brain,** which is encased in a skull, and a **spinal cord,** which runs through the spinal column of vertebrae. The cord widens out in front to form the base of the brain, the **medulla.** In front of that lies the **cerebellum.** Then come two large **optic lobes,** a small double **cerebrum,** and finally, small **olfactory lobes** way in front. These have nerves running to the nostrils. Nine other pairs of nerves go from the brain to parts of the head. As in other vertebrates, **pairs of spinal nerves** branch to other parts of the body. Compared to the crayfish or earthworm the fish has quite a brain, hasn't it? Turn back to Figure 33.17 to see how it differs from the brain of a mammal. Turn back to Chapter 26 for a discussion of reproduction in fish and other animals.

FROG
Class Amphibia
Subphylum Vertebrata
Phylum Chordata

How does the frog get and digest food? Put some fruit flies or smaller insects into a jar with a frog. You'll see a flash, the **tongue** darts out of the mouth and is withdrawn, with the insect caught in the forked point. When you examine the tongue of a frog, you will notice that it is attached at the front; that's why it can reach so far. Look for the small pointed **teeth** — a single row around the edge of the upper jaw and a small patch of teeth farther back, close to the inside opening of the **nostril.** All the teeth do is to keep the food from escaping. Watch the frog swallow. When its big bulging eyes sink into the roof of the mouth, the food is pushed down into the throat (**pharynx**). From here it passes through a short **esophagus** into a long muscular **stomach,** which runs down the left side. There are no salivary glands. The **small intestine** makes a letter U with the stomach and then is coiled until it widens into a **large intestine,** which is short. The large intestine opens into the **cloaca,** a chamber into which the **bladder** also opens. The **liver, gall bladder,** and **pancreas** are where you would expect them to be.

Breathing and circulation. One great difference between the frog's body cavity (**coelom**) and ours is that the frog has no diaphragm. The whole body cavity is lined with a very thin, smooth membrane, the **peritoneum.** Double layers of peritoneum, called **mesentery,** suspend the internal organs (just as in our bodies). The frog's large, pink lungs have much less absorbing surface inside than ours; they lack the complicated air sacs; they have a large cavity and the walls are raised into a network of ridges well supplied with capillaries. Remember that the frog does not depend only on its lungs for its supply of oxygen; while in water it absorbs oxygen through its thin skin. The frog's method of breathing is interesting. Watch its mouth and the sides of its body. As the floor of the mouth is lowered, air enters through the **nostrils.** Then the floor of the mouth is raised and the nostrils are closed. The air is forced through a short **larynx** into the **lungs.** When the muscles of the body wall contract forcibly, air is forced out of the lungs into the mouth.

The **heart** has two thin-walled **auricles** and a single, muscular **ventricle.** You will remember that your heart has two ventricles: the left ventricle pumps

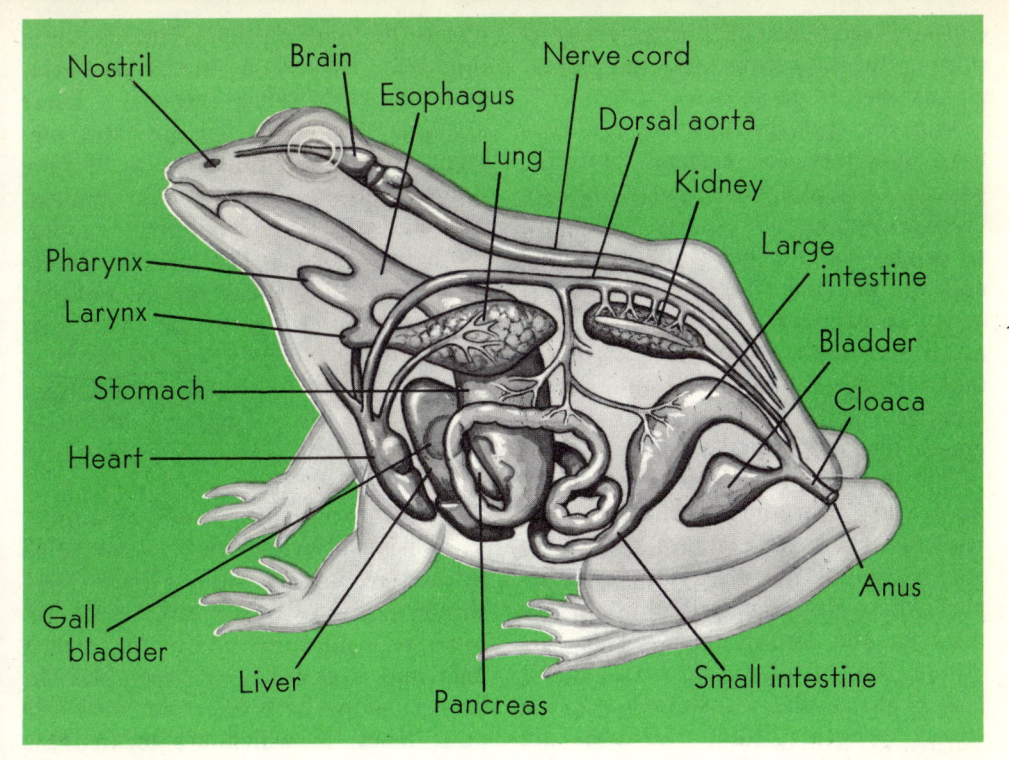

A.9 Male frog. Digestive, circulatory, reproductive, respiratory, and excretory systems.

aerated blood, which has just come from the lungs, to the rest of the body; the right ventricle pumps blood which has been through the body, and therefore contains little oxygen and much carbon dioxide, to the lungs. In the frog, a system of valves and of timing makes it possible for the single ventricle to pump aerated blood from the lungs to arteries that take it to most of the rest of the body and to pump blood received from the rest of the body to the lungs and skin. The frog's blood, like ours, consists of **plasma, white corpuscles,** and **red corpuscles** with hemoglobin. There are large **lymph spaces** which connect with the veins. The beating of four lymph hearts forces lymph into some of the veins.

Excretion. The frog has a pair of **kidneys** which take wastes out of the blood. The kidneys lie in the posterior part of the coelom against the dorsal wall. A **ureter** carries the waste (**urine**) from each kidney into the cloaca. A thin-walled **bladder** opens into the ventral side of the cloaca. By gravity the urine passes into this storage sac. Along the ventral side of each kidney is a long yellow organ, the **adrenal body,** a ductless gland.

See Chapter 26 for a discussion of reproduction in frogs and other animals.

Skin, bones, and muscles. The frog's skin, like ours, consists of an outer layer, the **epidermis,** and an inner layer, the **dermis.** The outer flattened cells of the epidermis come off in large pieces. The skin is much thinner and smoother than ours, and the blood comes much nearer to its surface. The

APPENDIX — THE STRUCTURE OF SOME ANIMALS

constant secretion of mucus keeps it slimy. But the dermis lacks hair, sweat glands, and oil glands.

Muscles, too, are like ours. Frogs have **voluntary,** or **skeletal,** muscles, which are attached to bones and are used in moving body parts. All have an **origin** (the end that is less movable) and an **insertion** (the more movable end). **Involuntary,** or **smooth,** muscles are found in the blood vessels, in the digestive system, and in some other internal organs. The heart has **cardiac muscle fibers** like ours.

The skeleton, in general plan, is like ours, too. But the vertebral column has only **nine vertebrae** and then a long flat extension, the **urostyle.** This begins where you see the hump in the back of the sitting frog. The frog differs, too, in having no ribs. But it has a breastbone, or **sternum,** and a strong **pectoral girdle;** the arms are attached to this. The arm has a **humerus,** a fused **radio-ulna,** six wrist bones (**carpals**), and four hand bones (**metacarpals**) to which are attached the finger bones (**phalanges**). The **pelvic girdle** has two long, narrow bones running parallel to the urostyle. At the posterior end of the body each bone ends in a ball and socket joint into which the hind leg fits. The leg has a thighbone (**femur**), a fused **tibio-fibula,** and two ankle bones (**tarsals**). These are long, giving the leg the extra segment, which is helpful both in its long jumps and its powerful swimming. There are five well-developed toes (**digits**), consisting of foot bones (**metatarsals**) and toes (**phalanges**). The toes are webbed. It would be interesting to count up all the ways in which a frog is adapted for rapid swimming.

Behavior and nervous system. Frogs perform reflex acts, responding to a variety of external and internal stimuli. They have been known to show some learned responses, too. Figure 33.17 shows that the frog's brain has a **cerebrum** without convolutions, a **cerebellum,** and a **medulla.** It resembles the fish in having both **olfactory lobes** and **optic lobes,** in which are located the senses of smell and sight. In our brain these lobes are quite small when compared with the cerebrum. The frog's body is well supplied with nerves which arise from these nerve centers. The frog has, too, an **antonomic nervous system** which "controls" the glands and involuntary muscles of the internal organs, as it does with us.

Glossary

A GLOSSARY IS A PARTIAL DICTIONARY of the words used in a book. In this glossary you will find short explanations or definitions of a great many of the biological words in this textbook. Some words have one meaning in biology and one or more meanings in other sciences or in ordinary conversation or writing. In this glossary the biological meaning of such words is given. Since the glossary would become too long if it included all the biological terms used, you will be obliged in some cases to consult the index and refer to the textbook for an explanation of a term. To help you pronounce some terms a phonetic pronunciation is given in parentheses.

abdomen (ab-doh′men): in an arthropod, the posterior (hind) region; in higher vertebrates the part of the body containing the stomach and lower digestive organs.

absorption: the movement of water, digested food, and other dissolved substances into the blood or cells of animals; in plants, diffusion of soil water and dissolved materials into any part of the plant.

acne (ack′knee): a skin condition which shows as an eruption, especially on the face.

acquired characters: characteristics or traits of an organism developed during its lifetime in response to environment.

acromegaly (ac′row-meg′al-ly): a condition in man and other mammals caused by excessive secretion of the pituitary gland, showing itself in enlargement of bones of feet, hands, and face.

activity and success learning: a form of behavior in which an animal learns after many repetitions; also called trial and error learning.

adaptation (a-dap-tay′shun): any change in the structure or activities of organisms which fits them for their environment.

adrenal (ad-ree′nal) **glands:** ductless glands, one on top of each kidney, secreting adrenalin, cortisone, and other hormones.

adrenalin (ad-ren′a-lin): hormone bringing about many changes in the body which help an animal in an emergency.

agar-agar (ah′gar): gelatinlike product of certain seaweeds used in raising bacteria. When food for bacteria is added, the product is nutrient agar.

agglutinin (ag-glu′tin-in): antibody which causes foreign cells (often bacteria) to clump.

agglutinogen (ag-glu-tin′o-jen): a substance in the body which causes formation of agglutinin.

air sacs: microscopic, thin-walled sacs making up the lungs in higher vertebrates. Each is the expansion of a tiny bronchial tube.

albino (al-bine′oh): person or other animal whose skin, hair, and eyes lack most or all pigment. There are also albino plants.

algae (al′jee): thallophytes with chlorophyll.

alimentary (al-i-men′tary) **canal:** food tube in an animal, from mouth to anus.

allergy (al′er-jee): a state of abnormal sensitiveness to a particular substance, such as pollen, foods, dust, etc.

alternation of generations: regular rotation of sexual and asexual reproduction in the life cycle of an organism; mostly in plants.

amino (am-ee′no) **acids:** complex compounds made by plants which, when chemically united in various combinations, make up the proteins of all organisms; also the end products in protein digestion.

amphibians (am-fib′i-ans): members of a class of vertebrates with soft, naked skins, usually breathing by means of gills in their early stages; later, breathing by means of lungs.

amylase (am′i-lace): one of several starch-splitting enzymes.

anaerobic (an-ay-ro′bic): as applied to bacteria, living in an environment which lacks free oxygen.

anatomy (an-at′o-me): study of the structure of plants and animals.

androgens (an′dro-jens): hormones made by sex glands of males and females but in larger amounts in males.

anemia (an-ee′me-a): condition in which there

GLOSSARY 569

is a deficiency of hemoglobin; often result of too few red blood cells.

angiosperms (an'jee-o-sperms): spermatophytes with seeds in an ovary; true flowering plants.

annelids (ann'ell-ids): members of a phylum of invertebrates which have ringed or segmented bodies, such as earthworms.

annual (an'you-el): plant that lives for only one growing season.

annual ring: easily distinguished ring forming each year in woody tissue of dicot trees and shrubs through growth of cambium cells.

anoxia (an-ox'ia): condition in which the body has an insufficient supply of oxygen; occurring mostly at high altitudes.

antenna: one of a pair of projecting sense organs on head of insects, crustaceans, etc.

anterior: applied to front or head end of an animal.

anther: the top of the stamen; the part which holds pollen.

anthropologist (an-throw-pol'oh-jist): one who studies the science that treats of the origin, classification, and culture of man.

antibiotics (an'ti-by-ot'ticks): substances produced by living organisms and used in medicine to kill or hinder growth of germs. Example is penicillin.

antibody: any of various substances which counteract foreign products in the body.

antihistamines: drugs for relieving symptoms of some allergies.

antiseptic: substance which prevents the action of germs and hinders their growth.

antitoxin: substance formed in the body of an animal which counteracts a particular toxin (poison) made by an organism.

aorta (ay-or'ta): single large artery in vertebrates which leads blood out of the heart to be sent to all parts except the lungs.

appendage (ap-pend'aj): any part of the body of an animal arising from the head or trunk.

appendix: in man and some other mammals, a narrow outgrowth from the blind sac at the beginning of the colon.

archaeornis (are-key-or'nis): extinct birdlike animal with teeth and a long tail with vertebrae.

artery: blood vessel that carries blood away from the heart to the capillaries.

arthropods (are'throw-pods): members of a large phylum of invertebrates with a segmented body, jointed legs, and a firm covering.

artifact (are'te-fact): any article made by man (especially prehistoric man) for his use.

ascorbic (ay-skor'bic) **acid:** vitamin C; prevents scurvy.

aseptic (ay-sep'tic): free from living microorganisms causing disease, fermentation, or decay.

asexual (ay-sek'shoo-al) **reproduction:** forming of a new individual without union of two cells.

assimilation (as-sim'il-ay'shun): changing food substances to protoplasm in the cell.

astigmatism (as-tig'mat-ism): an eye defect in which the lens does not focus equally well from all angles.

atom: the small particle making up a chemical element.

auricles (or'i-k'ls): chambers in the vertebrate heart which receive blood from veins and send it to the ventricles.

autogenous (aw-toj'en-us): applied to a vaccine made for a specific person from material taken from his own body.

autonomic (aw-toh-nom'ic) **nervous system:** system of nerves and ganglia which works closely with the central nervous system and controls the behavior of some of the internal organs.

auxin (awk'sin): class of substances which in very small amounts regulate the growth of particular parts of plants; sometimes called growth hormones.

axon: part of a neuron, usually long, which carries impulses out of the cell.

bacillus (ba-sill'us): rod-shaped bacterium.

bacteria, pl. of **bacterium:** microscopic fungi, of many species, very simple in structure; most are useful, some very harmful.

bacteriology (back-teer'iy-ol'o-jee): study of bacteria and their effects.

bacteriophage (back-teer'iy-o-faje): a filterable ultramicroscopic agent which breaks up certain bacteria.

570   GLOSSARY

balanced aquarium: aquarium in which under proper conditions of light and temperature the plants and animals produce substances necessary to each other in quantities that enable both kinds to survive.

barbiturate (bar-bit′you-rate): drugs used for quieting the nerves.

bark: tough, often hard, external covering of woody stems.

behavior: the sum total of the responses of an organism to its environment.

beriberi: deficiency disease caused by a deficiency of thiamin (vitamin B_1).

bicuspids: teeth with two points, lying between canines and molars in mammals. Also known as premolars.

biennial (by-en′i-al): plant that bears flowers and fruit the second year of its growth and then dies.

bilateral symmetry: arrangement of the parts of an animal in such a way that right and left sides are similar.

bile: bitter, greenish liquid secreted by the liver; stored in the gall bladder.

bile sac: see gall bladder.

binary fission (by′na-ree fish′un): division of a one-celled organism in half; one form of asexual reproduction.

biology: study of living things.

biotin (by′o-tin): one of the vitamins in the B complex group.

birds: members of a class of vertebrates distinguished by a covering of feathers.

blade: broad part of a leaf as distinguished from the petiole (stalk).

blastula (blast′you-la): an early stage (a hollow ball of cells) in the development of the embryo of many kinds of many-celled animals.

bleeders: persons who have hemophilia.

blending inheritance: inheritance in which there is no dominant or recessive character but a mixing of the two.

blood count: count of red or white blood cells in a small drop of blood. (White are counted to diagnose infection; red for anemia.)

botany: study of plants.

brachydactyly (brak′i-dak′te-lee): condition of having short fingers or toes with two bones.

breathing: in animals, inhaling and exhaling air.

breed: relatively homogeneous group of animals within a species, developed by man.

breed true: to have all the offspring show the same character as the parent or parents through the generations.

bronchi (brong′kye) pl.: two branches of the windpipe, one of which enters each lung.

bronchial (brong′kee-el) **tubes:** much branched tubes in the lung leading from each bronchus; the finest branches end in air sacs.

bryophytes (brye′o-fites): members of the phylum which includes mosses and liverworts.

bud: in higher plants, an outgrowth from the end of the stem (**terminal bud**) or from cells in axils of the leaves (**lateral bud**), containing undeveloped stem, leaves, and/or flowers; in lower organisms a small outgrowth that forms asexually and develops into a new organism; also applied to small structures like taste buds.

budding: form of asexual reproduction in some lower organisms in which a small outgrowth (bud) develops into a new organism; a kind of grafting in which the scion is a bud.

bulb: structure formed in some monocots, consisting of a bud with fleshy leaves and a reduced flattened stem, capable of producing a new organism by vegetative reproduction.

Calorie: The large Calorie (used to measure heat energy released by living things or by food) is the amount of heat required to raise the temperature of 1000 grams (a little more than a quart) of water 1° Centigrade.

calorimeter (cal′o-rim′e-ter): apparatus used to measure the number of Calories in foods.

calyx (kay′lix): name given to all the sepals together; they form the outermost circle of leaflike flower parts; usually green.

cambium (cam′be-um): narrow cylinder of thin-walled, actively growing cells between xylem and phloem in dicot stems and roots.

Cambrian (cam′bree-an) **period:** an early period of the Paleozoic era in which trilobites and many other aquatic animals flourished.

canines (cay′nines): teeth used for tearing flesh, as in some mammals; the eye teeth in man.

capillaries (cap′ill-a′rees): microscopic blood

GLOSSARY

vessels with thin walls, all over the body; receive blood from artery and give it to vein.

carbohydrates: group of compounds, such as sugars, starches, and others, composed of carbon, hydrogen, and oxygen, with the hydrogen and oxygen in the proportion of two to one.

Carboniferous (car-bon-if´er-us) **period:** a late period in the Paleozoic era in which the coal beds were formed.

carnivores (car´ni-vores): members of an order of mammals that are chiefly flesh eating, with well-developed canines.

carotene (care´o-teen): yellow substance found in some plants, such as carrots, which can be changed to vitamin A in animals.

carrier: person or other animal that carries germs of a particular disease without having the disease or without ever having had it.

cartilage (car´til-aj): firm, flexible connective tissue in animals, often found making up part of a bone and in some animals occurring instead of bone; gristle.

catalyst: any substance that speeds up chemical changes in some other substance without being used up in the process.

cattalo (cat´a-lo): species produced by crossing any of the domestic breeds of cattle with the American bison (buffalo).

Caucasoid (cau´kass-oyd) **stock:** one of the three main stocks of living men; it includes, among others, Nordics and Hindus.

cell: a small, usually microscopic, mass of protoplasm, normally consisting of nucleus, cytoplasm, and cell membrane; all organisms consist of one or more cells.

cell membrane: thin layer of firm living matter which surrounds every cell; also called **plasma membrane.**

cell sap: liquid in the vacuole of a plant cell.

cell theory: the belief that all living things are made throughout of cells and the products of cells. This theory has been so well established that it can be called the **cell doctrine.**

cell wall: lifeless material outside the cell membrane of most plant and some animal cells; secreted by cytoplasm.

cellulose (sell´you-lohss): a carbohydrate found in the cell walls of plant cells.

Cenozoic (see-no-zo´ic) **era:** era following the Mesozoic; the one in which mammals began to flourish.

central nervous system: the brain and spinal cord in a vertebrate.

centrosome: tiny protoplasmic body close to the nucleus, mostly in animal cells; it plays some part in mitosis.

cerebellum (ser-e-bel´lum): that part of the vertebrate brain which lies between the cerebrum and the medulla; it is concerned with coordination of voluntary muscle movements and equilibrium.

cerebrum (ser´e-brum): that part of the vertebrate brain in which lie the centers for voluntary acts, sensations, and conscious mental processes; in mammals, the most anterior part; it is particularly well developed in man.

chemical change: a change in the nature or composition of a substance or group of substances; opposed to physical change in which the composition remains unchanged.

chemistry: the science that deals with the composition of substances and the changes in composition.

chlorophyll (klor´oh-fill): green coloring matter in plants; necessary for making sugar.

chloroplast: small body of living matter containing chlorophyll; found in the green cells of leaves and other parts.

cholesterol (koh-less´ter-ole): fatty substance in tissues of man and other animals; ultraviolet rays change it to vitamin D.

chordates (core´dates): members of the animal phylum that includes backboned animals and a few kinds of simpler animals with a rodlike structure instead of a backbone.

choroid (core´oid) **coat:** layer in the wall of the vertebrate eyeball between the retina and the sclera.

chromatin (crow´mat-in): that substance in the nucleus that readily takes stain; at certain times found in the form of chromosomes.

chromosome (crow´mo-soam): one of several rodlike or threadlike bodies of chromatin that form during nuclear division.

chrysalis (kris´a-lis): hard-covered pupa of some insects, especially butterflies.

cilia (sil´ee-a) pl. of **cilium:** short, very fine

projections from a cell (usually animal), which by waving cause motion, as oars do.

class: in classification, the largest subdivision of a phylum or subphylum.

classification: grouping living things according to structure, origin, etc.; also the whole system of groups that has been developed.

cleavage (kleev'aj): repeated division (or partial division) of the fertilized egg of an animal, resulting in a mass of small cells.

club mosses: members of a small subdivision of pteridophytes; creeping plants with erect stems bearing spores in conelike structures.

coccus (kok'us); pl. **cocci** (kok'sye): spherical bacteria.

cochlea (kok'lee-a): that part of the inner ear in man and other mammals which contains the endings of the auditory nerve.

cocoon (kuh-coon'): silky covering spun by the larvae of many insects, which protects them in the pupal stage; the silky case in which certain spiders enclose their eggs.

coelenterates (see-len'ter-ates): members of a phylum of water-living invertebrates, such as jellyfish and corals, whose bodies have a single internal cavity.

colchicine (kol'chi-seen): a drug (extracted from a plant) which, when applied to plant tissues, doubles or triples the number of chromosomes in the cell by interfering with normal cell division.

cold-blooded: applied to an animal whose body temperature varies according to the temperature of its surroundings.

colon (koh'lon): large intestine.

colony: group of animals or plants of the same kind living together, usually descendants of the same parents.

community: a group of plants and animals living together. **Climax community:** the final community group after different species have come and gone.

composites: members of a family of flowering plants having two kinds of small flowers in one head, as in asters and daisies.

compound (chemical): a substance of which the molecules are made up of two or more kinds of atoms chemically united.

conditioned response or **conditioned reflex:** learned behavior in which there is a reflex response to a new stimulus. Thus dogs can be trained to have a flow of saliva when a bell is rung.

cone: a structure consisting of a mass of scales bearing the reproductive parts of such plants as pines, firs, and hemlocks.

conifers (kon'i-furs): cone-bearing trees and shrubs, such as pines, firs, etc.

conjugation: in sexual reproduction, the uniting of two cells similar in appearance.

connective tissue: animal tissue that connects, supports, or surrounds other tissues or organs; examples: white fibrous, yellow elastic.

conservation (kon-sir-vay'shun): using natural resources in such a way that they will not become exhausted.

contour (kon'toor) **planting:** planting on a slope in rows which follow the curve of the slope to reduce washing away of topsoil.

contractility (kon-trak-til'i-ty): that property of protoplasm which enables it to change its shape; developed best in muscle cells.

convolutions (kon-voh-lew'shuns): ridges or folds in the surface of the cerebrum or cerebellum in higher vertebrates.

cork: thick-walled cells under the epidermis of an older stem; their protoplasm dries up.

cornea (kor'nee-a): transparent layer that covers the front of the vertebrate eye.

corolla (ko-rol'a): whole group of petals of a flower; inner circle of leaflike flower parts, usually of some color other than green.

coronary (kor'o-ner-y): applied to arteries which start from the aorta and supply the heart tissues. **Coronary thrombosis:** clot forming in one of these arteries.

corpuscles (core'pus-ls): blood cells of vertebrates. Red corpuscles carry oxygen to the body cells; white corpuscles defend the body against bacteria.

cortex: the "rind" (outer layers) of an organ such as the brain or kidney. In plants, the region between conducting tissue and epidermis.

cortisone: one of the hormones made by the cortex of the adrenal glands. Used in medicine.

cotyledon (cot-e-lee'don): undeveloped leaf in the embryo of a seed plant; a monocot has one, a dicot has two, and gymnosperms several.

cranium (cray′nee-um): that part of the vertebrate skull that contains the brain.

cretinism (cree′ti-nism): abnormal condition in humans in which from birth there is a great deficiency of thyroxin, resulting in dwarfism and idiocy. An individual having such a condition is called a *cretin*.

crop: plants (or plant products) cultivated to supply food or materials for man or domesticated animals. Crop is also part of the digestive tract in many animals. **Cover crops:** plants raised mostly to bind the soil and prevent its loss.

crop rotation: planting different crops in one field in regular order year after year so that the soil's minerals may be used up slowly or be restored.

cross: a mating of two individuals.

crossbreeding: mating two individuals that have no family relationship but that belong to the same species or even the same variety; also called **outbreeding.**

crustaceans (crus-tay′shuns): members of a class within the phylum Arthropoda; mostly water-living forms with firm shells, such as crabs.

culture: the sum total of ways of living of a group of human beings handed on from one generation to another; also the growth of microorganisms or tissues for scientific study.

culture medium: a prepared material for raising microorganisms. **Pure culture:** a culture of only one kind of organism.

cyclotron (sigh′clo-tron): apparatus used for bombarding the nuclei of atoms; produces isotopes and artificial radioactivity.

cytoplasm (sigh′toe-plasm): that part of the living matter of a cell around the nucleus.

deciduous (de-sid′you-us): shedding the leaves every year, as occurs in many trees and shrubs.

deficiency (de-fish′en-see) **disease:** illness caused by an insufficient supply of some necessary substance in the diet, such as a vitamin.

dendrites (den′drites): thickly branched projections from the main part of a nerve cell which bring impulses into the cell.

denitrifying (dee-nye′tri-fy-ing): breaking down nitrates into nitrites, ammonium compounds, or free nitrogen by soil microorganisms.

dentine (den′teen): a hard substance making up the greater part of the tooth in vertebrates. In the crown it is covered by enamel; in the root, by cement.

depressant: a substance, like a narcotic, which has the opposite effect of a stimulant.

dermis: in mammals, a form of epithelium lying under the thinner epidermis and containing such structures as the roots of hairs, oil glands, secreting cells of sweat glands, etc.

diabetes (dye-a-bee′tees): disease in which sugar is not used normally by the body because of a deficiency of insulin.

diaphragm (dye′a-fram): thick sheet of muscle separating the chest from the abdominal cavity in mammals.

dicotyledons (dye-cot-e-lee′dons) or **dicots:** members of a subclass of angiosperms which have two seed leaves in the embryo, net-veined leaves, and stems which form annual rings.

differentiation (diff′er-en-she-ay′shun): processes by which embryonic cells develop the shapes and structures of specialized cells, such as muscle and nerve cells, etc.

diffusion (dif-you′zhun): spreading of molecules from a region where they are more concentrated to where they are less concentrated; this may occur through a membrane.

digestion: changing larger molecules into smaller molecules; this is often necessary to enable food to diffuse through a cell membrane and to make it usable by the cell.

dihybrid (die-high′brid): an organism that is hybrid in at least two characters.

dinosaurs (die′no-sores): extinct dragonlike reptiles of many species that lived toward the end of the Mesozoic era; some, such as **Brontosaurus,** were of gigantic size.

diploid number: number of chromosomes normally found in each of the cells of an organism other than the sex cells; a number of chromosomes twice as large as the number in a sex cell.

disinfectant: substance that destroys all bacteria.

dominant: in genetics, that character which, when combined with the contrasting character, shows up in the hybrid offspring; applied also to the gene of any pair of genes that produces the character that shows up.

donor: person furnishing blood for transfusions.

dormant: applied to living cells or organisms that are "resting," with a minimum of oxidation going on.

dorsal: in animals, applied to the back region as opposed to the under or ventral side.

ductless gland, also **gland of internal secretion** or **endocrine gland:** gland that secretes a hormone directly into the blood stream.

eardrum: membrane lying between the canal of the outer ear and the middle ear; it transmits vibrations to bones of the middle ear.

echinoderms (eh-kine′o-derms): members of a phylum of marine invertebrates with radial symmetry and spiny covering; starfish group.

ecology (ee-kol′o-jee): the field of biology that deals with the relationship of organisms to their physical surroundings and to each other.

ectoderm (ek′toe-derm): outermost layer of cells in the hollow cup stage of an animal embryo.

egg: structure with more or less substantial covering laid by the female of many kinds of animals, containing normally a fertilized egg cell.

egg cell: female sex cell, or ovum, before fertilization, in plants and animals.

electrocardiogram (e-lec-tro-car′di-o-gram): a photographic record of electrical currents showing the action of the heart.

electron: the negatively charged particle spinning around the nucleus of an atom.

electron microscope: microscope of extremely high power, using beams of electrons instead of rays of light and recording the image on a photographic plate or fluorescent screen.

element: a substance of which the molecules contain one kind of atom; at present 101 elements are recognized.

embryo (em′bree-oh): animal in the early stages of its development, before it is hatched or born; in a plant, stage before germination.

embryo sac: large cell in the plant ovule within which nuclear divisions result in the formation of the egg cell nucleus and other nuclei.

emotions: feelings of joy, sorrow, hate, and the like which involve important changes in the action of some internal organs and even some skeletal muscles.

emulsion (ee-mul′shun): condition of an oil in which it exists in tiny droplets, each surrounded by a thin film which gives the oil a milky appearance.

enamel: lifeless, hard outer layer of the crown of a tooth in many vertebrates.

end brush: branched endings of the axon through which a stimulus passes into the dendrites of another neuron or into the organ that responds.

end products: in digestion the smallest compounds into which food is broken down; these are then absorbed.

endocrine gland: see ductless gland.

endoderm: innermost layer of cells in the hollow cup stage of an animal embryo.

endosperm: group of food-storing cells outside the embryo in the seeds of some kinds of plants (mostly monocots).

energy: the ability to do work.

entomology (en-toe-mol′o-jee): study of insects.

environment (en-vie′run-ment): all the surroundings, living and lifeless, of an organism.

enzyme: substance made by living cells which brings about or hastens a chemical change, without being itself permanently affected; some enzymes are digestive, such as pepsin, ptyalin, etc.

eohippus (ee-oh-hip′us): small extinct animal found to be the ancestor of the horse.

epidemic: the rapid spread of an infectious disease to large numbers of people or animals.

epidermis (ep-i-der′mis): outermost layer or layers of cells in an animal or plant.

epiglottis (ep-ee-glot′tis): flap of tissue that is folded down over the top of the windpipe (voice box) during swallowing.

epithelial (ep-e-thee′lee-al) **tissue:** covering tissue in plants and animals; includes also lining tissues in animals.

era: a major division of time in the history of the earth; many geologists divide time since the beginning of the earth into six eras.

ergosterol (er-goss′ter-ohl): substance produced by and found in many plants, which can be turned into vitamin D by ultraviolet rays.

erosion (e-row′zhun): wearing away of the surface of the earth by agents such as water and glaciers. **Sheet erosion:** floating away of top soil in a sheet. **Gully erosion:** erosion in which water makes deep cuts in the soil as it runs off.

esophagus (ee-sof′a-gus): food pipe or gullet in many animals; in man, the tube connecting the throat with the stomach.

essential organs: in a flower, the organs directly concerned with sexual reproduction; stamens and pistils.

estrogens (es′tro-jens): hormones made by sex glands in both males and females, but in larger amounts in females.

eugenics (you-jen′ics): improvement of the human race by breeding.

Eustachian (you-stake′ee-an) **tube:** tube connecting the middle ear with the throat.

euthenics: improvement of the human race through improvement of the environment.

evolution: change or development. **Organic evolution:** theory that all living things are descended from earlier forms, that the first organisms to appear on the earth were simple, and that they gave rise throughout the ages to more and more complex forms.

excretion: giving off wastes formed in oxidation by animal or plant bodies or cells.

exoskeleton (ex-oh-skel′e-tun): a hard protective covering, as in arthropods.

extensor: a muscle which extends across a hinge joint in such a way that by contracting it a part of the body is extended.

Fallopian tubes: the oviducts in the human leading from the ovaries to the uterus.

family: in classification, the major subdivision of an order, usually composed of several genera.

fang: sharp, hollow, or grooved tooth by which venom is injected by poisonous snakes.

feeble-minded: having so low an intelligence that the person is unable to meet the conditions of life satisfactorily.

fermentation: changing of sugar by some microorganisms, especially yeasts, into alcohol and carbon dioxide; by this process energy is released. Also changing of other organic compounds by microorganisms, with production of a gas.

ferns: plants of many species belonging to the pteridophyte group, with true leaves, roots, and horizontal stems having conducting tissue much like that in higher plants; spores borne on leaves or modified leaves.

fertilization: union of two unlike gametes to form a fertilized egg, or zygote.

fibrin: the fibers which harden out of fibrinogen.

fibrinogen (fye-brin′o-jen): protein in blood plasma which under certain conditions thickens and forms fibers as part of the blood clot.

filament: slender stalklike part of a stamen; thread of an alga or fungus consisting of a single row of cells.

filial (fill′i-al) **generations:** generations of offspring of a cross; first filial (F_1) is the first generation of offspring; second filial (F_2) is the offspring of two individuals belonging to the F_1 generation.

fishes: members of a class of vertebrates that have gills, commonly have fins, and a body usually covered with slimy scales.

flagellum (fla-jell′um); pl. **flagella:** long, whip-like projection from a cell.

flexor: a muscle which extends across a hinge joint in such a way that by contracting it bends a part of the body.

folic acid: a vitamin belonging to the B complex group; found in green leaves.

food: any substance that can be used by a cell for oxidation, assimilation, or secretion.

food chain: series of organisms (always starting with a green plant), with each organism serving as food for the one above it in the series.

fossil: any remains, impression, or trace of an animal or plant of an earlier geological age; most often found in rock.

fractionation (frac-shun-ay′shun): applied to blood, the separation of blood into its parts and ingredients.

fraternal twins: developed from two distinct eggs, each egg fertilized by a separate sperm; distinguished from identical twins.

frond: leaf of a fern; also a leaflike part in seaweeds and other lower plants.

fruit: ripened ovary. Sometimes other flower parts become attached and form part of the fruit.

function (fungk'shun): activity or useful action of some organ, tissue, cell, or part of a cell.

fungi (fun'jeye): thallophytes which lack chlorophyll; mushrooms are one example.

gall bladder: sac attached to the liver in vertebrates; holds bile secreted by liver.

gamete (gam'eat): either of the two cells that unite in sexual reproduction to form a new organism. The male gamete is the sperm; the female is the egg or ovum. In conjugation, where the gametes are similar in structure, one may be an active or supplying gamete, the other a passive or receiving gamete.

gamma globulin (glob'you-lin): a protein in blood not used for building protoplasm, but as a protection against disease.

ganglion (gang'glee-on); pl. **ganglia**: small group of neurons. In vertebrates, ganglia lie outside the brain and cord, some of them being part of the autonomic system. In invertebrates, together with nerves, they constitute the nervous system.

gastric juice: digestive juice of the stomach secreted by **gastric glands** in the stomach walls.

gastrula (gast'roo-la): cuplike stage of the embryo in many-celled animals; at first two-layered, later three-layered.

gene (jean): unit of heredity; substance located in the chromosome and transmitted with it; acting with the environment and other genes it produces one or more characters in the organism.

genetics (jen-et'ics): the science of heredity.

genus (jee'nus); pl. **genera**: in classification, the usual major subdivision of a family, consisting of one or more species. The name of the genus is first in the scientific name.

geologist (jee-ol'oh-jist): scientist who makes a study of the earth, the rocks of which it is composed, and the changes it is undergoing or has undergone.

geotropism (jee-ot'ro-pism): tropism in which the stimulus is gravity.

germ: microscopic organism that causes disease; also the beginning of an organism.

germ cells: sex cells of an animal or plant.

germ layers (primary): the three layers of cells in the cup stage of the embryo of many-celled animals; from each layer are formed particular organs and tissues.

germ plasm: protoplasm of the reproductive cells and of those cells in the early stages of development which become reproductive cells.

germ theory: the belief that every infectious disease is caused by a specific germ.

germination (jer-min-ay'shun): sprouting of a seed or spore.

gestation (jes-tay'shun): in mammals, the period of development of the embryo within the body of the parent.

gills: breathing organs of aquatic animals, suited to taking dissolved oxygen out of water. Fish gills have an **arch** which holds **filaments** containing capillaries, and **rakers** which strain water taken through the mouth.

gill slits: in fish, the openings back of the head.

gland: a group of epithelial cells (or a cell) that secretes a substance for the body. There are ductless glands and glands with ducts.

glucose (gloo'cose): grape sugar; a simple sugar with the formula $C_6H_{12}O_6$.

glycogen (gly'co-jen): "animal starch" stored in the liver; found also in muscles.

goiter: enlarged thyroid gland which may be accompanied by an undersecretion of thyroxin (**endemic goiter**) or an oversecretion (**exophthalmic goiter**).

grafting: transplanting living tissue from one plant to another to maintain or produce more of a desired type. In animals, skin or other organs may be grafted.

guard cells: the two cells on either side of a leaf stoma, which regulate size of the stoma.

gymnosperms (jim'no-sperms): plants of the spermatophyte group that have uncovered or "naked" seeds, such as the cone bearers.

habit: behavior that has been learned so well that it has become automatic.

habitat: natural home in which an organism lives.

haploid number: the half number of chromosomes; the number found in every sex cell. Compare **diploid number**.

heartwood: the hard, older part of the xylem in the center of a tree trunk.

hemoglobin (he′mo-globe′in): protein containing iron found in the red blood cells of vertebrates; it carries oxygen by combining loosely with it. See **oxyhemoglobin**.

hemophilia (he-mo-fill′e-a): condition in which the reduced ability of the blood to clot may result in severe bleeding. It is sex-linked.

herb (erb): seed plant with a stem above ground which does not become woody.

heredity: passing on genes, and thus characters, from parents to offspring; the word is used also for the resemblance as well as for the process.

hibernation (high-ber-nay′shun): a resting or "sleeping" stage occurring in some animals during the winter.

hilum (high′lum): scar left on seeds by the breaking off of the stalk which attached the seed to the fruit.

Homo sapiens (hoh′mo say′pee-enz): the single species within the genus Homo which includes all living men and some prehistoric forms.

hormone: substance secreted by the cells of an animal directly into the blood and carried to other parts of the body where it regulates and modifies activities. In plants the growth substances are often called hormones.

humus: decaying plant and animal material in soil.

hybrid (high′brid): having a "pair" of different genes. The opposite of pure in genetics.

hybrid vigor: the increased hardiness and size which sometimes results from outbreeding or crossbreeding.

hybridization (high′brid-iz-ay′shun): crossing of individuals with contrasting characters.

hydrotropism (hy-drot′ro-pism): tropism in which the stimulus is moisture or water.

hypertension (hy-per-ten′shun): chronic high blood pressure.

hypha (high′fa): a threadlike part of a mold.

hypocotyl (high-po-cot′il): that part of the plant embryo or seedling which lies between the point where the cotyledons are attached and the upper part of the undeveloped root.

identical twins: twins developed from a single fertilized egg. See **fraternal twins**.

igneous (ig′nee-us) **rock**: very hard rock formed from the cooling of molten rock.

immunity: not being susceptible to a particular disease. **Natural immunity**: immunity which one has without treatment or without having had the disease. **Acquired immunity**: immunity which one gets through recovery from a disease or by appropriate inoculation. **Active immunity**: immunity acquired after introduction of germs or their products. **Passive immunity**: immunity acquired by inoculation of antibodies made by some other animal.

impulse: as applied to a nerve, is that which is carried along the axon either into or out of the main part of the nerve cell.

inbreeding: mating of close relatives; in plants, usually by self-fertilization.

incisor (in-size′er): in mammals, the front teeth in both jaws used for cutting; particularly well developed in rodents.

incomplete dominance: another name for blending inheritance.

incubation (in-kew-bay′shun): keeping eggs, embryos, or young colonies of cells at an even favorable temperature during development.

independent assortment: Mendelian law of heredity which states that genes lying in different pairs of chromosomes are segregated independently of one another; also law of unit characters.

infectious (in-fek′shus) **disease**: any disease which may be caused by the entrance of a microorganism into the body; frequently passed from one person to another; contagious.

inoculation (in-oc′you-lay′shun): introduction of bacteria or viruses into the body or into media suited to their growth; also introduction of antibodies into the body.

insects: members of a very large class of arthropods, having three distinct body regions, three pairs of legs, and often wings.

instinctive behavior: complicated inherited behavior in which there is a series of reflexes, each reflex serving as a stimulus to the next, as in web spinning or nest building.

insulin: hormone secreted by the "islands of Langerhans"; regulates sugar metabolism.

578　　　　　　　　　　　　　　　　GLOSSARY

intelligence quotient or **I.Q.:** score obtained on an intelligence test compared with scores made by many people of the same age.

intercellular matter: material secreted by certain tissue cells and piled up between them.

intermediate products: the compounds into which food is broken down by digestive enzymes before it is completely broken down.

internode: portion of stem between two nodes.

invasion: the moving of plants or animals into a community to replace other organisms.

invertebrates: animals that have no backbone (or rodlike structure called a notochord).

iris (eye′ris): in vertebrates, the colored portion of the eye around the pupil.

iron lung: apparatus for producing breathing movements in paralyzed people.

irradiation (ir-ray-dee-ay′shun): exposing food to ultraviolet light in order to produce vitamin D in the food.

irritability: in protoplasm, being sensitive to surroundings and able to respond to stimuli.

islands of Langerhans: small groups of cells constituting a ductless gland in the pancreas; they secrete insulin into the blood.

isotopes (ice′oh-topes): any of two or more forms of a chemical element which differ in the number of neutrons in the atom of that element. Some isotopes are **radioactive**, such as radioactive iodine or phosphorus.

lacteal (lack′tee-al): tiny lymphatic in the villus; absorbs digested fats.

larva: in insects, the form which hatches from the egg in complete metamorphosis; also in some lower animals the young when it is very different from the parent.

larynx (lar′inks) or *voice box:* top part of the windpipe containing the vocal cords.

layering: form of vegetative reproduction in which a twig still attached to the main plant touches the ground and takes root.

learning: changing of behavior as a direct or indirect response to the environment; also the acquiring of knowledge.

legumes (leg′youms): a large family of pod-bearing plants, such as peas, beans, clover, etc.

lens (of the eye): lies near the front of the eyeball in vertebrates; focuses light rays on the sensitive cells of the retina.

lenticel (len′ti-sel): opening through the bark of dicot stems; permits passage of gases into and out of the stem.

leucocyte (lew′ko-site): another name for white blood cells, of which there are several kinds.

lichens (lie′kens): "compound" plants consisting of an alga and a fungus (or sometimes a species of bacteria) living together.

life activities: activities carried on by all living matter, such as food getting, food manufacture, digestion, assimilation, respiration, excretion, irritability, reproduction.

ligament: band of fibrous tissue connecting bones.

lignin: a substance in the plant cell wall that strengthens it.

linkage: condition in which two characters are not assorted independently of one another because the determining genes lie in the same chromosome and therefore tend to remain together in reduction division.

lipases (lie′pases): fat-digesting enzymes.

lymph: liquid which surrounds the tissue cells in vertebrates; it is largely blood plasma which has diffused from the capillaries.

lymph node or **gland:** one of the glandlike structures occurring in many places along a lymphatic; it filters out certain white blood cells and makes new ones.

lymphatic (lim-fat′ick): tube carrying lymph.

lysin (lie′sin): antibody which breaks up bacterial cells or other cells which have entered the body.

macrospore (mac′roh-spore): large spore in certain ferns which grows into the female prothallus; in seed plants, it grows into an embryo sac.

maggot: larval stage of flies.

maltose: a sugar formed by the action of diastase on starch.

mammals: members of a class of vertebrates having hair, a diaphragm, and milk glands used in feeding the young.

manure, green: plants plowed under which decay and supply minerals to the soil.

marsupials (mar-soo′pee-els): "pouched" mammals; in most cases the young are born

GLOSSARY 579

in an immature state and live in the pouch for a long time after birth.

maturation (mat-you-ray′shun): process by which eggs and sperms are formed from primary sex cells; in this process the number of chromosomes is reduced to the half number.

medulla oblongata (med-dull′a ob-long-gah′ta): the hindmost part of the brain continuous with the spinal cord; center for heartbeat, breathing, etc.

meninges (men-in′jees): three membranes covering the brain and cord of vertebrates.

mesentery (mes-en-ter′ree): folds of thin membrane attached to the wall of the abdomen of a vertebrate; it holds the organs in place.

mesoderm: middle layer of cells which forms between the ectoderm and the endoderm in the embryo of a many-celled animal.

Mesozoic era: the era in the history of the earth following the Paleozoic; the one in which reptiles flourished.

metabolic (met-ah-bol′ic) **disease:** a pronounced abnormal building up or breaking down of living matter in the animal body.

metabolism (met-ab′o-lism): sum of all chemical changes going on in a cell or organism. **Basal metabolism:** amount of metabolism when the body is as nearly at rest as possible; a test for this is often made to diagnose thyroid activity.

metamorphic (met-e-mor′fic) **rocks:** rocks which have been changed in structure by terrific pressure or heat; thus marble, a metamorphic rock, is made from limestone.

metamorphosis (met-e-mor′fo-sis): in zoology, changes in an animal after its embryonic stages by which it is adapted to a different way of living, as the change from an insect larva into the adult or a tadpole into a frog. In **incomplete metamorphosis** in insects the form hatching from the egg is much like the adult; in **complete metamorphosis** there is little resemblance between young and adult.

microorganism (my-cro-or′gan-ism): organism whose structure can be seen only with the aid of a microscope.

micropyle (my′cro-pile): tiny opening in the coats of an ovule (and later the seed); pollen tubes can enter through it.

microspore: small spore in certain ferns, developing into the male prothallus; in seed plants, it grows into the pollen tube.

migration: the moving of animals in a body from one place to another.

mitosis (mit-toe′sis): complicated nuclear division occurring in normal cell division in all animals and plants, except possibly some of the simplest; in mitosis each chromosome and gene reproduces.

mixture: a substance consisting of two or more chemical elements not chemically united.

molars: grinding teeth of mammals.

molds: any of the fungi that produce a downy or fuzzy growth on vegetable or animal matter.

molecule (moll′e-kewl): smallest particle of a substance that has the characteristics of the substance, consisting of one or many atoms.

mollusks: phylum of invertebrates with a soft, unsegmented body, gills, mantle, and foot, usually covered with a shell of lime; includes clams, snails, and octopuses.

Mongoloid: one of the three main stocks of living men; it includes, among others, Mongolians and American Indians.

monocotyledons (mono-cot-i-lee′dons) or **monocots:** members of a subclass of flowering plants with one cotyledon in seed, scattered bundles of tubes, and parallel-veined leaves.

mosses: plants of many species belonging to the Bryophytes, with simple leaflike, rootlike, and stemlike parts; mosses have an alternation of generations in their life cycle.

mucous (mew′kus) **membrane:** lubricating membrane that lines the alimentary canal and some other organs in higher animals.

mucus: slimy substance secreted by mucous membrane.

muscle tissue: tissue consisting of contractile fibers. **Striated, voluntary,** or **skeletal muscle** is attached to bones. **Smooth,** or **involuntary, muscle** is found in internal organs. **Cardiac muscle** found in heart.

mutant: organism that shows a mutation.

mutation (mew-tay′shun): a change in a gene which will at some time produce a new character in the offspring, such as white-eyedness among red-eyed Drosophila.

narcotic: any of a group of substances that act as depressants.

natural selection, Darwin's theory of: theory to explain how new types of living things appear on the earth.

nectar: sweet liquid in many flowers which attracts some insects and birds; made into honey by bees.

Negroid: one of the three main stocks of living men; it includes, among others, the Negro and Melanesian races.

nerve: a bundle of nerve fibers or axons arising in the brain, spinal cord, or ganglia and ending among other cells of the body.

nerve centers: the name given to brain and spinal cord where most nerve cells are located.

nerve fiber: a projection of protoplasm from the main part of a neuron.

neuron (new'ron): a nerve cell. **Sensory (or afferent)** neurons send the impulse toward brain or cord. **Motor (or efferent)** neurons carry the impulse away from brain or cord; **intermediary** neurons lie between sensory and motor.

neurosis: mental illness which is a result of an emotional disturbance.

neutron: neutral particle often found with the proton in the "nucleus" of the atom.

New Stone, or Neolithic, Age: period in the history of civilization which followed the Old Stone Age. Shelters and boats were built, plants were cultivated, and animals were domesticated. It ended about 6000 years ago.

niacin (nye'a-sin): vitamin of the B complex group; deficiency may cause pellagra.

nicotine: strong poison found in tobacco plant.

nitrate: compound containing nitrogen, oxygen, and at least one other element; used by plants in making proteins.

nitrifying (nye'tri-fy-ing) **bacteria:** bacteria in the soil that build up ammonium compounds into nitrates.

nitrogen cycle: passage of nitrogen atoms from the air through more and more complex compounds into living matter and back again to free nitrogen.

nitrogen-fixing bacteria: those that build up proteins from free nitrogen; some live free in the soil; others in root nodules of legumes.

node: that region of a woody stem where a leaf grows. See **internode.**

nodule (nod'youl): small rounded mass, as on the roots of legumes in which live nitrogen-fixing bacteria.

nuclear (new'klee-er) **membrane:** thin layer of slightly denser protoplasm around nucleus.

nucleolus (new-klee'o-lus): rounded body within the nucleus that takes stain like chromatin but is different from chromatin.

nucleus: small ball of denser protoplasm, lying within the cytoplasm, containing chromatin material.

nymph: the young of an insect that has incomplete metamorphosis.

Old Stone, or Paleolithic (pay-lee-oh-lith'ic), **Age:** first period in the history of civilization; ended about 10,000 years ago.

olfactory (ohl-fac'to-ree) **lobes:** most anterior part of the vertebrate brain, containing centers of smell; concealed in human brain.

opsonin (op'soh-nin): antibody which makes a particular kind of invading germ more easily engulfed by phagocytes; it is specific.

optic lobes: in vertebrates below mammals, two distinct spherical portions of the brain behind the cerebrum, containing the centers of sight; in mammals, optic lobes are small and inconspicuous.

order: in classification, the largest subdivision within a class.

organ: distinct part of the body of a plant or animal, which consists of tissues working together to carry on some activity.

organic compounds: complex carbon compounds made by living things; some can be made by man in the laboratory.

organic disease: disease caused by the improper working of some particular organ.

organism: any single living thing.

ornithologist (or-nith-ol'o-jist): scientist who studies birds.

osmosis (oss-moh'sis): technically the diffusion of water through a membrane; also used for diffusion of dissolved substances through a membrane.

outbreeding: see **crossbreeding.**

ovary (oh'va-ree): in many-celled animals, the

organ in which eggs or ova develop. In higher forms it also secretes sex hormones. In seed plants, the lowest part of the pistil in which ovules with eggs develop.

overproduction: the reproduction by animals and plants of more offspring than can survive. Darwin pointed out that this results in a **struggle for existence.**

oviduct: tube leading from the ovary through which eggs pass toward the exterior.

ovule (oh′vule): in seed plants, that structure which normally grows into the seed after fertilization; in the true flowering plants it lies within the ovary and contains the embryo sac with its egg cell.

ovum; pl. **ova:** an egg cell in plant or animal.

oxidase: enzyme made by protoplasm which makes possible oxidation in cells.

oxidation: chemical union of a substance with oxygen; results in release of energy.

oxyhemoglobin (ox-ee-he-mo-glo′bin): hemoglobin carrying oxygen; red in color.

P$_1$ generation: parental generation or the first two individuals crossed in a breeding experiment.

Paleolithic (pay-lee-oh-lith′ic) **Age:** Old Stone Age.

paleontologist (pay-lee-on-tol′o-jist): scientist who studies organisms that lived in former ages.

Paleozoic era: the fourth era in the history of the earth, in which occurred the Cambrian and Carboniferous periods.

palisade cells: in a green leaf, the regular, upright cells just under the upper epidermis.

pancreas (pan′cree-as): digestive gland near the stomach, which pours its juice into the upper end of the small intestine; other cells in the pancreas are ductless gland cells secreting insulin into the blood.

parasite: plant or animal that lives in or on a living organism (its *host*), taking its food from the host. Also **parasitism.**

parathyroids (par-a-thy′roids): two pairs of small ductless glands lying close to the thyroid; their secretion regulates the assimilation of calcium by the body.

parenchyma (per-en′kim-ma): tissue in plants that consists of thin-walled cells with large vacuoles; with or without chloroplasts.

parthenogenesis (parth-en-oh-jen′e-sis): development of an egg without fertilization, as in some insects and other animals.

pasteurization (pas-ture-iz-ay′shun): heating a liquid, such as milk, to a temperature of about 150 degrees F., followed by chilling; kills germs that do not form spores.

pathogenic (path-oh-jen′ik): causing disease; term applies to certain microorganisms.

peat: partly decomposed vegetable matter found in marshy regions; used as fuel when dried.

pedigree: table or chart showing the line of ancestors of a person or some other organism; record of family history.

pellagra (pe-lay′gra): deficiency disease caused by insufficient intake of niacin.

penicillin: a powerful antibiotic made from the mold **Penicillium;** used in medicine.

pepsin: enzyme in gastric juice which, in presence of hydrochloric acid, changes protein into smaller molecules, such as peptones.

peptones: diffusible, soluble substances into which proteins are changed by enzymes; intermediate products of digestion.

perennial (peh-ren′ee-el): plant that normally lives more than two years.

perianth (per′ee-anth): name given to calyx and corolla together.

period: subdivision of time within a geologic era.

peristalsis (perr-i-stall′sis): wavelike series of contractions of the rings of muscle in a tubular organ in an animal; in man, food is pushed along the food canal in this way.

petals: leaflike parts of a flower lying within the sepals; usually white or brightly colored.

petiole: stalk of a leaf which attaches it to the stem of a plant.

petrification (pet-rih-fi-cay′shun): process by which parts of living things are turned to stone.

phagocyte (fag′o-site): one of the white blood cells that engulf and destroy bacteria and other foreign particles.

phloem (flow′em): outer portion of the vascular cylinder in the roots and stems of ferns and seed plants; contains food-conducting cells (sieve tubes) and fibers.

photosynthesis (foe-toe-sin'the-sis): manufacture of carbohydrates out of carbon dioxide and water by chlorophyll, using light energy.

phototropism (fo-tot'row-pism): tropism in which the stimulus is light.

phylum (fy'lum): used in classification; largest division within the animal or plant kingdom.

pistil: organ in the center of a flower within which the egg cell or cells are held.

pistillate: applied to flowers having pistils but no stamens.

pith: tissue of thin-walled cells sometimes found in the center of dicot stems.

pituitary (pit-two'i-ter-ree) **gland:** ductless gland at base of the brain, secreting many hormones, one of which regulates the growth of the skeleton; often called the "master gland."

placenta (pla-sen'ta): in mammals, that part of the wall of the uterus to which the embryo is attached and through which it is nourished. The placenta consists of membranes formed by the uterus and by the embryo. In the ovary of plants, the placenta is the place of attachment of the ovules.

plankton: floating mass of small living organisms in water.

plasma (plaz'ma): liquid part of the blood, usually straw colored.

plasma membrane: see **cell membrane.**

platelets (plate'lets): tiny blood cells that start the process of blood clotting; under certain conditions they break down and release a substance that aids the clotting.

pleura (ploo'ra): thin, moist membrane that covers each lung and lines the chest cavity in mammals.

plexus: in the autonomic nervous system of higher vertebrates, it is a network of ganglia and nerves lying near or within the walls of some of the internal organs; in the central nervous system, a network of nerve fibers.

plumule: in the embryo of a seed plant, the part that will grow into the shoot.

pollen: tiny grains produced by the anther of the stamen of a flower (in conifers by the male cone); within each grain there is formed, besides other nuclei, the sperm nucleus which will unite with the egg nucleus.

pollen tube: tube that grows from the pollen when on the stigma; normally, it extends to an ovule, carrying the sperm nucleus and the other nuclei toward the egg cell.

pollination: transfer of pollen from anther (of stamen) to stigma (of pistil). **Self-pollination:** transfer within the same flower or between different flowers of the same plant. **Cross-pollination:** transfer between flowers of different plants.

polydactyly (polly-dak'til-lee): condition of having more than five fingers or toes.

Porifera (pore-if'er-a): phylum of invertebrates whose bodies are pierced with many holes, such as sponges.

portal circulation: circulation through the loop of blood vessels which bring blood from digestive organs through the liver into the vein going to the heart.

posterior: hind end; referring to the trunk of an animal, the end opposite the head.

primates (pry-may'tees): order of mammals including those with the best developed brains, such as monkeys, great apes, and man.

protective resemblance: an animal's being inconspicuous in its environment. These adaptations protect it from its enemies.

proteins: group of nitrogenous organic compounds needed by all living things for making protoplasm; plants make proteins from minerals and carbohydrates.

prothallus (pro-thall'us): sexual phase in life history of ferns and their relatives; a tiny, flat, green plant that grows out of a spore and produces eggs and sperms.

proton: the particle bearing a positive charge, found in the "nucleus" of an atom.

protonema (pro-toh-nee'ma): in mosses and their relatives, a tiny green branching filament that grows out of a spore; buds forming on the filament grow into leafy plants.

protoplasm (proe'toh-plasm): the living matter that makes up all plants and animals.

Protozoa (proe-toe-zoe'ah): phylum of single-celled animals.

pseudopod (siu'doe-pod): temporary projection from the body of certain cells; used in locomotion and food getting.

psychiatrist (sy-kye′a-trist): physician who is an expert on mental illness.

psychologist (sy-kol′o-jist): person trained in the science of human and animal behavior.

psychosis (sy-koh′sis): severe mental illness.

pteridophytes (ter-id′oh-fites): in plant classification, the group or phylum that includes the ferns, club mosses, and horsetails.

ptomaine (toe′main): a poisonous substance formed at one stage in decay of food.

ptyalin (ty′a-lin): digestive enzyme in saliva that changes starch into maltose (a sugar).

pulse: regular expansion (and relaxation) of the arteries caused by the successive contractions of the heart; can be easily felt in the wrist.

pupa (pew′pa): in the complete metamorphosis of insects, the stage between larva and adult in which the insect does not feed.

pure: in genetics, a term applied to an organism in which the two genes of a pair are alike; the organism is then pure with respect to that one pair of genes and to the character they determine. The **organism** can be pure only if this is true of each pair of genes.

pus: yellowish white substance that may form in an infected part of the body; it consists of dead white cells, dead and living germs, and a little plasma.

pyloric sphincter (pie-lor′ik sfingk′ter): a circular band of muscle in the stomach where it opens into the small intestine; when relaxed, food can pass into the intestine.

quarantine (kwar′un-teen): prevention by those in authority of free movement of people, other living things, or goods in order to stop the spread of disease.

race: in the classification of man, a subdivision of a stock; composed of people who tend to have certain inborn physical characters in common, such as Nordic and Hindu races.

radial symmetry: arrangement of parts in an animal in such a way that the parts radiate from a central point, as arms of starfish.

radioactive: having the property of giving off particles (or radiation) from an atom.

receptors: sense organs which keep an animal in touch with the environment, such as the eyes, ears, taste buds, etc.

recessive: in genetics, that character of a pair of contrasting characters that does not show in the hybrid offspring, as shortness in pea plants; applied also to the gene.

reduction division: nuclear division in which the number of chromosomes is reduced to half; in higher plants and animals it occurs just before or at the time of development of eggs and sperms.

reflex act: in an animal, a direct response to a stimulus; it is immediate, and inborn, and therefore predictable. It may or may not be accompanied by consciousness of the act.

regeneration (ree-jen-er-ay′shun): growing back of a part of an organism or a part of a cell which has been lost by injury, as the arm of a starfish, healing tissues, or the axon of a nerve cell.

rennin: enzyme found in our gastric juice; curdles milk.

reproduction: process by which living things make more of their own kind.

reptiles: members of a class of vertebrates with lungs and a covering of dry scales, such as snakes, lizards, turtles, etc.

respiration: in animals and in individual cells, the process by which oxygen is taken in and used in oxidation, together with the release of the products of oxidation from the body and from the cell. In plants, respiration is merely the oxidation of foods in the cell.

response: behavior in living things brought about by a stimulus.

retina: innermost layer of the eyeball in vertebrates, containing the cells sensitive to light.

Rh factor (R-H factor): substance in the blood of most people; persons who lack it are said to be Rh negative. (Discovered in the Rhesus monkey; hence its name.)

riboflavin (rye-bo-flay′vin): vitamin in the B complex group; formerly called vitamin G.

rickets: condition in which the bones fail to develop properly, remaining soft; caused by deficiency of vitamin D or calcium or both.

Rickettsia (ri-ket′see-a): a type of microorganism which causes certain diseases; example, Rocky Mountain spotted fever.

rodents: members of the order of gnawing mammals with strong incisors, such as rats and beavers.

root hair: microscopic outgrowth from an epidermal cell of a root; absorbs soil water.

root pressure: the pressure by which water rises into the stems of plants from the roots.

runner: slender stem growing along the ground, taking root at intervals, and producing new plants at such points, as in the strawberry.

salivary (sal′i-very) **gland:** one of three pairs of glands emptying its secretion into the mouth.

sanctuary (sank′chew-e-ree): area set aside, usually by the government, for protection of wildlife; refuge.

saprophyte (sap′row-fite): plant that lives and feeds on dead organic matter.

sapwood: in the trunk of a tree, the more recent rings of wood surrounding the heartwood.

science: organized facts and "laws" about the world and living things; also the method by which men reach understandings about the world and living things.

scion (sy′on): in grafting, the twig or bud attached to the growing plant (or **stock**).

sclera, or **sclerotic coat:** dense fibrous membrane forming, with the cornea, the outermost coat of the eyeball.

scurvy: deficiency disease caused by insufficient intake of vitamin C.

secondary sex characters: bodily characteristics, other than the sex organs themselves, which distinguish the male from the female, such as bright plumage in male birds.

secretin (see-cree′tin): hormone produced by the small intestine which stimulates the pancreas to secrete its digestive juice.

secretion: producing and giving off useful substances by cells or groups of cells in plants and animals; special cells or groups of cells are called **glands**.

sedimentary rock: rock formed from sand or mud laid down as a sediment in water and finally compressed into rock.

seed: ripened ovule containing an embryo plant.

seedling: young plant from the time it emerges from the seed until it is entirely dependent on food made by itself.

segment: one of the rings that compose the body of annelids, most arthropods, and chordates.

segregation, law of: law stating that the two members of a pair of genes separate in reduction division without having changed one another. As stated by Mendel: in the crossing of hybrids the recessive character shows up in the offspring, the ratio in the offspring being 1 pure dominant to 2 hybrids to 1 pure recessive.

selection: in breeding, the choosing of certain organisms with desirable characters to be the parents of future generations.

semicircular canals: three arches lying in different planes in the inner ear; concerned with the sense of balance.

sepals (see′pals): leaflike parts forming the outermost circle of most flowers, usually green; together they form the **calyx**.

serous (sear′us) **membrane:** very thin, smooth membrane lining the blood vessels and body cavity in man and other animals; also covers internal organs.

serum: in general, any watery animal fluid; in clotting, the blood serum is the clear liquid which separates from the clot; when containing special immune substances serum is used for inoculation.

sex cells: male and female reproductive cells; eggs and sperms; contained in male and female **sex organs**. **Primary sex cells:** the cells which eventually by maturation develop into sex cells.

sex chromosomes: the "pair" of unlike chromosomes (X and Y) in men, which determine the sex of the offspring.

sex linked: applied to all the other genes which lie in a sex chromosome.

sexual reproduction: commonest method of reproduction among simple and complex organisms in which the life of the new individual starts with the union of two cells (gametes).

sheet erosion: the floating or steady downhill moving of a well-soaked layer of topsoil.

shrub: woody, perennial seed plant with stems branching just above the ground; usually smaller than trees.

sieve (siv) **tubes:** tubes in the phloem consist-

GLOSSARY

585

ing of living cells through which manufactured foods pass. **Sieve plates,** or cell walls with holes, form at the top and bottom of each cell of a sieve tube.

sinusitis (sigh-nu-sigh'tis): inflammation of sinuses, or cavities in front part of skull.

slip, or cutting: piece of a stem or leaf suitable for propagation of a new plant.

somatic cells: cells in a higher animal that make up the body as distinguished from sex cells.

somatic mutation: a mutation in cells other than reproductive cells. In organisms reproducing vegetatively this mutation may be passed on.

spawning: releasing of eggs into the water by aquatic animals.

species (sing. and pl.): the subdivision of a genus; often the final subdivision. Every species has a name of at least two words, the first being the genus name.

spermary (sperm'a-ree): male reproductive organ in animals; testis. Produces **sperm cells** which pass to exterior through **sperm ducts.**

spermatophytes (sperm'at-oh-fites): members of a large group or phylum of plants that produce seeds; the "highest" plant group.

spinal column: series of vertebrae in the region of the back which enclose the spinal cord.

spinal cord: nerve tissue which is the continuation of the brain; it lies in the spinal column.

spindle: in mitosis, the structure on which chromosomes are arranged, in certain stages.

spiracles (spy're-k'ls): in insects and some other arthropods, the openings on the surface of the body leading into the breathing tubes.

spirillum (spy-ril'lum): spiral-shaped bacterium.

spleen: an abdominal organ in higher animals; stores blood, especially red cells, makes certain white blood cells, and destroys old red blood cells.

spontaneous generation, theory of: living things can arise from dead matter; now disproved.

sporangium (spore-an'jee-um) or **spore case:** spore-forming organ in many plants.

spore: in reproduction, a one- or two-celled body formed sexually or asexually in plants and some protozoa; in some cases it has a resistant wall. Also a bacterium in a stage in which it has a thick, resistant wall.

sporulation: (spore'you-lay'shun): multiple division of a cell resulting in the production of spores, as in bread mold; form of asexual reproduction.

stamen (stay'men): organ of a flower that produces pollen; one of the essential organs.

staminate (stam'e-nate): applied to flowers which have stamens but lack pistils.

sterile: free from bacteria; also means unable to reproduce.

stigma: somewhat expanded top of a pistil on which pollen must land.

stimulant: something that temporarily quickens a process or activity of some organ or tissue.

stimulus (stim'you-luss); pl. **stimuli:** anything that calls forth a response in a living thing.

stock: in grafting, a stem to which a scion is attached and which is its support. Also a major division in the classification of mankind, such as Caucasoid, etc.

stoma (stoh'ma); pl. **stomata:** tiny opening in the epidermis of a leaf through which gases pass.

strain: a variety, especially in microorganisms. Or a variety of domestic animal or cultivated plant produced by a breeder.

strata (stray'ta): parallel layers of sedimentary rock, each generally consisting of one kind of sediment deposited continuously over a long period of time.

streptomycin (strep-toh-my'sin): drug made from soil bacteria; an antibiotic.

striated (stry'ay-ted) **muscle:** voluntary muscle; muscle under the control of the central nervous system. The fibers have cross lines.

strip cropping: alternating strips of soil binding plants with other crops on a slope to prevent erosion.

structure: construction and arrangement of parts or organs of an organism.

style: usually slender portion found in many pistils between ovary and stigma.

sulfa drugs: large variety of compounds (sulfanilamide, etc.) in common use since the 1930's in treating various diseases and infections.

survival of the fittest: according to Darwin's

theory of natural selection, the survival in the struggle for existence of the best adapted organisms, which thus become the parents of the next generation.

symbiosis (sim-by-oh′sis): intimate living together of two species of organisms to the advantage of each, as the alga and fungus in a lichen.

synapse (sin′aps): region where a nerve impulse is transferred from one neuron to another; includes the end brush of one cell and the dendrites of another.

tadpole: water-living form in the life history of frogs, toads, etc.; it hatches from the egg.

tagged atoms: also called **tracers;** radioactive isotopes which, when introduced into the body, can be traced and thus help in explaining the use of various elements in body processes.

taproot: long, main root of a plant, corresponding to a main stem.

tendril: thin, stemlike part of many climbing plants; responsive to contact and twining around any other object.

tentacles (ten′ta-c′ls): slender, flexible projections of an animal; hydra and jellyfish use them for food-getting and protection.

testis; pl. **testes:** see **spermary.**

tethelin (teth′e-lin): the pituitary hormone which is concerned with the growth of the skeleton.

thallophytes (thal′oh-fites): members of a phylum of simple plants without true stem, root, or leaf, such as algae, fungi, and lichens.

thiamin (thigh′a-min): a vitamin of the B complex group (B_1); needed in the diet to prevent beriberi.

thoracic (thor-as′sick) **duct:** vessel that empties lymph into a vein under the left collarbone.

thorax: (thor′aks): in higher vertebrates, the part of the body between the neck and abdomen, containing the heart and lungs; in insects, the part between the head and abdomen.

thoroughbred (thor′oh-bred): animal bred from parents with certain desirable traits and whose pedigrees are registered.

thymus (thigh′mus): organ in man lying behind the upper part of the breastbone; plays an important role in children; may be a ductless gland.

thyroid (thigh′royd) **gland:** ductless gland just below the voice box; secretes thyroxin.

thyroxin (thigh-rox′in): hormone secreted by the thyroid gland, containing comparatively large amounts of iodine. It speeds up oxidation.

tissue: group of cells, sometimes including cell products, which are alike in structure and do the same kind of work.

toxin (tock′sin): specific poison made by pathogenic microorganisms and causing a specific disease; also, poisons produced by certain animals and plants.

toxoid (tock′soid): weakened toxin used for inoculation into people and animals against diphtheria, tetanus, etc.

tracers: see **tagged atoms.**

trachea (tray′kee-a): in higher vertebrates, the windpipe; in insects, one of the tubes that branch throughout the body carrying air.

transpiration (trans-pir-ay′shun): diffusion into the surrounding air of water from the cells of a leaf.

trichinosis (trick-i-noh′sis): disease of men, pigs, and some other animals caused by the **trichina worm** which enters the digestive tract and settles in the muscles.

trilobite (try′lo-bite): any of a group of extinct arthropods that lived in great abundance in the seas during the Paleozoic era.

tropism (troh′pism): the turning of a plant or animal or one of its parts toward (**positive tropism**) or away from (**negative tropism**) the source of a stimulus.

trypsin (trip′sin): digestive enzyme in pancreatic juice that breaks down proteins and peptones into smaller molecules.

tuber (too′ber): fleshy underground stem capable of producing new plants by vegetative reproduction, as the white potato.

twins: see **fraternal twins** and **identical twins.**

ultraviolet: light rays invisible to us, lying just beyond the violet end of the spectrum.

umbilical (um-bil′ick-el) **cord:** in a mammal, the cord that connects the embryo with the placenta; blood vessels from the placenta to the embryo run through it.

GLOSSARY

unit characters: see **independent assortment.**

urea (you-ree′a): nitrogen compound produced and given off as a waste in animals when proteins are oxidized or when amino acids are broken down in the liver.

ureter (you-ree′ter): in vertebrates, a tube leading from the kidney to the bladder.

"use and disuse": name given to Lamarck's theory of how organisms change through the ages.

uterus (you′ter-us): in mammals, the organ in which the embryo lies during its development.

vaccination: process of making a person immune to smallpox; now applied to active immunization against other diseases like typhoid.

vaccine (vax′seen): virus of cowpox, used for preventing smallpox; nowadays any modified disease-producing material used to prevent a specific disease.

vacuole (vak′you-ohl): drop of liquid in the cytoplasm of plant cells particularly; **contractile vacuole:** special vacuole in protozoa used in excretion of liquid wastes; **food vacuole:** also in protozoa, particle of food surrounded by water within the cell.

vagina (va-jeye′na): in mammals, the passage from the uterus to the outside of the body through which the embryo passes at birth.

variation: often used to indicate a change in an organism produced by the environment, as distinguished from a mutation.

variety (var-eye′e-tee): subdivision within a species based on some hereditary difference considered too small to make a new species.

vascular (vas′cue-lar) **bundle:** a group of conducting tubes and wood cells in a young dicot stem and root and leaf or in a monocot stem. In older stems they are replaced by the vascular cylinder.

vascular (vas′cue-lar) **cylinder:** the cylinder in or near the center of a dicot root and stem, holding the water-conducting tubes.

vegetative propagation (vej′a-tay′tiv prop-a-gay′shun) or **reproduction:** asexual reproduction in higher plants from parts other than the reproductive organs, such as roots.

vein (vain): vessel that carries blood toward the heart. In a leaf the vein consists of conducting tissues and wood fibers.

venereal (ven-ee′ree-al) **disease:** disease spread commonly through the sex organs, such as syphilis and gonorrhea.

ventral: under or belly side of an animal; opposite of *dorsal.*

ventricle (ven′tri-k′l): in the vertebrate heart, the chamber (in higher vertebrates there are two ventricles) which pumps blood into the artery or arteries.

vertebra (ver′te-bra): one of the bones composing the backbone of vertebrates.

vertebrates (ver′te-brayts): animals with backbones, making up a subphylum of the chordate phylum.

vestigial (ves-tij′ee-al) **structures:** in animals or plants, imperfectly developed structures having little or no use, but which were useful in preceding organisms.

villus (vill′us): one of the many tiny projections of the lining of the small intestine into which digested foods are absorbed.

virus (vy′rus), or **filterable virus:** ultramicroscopic agents of infection, requiring living cells for multiplication; small enough to pass through a porcelain filter.

vitamin (vye′te-min): one of a group of substances in foods occurring in small amounts and necessary to keep the body in a healthy condition.

warm-blooded: applied to animals whose body temperature remains relatively constant.

weathering: breaking up of rocks or changes in their composition caused by the action of the atmosphere.

weed: a plant "out of place," that is, a plant growing where it is not wanted.

xylem (zye′lem): woody inner portion of the vascular cylinder in root and stem of ferns and seed plants.

yolk: that part of the egg of some animals, such as the fish, frog, bird, and others, which supplies food to the developing embryo.

zoologist (zoh-ol′o-jist): person who makes a special study of animals.

zygospore (zeye′go-spore): cell with a thick cell wall formed by the fusion of two similar gametes in plants.

zygote (zeye′goat): fertilized egg cell in plants and animals.

Index

Figures in **boldface** indicate pages on which there are illustrations. Figures preceded by "def." indicate pages where definitions are found.

Abdomen, bird, **116;** grasshopper, 94, **94;** insect, 94
Abdominal cavity, 190
Absorption, def., 46, 199; of food, 190, 199–200
Accidents, 350–351; and alcohol, 354–355, **355**
Acetylcholine, 276
Acne, 240–241
Acquired characters, and evolution, 490–492; and heredity, 428–431, **429**
Acquired immunity, 318; active, 318; passive, 318
Acromegaly, 243
ACTH, pituitary hormone, 252
Active immunity, 312–317
Activity and success learning, 279–283, **281, 282, 285**
Adaptations, 492–493, **492, 493**
Adenoids, 229, **230**
Adolescents, and mental health, 294–296
Adrenal glands, 236, 243, 249–251, **249,** 252
Adrenalin, 208, 249–251, 252
Aeration, of drinking water, 333
African sleeping sickness, 337–338
African tribe, and disease, **307**
Agar-agar, 61–62, 302; plate, 302, **303;** slant, 302
Agate, Dr. Luis, and blood banks, 210
Age of Mammals, 474–476, **475, 476**
Age of Man, 496–502
Age of Reptiles, 474, **475**
Agglutinins, 208–210, 311
Agglutinogen, 209–210
Agriculture, U.S. Department of, 436, 533, 537, 542
Air, in breathing, 228–229; changes of, in breathing, 229; passages, 229–230, **230**
Air pressure, and breathing, 228–229
Air sacs, 226, 227, 229, **229**
Albino, heredity, **448,** 449
Albumen, 394
Alcohol, 354–356; and accidents, 355, **355;** and alcoholism, 355–356
"Alcoholics Anonymous," 356

Alfalfa, 77, 511, 532
Algae, 59–63, **59, 60, 61, 62,** 64, 135
Alimentary canal, 190, **191;** absorption in, 190, 199–201; digestion in, 190–202
Allergy, 351, **351,** 352, **352;** tests for, 352, **352**
Alligator, 111; brain, **481**
Alpine, race, 502
Alternation of generations, in fern, 381, **381,** 383; in flowering plants, 381–382; in moss, 382, **382,** 383
Altitude, and plants, 515–516; and respiration, 231–233
Amanita, 62
Amber, fossils in, 465
Ameba, 45–47, **45,** 81, 84; behavior, 46, 263–264, **264;** reproduction, 46, 364, **365**
American Forestry Association, 550
American Indian, 502
Amino acids, 146, 198; and diet, 174–175
Ammonia, 37, **510,** 511
Amnion, 396
Amphibians, 110–111, **110, 111,** 135 (see Frog)
Amylase, 198
Anaerobic bacteria, 320
Anatomy, def., 480
Ancon sheep, 440, **441**
Andalusian fowl, heredity in, 414
Androgens, 251, 252
Anemia, 207; and hookworm, 341–342; in malaria, 338
Anemone, sea, 85, **85**
Angiosperms, 72, 73–74, 75–78, 136
Animals, with backbones, 107–122; without backbones, 81, 82–106; behavior, 254–264; breeding, 434–438, 440–442; desert, **26;** reproduction of, 386–401; review of, 122; survey of, 82–122; tracks of, **22**
Annelids, 81, 87, 88–89, **89,** 133
Annual rings, 157, **157**
Annuals, 71–72
Anopheles, chromosome number,

408; and malaria, 338–340, **339,** 341
Anoxia, 232
Anteater, skull, **194;** spiny, **118**
Antenna (feeler), 94, 96; of grasshopper, **94**
Anther, 372, **372**
Ant hill, 101
Anthrax, and Koch, 305; and Pasteur, 312
Anthropologist, def., 496
Antibiotics, 324–327, 350; def., 325
Antibodies, 310, 311–323; "borrowing," 320
Antihistamines, 352
Antiseptic surgery, 320
Antiseptics, 303; for wounds, 303, 310
Antitoxin, def., 311; and diphtheria, 317–318; and diphtheria deaths, **319;** preparation, **318;** for tetanus, 320
Ants, with aphids, **101;** kinds of, 101; life cycle of, **100,** 101; tending mealy bug, **101**
Anus, 190
Anvil (bone of ear), 274, **275**
Aorta, 211, 217–218, 219
Apes, 121, 122; and learning, 284–286, **286**
Aphids, 101, **101;** control of, 524–525
Appendage, bat, **481;** cat, **481;** def., 94; insect, 94; man, 480, **480;** monkey, **481;** seal, **481;** whale, 480, **480**
Appendicitis, 349–350
Appendix, in man, 190, 349–350, **349**
Apple, 370, **376,** 377, 434; and codling moth, 524; effect of spraying, **524**
Aquarium, balanced, 518, **518**
Arachnids (see Spiders)
Arbor vitae, 71
Archaeornis, fossil, **474**
Archaeozoic era, 468, **471**
Arctic tern, migration, 116
Arctic zone, 66
Aristotle, 127
Arm, bones of, **480;** of starfish, 89; tissues of, **51**
Armadillo, skull, **194**
Arsenic, and syphilis, 327

INDEX 589

Arteries, 204, 205, 214–215, **214,** 216; and blood movement, 219–222; and blood pressure, 215–216; hardening of, 216
Arthritis, 243
Arthropods, 93–106, 134; examples of, **81, 93,** 134
Artifacts, 495, 496, 500, 501; def., 495
Artificial respiration, 231, **232**
Aryan "race," 503
Ascorbic acid, 180; in common foods, 186, 187
Aseptic surgery, 320
Asexual reproduction, 360–366; def., 366; in fern, 381; in flowering plant, 381–382; in moss, 382; by vegetative reproduction, 377–379
Asparagus, 71
Assimilation, 147; def., 46
Asthma, and allergy, 352
Astigmatism, 274
Atabrine, and malaria, 327
Atomic bomb radiation, and organisms, 424, **425**
Atoms, 33, **33,** 34; tagged, 247; tracer, 247
Auditory nerve, 274–275
Auricle, 211, 212–213, **212,** 217
Australian mammals, explanation of, 484–485
Australoid, 502
Autogenous vaccine, 353
Autonomic nervous system, 272, 275–276, **276,** 277, 291
Auxin, 264
Aves (see Birds)
Aviators, and altitude, 231–233; and blackout, 216
Axon, 258, 259, **261,** 277
Azoic era, 468, **471**

Baby, and emotions, 291, 291–292; and learning, 279–281, 282; and responses, 257
Bacillus, 300, **301**
Backbone, animals with, 107–122; def., 107; of man, **230,** 272; of snake, 113
Bacon, Francis, and food preservation, 304
Bacteria, 64–66, 298–345, 349–350; and antibiotics, 324–326; and body's defenses, 310–323, **310;** and cheese, 301; colonies, 302, **303;** conditions of growth, 303–304; def., 300; digestion, 300, **301;** entry to body, 310; food-getting, 300, 301, **301;** germ theory, 307–308; methods of identifying, 302, 305; methods of studying, 302, **303,** 304–305; and milk supply, **336;** and nitrogen cycle, 510–511, **510, 511;** and pasteurization, 333–334; and phagocytes, 207, **207;** recent discoveries, 324–330; size, 64; and soil restoration, 510–511, **511;** spores, 303; and surgery, 320, **321,** 350; types, 300, **301;** typhoid, **301,** 314, 332; uses, 64, 300–302
Bacteriology, def., 304; and length of life, 331–337, 346–347; recent discoveries, 324–330; and study of viruses, 327–329
Bacteriophage, 328–329
Baking, and yeast, 64
Balance, sense of, 275
Balanced aquarium, 518, **518**
Bamboo, 75; stems, 164–165
Banana, 75; lack of seeds in, 380
Banting, and insulin, 248
Barbiturates, 356
Bark, 153, 154–156, **155;** of trees, 155
Barley, 75; mutation, **425**
Barnacle, 106, **106**
Basal metabolism, 172–173, **173;** and thyroid, 244–246
Basic Seven, in diet, **183**
Bats, 122; appendage of, **481**
BCG, vaccine for tuberculosis, 317
"Beagle," and Charles R. Darwin, 488
Bean, seed, **375;** variation in, 427–428, **428**
Bear, 119, **548;** California grizzly, 545
Beaumont, Dr. William, and gastric digestion, 197–198, **197**
Beaver, dam-building, 262, 263
Bees, 102, **102, 103;** keeping, 102; nervous system of, **261;** and pollination, **374;** swarming, **102**
Beet, plant, 162, **163;** root, **163**
Beetles, 100; Colorado potato, 100, **100;** and Dutch elm disease, 522; ladybird, 100
Begonia, 377–378
Behavior, 254–297, **256,** 262, **263, 264, 265, 266, 267, 268, 280, 282, 285, 286, 290, 293, 294;** of ameba, 264, **264;** of baby, 279–281, 282, **282, 285;** def., 257; and emotions, 290–297; of invertebrates, 260–262, **262;** learned, 279–289, **282, 285;** of lower animals, 260–264, **262, 263, 264,** 279, 280, 281; of man, 257–260, 270–281, 282–284, 286–288, 291–296; of mimosa, **267;** and nervous system, 270–278; of paramecium, 263, **263;** Pavlov's experiments, 279; plant and animal compared, 265; in plants, 264–265, **265, 266, 267, 268;** in protozoa, 263–264, **263, 264;** unlearned, 257, 260–265; of vertebrates, 263, **263,** 281, **281;** of vorticella, **83**
"Bends," 233
Benedict's solution, 37
Benign tumor, 347
Benzoate of soda, 304
Beriberi, 177–178, **177**
Bernard, Claude, and diabetes, 247–248
Best, and insulin, 248
Biceps (muscle), 51, 52; as flexor, **51**
Bicuspids, 193–194
Biennials, 72
Bile, 198–199; duct, **196;** salts, 199
Binary fission (see Fission)
Biologists, 2, 3, 5
Biology, def., 1
Biotin, 182
Birch, bark, **155;** water loss, 161
Bird laws, 546–547
Birds, 18, 114–117, 135; bills (beaks), **115;** brain of, **481;** calendar, **116;** characteristics of, 116; embryo, **482;** "family life," 394–395; identification, 115; importance, 115; and insect control, 115; migration of, 116; migration routes of, **117;** parts of, **116;** perching, **114;** of prey, 115; recognition, 115; reproduction of, 393–395, **395;** as scavengers, 115
Bird's-foot violet, 551
Birth, in rabbit, 396
Bismuth, and syphilis, 327
Bison, 545; hybridization with, 437
Black ant, life history, **100**
Black Death, 331
"Blackheads," 240
Black raspberry, vegetative reproduction of, 378
"Blackout," of aviators, 216
Black widow spider, 104, **104**
Bladder, 235–237, **236;** of frog, 392
Blade, of leaf, 140, **141**
Blastula, 386–388, **388**
"Bleeders," 207–208; heredity of, 450
Bleeding, first aid for, 214
Blending inheritance, def., 413; in Andalusian fowl, **414;** in four o'clock, 413

590   INDEX

Blister, and lymph, 218
Blister rust, of pine, **523**, 524
Blood, 205–224; and adrenin, 208; cells, **49**, 206–207, **206**, 219; circulation, 219–222, **220, 221**; clotting, 207–208, **208**; composition, 205–207; and diabetes, 248; donations, 208–210, **209**; groups, 209–210; platelets, **206**, 207–208; poisoning, 320; pressure, 215–216, **216**; Rh factor, 210; tissues, 54; transfusions, 208–211; types, 208–210, 449; vessels, **204**, 205, **205**, 214–218, **214, 215**
Blood banks, 208–210
Blood plasma, in transfusions, 210–211
Blood pressure, 215–216, **216**
Blood protein, in transfusions, 211
Blood vessels, of cat's intestine, **214**; of crayfish, 561–562; of earthworm, 558; of fish, 565; of frog, 566–567; of grasshopper, 564; of man, **215**; of skin, 238, **238**
Blubber, of whale, 118
Blueberry, improved by breeders, 439, **440**
Board of Health, 331–332; inspections, 334, 335; inspector in milk plant, **334**; worker in laboratory, 336
Bobcat, 121
Body louse, 337
Body temperature, 41–42; regulation of, 239–240
Boll weevil, cotton, 520, **520**
Bone, cells, **49**; tissue, 50, **50**, 54
Bones, arm, **480**; ear, 275
Boston, bird calendar, **116**; water supply, 333
Brachydactyly, 448–449
Bracket fungus, 62
Brahman cattle, 436–437; bull, **436**; Hereford hybrid, **436**; Jersey hybrid, **437**
Brain, alligator, **481**; dog, **481**; fish, **481**; frog, **481**; human, 259, **259**, 270–272, **271**, 277; protection of, 272; sheep, **271**; sparrow, **481**
Brain hemorrhage, 216
Brain stem, 270, **271**
Bread mold, 58, 63, 65; reproduction of, 63, 365–366, **365**, 367, **367**
Breaking habits, 284
Breast bone, 227
Breathing, 224–233; air changes by, 229, **229**; and air pressure, 227–229; center, 228; def., 230–231; in high altitudes, 224, 225, 231–233; mechanics of,
227–229; models of, **234**; movements, 227–228; rate, 229; regulation of, 229, 271, 277
Breed, of cattle, 436
"Breed true," def., 412
Breeders, early achievements of, 434–436; methods of, 434–446
Breeding, 434–446; summary of, 444–445
Brine, as preservative, 304
Bronchi, 225, 226
Bronchial tubes, of man, **225**, 226–227, **226**
Brontosaurus, 474
Bronze Age, 501
Broth, for raising bacteria, 302
Brown algae, 59–61
Brown-tail moth, 522
Bryophyllum, vegetative reproduction of, 379, **379**
Bryophytes, 66–68, **68**, 135–136 (see Moss)
Bubonic plague, 331; and carriers, 337, **337**
Budding, def., 364; of hydra, 364; of yeast, 364, **365**
Buds, 152, **152**; dormant, 152; lateral, 152, **152**; mutation in, 423–424, **424**; potato (eyes), **162,** 163, 378–379, **378**; terminal, 152, **152**; of yeast, 364, 365
Bulb, def., 379; of onion, **162**, 379; of tulip, 379, **379**
Bull, 436, 437, **437, 438**
Burbank, Luther, and plant breeding, 439
Burdock, fruits, **376**
Burning, 40–41, **40**
Bush turkey, behavior of, 285
Bushes, 70
Bushman, 502
Buttercup, 370
Butterfly, 96–97; life cycle of, **95**; Monarch (milkweed), 95, **95**

Cactus, 77, 140, 493; barrel, **70**; family, 77; prickly pear, **141**, 523
Calcium, 36; in common foods, 186–187; in diet, 175; dietary experiment with, **176**; and parathyroids, 251, 252
California redwoods, 538
Calories, average daily need, 173; in basal metabolism, 174; calculation of, 171–172; in common foods, 172; def., 172; need for, 173–174; output, 172–173; used in activities, 174
Calorimeter, 172, **172**
Calyx, 370, **371**, 375
Cambium, and grafting, **442**, 443;
of root, 158, **159**; of stem, 154, **154**
Cambrian period, 472, **472, 473**; underwater scene of, **472**
Camel, 121
Camomile, 77
Canada goose, 117
Canada lynx (bobcat), 121
Cancer, 347–349, **347, 348**; and smoking, 354
Canine, tooth, 193
Canis, 129, **129**; dingo, 129, **130**; familiaris, 129, **129**
Canning, of food, and vitamin C, 180
Cannon, Dr. Walter B., 201–202; and adrenin, 249–250
Capillaries, 205, 213–214, 215, **215**; of air sacs, 229; of frog, 205; of lung, **226,** 227; of stomach, **193**; structure of, 205, **215**; of sweat glands, 238, **239**; of villus, **200**; and wastes, 237, 240
Capillary action, in plants, 162
Carbohydrates, 36, 37, 41, 143–145, **144**; in common foods, 186; in diet, 175; manufacture of, 143–145
Carbolic acid, and surgery, 320
Carbon, 35, 36, 37, 496; atom, **33**; compounds, 36, 37; cycle, 511–512, **512**
Carbon dioxide, and breathing rate, 228; in oxidation, 40, 41; in photosynthesis, 143–145; as waste, 235, 240
Carboniferous period, 473, **473**; scene of, **473**
Cardiac muscle, 51
Carnivores, 119, 130
Carotene, 142; and vitamin A, 179
Carriers, of disease, 337; other than man, 337–341
Carrot, 162; wild, **76**
Cartilage (gristle), 272; tissue, **49**, 50–51, **50**, 54; of windpipe, 230
Castings, of earthworms, 558
Cat, appendage of, **481**; blood vessels of intestine, **214**; classification of, 128, 129, **129**; continuity of germ plasm in, 429, **429**; and heredity, **411**; Persian, 129
Catalyst, 192
Caterpillars, 95, **95**; codling moth, 524, **524**; Monarch (milkweed), 95, **95**; silkworm moth, 96
Cattalo, 437
Cattle, Brahman-Hereford cross, 436, **436**; Brahman-Jersey cross, **437**; effects of selection on, 436; and environment, 443–444, **444**; mutation in, 440

Caucasoid, 502
Causes of death, chart of, 347
Cave dwellers, 498, 499–501, **500**, 501
Cedar, red, 73, **73**
Cell, 31; bacterial, 300, **301**, 303; body of neuron, 258, **258**; def., 31, 32; doctrine (theory), 47; functions, 40–49; and growth hormones, 264; membrane, 45; membrane in diffusion, 44, 45; parts of, 31–33; protozoan, 82–84, **82**, **83**; sap, 32; structure, 31–33, **31**, **32**; typical animal, 32, **32**; typical plant, 32, **32**; use of food in, **171**; wall, 32; wastes, 235
Cell division, 405–407, **406**, **407**
Cells, 28, 30–55; activities of, 40–48; algae, 59, **59**, 60; animal, 31, 32, **32**, 37; blood, **49**, 206–207, **206**; in blood vessels, 205; body, 49–53; bone, **49**; cartilage, **49**, 50–51, **50**; chlorophyll in, 141, **141**; comparison between plant and animal, 32, **32**, 37; conjugation of, 366–367, **367**; def., 31–32; diagrams, **32**; differentiation of, 375, 386, 388; egg, **340**, 341, 372, **373**, 388–389, **389**, 391–393, **392**; embryo sac, 372, **373**, **374**, 375; epithelial, 38, **49**; fat, **49**; fertilization of, 367–368, **368**, 374–375, **374**, 381, 382, 386, 389, 391, 393, 395; germ plasm, 390, **390**, 429, **429**; guard, 142, **142**; and heredity, 408–457; leaf, 140–143, **141**, **142**; malaria, **339**, 367–368, **368**; mouth, **31**, 38; mucous membrane, 38; muscle, **49**; nerve, **49**, 258–259, **258**; onion skin, **53**; palisade, 141, **141**; parts of, 31; phloem, 156, **156**; plant, 32, 37; and plant tropisms, 264–265; pollen, 372–373, **373**; reproduction of, 360–401; respiration in, 41, 42; root, 160–161, **161**; sap, 161; skin, 238–239, **238**; sperm, **387**; spongy, **141**; staining, 305; stem, 154–155, 156–157, **156**; stomach, 193; summary of, 37–38; sweat gland, **239**; tissue, 49–54; villus, **200**; voluntary muscle, 51–54; xylem, 156–157; yeast, **365**
Cellular respiration, 41, 42, 48, 231
Cellulose, 32, 36
Cell wall, 32
Cement, of tooth, **195**
Cenozoic era, 468, 474–476, **475**, **476**, **477**

Centipede, 93, 105, **105**, 134
Central nervous system, of man, 259, **259**, 270–275, 277
Centrifuge, 210–211
Centrosome, 407, **407**
Cereals, 75
Cerebellum, 259, 270–272, **271**, 277, **481**
Cerebral hemorrhage, 216
Cerebrum, **259**, 270–271, **271**, 277, **481**; centers of, **271**; functions of, 270–271; motor areas, **271**; and "seeing," 270; sensory areas, **271**; of sheep, **271**; of vertebrates, 481
Chalk cliffs, 82–83
Chance, effect on heredity, 414–417
Change, in living things, 422–445, 458–505
Characteristics, acquired, 428–431, **429**; and breeding, 434–445; and chromosome changes, 422–433; and chromosomes, 404–421; in classification, 127–128; and environment, 426–429; heredity of, 404–457; secondary sexual, 386, **387**; sex-linked, 450, **450**
Chemical, action, 34–35, **34**; change, def., 34–35; energy, 144–147; "messenger," 242; regulators, 242–253; resemblances, 483
Chemicals, and bacteria, 303; and tropisms, 266
Chemistry, 33–35
Chemists, 33
Chemotropism, 266
Chest, in breathing, 227–229, **227**; x-ray of, 306, **306**
Chewing, of food, 194
Chickadee, 114
Chicken, cholera, 311–312; chromosome number of, **408**; learning in, 281, **281**; and polyneuritis, 177, **177**
Children, and gonorrhea, 327; and learning, 257, 260, 279–280, 282–284, 286–288; and syphilis, 327
Chimpanzee, **107**, 122; and reasoning, 284–286, **286**
Chlorine, 35, 36; and water supply, 333
Chlorophyll, 32, 142–145, 146; composition of, 142
Chloroplasts, 32, 138, 141, **141**, 142, 143–145, **142**, **145**
Cholera, in chickens, 311–312; epidemic, 331; spirillum of, 301
Cholesterol, and vitamin D, 180
Chordates, 107–122, **107**, 134–135

Choroid coat, of eye, 273
Chromatin, **32**; in cell division, 405–407, **405**, **406**, **407**; def., 33
Chromosome changes, effect of, 422–426
Chromosome number, 408, **408**; keeping constant, 408–409
Chromosomes, and cell division, 405–407, **405**, **406**, **407**; changes in, 423–426; def., 405; and fertilization, 409; giant, **405**; and heredity, 407–408, 414–419; map of, 417–418; in reduction division, 408–409, **409**; and sex, 450; X, Y, 450–451
Chronic alcoholics, 355–356
Chrysalis, **95**, 96
Cilia, of epithelium, 230; of paramecium, **82**, **83**; of vorticella, **83**
Cinchona tree, 327
Circulation, diagrams of blood, in man, **204**, **220**, **221**
Circulatory diseases, 347, 349
Circulatory system, 204–224, **204**, **220**, **221**; blood, 204–218, 219–224; lymph, 218–219, **218**; main, **204**, 219–222, **220**; pulmonary, 220–221, **221**; systemic, **220**
Citrus fruits, and vitamin C, 180
Civilization, and ecology (see Culture)
Clam, 91, **91**, 92, 335
Class, def., 128
Classification, 127–135; of animals, 81–126, 128–130, 131, **132**; of cat, 484; of coins, 127–128, **127**; explanation of, 483–484; of gray squirrel, **132**; Linnaeus' scheme of, 127, 128–130; of man, 502–504; of plants, 59–79, 130; principles of, 128; and resemblances, 483–484; of squirrel, **132**; of stamps, 127–128
Clay, 515
Cleavage, 386–388, **388**, 395
Climax communities, 518–520, **519**
Cloaca, of frog, **392**
Clotting, of blood, 207–208, **208**
Clover, 76, 532
"Club mosses," 69, 136
Coal, and carbon cycle, 512; formation of, 464; fossils in, 464
Coat color, heredity in cats, **411**; heredity in guinea pigs, **416**; heredity in mink, **441**; heredity in rats, **415**
Cobalt, 36
Cobra, 113
Coccus, 300, 301
Cochlea, of ear, 275, **275**

592 INDEX

Cockroach, 99; of Carboniferous period, 473, **473**
Coconut, 75; palm, 75
Cocoon, 20–21, 96, **96**; silkworm, 96, **96**
Codling moth, control of, 524, **524**; larva, 524, **524**; life history of, 524
Cod liver oil, **178**, 179
Coelenterates, **81**, 84, 85–87, **85, 86**, 133
Cohesion, 162
Cohn, Professor Edwin, 210
Colchicine, and chromosome number, 425, **425**
Cold-blooded, 111
Colds, 327, 352–353
Collie, **130**
Colon, 190
Colony, of bacteria, 302, **303**; of mold, **303**
Color blindness, heredity in man, 450, **451**
Colorado potato beetle, 100, **100**
Combustion, 40–41, **40**
Communities, of organisms, 517–520; climax, 518–520, **519**; cycles within, 520; succession in, 518, **518**; in water, **519**
Community, and disease, 331–345, 349, 350–351, 357
Companion cell, **156**
Composite family, 77
Compound leaf, 70, **71**
Compounds, 34–38; food, used in cell, 170–171, **171**; organic, 37; tests for, 37
Conditioned responses (reflexes), 279, **280**
Conduction, in plants, 153, 155; tissues, **156**
Conifers (cone-bearers), 72, 73, 140, 538; tracheids in, **156**
Conjugation, bread mold, 367, **367**; def., 367; of paramecium, 367, **367**; of spirogyra, 366–367, **367**
Connective tissue, 54
Conservation, 506–555; agencies and careers, 550; Commission, 529; early programs, 546–547; of forests, 537–545; of gifted people, 455; of health, 357; and land grading, 532–533, **532**; modern programs, 548–549; need for, 528; and planting, 532–533, **533**; by pupils, 550–552, **551**; soil, 529–533; soil services, 533; of water, 534–537, **534, 535, 536, 537**; of water life, 549–550; what you can do, 550–553; whose concern, 528–529; of wildlife, 545–552

Contact poisons, 524–525
Continuity of germ plasm, 390, **390**, 429, **429**
Contour planting, 533, **533**
Contrasting characters, 412–413
Convolutions, 270, **271**
Convulsions, 251
Cooking, and vitamins, 180
Coordination, and cerebellum, 271, 277
Copper, 36, 175
Copperhead, 113
Coral reefs (islands), 86–87
Coral snake, 113
Corals, 86–87; organ pipe, **87**
Cork, 31, **31**; of roots, 155; of stems, **154**
Corn, 75, **139**, 520, 532; chromosome number of, **408**; and corn borer, 520–521; effects of radiation, **425**; flowers of, 370, **371**; fruit, 377; gene and light, 426, **427**; hybrid vigor, 438, **439**; seed, **375**; stem, 164–165, **165**; water loss in, 161
Corn borer, 520–521; larvae, **521**
Cornea, of eye, 273, **273**
Corolla, 370, **371**
Coronary, arteries, 208; thrombosis, 208
Cortex, of adrenals, 251, 252; of brain, 270–271, **271**; root, **159**; stem, **154**, 155
Cortisone, of adrenals, 251, 252
Cotton, 77, 520, 523; fruits, **520**
Cotton boll weevil, 520; history of, 520
Cotyledons, **375**
Cousin marriages, 449
Cowpox, and smallpox, 313–314
Cows, in model farm, 335, **444**; and selection, 436
Coyote, **129**, 130
Crab, 106, **106**
Cranium, 107, 270
Crayfish, 559–562, **559, 561**
Creosote, use against termites, 104
Cretinism, 244, 252
Cricket, 99
Crocodiles, 111
Cro-Magnon man, 499–501; art, **501**; artist at work, **500**
Crops, rotation of, 532
Crossbreeding, def., 438
Crosses, 411–421; Andalusian fowl, **414**; cat, **411**; cattle, **436, 437**; dihybrid, **417**; four o'clock, 413; fruit fly, **418**; guinea pig, **416**; onion, **412**; pea, **413, 415, 416, 417**; in plant breeding, 412; rat, **415**; squash, **414**
Crossing over, 418, **419**

Cross-pollination, 374; and bees, 102, **374**
Crow, 115
Crustaceans, 93, 106, **106**, 134
Cud, chewing, 119
Culex (mosquito), 339; life history of, **340**
Culture, Bronze and Iron Age, 501–502; def., 496; of early man, 500–501; New Stone Age, 501–502; Old Stone Age, 501
Culturing bacteria, 302, **303**; medium used, 302
Cutting, def., 378
Cyclotron, 247
Cypress tree, 70, **71**
Cyst, trichina, 342, **342**
Cytoplasm, 31, **32**

"Daddy longlegs," 105
Daisy, 77, **490**; Shasta, **439**
Dam, beaver, **262**; and water supply, 536, **536**
Dandelion, 162; parthenogenesis in, 379; seeds, **376**
"Darning needle," insect, 95
Darwin, Charles R., family pedigree, 452–453, **453**; theory of evolution of, 488–490
Darwin-Wedgwood pedigree, 452–453, **453**
Datura, and heredity, **425**
"Daughter" cell, in reproduction, 364
Daydreaming, 295
Daylight, and plant growth, 516
DDT, and insect control, 338, 341, 525, **525**
Deafness, heredity, 449
Death, by accident, 350–351; Black, 331; from bubonic plague, 331; causes of, 347, **347**; causes of in children, 350; from diphtheria, **318, 319**; and tobacco, 354; from tuberlosis, **305**, 306, 347
Decay, and cycles, 508–511, 512–513; and nitrogen cycle, **510**
Deciduous, 75
Deer, 387
Deficiency diseases, 176–182, 300; def., 178
Delphinium, bud mutation, **424**
Delta, formation of, 461
Dendrites, 258–259, **258, 283**; and nerve impulse, 260
Denitrifying bacteria, 511
Dentine, of tooth, **195**
Depressant, 355
Dermis, of skin, 238, **238**
De Vries, Hugo, and mutations, 490; and theory of evolution, 490

INDEX 593

Diabetes, 247–248, 252; use of insulin in, 247–249, 252
Diaphragm, human, **195,** 227–228, **227**
Diatoms, 58, 60, 62–63, **62;** and food chains, 508–509
Dicot (dicotyledon), 74–78, 136; families, 77; seed, **375;** uses, 77
Diet, 170–187; Basic Seven, **183;** and calories, 171–174; carbohydrates in, 175; experiments, 175–176, **176;** fats in, 175; minerals in, 175–178; proteins in, 174–175; roughage in, 200–201; vitamins in, 176–184; water in, 175
Differentiation, 53; in animals, 386, 390, **390;** in plants, 375
Diffusion, 42–45; of air in lungs, 227; and blood, 205; and capillaries, 205; in cells, 44, **44,** 45; conditions of, 43, **43,** 48; experiment, 43–44, **43,** 48; in liquids, 43, **43, 44;** and lymph, 218; through membrane, 43–45, **43, 44;** and molecules, 43, **43,** 44; and osmosis, 45; in root hairs, 161
Digestion, 190–202, **191;** by bacteria, 300, **301;** def., 46, 191–192; and enzymes, 192–193; of fats, 199; in mouth, 193–194; products of, 198; of protein, 198–199, **198;** in small intestine, 198–199; of starches, 192, **198,** 199; in stomach, 196–198; table of, **198;** in test tube, 192
Digestive enzymes, 192, 196–198; table of, **198**
Digestive glands, 192–193, **193, 60;** stimulation of, 201–202
Digestive juice, 192–193, 196–198; table of, **198**
Digestive system, of man, 190, **191**
Dihybrid, 416; cross, **416, 417;** gametes, **416, 419**
Dingo, 130
Dinosaurs, 458, 466, 474, **475;** footprints of, **464**
Diphtheria, 317–319; and active immunity, 318; carriers, 337; death rate, **318, 319;** effect of antitoxin on, 318, **319;** and passive immunity, 317–318; susceptibility test, 319
Diploid, 409
Disease, 298–359; and body defenses, 310–323; and carriers, 337–341; circulatory, 347–349; communicable, 300–309; deficiency, 176–182, 300; and drugs, 326–327; epidemics, 331; and future, 346–359; germ theory of, 307–308; infectious, 300–309; and laws, 335–337; metabolic, 242–243, 244–249; and milk supply, 333–335, **334, 335;** organic, 300, 347; recent discoveries, 324–329; summary of conquest, 320–322; table of information, 343; venereal, 327; virus, 298, 327–328; and water, 333
Disinfectants, 303; and surgery, 320
Dispersal, seed, **376,** 377
Distribution, of organisms, 484–485
Diver, 80; and "bends," 233
Division, ameba, 364, **365;** cell, 405–407; embryo sac, 372, **373;** nuclear, 405–407; paramecium, 364, **364;** pollen grain, 372–373, **373;** reduction, 408–409, **409;** yeast, 364, **365;** zygospore, 366 (see Reproduction)
Dodder, 509
Dog, 129, **129,** 501; brain, **481;** breeds and hormones, **251;** conditioned response, 279; rabies, 312–313; skull, **194**
Dogfish, 109
Dominance, 413, 414, 415, 416, 417; in fruit fly, **418;** law of, 412–413, **413**
Dominant, def., 412; species, 517–518
Donkey, 437
Donor, of blood, **209**
Dormant, buds, 152; seeds, 377
Double nucleus, 372, **373**
Draftees, causes of rejection of, 353; rejection of, 354
Drawing, prehistoric, **500, 501**
Drosophila melanogaster (see Fruit fly)
Drugs, addicts, 356–357; and disease, 326–327; laws about, 335–337; sulfa, 326–327
Duckbill, 119
Ducks, in refuge, **547;** shape of bill, **115**
Ductless glands, 242–253, **243, 244;** and dog breeds, **251;** table of, 252
Dutch elm disease, 522
Dutrochet, (Henry Joachim), 47
Dyeing, bacteria, 305

Ear, 274–275, **275,** 277; and balance, 275; of corn, **427**
Eardrum, 94, 274
Earth, changes in surface of, 460–461; estimating age of, 460; history of, 458–505; studying history of, 466–468; table of eras of, 468
Earthworm, 81, 88–89, **89,** 557–559, **557**
Echinoderms, 81, 89–90, **89, 90,** 133
Ecology, 515–527; def., 515
Ectoderm, 388, **388**
Eczema, and allergy, 352
Eels, life cycle of, 109
Efferent neuron, 260, **261**
Egg cell, 387; animal, 386; of flower, 372, **373;** hen, 393–394
Egg nucleus, of flower, 372, **373,** 374–375, **374**
Eggs, ant, **100;** development of hen's, 393–394, **395;** development of plant, 370–372, **373;** fish, 388–389, **389;** flowering plant, 372, **373;** formation of, 408–409; frog, **387,** 391–393, **392;** human, **387;** hydra, **387;** for measles vaccine, 317; mosquito, **340,** 341; for typhus vaccine, **317**
Ehrlich, Paul, and syphilis, 327
Eijkman, Christiaan, and beriberi, 177
Elastic tissue, 54
Electrical energy, 41
Electrocardiogram, 349
Electron, 33, **33**
Elements, def., 34; in protoplasm, 35
Elephant, fossil history, 478
Elimination, vs. excretion, 235
Elk, 545, **546**
Elm, leaf, **71,** 74; netted veined, 71, **74;** trees, **153,** 164
Elodea, 146
Embryo, 386–388; chick, **482;** development of bird, 393–394; of fish, 389–390, **390;** of flowering plant, 370, 375–377, **375;** of frog, **392,** 393; of human, 397; of mammal, **396, 482;** of rabbit, 395–396; of starfish, 386–388; of turtle, **482**
Embryos, resemblances among vertebrate, 482, **482**
Embryo sac, of plant, 372–373, **373,** 374
Emotions, 290–297, **290, 291;** and behavior, 290–297; in child, 291–292; and growing up, 290–297; and habits, 284; healthy, 294; and maturity, 292; and nervous system, 275–276; and success, 292–293
Emulsion, 199
Enamel, of tooth, **195**
End-brush, 258, 259; in reflex arc, **261;** and synapse, 261
Enders, John F., and polio, 316

End products, of digestion, 192, 198
Endocrine glands, 242–253, **243, 244**
Endoderm, 388, 388
Endosperm, 375, **375,** 377
Energy, in breaking log jam, 41; changes in, 41; in common foods, 170–171; def., 41; measurement of heat, 171–172; measuring in food, 172; measuring in man, 172–174; mechanical, **42;** in nerve impulses, 260; in photosynthesis, 144–145; radiant, 144; in respiration, 230–231; in resting cow, **42;** from sun, 143–145; transformation of, 41–42
English sparrow, 115
Entomologist, 93; def., 93
Environment, adaptations to, 492–493, **492, 493;** and breeding, 443–444, **444;** and changes, 426–432; and chromosomes, 424, **425,** 426–431; def., 110; effect on gene, 426–427; effect on organisms, 427–428, **427, 428, 429;** and human improvement, **430,** 431–432, 453–455; and plants, 515–520
Enzymes, 192, 243; digestive, 192–193, 198–199
Eohippus, 478–479, **478, 479;** leg bones, **479;** skeleton, **478**
Epidemics, 331
Epidermis, of leaf, 140, 141, **141,** 142, **142;** of root, **159;** of skin, 238, **238;** of stem, 155; tissue, 54
Epiglottis, of man, **230**
Epithelial, cells, **49;** tissue, 54
Epithelium, of lungs, 227; of skin, 238, **238;** of stomach, 196; of windpipe, 230
Eras, def., 468; described, 471–476; diagram of, **471;** organisms in, **477;** pictured, **472, 473, 475, 476;** table of, 468
Erepsin, 198
Ergosterol, and vitamin D, 180
Erosion, 460–461, **460,** 529–530, **529;** def., 460; and forests, 537–538; gully, 530, **531;** on hillside, **531;** map of U.S., **529;** sheet, 530; by wind, 530, **531**
Esophagus (food pipe), of man, 190, 194, **195, 196,** 230, **230**
Essential organs (flower), def., 370
Estrogens, 251, 252
Eucalyptus, 73
Eugenics, 431
European corn borer (see Corn borer)

Eustachian tube, 274
Euthenics, 431–432
Evaporation, from leaf, 161–162; of sweat, 239–240
Evening primrose, 490, **491;** chromosome number, **408;** mutant, **491**
Everest, Mt., 224
Evergreens, 73, **73**
"E" vitamins, 182
Evolution, and adaptations, 492–493, **492, 493;** def., 480; evidences for, 480–486; of man, 495–502; significance of fossils in, 478–479, 485; summary of, 485–486; theories of, 488–494
Excavating, for fossils, **467**
Excretion, 46, 235–241; and typhoid, 314, 337
Excretory system, 235–237, **236;** of frog, **392**
Exhaling, 228–229
Experience, and learning, 285–286
Extensor, 51, 52
Extinction, of wild life, 545–546
Eye, compound, **94;** grasshopper, 94, **94;** heredity of color, 447–448; heredity of color blindness, 450, **451;** human, 272–274, **273, 274,** 277; of white potato, **162**

F_1, def., 413, **413**
F_2, def., 413, **413**
Fainting, 216
Fallopian tubes, 397
False Solomon's seal, 551
Families, 128, 130, 131, **132;** plant, 77
Family, in classification, 128, 130, 131, **132**
Family life, animal, 395
Farming, and soil destruction, 530–533
Farms, inspection of milk, 334, 335
Far-sightedness, 274, 448
Fat cells, 49
Fats, 36, 37, 147; absorption of, 199–200; in common foods, **186;** composition of, 36; in diet, 175; diffusion of, 45; synthesis of, 147; test for, 37
Fat tissue, 54
Fatty acids, 198
Federal Bureau of Fisheries, 109
Federal Food, Drug and Cosmetic Act, 304, 336
Feeble-mindedness, heredity of, 452–455
Feelers, 94; butterfly, 97; moth, 97, **97**
Felis (cats), 129, **129;** cougar,

129, **129;** domestica, 129, **129;** leo, 129
Female, ant, **100;** deer, **387;** gametes, 286; malarial protozoan, 367–368, **368;** sex organs, 286, **392**
Fermentation, 64; and Pasteur, 306–307
Ferns, 16–17, 68–69, **69,** 136; bracken, 68; classification of, 68–69; hay-scented, 69, **69;** prothallus, 381, **381;** reproduction of, **380,** 381, **381,** 383; spore cases, **69,** 380, 381, **381;** tree, 69, 473, **473;** young plant, **381**
Fertilization, 386; in bird, 393–394; and chromosome number, 408–409; def., 367–368; and development, 374–377, 381, 382, 383, 386–390, 392, 394–396, 397; external, 388–389, 391; in fern, 381; in fish, 388–389; in flowering plants, 374–375, **374;** and heredity, 404–410; internal, 393–394, 395; in land-living animals, 393; in malarial protozoan, 367–368, **368;** in moss, 382; in rabbit, 395
Fertilization membrane, 389
Fertilized egg cell, 386, **388;** of fern, **381;** of flowering plant, 374–375
Fertilizer, 161; and soil restoration, 530–531
Fever, malaria, 338; typhoid, 314
Fibrin, 208
Fibrinogen, 206
Fibrous, tissue, 54
Field trips, 10–27; to a city lot, 19; to the desert, 27; in the fall, 11; in the late fall, 21; to a marsh, 25; in midwinter, 23; to a pond, 13; to the seashore, 15; to the woods, 17
Filament, flower, 372, **372;** spirogyra, 366, **367**
Filial, def., 413
Filterable virus, 328 (see also Virus)
Filters, for water supply, 333, **333;** porcelain, 328
Fins, fish, **107**
Fir, western Douglas, 71
Firefly, 100
First aid, 214
Fish, 107–109, **107, 108,** 134, 564–566, **565;** in balanced aquarium, **518;** brain, **481;** classification, 108; development of, 389–390, **390;** embryo, **482;** fossil, **463;** hatcheries, 549–550; "ladders," 109; and learn-

INDEX 595

ing, 281; migration, 109; parental care, 390–391, **391**; reproduction of, 388–391, **389, 390, 391**; sperm, 387
Fish hawk, bill, **115**
Fission, in ameba, 364, **365**; binary, def., 364; in paramecium, 364, **364**
Fissure, of cerebrum, 270
Fitness (see Adaptations)
Flagellum, of bacteria, 300, **301**
Flatfish, 108
Flatworm, 87, **88,** 133
Flax, 302
Fleas, as germ carriers, 337
Fleming, Alexander, 324–325, **324**
Flexor (muscle), **51,** 52
Flies, 97–98, **98,** 332, 337, 362, 363 (see Fruit fly)
Floods, 535, 535–536; and forests, 539
Flounder, 108
Flower, structure, 370, **371, 372, 374**
Flower color, inheritance, 413, **413**
Flowering plants, 69–78, **76, 77**; ages, 71; alternation of generations, 381–382; characteristics, 70; classification of, 70, 72–77; families, 77; life cycle, 370–377, 381–382; reproduction, 370–381, 381–382, 383
Flowers, needing protection, **551**
Fly, and spontaneous generation, 362–364, **363**
Flycatcher, bill, **115**
"Flying" fish, 108
Focus, of eye, 273, **274**
Folic acid, 182
Food, 170–189; absorption of, 190, 199–200; Basic Seven, **183**; calories, 171–174; canning, 180; choosing of (diet), 174–176; compounds, 170–171; diffusion into capillaries, 199–200; digestion, 190–199; energy in, 171–174; movement in canal, 194, 196–197; preservation of, 304; pure, 335–337; and reflexes, 281; sources of man's, 170; table of information, 186–187; and typhoid, 314; use in body, 170–171; use in cell, **171**; and vitamins, 176–184, 187
Food chains, 89, 508–510, **509,** 520–521; and earth history, 509–510
Food pipe (see Esophagus)
Food vacuole, of paramecium, **82,** 83
Foot, of mollusks, **90,** 91
Forest fires, 541–542; effect, **541**; fighting, **543, 544**

Forest ranger, at work, **542**
Forests, climax community, **519**; conservation of, 537–545; destruction of, 437–438; and flood prevention, 539; and humus, 539; need for, 539; second growth, 537; services, 543–545; and soil erosion, 539; uses of, 538–539; virgin, 537, **538**
Formula, of various compounds, 36, 37; of water, 34
Fossils, 458–469, 471–479; Cenozoic, **475**; def., 465; early man, 495–501; fern, **464**; formation of, 462–464; how discovered, **466**; hunting, 465–466, **467**; illustrations of, **463, 464, 465, 473, 474, 478, 479**; Mesozoic, 474, **475**; Paleozoic, **472, 473**; Proterozoic, **471**; reconstruction of, **467**; series of, 478, **479**; significance of, 479; snail series, 478, **479**; succession in rocks, **477**; summary of, 477; and tar pool, **465**; tree, **463**; types of, 465
Four o'clock, blossom, **413**; heredity in, 413; hybrid cross of, 413
Fox, mutation, 440–441; red, **130**
Fractionation, of blood, 211
Fraternal twins, 455
Friends of the Land, 550
Fringed gentian, response to light, 264, **266**
Frog, 107, 110–111, **110, 111,** 566–568, **567**; brain, **481**; capillaries, **205**; chromosome number (leopard frog), **408**; classification of, 110–111; development of, 391–393, **392, 393**; egg, **387, 392**; embryo, **482**; excretory organs, 567, **567**; metamorphosis of, 393, **393**; reproduction, 391–393, **392, 393**; reproductive organs, **392**; sperm, **387**; and thyroxin, 244
Fronds, of fern, 68, **69**
Fruit, 375–377, **375, 376**; cotton, **520**; development, **375**; seedless, 380
Fruit fly, chromosome number of, **408**; giant chromosome, **405**; heredity, 417–418, **418, 419,** 426; in milk bottles, **417**; mutations, 422, **423**; use in genetics, 417–418; x-rayed, 424, **424**
Fucus, 59–60
Function, def., 49
Fungi, 63–64, **66,** 135; bracket, **62**; and decay, 64; and disease, 63–64, 307–308; and nitrogen cycle, 510; as plant

parasites, **63,** 158, **522**; and symbiosis, 64
Funk, Casimir, "vitamine," 177–178
Fused nucleus, def., 372

Gall (bile), 198; bladder, **196, 198**
Game laws, 547
Gametes, active (supplying), 366, **367**; bird, 393–394; and chromosomes, 408–410, **409,** 414–420; conjugation of, 366–367, **367**; def., 366; of dihybrid, **416, 419**; eggs, 372, 381, 382, 383, 386, **387,** 388; fertilization of, 374–375; fish, 388–389; formation, 408–409; frog, 391, **392**; and germ plasm, **429**; and heredity, 404–410, 414–416, **413, 416, 419**; like, 366–367; mammalian, 395, 397; maturation, 408–409, **409**; passive (receiving), 366, 367; plant, 370–373, **372, 373**; sperm, 372, 381, 382, 383, 386, **387,** 389; spirogyra, 366–367, **367**; unlike, 367–389
Gamma globulin, 206, 315–316, 318, 320
Ganglia, 259, 260; autonomic, 276, **276,** 277; bee, **261**; earthworm, **557**; in reflex arc, 260, **261**
Garden spider, and web, **105**
Garter snake, 112
Gastric glands, 192, **193**; duct, **193**; stimulation of, 201
Gastric juice, 196, 197, 198
Gastrula, 388, **388**
Gene, def., 404; action of, 426, 427; and breeding, 435–443; changes in, 422–423; and chromosome, 405, 406; effect of environment on, 426–427; and grafting, 442–443; and heredity, 404; and light, 426, **427**; and mitosis, 405–407; revisions in theory of, 426–427; and selection, 435; and temperature, 426; theory of, 404–405
Genetics (see Heredity)
Genus (genera, pl.), 128
Geographic distribution, of organisms, 484–485
Geologist, 460
Geometrid moth caterpillar, and adaptation, **492**
Geotropism, 266; in sunflower, **265**
Geranium, 377–378
Germ cells (see Gametes)
Germination, 377, **377**

Germ layers, in animal development, 388, **388**
Germ plasm, and acquired characters, 428–429; continuity of, 390, **390**, 429, **429**
Germs, 64; def., 300; and disease, 300–345, 349–350; spread of, 310
Germ theory of disease, 307–308; and Koch's postulates, 305–306
Gestation, 396
Giantism, **242**
Gills, fish, **107**, 108; tadpole, **392**, 393
Giraffe, **491**
Glacial period, 476
Glacier, **460**; and ice sheet, **476**
Gland, cells, 193, **193**; def., 193, **193**; tissue, 54, 193
Glands, "of Combat," 250; gastric, 192, **193**; of internal secretion (endocrine), 201, 242–253; intestinal, 192, 201–202; oil, 238, **238**; salivary, 193, 201; sweat, 238–239, **238**, **239**
Glasses, to correct vision, 274
Glowworm, 100
Glucose, 36, 37, 143, 198; formula, 36
Glycerin, 198
Glycogen, 36, 201; and insulin, 247
Gneiss, 462
Goat, 121
Gobi Desert, and fossils, 466, **467**
Goblet cells, 230, **231**
Goiter, 245–247, **245**, **246**, 252; exophthalmic, 245–247; map of distribution, 245, **246**; treatment of, 246–247
Golden plover, migration, 116, **117**
Goldenrod, **509**
Gonorrhea, 327
Gooseberry, and blister rust, **523**
"Gopher," 128
Gorilla, **121**, 122
Grafting, 379; and plant breeding, 442–443, **442**, **443**
Grains, 75
Grand Canyon, and fossils, 466
Granite, 460, 462
Graph, of bean length, 427–428, **428**; of intelligence quotients, 452
Grasses, 75; and allergies, 351
Grasshopper, 81, **94**, 95, 99–100, **562**, 563–564, **563**; life history, 96
Gravity, and plant hormones, 264, **265**; and tropisms, 266
Gray matter, of brain, 270, **271**
Greenland, ice cap, **476**

Green plants, and food chains, 508–510
Gristle (see Cartilage)
"Ground pines," 69
Ground sloth, **465**
Grouse, hatching, **395**; protective adaptation, **492**
Growing point, of root, **159**, 160; of stem, 152, 157
Growing up, and emotions, 290–297
Growth, of bacteria, 302–305, **303**; and plant behavior, 264
Growth hormones, 264
Guard cells, 142, **142**
Guinea pigs, and acquired characters, 428; heredity of, **416**; and scurvy, **178**
Gull, 395
Gullet (see Esophagus), of paramecium, **82**
Guppies, 108
Gymnosperms, 72–73, 74, 136

Habitat, def., 66
Habits, 283–284; breaking (unlearning), 284; compared with reflexes, 283; formation of, 283–284
Hair, 238; follicle, **238**; heredity in cats, **411**; heredity in man, 448
Halibut liver oil, and vitamin D, 180
Halters, of flies, 98, **98**
Hammer, bone of ear, 274, **275**
Haploid, 409; effect on organism, **425**; in maturation of gametes, 408–409, **409**
Hardwoods, 75, 77, 538
Harvey, William, and blood circulation, 213–214, **213**, 222
Hatchet foot mollusks, 91–92
Hawks, and conservation, 546–547
Hay fever, 351, 352
Hay infusion, 83
Health, 298–359; and alcohol, 354–356; laws, 335–337; mental, 295–296; poor, 352–353; and poverty, 357, **357**; and social problems, 357; and tobacco, 354; workers of Board of, 331–332, **336**
Health officers, 331–332; and disease prevention, 331–332
Heart, 51, **204**, 205, 211–214, **211**, **212**; beat, 212–213, 214; disease, 216, 349; muscle, 51; structure of, **211**, 212, **212**; valves of, **212**, 217–218, **217**; work of, 51, 211–213
Heartwood, 157–158, **157**
Heat, different from temperature, 171; energy, 41, 171–174; unit of, 171–173, **172**, **173**
Heath hen, extinction of, 545
Helicopter, and DDT dusting, **525**
Hemlock, 140
Hemoglobin, 206–207; formula of, 36
Hemophilia, heredity of, 450
Hemorrhage, cerebral, 216
Hemp, 302, 356
Hepatica, **551**
Herbs, def., 70; stem, 164
Heredity, 402–457; and acquired characters, 428–431, **429**; and breeding, 434–446; diagram of simple case, **415**; in dihybrids, 415–416; of disease in man, 348; and environment, 443–444; in fruit fly, **418**; and gene theory, 404–405; and improvement of man, 452–456; laws of, 411–416, **413**, **414**, **415**, **416**, **417**; in man, 447–457; mental traits in man, 451–454; and organisms studied, 417; of sex, 450; sex-linked, 450, **451**; and variation, 416–417
Hereford, cattle, **436**, 437, 440
Herelle, Felix H. d', and bacteriophage, 328–329
Herring, 107, 508
Hessian fly, 97–98, **98**, 522
Hibernation, 112
Hickory, 519; shagbark leaf, **71**; shagbark trunk, **155**
Hillary, Sir Edmund, 225
Himalayas, 476
Hippopotamus, and young, 404, **404**
Hives, and allergy, 352
Hobbies, 295
Hog (see Pig)
Hog-nosed snake, **113**
Homo, Neandertalensis, 497–499, **498**, **499**; sapiens, 495, 499–505
Honeybee, 102, **102**, **103**
Honeycomb, of bees, 102
Honeydew, ant food, 101
Hooke, Robert, 30, 31, 47
Hookworm, **81**, 88; disease, 341–342
Hormones, 201, 242–253; def., 201, 242; and growth, 242–243, **242**; plant, 251; and secondary sex characters, 250, 251; similarity in animals, 483; table of, 252
Hornlessness, in cattle, 422, 440
Horse, and antitoxin, 317–318, 320; bleeding for antitoxin, **318**; breeding of, 434, **434**; fossil history, **476**, 478–479,

INDEX **597**

478, **479**; hybridization of, 437; leg bones, **479**; and selection, 435–436; skeleton, **478**; skull, **194**; and tetanus, 319; thoroughbred, **434**; wild, **434**
Horse chestnut twig, 151–154, **152**
Horsetails, 69, 136
Host, 300, 508, **509**, **523**; def., 63
Housefly, 98, **98**; chromosome number of, **408**
Human, brain, 259, **259**, 270–272, **271**, 277; egg, **387**; gametes, **387**; history, 495–502; races, 502–504; reproduction, 397–398
Human heredity, 447–457; of albinism, **448**, 449; of blood types, 449; of complex characters, 449; difficulties, 447; how studied, 447–448; of mental traits, 451–455; Rh factor, 449–450; of sex, 450; of sex-linked characters, 450, **451**; table, 448; use of pedigrees, **446**, 446
Hummingbird, bill, **115**; nest, 114
Humus, 515, 531–532, 539, **539**
Huxley, Thomas Henry, 47, 168
Hybrid, 413–416, 436–440, **436**, **437**, **439**; def., 414; vigor, 438, **439**
Hybridization, animal, 436–438; in cattle, 436–437, **436**, **437**; def., 436; plant, 438–440, **439**, **440**; used by breeders, 436–437, 438–440
Hydra, 86, 87, 423, 556–557, **556**; budding in, 364; egg, **387**
Hydrochloric acid, of stomach, 198
Hydrogen, 34, 35, 36, 37; atom, **33**; cycle, 512, **512**
Hydrophobia (see Rabies)
Hydrotropism, 266
Hypertension, 216
Hypha, 63, 365–366, **365**
Hypothesis, in vitamin experiment, 177

Ice, river of (glacier), **460**; sheets, 476
Ichneumon fly, and adaptations, 493, **493**
Identical twins, **454**, 454–455
Igneous rock, 460
Illness rate, among occupations, 357, **357**
Immunity, 312; acquired, 318; active, 312–317; to anthrax, 312; to chicken cholera, 311–312; to measles, 317; natural, 318; passive, acquired, 318; to polio, 314–317; to rabies, 312–313; to scarlet fever, 317; to smallpox, 313–314; to tuberculosis, 317; to typhoid, 314; to whooping cough, 317
Imprints, fossil, 464, **464**
Impulse, in nerve, 260, **261**
Inbreeding, 437–438; def., 436
Incisor, 119, 193, **195**
Incomplete dominance, def., 413
Incomplete metamorphosis, 96
Incubation, 394
Independent assortment, 415–416, **416**, **417**
Industrial revolution, and tuberculosis, 306
Infantile paralysis (see Poliomyelitis)
Infectious disease, 300–309
Influenza, 327, 347; epidemic, 331; vaccines, 317; virus, **328**
Inhaling, 227–229
Inheritance of variations, and evolution, 489–490
Inner ear, 274–275, **275**
Inoculation, for immunity, 311–317
Insect-eating plants, 265, **267**, **268**
Insects, **12**, 93–104; as allies, 523; classification, 94, 134; communities, 101–104, **101**; contact poisons, 524–525; control, 524–525; as disease carriers, 337–341, **339**; economic effects, 99, 103; fossils, 465; harm, 103; importations, 521–522; life cycle of, 95–96; and man, 96, 97, 98, 99, **99**, 100, 103, 520–522; mouth parts, 96, **96**, 98, **98**, 99; noises, 95; origin of problem, 520–521; reflexes, 260; scale, 96–97; scaly winged, 96–97; social, 101–104; stomach poisons, 524; structure, 94; usefulness, 103
Insoluble substances, 45
Inspection, for health purposes, 335
Instinct, 260–263, **262**
Instinctive behavior, 260–263, **262**, **263**
Insulin, 247–249, **248**, 252; injection of, 247, **248**
Intelligence, conservation of, 455; def., 451; of identical twins, 445; tests, 451–452
Intelligence quotient, def., 451–452; graph, **452**
Intercellular matter, 50–51, **50**
Intermediate products, of digestion, 192, 198
Internal secretions (see Hormones)
Internode, of stem, 152
Intestinal, glands, 192, 198–199, **200**; juice, 192, 198–199
Intestine, absorption in small, 199–200; blood vessels of cat's, **214**; digestion in small, 198–199; large, 190, 200–201; of man, 198–201; small, 190, **196**, 198–200
Invertebrates, 80–106; behavior, 260–262, **262**; def., 80; examples of, **81**
Involuntary muscle, 51, 52, **52**, 275–276
Involuntary nervous system (see Autonomic nervous system)
Iodine, 36, 61; and goiter, 244–247, **246**; radioactive, 246–247; as testing agent, 37; in thyroxin, 244
Iris, of eye, 273, **273**
Iron, 36; Age, 501; in common foods, **187**; in diet, 175
Iron lung, 227, **228**
Irradiation, and vitamin D, 180
Irrigation, 536, **537**
Irritability, 46, 47, 258, 259
Islands of Langerhans, and insulin, 248, 252
Isolation (quarantine), and disease, 331
Isoniazid, 306
Isotopes, 246–247; and cancer, 349; and goiter, 247; radioactive, 247, 349
Italian "race," 503
Izaak Walton League, 550

Jack-in-the-pulpit, **551**
Japanese beetle, 521–522, **522**; quarantine sign, 522
Java ape man, 496; head, **498**
Jellyfish, **81**, 85–86, **86**
Jenner, Edward, and smallpox, 313–314
Jersey cow, and breeding, **437**
Jewish "race," 503
Jimson weed, and chromosomes, **425**
Johannsen, Wilhelm L., 427
Jointed-legged invertebrates (see Arthropods)
Juice, digestive, 192–193, 196–199
Jukes family, 453
Junco, Sierra, **114**
Jute, 302

Kallikak family, 453
Kangaroo, 118, **121**, 484; reproduction, 397, **397**
Katydid, 99
Kelp, 61
Kidneys, 235–237, **236**, 240; of frog, **392**; of sheep, **237**
Kingdoms, animal, 82–122; plant, 58–79
Kissinger, John R., and yellow fever, 340

Knee jerk, 257
Koala, and young, 484, **485**
Koch, Robert, 304–306; and culture media, 304; postulates, 305–306; staining bacteria, 305
Köhler, Dr. Wolfgang, and behavior, 284–285
Krilium, 532
"K" vitamins, 182

Lacteals, of villus, 200, **200**, 218
Ladybird beetle, in insect control, 100
Lady's slipper, 74
Lamarck, Jean Baptiste (Chevalier de), theory of evolution, 490–492; and variation, 430
Lamprey eel, 549
Landsteiner, Karl, 208–209
Langerhans, Paul, and diabetes, 248
Larva, ant, **100**; bee, 102; corn borer, **521**; insect, 95, **95**, 96, **96**; Japanese beetle, 521; Monarch (milkweed) butterfly, 95, **95**; mosquito, **340**, 341; potato beetle, **521**; silkworm, **96**
Larynx, **225**, 229, **230**, 244
Laveran, Alphonse, and malaria, 338
Law, "of dominance," 412–413; of independent assortment, 415–416; of segregation, 413–415; of unit characters, 415–416
Laws, to protect wildlife, 546–550; pure drugs, 335–337; pure foods, 335–337
Layering, def., 378
Leaching, of soil, 530
Lead, 460
Leaf scar, 152
Learned acts, 279–288; conditioned response, 279
Learning, 279–289; activity and success, 279–283, **281**, **282**, **285**; by chickens, 281, **281**; in children, 279; and experience, 285–286; in fish, 281; and habits, 283–284; and maze, 281, **281**; and memory, 287–288; and rat, 281; by reasoning, 284–286; rules for, 286–287; trial and error, 279–283, **281**, **282**, **285**; by wild animals, 280
Leaves, 140–148; angiosperm, 73–74; color in fall, 142–143; compound, 70, **71**; differences among, 73–77; gymnosperm, 72–73, 140; internal structure, 140–143, **141**; needlelike, 72–73, **73**, 140; net veining, 74, **74**; parallel veining, 74, **74**; parts of, 140; in photosynthesis, 144–145; simple, 70, **71**; sizes, 140; stomata, 142, **142**; structure, 140–143, **141**; use to plant, 143–145, 147–148; veining, 74; veins of, 159; work of, 140–150
Leeuwenhoek, Anton van, 30; and spontaneous generation, 362
Legs, Eohippus, **479**; grasshopper, **94**; horse, **479**
Legume, 175, 511, **511**, 532; family, 77
Lemurs, 122
Length of life, 346–347, **346**
Lens (eyes), 273–274, **273**, **274**
Lenticels, 152–153, **152**
Leopard, 128, **129**
Lepers, and community action, 331
Lepidoptera, 96–97
Leucocytes, 207, **207**
Lichen, 64, **67**, 493, 518–519
Life, 40; defined as cell activities, 40–47; length of, 346–347, **346**
Ligaments, 272
Light, and eye, 272–274; form of energy, 41; and fringed gentian, 264, **266**; and gene action, 426, **427**; and plant growth, 264; and plant responses, 264–265, 266, **265**, **266**; response of nasturtium, **265**; as stimulus, 264, 266; and tropisms, 264–265, 266
Lightning, and nitrogen cycle, 511
Lignin, 32
Lily, flower, 370, **371**, **372**; flower x-ray, **371**
Limestone, 82–83, 462
Linkage, 418, **419**; sex-linked heredity, 450, **451**
Linnaeus, Carolus, 127, 483–484; scheme of classification, 128–130; work of, 56
Lipase, 198
Lister, Sir Joseph, 320
Liver, 198, 201
Liver flukes, 87
Liverworts, 68, **68**, 135
Living matter (see Protoplasm)
Living things, difference from lifeless, 40; general structure, 31–39
Lizards, 107, 111, **112**
Lobster, 106, **106**
Lockjaw (see Tetanus)
Locomotion, 46
Locust, 99–100 (see Grasshopper)
Los Angeles, tar pits, 465, **465**; water supply, 333, 536
Louse, and typhus, 337
Lumber, 153
Lumbering, 539–540, **539**
Luna moth, **97**
Lungfish, 109
Lungs, 225–227, **225**, **226**; in amphibia, 110; blood circulation, 220–221, **221**; and excretion, 240; in reptiles, 111; and tuberculosis, 306, **306**
Lymph, 205, 218–219, **218**, **219**; glands (nodes), 219, **219**
Lymphatics, 205, 218–219, **218**, **219**; of villus, 200
Lysins, 311

Mackerel, 508
Macrospore, def., 381
Maggot, 98; and spontaneous generation, 362, **363**
Magnesium, 36
Maize (see Corn)
Malaria, 327, 328–341; deaths from, 338; mosquito, **339**
Malarial protozoan, life history, **339**, 367–368, **368**; reproduction, 367–368, **368**
Malaysian, 502
Male, ant, **100**; deer, **387**; gametes, 286, 372, **373**, 386; malarial protozoan, 367–368, **368**; sex organs, 286, 372–373, **373**, 386; stickleback, **391**; toad, **393**
Malignant, tumor, 347–348
Malnutrition, 353
Maltose, 192
Mammals, 118–122, **118**, **119**, **120**, **121**, **122**, 135; Age of, 474–476; behavior, 257–259, 270–278, 279–280, 282–297; brain, **481**; characteristics, 118; embryo, **482**; embryo in uterus, 395–396, **396**; explanation of distribution, 484–485; family life, 397–398; flying, **122**; gnawing, 119; with grinding teeth, 119; importance, 118; with long eyeteeth, 119; marine, 118; parental care, 397, **397**, 397–398; pouched, 484–485, **485**; reproduction, 395–398; simple, 118–119, **118**, **119**
Mammary glands, 118, 397
Mammoth, fossils, 465
Man, arm bones of, **480**; behavior of, 257–259, 270–278, 279–280, 282–297; breathing of, 224–233; cells and tissues of, 49–53, **49**, **50**, **52**; chromosome number, **408**; classification of, 502–503; diet of, 168–187; digestion of, 190–202; and disease, 298–359; egg of, **387**; embryo of, **482**; endocrine glands of, 242–253; and environment, 431–432; excretion of, 235–241; heredity

INDEX

599

in, 447–457; history of, 495–502; improving mankind, 431–432; and insects, 520–522, 524–525; and population growth, 528; and racial classification, 502–504; reproduction, 397–398; skull of, **194**; sperm of, 387; time clock for, **495**

Manson, Patrick, and malaria, 338

Manure, green, 530–531; and tetanus, 319

Maple, classification of, 130; flow of sap, 162; fruits, **376**; leaf of red, **71**

Marble, 462

Marchantia (a liverwort), **68**

Marijuana, 356

Market hunting, 545

Marriage, regulation of, and syphilis, 327

Marsupials, 118–119; geographic distribution of, 484–485

"Master gland," 251–252

Maturation, of gametes, 408–409, **409**

Maze, 281, **281**

McGregor, Prof. J. H., and fossil man, **498**

Measles, 317, 327

Mechanical, energy, 41; stimulus, 266

Media, for raising bacteria, 302; solid, 302

Mediterranean, fruit fly, 522; race, 502

Medulla, **481**; and breathing, 228; human, 270–272, **271**, 277; sheep, **211**; vertebrate, **481**

Melanesian, race, 502

Membranes, of blood vessels, cell, **32**, 45; in diffusion, 43–45; embryonic, **396**; fertilization, 389; of lungs, 225–227; mucous, 54, 193; nervous system, 272; nuclear, 32–33; plant epidermis, 140–141; serous, 196

Memory (memorizing), 287–288

Mendel, Gregor, and heredity, 411–416

Mendelian ratio, 413–416, **413**, **414**, **415**, **416**, **417**; explained, 414–416

Meninges, 272, 277

Mental health, 295–296; of adolescents, 290–297; and alcohol, 354–356

Mental illness, 295–296

Mental traits, heredity, 451–455

Mesoderm, 388, **388**

Mesozoic era, 468, 474, **474**, 475, **477**

Metabolism, 172–174; basal, 173, **173, 174**; def., 173

Metamorphic rock, 462

Metamorphosis, complete, 96; def., 96, 393; of frog, 391–393, **392**; incomplete, 96; of insect, 96

Metchnikoff, Eli, and phagocytes, 207

Microneedles, 32

Microorganisms, 64–65, 82–84, 300–305, 310–323, 327–329, 338–340; and man, 300–305, 310–323, 327–329, 338–340

Micropyle, 374, **374**

Microscope, effect on image, 30; electron, 40; learning to use, 38; Leeuwenhoek's, 30; modern, 30, **30**

Microspore, def., 381

Midget, **242**, 243

Migration, of birds, 116; of fish, 109; laws about hunting, 547; routes, **117**

Milk, bottling of, **334**; breeding for, **438**; certified, 334–335; counting bacteria in, **336**; inspection of, **336**; raw, 334–335

Milk supply, and public health, 333–335, **334**, **335**, **336**

Milkweed, butterfly, 95–96, **95**; fruit, **376**

Millipedes, 93, 105, 134

Mimosa, behavior of, **267**

Minerals, 36, 198; in diet, 175–176; experiments on, **176**; movement in plants, 153, 161–162; in protein synthesis, 146–147; in soil, 146, 147, 161; test for, 37

Mink, mutation, **441**

Mint family, 77

Mistletoe, 493

Mitosis, 405–407, **406**, **407**, 425; def., 406

Mixture, 35; and compound, 35; sugar and water, **35**

Mockingbird, diagrammed, **116**

Molars, 194

Molasses, 43, 44

Molds, 63; breed, 63; colonies, **303**; in heredity, 417; of penicillin, 63, **65**; reproduction of, 365–366, **365**, **367**, **367**; and skin disorders, 63

Molecules, 33; not diffusible, 45; in diffusion, 43, 44

Mollusks, **81**, 90, 91–93, **91**, **92**, 134

Monarch butterfly (see Milkweed butterfly)

Mongoloid, 502

Monkey, 121; appendage, **481**; chromosome number of, **408**

Monocots (monocotyledons), 74–75, 136; as food, 75; leaves, 74, **74**; stems, 164–165, **165**

Moran, John J., and yellow fever, 340

Morgan, Thomas Hunt, **405**; and fruit fly, 422; and gene theory, 404–405

Moron, def., 452

Mosaic disease, of tobacco, 328

Mosquito, 97, **98**; chromosome number, **408**; control, 341, **341**; extermination of, 341, **341**; life history, 340, 341; and malaria, 338–341; mouth parts, **98**; sucking blood, **98**, **339**; and yellow fever, 338, 340

Mosses, 66–68, **67**, 136, **382**; classification of, 66; pigeon wheat, **382**; "reindeer," 64; reproduction of, 382, **382**, 383

Moth, 96–97, **97**; life cycle, **96**; sucking tube, **96**; tropism, 264

Mother cell, in reproduction, 364

Motor areas, of brain, 270–271

Motor neuron, 260, 261, **261**

Mountain laurel, 551

Mouth, anemone, 85, **85**; frog, 393; insect, 95, 97, 98, 99; man, 193, 229; paramecium, **82**, 83; tadpole, 393

Mucous membrane, 54, **231**; of mouth, 193; of villus, **200**

Mucus, 110, 193, 230

Mule, 437

Muller, Hermann J., **424**; and mutation, 424

Muscle, of arm, 51; cells, **49**, 51; of esophagus, 194; heart (cardiac), 51, 54; involuntary (smooth), 51, **52**, 54, 196, **196**, 275, 276; nervous control of, 275–276, **276**; in reflex arc, 260; skeletal, 51; of stomach, 196, **196**; tissue, 51–52, 54; voluntary (striated), 51, 54; work of, 51–52

Mushrooms, 58, 62, 63

Mussels, 91, 92

Mustard, family, 77; gas, 424

Mutant, barley, **425**; cattle, 441; corn, **425**; def., 422; Delphinium, **424**; evening primrose, 490, **491**; fox, 440–441; fruit fly, **423**; mink, **441**; oats, 442; sheep, 440; tobacco, **441**

Mutation, 422–424; barley, **425**; and breeder, 440–442, **441**; and cattle, 440; def., 422; effect of, 422–423; and evolution, 490; fox, 440–441; fruit fly, 422, **423**, 424; human, 449; induced, 442; mink, **441**; and organism studied, 422–424;

sheep, 440; somatic, 423–424, **424**; tobacco, **441**; and x-ray, 424, **424**, 425
Mutation theory, of evolution, 490
Myxedema, 245, 252
Myxomatosis, 522–523

Naming organisms (see Classification)
Narcotic, 356
Nasturtium, behavior, **265**
National Audubon Society, 550
National Monuments, 548
National Parks, 548
National Parks Association, 550
National Park Service, 548
National Wildlife Institute, 550
Natural immunity, 318
Natural resources, 508, 528–555; nonrenewable, 528; renewable, 528
Natural selection, Darwin's theory, 488–490
Neandertal man, 497–499; head of, **498**; hunting, **499**
Near-sightedness, 274, 448
Nebraska, in Cenozoic era, **476**
Nectar, 97, **374**
Needles, cedar, 73, **73**; evergreen, 73; hemlock, 140; pine, 72–73, **73**
Negative tropisms, def., 264; in paramecium, **263**
Negroid (stock), 502
Nemathelminths (round worms), **81**, 87–88, 133
Neolithic, 501–502
Nerve, auditory, **275**; cells, 258–259, **258**, 261; def., 259; impulse, 260, **261**; and nerve cells, 259; optic, **273**; tissue, 54, 257–259
Nerve centers, of man, 259, **259**, 270–272; protection of, 272
Nerve impulse, 260, **251**; in reflex arc, 260–263
Nerves, 272; man, 259, **259**, 277; skin, 238
Nervous system, 270–278; autonomic, 272, 275–276, **276**, 277; of bee, **261**; central, 259, **259**, 270–275, 277; involuntary, 272, 275–276, **276**, 277; of man, 254–269, 270–277; table, 277
Nests, ant, 101; bird, 394, **395**; fish, **389**, 391; praying mantis, **99**; spider (web), 105, **105**
Neuron, 258–259, **258**, 270–272; afferent (sensory), 260, **261**; efferent (motor), 260, **261**; of human cortex, 270; motor, 260, **261**; sensory, 260, **261**
Neurosis, 296

Neurospora, 417
Neutrons, 33, **33**
New Stone Age, 501–502; artifacts from, **496**
Newts, 111
New York City, diphtheria death rate, **319**; tuberculosis, **305**; water supply, 333
Niacin, 181–182; in common foods, 187
Nicotine, effects of, 354
Nicotinic acid (see Niacin)
Nitric acid, 37
Nitrifying bacteria, 511
Nitrogen, and bends, 233; cycle, 510–511, **510**, **511**
Nitrogen-fixing bacteria, 511, **511**
Nitrogenous wastes, 235–237, 240
Noctiluca, 82
Node, of stem, 152, **152**
Nodules, def., 511; of peanut, **511**
Nordic race, 502, 503
North America, in Paleozoic era, 472, **472**
Nose, 229, **230**, 272; cavity, 229, **230**
Nuclear division, 405–407, **406**, **407**
Nuclear membrane, 32–33, **32**
Nucleus, 31, 32, **32**, 33; of animal eggs, **387**; of flowering plant egg, 372; of flowering plant sperm, 372, 372–373, **373**, 374, 374–375; of white corpuscle, **206**, **207**
Nutrient, agar, 302; def., 170
Nymph, insect, 96

Oak, 71, **71**, 73, 519; classification of, 130; cork of, 155; leaf, **71**; root, 162; seedling, **377**; trunk, **155**
Oats, 75; breeding difficulties, 439–440
Octopus, 91, **92**
Oedogonium, 60
Oesophagus (see Esophagus)
Offspring, 362–369, 375–385, 386–401, 404–421
Oil glands, of skin, 238, **238**
Oils (fats), 147
Okapi, **491**
Old age, and disease, 346
Old Stone Age, 500; artifacts from, **496**
Olfactory lobes, of vertebrates, **481**
One-celled organisms (see Algae, Bacteria, Protozoa)
Onion, 75, **162**; chromosome number of, **408**; experiment with, **412**; mitosis in root tip, **406**; skin cells, 53
Operation, 321, 350

Opium, 356
Opossum, 119, **121**; reproduction, 397
Opsonins, 311
Optic lobes, of vertebrates, **481**
Optic nerve, in man, 273, **273**
Orange, seedless mutation, 441, 443
Order, in classification, 128
Organ, def., 51
Organic disease, 300, 347, 349
Organic evolution (see Evolution)
Organisms, behavior of, 254–297; classification of, 127–137; def., 51; and disease, 298–359; functioning of, 138–167, 168–253; heredity in, 402–457; kinds, 56–126; origin of, 458–505; relationships of, 515–527, 537–555; and reproduction, 360–401; structure of, 556–568; survey of, 56–126
Organs, bird, **116**; breathing, 225–234; circulatory, 205–224; def., 51; digestive, 190–204; endocrine, 242–253; excretory, 235–241; grasshopper, **94**; of nervous system, 270–278; origin in embryo, 388, **390**; plant, **52**, 140–167; reproductive, 370–373, 377–379, 381, 382, 386–397, **392**
Origin, of earth, 460; of species, 488–494
Ornithologists, 115
Osmosis, 45 (see Diffusion)
Outbreeding, 437–438
Ova (ovum, sing.), 386, **387**
Ovary, animal, **243**, 386, 390, **392**, 393–396; of flower, 371–372, **371**, 372, 374, 375–377, **375**, **376**; growth of plant, 375–377
Overgrazing, and soil erosion, 532–533
Overproduction, daisy, **490**; and evolution, 488–489, **489**
Oviducts, 386; bird, 393–394; fish, 388; frog, 391–393, **392**; human, 397; mammal, 395–396, 397; rabbit, 395–396
Ovules, 372, **372**, 374–377, **374**, 375
Owls, and conservation, 546–547
Oxidases, 41
Oxidation, 40–41; in cells, 40, 41, **235**; compared with photosynthesis, 147–148; and excretion, 235, 240; rapid, 40–41, **40**; slow, 41; and thyroid, 245–246
Oxide, 41
Oxygen, 34, 35; and altitude, **224**, 225, 231–232; and artificial respiration, 231, **232**;

atom, **33;** and breathing, **224,** 225–226; cycle, 512, **512;** in oxidation, 40–41; in photosynthesis, 145, 148
Oxyhemoglobin, 207
Oyster, 91, 92, 335; and starfish, 90

P₁, def., 413, **413**
Paleolithic, def., 501 (see Stone Age)
Paleontologist, 481, 482; def., 465; at work, **467**
Paleozoic era, 468, 471–473, **472, 473, 477**
Palisade cells, of leaves, 141, **141,** 144
Palm (trees), 73; coconut, **75;** date, 75; stems, 164–165
Pancreas, 198–199, 243; and diabetes, 248–249, 252; ducts, **196;** stimulation of, 201
Pancreatic, activation of juice, 201; ducts, **196;** juice, **198,** 199
Paramecium, 82, 83–84; behavior of, 263, **263;** conjugation of, 367, **367;** reproduction of, 364, **364,** 367, **367**
Parasites, 66, 82, 300, 508; causing disease, 63, 300–330, 331–345; large, 341–343; of plants, 63, **509**
Parasitism, 63–64, 300
Parathyroid, 243, 251, 252
Paratyphoid, statistics, 315
Parental care, in birds, 394–395, **395;** in fish, 390–391, **391;** in frogs, 393, **393;** in insects, 101–102, **493;** in mammals, 397–398
Parsley family, 77
Parthenogenesis, 379; def., 379; in plants, 379
Passenger pigeons, extinction of, 545
Passive immunity, 317–318; for tetanus, 320
Pasteur, Louis, 306–308; and disease, 307, 311–313; and immunity, 311–313; and pasteurization, 334; and rabies, 312–313; and spontaneous generation, 362–364, **363;** treatment, 312–313; and wine, 307
Pasteurization, of milk, 333–334; test of, 334
Pavlov, Ivan, and conditioned response, 279
Pea, chromosome number of, **408;** heredity in, 412–416, **413, 415, 416, 417;** pod, 377; tall X short cross, **413**
Peanut plant, 511

Pearl, Raymond, and tobacco, 354
Pearls, 92
Peat, 67–68
Pecan tree, grafting, **443**
Pedigree, def., 437; of famous family, 452–453, **453;** of man, 447; and shortsightedness in man, **446;** and skin condition in man, **446**
Peking man, 496–497, **497, 498;** excavating for, **497**
Pelican, and conservation, 546; feeding young, **395**
Pellagra, 182
Penicillin, 63, 324; and mold, 63, 65
Penicillium, 65, 324
Pepsin, 198
Peptone, 198
Perch, 107
Perching birds, 114
Perennials, 71, 73
Perianth, 370, **371**
Periods, geologic, 468
Peristalsis, 194, 196–197, 200
Permeable, def., 45
Persian cat, heredity, **411**
Petals, 370, 375; of lily, **371**
Petiole, 140; scar, **151**
Petri dish, for studying bacteria, 302; used in high school experiment, **329**
Petrifaction, def., 463
Petrified, Forest, 474; tree, **463**
Phagocytes, 207, **310,** 311; and bacteria, **207**
Phloem, of root, 158–159, **159;** of stem, **154,** 155, 156, **156**
Phosphatase, in milk, 334
Phosphorus (P), 36; in common foods, 187; in diet, 175
Photosynthesis, 143–145, **146;** equation, 145; experiment, **143;** in leaf, **143;** and respiration compared, 148; summarized, 148
Phototropism, 264, 266; of nasturtium, **265;** negative, 264; positive, 264
Phylum, annelids, 88–89; arthropods, 93–106; bryophytes, 66–68; in classification, 128; coelenterates, 85–87; def., 128; echinoderms, 89–90; flatworms, 87; invertebrates, 82–106; mollusks, 91–93; porifera (sponges), 84–85; protozoa, 82–84; pteridophytes, 68–69; roundworms, 87–88; spermatophytes, 69–77; thallophytes, 58–66; vertebrates, 107–122
Pig, effect of environment on, **429;** embryo, **482;** and hybrid

vigor, 438; and rickets, **178,** 179–180; and tapeworm, 343; and trichina worm, 341, 342–343
Pigeons, 115
Pimples, 240–241
Pine, 72–73, **73,** 164; and environment, **427;** needles, 72–73, **73;** and rust, **523**
Pineal gland, human, 243, 271
Pioneers, in plant communities, 518–519
Pisces (see Fish)
Pistil, 370–372, **371, 372;** after fertilization, **375**
Pistillate, def., 370; flower, **371**
Pith, 153, **154;** in monocots, 164–165, **165;** rays, 157
Pithecanthropus erectus, 496, **498**
Pituitary gland, 242–243, **243,** 251–252, **271**
Placenta, 396, **396,** 397
Plague, bubonic, 331; and quarantine, 331
Planaria, 81, 87, **88**
Plankton, 62–63
Plant lice (see Aphids)
Plants, 58–79, 138–167; behavior of, 264–268, **265, 266, 267, 268;** breeding, 434–435, 437–440, 442–443; Bryophytes, 66–68; classification of, 130; and environment, 515–520; families, 77; in food chains, 508–510; food-making in, 142–147, **144, 146;** and growth hormones, 251; importance of green, 138, 142–147, 148, 151; insect-eating, **267;** movement of water in, 161–162; organs, **52;** parasites on, **509;** phyla, 59–79; reproduction of, 370–385; simplest (Thallophytes), 58–66; structure of, 140–167; tissues, 140–167; tropisms, 264–268, **265, 266, 267, 268;** unusual behavior of, 264–265, **266, 267;** useful, 75, 77; uses of, 75, 77, 138, 148
Plasma, of blood, 205–206, 211; membrane, 31
Platelets, 206, 207; and clotting, 207–208
Platyhelminths (flatworms), **81,** 87, **88,** 133
Pleura, 226
Pleurisy, 226
Pleurococcus, 59
Plexus, of autonomic system, 276, **276, 277**
Plumule, 375
Pneumonia, 326, 347
Poisons, contact, 524–525; stomach, 524

Poliomyelitis (polio), 298, 314–317, 318, 327; carriers, 337; and iron lung, 227, **228**
Polled cattle, 440; def., 422
Pollen, and allergy, 351–352; case, 372, **372**; development of grain, 372, **373**; grain, **373**; tube, 372, **373**, 374–375, **374**
Pollination, 373–374, **374**
Pollution, 332; of water supply, **534**, 535
"Pollywog," 110, **111**, 393, **393**
Polydactyly, 448–449, **448**
Polynesian, 502
Polyneuritis, 177–178, **177**
Pond scums (simple plants), 59
Poplar, 73; leaf, **71**
Pores, of skin, 238–239, **238**
Porifera (sponges), 84–85, 133
Pork, and parasites, 342–343
Portal circulation, **220**, 221
Positive tropism, 264
Postulates of Koch, 305–306
Potassium, 36
Potato, 76, **162**, 163; beetle, 520, **521**; family, 77; vegetative reproduction of, 378–379, **378**
Pouched mammals, 118–119, **397**, 484–485, **485**
Poverty and health, 182, 342, 357, **357**
Prairie dog, **121**
Praying mantis, 99, **99**
Pregnancy, 397–398
Prehistoric, ages, 466–468, 471–477; man, 495–500
Prejudice, 503–504
Preservation of food, 304
Prevention of disease, 311–320, 324–329, 331–343
Primary germ layers, 388, **388**
Primary sex cells, 408–409, **409**, 422, **429**; dihybrid, **419**
Primates, 122
Primrose, and heredity, 426
Protective resemblance, 492–493, **492, 493**
Proteins, 36, 37, 40; in common foods, 186; in diet, 174–175; diffusion of, 45; digestion of, 190, 198, 199; synthesis of, 146–147, **147**; test for, 37
Proterozoic era, 468, 471, **477**
Prothallus, of fern, 381, **381**; of flowering plant, 381–382
Protonema, 382, **382**, 383
Protons, 33, **33**
Protoplasm, 31–38, 146; composition of, 35–37, **35**, 40; compounds in, 36, 37; elements in, **35**, 36; irritability of, 46, 257–258; and living things, 47; parts of, 31, **32**; streaming of,

48; structure of, **33**; summary of, 37
Protozoa, 82–84, 133; ameba, 45–47; behavior of, 263–264, **263, 264**; of malaria, 338–340, **339**, 367–368, **368**; reproduction, 364, **364**, 365, 367–368, **368**; tropisms of, 263, **263**, 264, **264**
Pseudopod, **45**, 46
Psychiatrist, 295
Psychologist, def., 286
Psychosis, 296
Pteridophytes (ferns), 68–69, **69**, 136
Ptomaines, 335
Ptyalin, 192, 198
Public health, 331–345; disposal of sewage, 332–333, **332**
Puffball, and spores, **489**
Pulmonary, artery, **211**, 220, **221**; circulation, 220–221, **221**; tuberculosis, 306, 347; vein, 221, **221**
Pulse, 214
Puma, 128, **129**
Pupa, of ant, **100**; of butterfly, **95**, 96; of mosquito, **340**, 341
Pupil, of eye, 273, **273**
Pure Food and Drug Act, 336
Pus, 207; bacteria, **301**
Pustules, of cowpox, 313
Pygmy black race, 502
Pyloric sphincter, 196, **196**
Pythons, 113

Quail, 263, **263**
Quarantine (isolation), 331, 332; def., 331
Queen Anne's lace (wild carrot), 76
Quinine and malaria, 327

Rabbit, chromosome number, **408**; reproduction of, 395–397; and web of life, 522–523, **523**
Rabies, 312–313, 327
Races, blood groups in, 503; classification of, 502; of man, 502–503; misuse of term, 503; prejudice, 503–504; table of human, 502; variations in, 503
Radiations, and chromosome number, 425; and mutation, 424
Radicle, of seed, **375**
Radioactive elements, 247, 349
Radiolarian (a protozoan), **84**
Radium, and cancer, 349; and mutation, 424
Ragweed, 351; and hay fever, 351
Ratios, Mendelian, 413–416; dihybrid, 415–416, **416**
Rats, dietary experiments on,

175–176, **176**, 178; as germ carriers, 337, **337**; heredity in, **415**; and hormones, 242–243; and learning, 281
Rattlesnake, 113, **113**
Ray flowers, 77
Reasoning, 284–286, **285**, **286**; in chimpanzees, 285–286, **286**
Receiving gamete, 366, 367
Receptors, 257, **258**, 272–275, **273**, **274**, **275**; of ear, 274–275, **275**; of eye, 272–274, **273**, **274**; internal, 272; in reflex arc, 260, 261
Recessive characters, 412, **413**, 414, **414**, 415, **415**, 416, **417**, 418, **418**, 438; in man, 448, 449–450, **451**; mutations, 422–423
Recombination and variation, 416–417
Rectum, 190
Red corpuscles, 206–207, **206**; and malaria, 338
Redi, and spontaneous generation, 362, **363**
Reduction, of chromosome number, 408–409, **409**
Reduction division, 408–409, **409**; and heredity, 409–410, 413–417, **413**, **415**, **416**, **417**, 425; and independent assortment, 415–417, **416**, **417**
Redwoods, forest, **538**; giant, 158, **158**
Reed, Walter, and yellow fever, 340
Reflex, act, 260–263; arc, **261**; conditioned, 279, **280**
Reflexes, 257, 260–263, **261**, 279, **280**, 285; and habits, 283; in insects, 260; in protozoa, 263–264, **263**, **264**; in spiders, 260–261
Reforestation, 540, **540**
Refrigeration, and bacteria, 304
Refuges, 546, **547**, 548, **548**
Regeneration, in starfish, 90
"Reindeer moss," 64
Relationships of living things (ecology), 515–527
Rennin, 198
Reproduction, 47, 360–401; ameba, 46, 364, **365**; animal, 386–401; asexual, 360–366, 377–379; bird, 393–395, **395**; bread mold, 365–366, **365**; fern, **380**, 381, **381**; fish, 388–391, **389, 390, 391**; flowering plant, 370–381, **373**, 381–383; frog, 391–393, **392, 393**; human, 397–398; and insect life histories, 95–96, 98, 101, **101**, 102; malarial protozoan, 367; mam-

INDEX

603

mal, 395–398, **396, 397;** molds, 365–366, **365,** 367, **367;** moss, 382, **382;** organs of, 370–373, 381, 382, 386–397, **392;** paramecium, 364, **364;** preview of animal, 386; protozoa, 364, **364, 365;** rabbit, 395–397; sexual, 366–401; spirogyra, 366–367, **367;** by spore formation, 365–366, **365;** and survival, 398; table of plant, 383; variations in, 379–381; vegetative, 377–379; yeast, 364, **365**

Reproductive organs, animal, 386; bird, 393–394; flowering plant, 370–373, **371, 372, 373;** frog, **392;** origin in embryo, 388; rabbit, 395–396, **396**

Reptiles, 111–113, 135; Age of, 474; brain, 481; embryo, **482;** fossil, **464,** 466; reproduction, 394, **394;** usefulness, 111

Resemblances, and classification, 127–137, 483–484; chemical, 483; in embryos, 482, **482;** hereditary, 402–410; protective, 492–493; in skeleton, 480, **481;** among vertebrates, 480–482, **480, 481, 482**

Reservoirs and water supply, 333

Respiration, 46, 147–148, 224–233; and breathing, 230–231; cellular, 147–148; compared with photosynthesis, 147–148; plant, 147–148

Response, 256, 257–258, 261; ameba, **264;** conditioned, 279, **280;** learned, 279–288; paramecium, 263, **263;** plant, 264–265, **265, 266, 267;** to stimulus, 257–258, 279; unlearned, 257, 260–265; vorticella, **83**

Retina, of eye, 273–274, **273, 274**

Retted, def., 302

Rheumatic fever, 349

Rh factor, 210; heredity of, 449–450

Rhizopus, 63, **65;** reproduction of, 63, 365–366, **365**

Riboflavin, 182; in common foods, 187; formula of, 36

Ribs, 227, **227**

Rice, 75; and beriberi, 177–178

Rickets, 178, 179–180, **179**

Rickettsiae, 327–328

Ringworm, 63

Robbins, Frederick C., and polio, 316

Robin, 107, 115

Rocks, age of, 460; and earth history, 460–470; formation of, 460–462; formation of sedimentary, 461–462, **461;** kinds of, 460–462; molten, 460; strata of, 462, **462;** tilted strata of, **462**

Rockweed (Fucus), 59–60, **61**

Rocky Mountain spotted fever, 328

Rodents, 119

Roosevelt, Pres. Theodore, 529

Rooster, 250, 251

Roots, 151, **151,** 158–166, **159;** cap, **159,** 160; as food, 162; growing point, **159,** 160; hairs, 160–161, **160, 161;** length, 138, **151;** and plant responses, 264; pressure, 162; and soil, 159–160; structure of, 159–161, **159;** sugar beet, **163;** summary, 165–166; tap, 162, **163;** tip, **159,** 160–161; use to plant, 151, 159, 160–161; wheat, **159**

Rose, family, 77; wild, **76**

Ross, Ronald, and malaria, 338–339

Roughage, 200–201

Roundworms, 87–88, 133

Runner, of strawberry, 378, **378**

Rusts, 523, 524

Rye, 161

Saber-toothed tiger, 465

Safety, home check list for, **350;** suit, **351**

St. Martin, Alexis, and gastric digestion, 197–198, **197**

Salamanders, 111

Saliva, 192, 194

Salivary glands, of man, **191,** 193; of mosquito, **98;** stimulation of, 194, 201

Salk, Dr. Jonas, 298, 316

Salmon, life cycle, 109; stocking of, **549**

Salts, as wastes, 235, **235,** 238, 240

Salvarsan ("606"), 327

Sanctuaries, def., 548

Sand dollar, 90

Sandpiper, bill, **115**

Sandstone, 461

Sanitation, 332

Sap, 73; cell, 32

Saprophytes, 64, 301–302

Sapwood, 157–158, **157**

Scale insects, control of, 524–525

Scales, bird, 116, **116;** fish, 108; of insect wings, 96–97; reptile, 111

Scarlet fever, 317; immunity, 317

Scavengers, 88, 100, 105, 115, 509

Schick, Bela, and diphtheria, 318–319; test, 319

Schleiden, Matthias, 47

Schwann, Theodor, 47

Science, and improvement of man, 455–456

Scientific method, and betterment of man, 455–456

Scion, 442, 443, **443**

Sclerotic coat, of eye (sclera), **273**

Scorpion, 105, **105**

"Scouring rush," 70

Scurvy, 176–177, **178,** 180

Sea, anemones, 85, **85;** horse, **108;** lettuce (Ulva), 61; lion, **121;** urchin, 90, **90**

Seal, appendage, **481**

Seasons, and plant growth, 516

Seaweeds, 58, 59–62, **61**

Secondary sexual characteristics, 386; in birds, 386; in deer, 386, **387;** and hormones, 250, 251; in mammals, 386, **387;** in spiders, **104**

Secretin, 201, 242

Secretion, as conditioned response, 201–202; def., 46; as reflex, 201

Secretions, digestive, 192–193; internal, 242–253

Sediment, 461; and fossil formation, 462–463, 464, **464**

Sedimentary rock, formation of, 461–462, **461, 462;** strata of, **461;** tilted, **462**

Sedum, 140

Seedless, fruits, 380; vegetables, 380–381

Seedling, 377, **377**

Seed plants (see Flowering plants), classification, 74

Seeds, 10, 72, 375–377, **375;** agents of dispersal, **376,** 377; bean, **375;** coats, **375;** corn, **375;** development of pea, **375;** dispersal, **376,** 377; formation, 375–377; "naked," 72; in plant life cycle, 370, 375–377; sprouting, **160**

Segments, 94; grasshopper, **94;** worm, 88, **89**

Segregation, in four o'clock, 413; in fruit fly, **418;** in garden pea, **413, 415;** in guinea pigs, **416;** in squash, **414;** in rats, **415;** law of, 413–415, **413, 414, 415**

Selection, animals, 435–436; in breeding, 434–436, **435;** effects explained, 435; natural, 488–490; in plants, 434–435; procedure, 434–435; in soybeans, 434–435; of strawberry, **435**

Selective cutting, of trees, 539–540, **540**

Self-pollination, 374

Semicircular canals, 275

Semmelweiss, Ignaz, and blood poisoning, 320

Sensation, and brain, 270; and

receptors, 265; and reflex arc, 260, **261**; and skin, 238, 239
Sense organs, 260, 272–275, **273, 274, 275,** 277; and stimuli, 257
Sensitive plant, 265, **267**
Sensory neuron, 260, **261**
Sensory region, of brain, 270
Sepals, 370, **371**
Sequoia, 71
Serous membrane, 54, 196
Serum, blood, 208, 209–210; immune, 320
Sewage, 332–333, **332;** disposal, 332–333, **332;** and typhoid, 314; and water supply, 535
Sex, chromosomes, 450; effect of removal of glands, **250;** glands, 250, 251, 252; heredity of, 450; organs, fish, 390
Sex-linked heredity, 450, **451**
Sexual reproduction, 366–401; animal, 386–401; def., 366; plant, 370–385; simplest, 366–369
Shale, 461, 462
Shark, 109, **109;** suckers, 109, **109**
Sheath, of neuron, **258**
Sheep, Ancon mutation, 440, 441; and anthrax, 305, 312; Bighorn Mountain, **131, 548;** brain, **271;** hybridization, 438
Sheeting, and soil erosion, 530
Shelled invertebrates (see Mollusks)
Shells, 82–83, 86–87, **87,** 91, **91,** 106, **106, 479**
"Shelter belts," 530
Shipworm, 93
Shore life, 14
Shortfingeredness, 448–449
Shortsightedness, pedigree, **446**
Shrubs, 70
Siamese cat, heredity, **411**
Sieve plate, 156
Sieve tubes, of stem, 156, **156**
Silkworms, and disease, 307–308; life cycle, **96**
Silt, 536, **536**
Sinanthropus pekinensis, 496–497, **497**
Sinuses, 230, 353
Sinusitis, def., 353
Sire, def., 437
606, a drug, 327
Sixfingeredness, 448, 448–449
Skeleton, Eohippus, **478;** fossil fish, **463;** horse, **478;** protozoan, **84;** snake, 113
Skin, 238–241, **238, 239;** and body temperature, 239–240; care of, 240–241; and excretion, 240; as receptors, 272; and ventilation, 240
Skin condition, pedigree, **446**

Skull, 107; anteater, **194;** armadillo, **194;** dog, **194;** horse, **194;** man, **194,** 270, 272, 277
Slate, 462
Slip, 377–378, def., **378**
Slugs, 91, 92, **92,** 93
Small intestine, 190, **196,** 198–200, **200**
Smallpox, 313–314, 327; cases in U.S., 314; immunity, 313–314; and India, **313;** vaccine, 314, **315**
Smell, 272
Smoking, as habit, 284; and health, 354
Smooth muscle, 52; control of, 275–276, **276**
Smut, corn, 66
Snails, 81, 90, 91; fossil series, 478, **479**
Snakes, 111, 112–113, **112, 113;** poisonous, 113, **113;** shedding skin, **113;** sperm, **387;** x-ray, **113**
Snapping turtle, 112; hatching, **394**
Social insects, 101–104
Sodium, 35, 36, 175; chloride, 35, 238
"Softwoods," 73
Soil, 515; bacteria, 326; conservation of, 529–533; conservation services, 533; destruction of, 530; erosion, **529,** 530; formation of, 529–530; improvement of, 530–532; leaching of, 530; minerals, 146, 147; and roots, 159–160; top, 529–530, **529;** water in, 534–535
Soil Conservation Society, 550
Soluble, 45
Somatic, mutations, 423–424, **424**
Sorting (see Classification)
Sound and hearing, 274–275, **275**
Souring, of wine, 307
Soybean, and selection, 434–435; uses of, 147
Sparrow, 115; bill, **115;** brain, **481**
Spawning, 109, 388–389, **389**
Specialization (of function), 53
Species, 128, 436–437; chromosome number, 408, **408;** def., 128; origin of, 460–505; survival, 398
Specific antibodies, 311
Specific toxins, 311
Speech, aid to learning, 286
Sperm, 386, **387;** birds, 393–394; ducts, 386, **392;** in fertilization, 386; fish, **387,** 389; flowering plant, 372–373, **373,** 374–375, **374;** frog, **387,** 391; human, **387;** maturation, 408–409, **409;** snake, **387;** worm, 387

Spermary, 386, 390; frog, **392**
Spermatophytes, 69–78; classification of, 74, 136
Sphagnum, 67, 68
Spiders, 93, 104–105, **104, 105,** 134; house, 105; instincts, 260–262, **261;** trapdoor, 105; webs, 105, **105, 262**
Spinal column, 107, 272
Spinal cord, in man, 230, 259, **259,** 270–272, **271,** 277; in reflex arc, 260, **261;** in sheep, **271;** in vertebrates, **481**
Spindle, in mitosis, 407
Spiny-skinned animals (see Echinoderms)
Spirillum, 300, **301**
Spirogyra, 58, 59, **59,** 142; reproduction of, 366–367, **367**
Spleen, 207
Sponges (Porifera), 81, 84–85, 133
Spongy cells, of leaves, 141, **141**
Spontaneous generation, 362–364; experiments, 363
Sporangium, bread mold, 366; moss, 382, **382**
Spore cases, fern, **69, 380,** 381, **381;** mold, 63, 365–366, **365;** moss, 66, **67,** 382, **382**
Spores, bacteria, 303; bread mold, 63, **65,** 365–366, **365;** def., 63; malarial protozoan, **339;** moss, 66; of penicillium, **65;** puffball, **489;** reproduction by, 365–366, **365;** tetanus, 319, **319**
Sporulation, def., 365; in various organisms, 366
Spraying, and apples, **524**
Sprouting seeds, 377
Spruce, 73, 164
Squash, heredity of shape, **414;** tendrils, **266**
Squid, 91
Squirrel, 121; gray, classification of, **132**
Staining, bacteria, 305; chromatin, 33
Stamens, 370, **371,** 372–373, **372**
Staminate, def., 370; flower, **371**
Stanley, W. M., and viruses, 328
Starches, 36, 37, 143; chemical formula of, 36; in diet, 170–171, 175; in diffusion, 45; plant sources of, **144;** production in plants, 143; test for, 37
Starfishes, 81, 89–90, **89;** chromosome number, **408;** development, 386–388
Statistics, def. (vital), 331
Stearin, formula of, 36
Stems, 151–159, **151, 152, 153, 155, 158,** 162–166; bamboo, 164–165; conducting cells, 153–155, 156–157; corn, 164–165,

INDEX **605**

165; cross-section, **157, 164;** diagram, **154;** growth of, 151; monocot, 164–165, **165;** palm, 164–165; structure of, 153–158, **154;** summary, 165–166; underground, 162, **162;** variations in, 162–165; vegetative reproduction by, 377–379, **378;** white potato, **162;** woody, 151–159
Sterile, def., 302
Sterilization, methods, 302–303, 304; and surgery, 320
Stickleback, male at nest, **391**
Stigma, 370–372, **371, 372,** 375
Stimulant, 355
Stimulus, 256, 257–258, 272, 279, 291; def., 257; plant responses, 264–265, **265, 266, 267, 268;** in reflex arc, 260–263, **261;** responses of protozoa, 263, **263, 264**
Stirrup, 274, **275**
Stock, 442, 443, **443;** in grafting, 442–443, **443;** races of man, 502, **502, 503**
Stoma (pl. stomata), 142, **142**
Stomach, 190, **196;** digestion in, 192, 196–198; functions, 190, 192, 196–198; glands, **193,** 196; lining, **193;** movements, 196–197; muscles, **196;** structure, **196;** tissues, 196
Stomach poisons, for insects, 524
Stone Age, artifacts from, **496;** history of, 500–502
Strain, of bacteria, 325; plus and minus in reproduction, 367, **367**
Strata, rock, **461,** 466–468; def., 462
Strawberry, and selection, **435;** vegetative reproduction, 378, **378**
Streptococcus, of pus, **301;** and sulfa drugs, 326
Streptomycin, 306, 326
Striated muscle (see Voluntary muscle)
Strip cropping, 533
Struggle for existence, and evolution, 489
Style, 370, **371,** 372
Successful reproduction, 398
Succession of organisms, 518, **519**
Sucrose, 36, 37, 143; formula of, 36
Sugar beet, 144, 163
Sugar cane, 71, 75, 43, **144;** breeding, 438–439
Sugars, 36, 37; in diet, 170–171, **171,** 175; and diffusion, 42–45, **43;** and digestion, 192, 198–199; formula of, 36; and in-

sulin, 247–249; and metabolism, 170–171, 175; movement in plants, 156; in photosynthesis, 143–145, **144;** sources of, 143, **144, 145;** test for simple, 37
Sulfa drugs, 326–327
Sulfanilamide, 326
Sulfur, 36
Sulfuric acid, 34
Sun, and chlorophyll, 142–143; and gene action, 426, **427;** and photosynthesis, 143–145; and vitamin D, 180
Sunburn, 240
Sundew, 265, **268**
Sunfish, male at nest, **391**
Sunflower, behavior, **265;** stem, **164**
Supplying gamete, 366, **367**
Surgery, and appendicitis, 350; and cancer, 347, 349; and infection, 320, **321**
Survival of the fittest, and evolution, 489; and daisy, **490**
Sustained yield, in forests, 539–540
Swallow, cliff, nest, **114**
Swallowing, 194, 230
Swarming, of bees, 102, **102**
Sweat, glands, 238–239, **238, 239,** 241
Swedes, 503
Swift, a lizard, **112**
Symbiosis, 64
Symbols, of elements, 36
Symmetry, bilateral, 90; radial, **89,** 90
Sympathin, 276
Synapse, def., 260; in reflex arc, 260, **261**
Synthesis, of compounds, 144
Syphilis, 327

Tables, of animal tissues, 54; of blood types, 210; of calorie needs, 173, 174; chromosome numbers, 408; comparing photosynthesis and respiration, 148; on disease, 343; of eras, 468; of excretion of wastes, 240; of food values, 186–187; of food substances, 36; of insect use and harm, 103; of nervous system, 277; plant tropisms, 266; simple inheritance in man, 448; tests for compounds, 37
Tadpoles, 110–111, **111,** 393; changing to frog, **393;** and thyroxin, 244
Tagged atoms, 247
Tail, in embryos, **482**
Tapeworm, 87, **342,** 343

Taproot, beet, **163;** oak, 162
Tar pit, 465, **465**
Tarantula, 104–105
Taste buds, 193, 272
Technique, 304
Teeth, armadillo, **194;** dog, **194;** Eohippus, 478; grinding, 119; horse, **194;** human, 193–194, **195;** infected, **353,** 354
Temperature, 41; and bacterial growth, 302, 303, 304; body, 41–42, 239–240, 303; and gene action, 426; and plant growth, 516; regulation, 239–240
Tendon, 51, 52
Tendrils, plant, 264; squash, **266**
Tentacles, anemone, 85, **85;** jellyfish, 86, **86;** octopus, **92**
Tenzing Norgay, and Everest, 225
Terminal branches, of neurons, 258–259, **258, 261**
Termites, 102, 104, **104;** damage by, 103, **104**
Testis, 243, 386
Tests for compounds, 37
Tetanus, 319–320; bacilli, **319**
Tethelin, 242, 252
Thallophytes, 58–66, **58, 60, 61, 62, 65, 66,** 135
Thiamin, 178, 180–181; in common foods, 187
Thigmotropism, 266
Thinking (see Reasoning)
Thistle tube, 43, **43,** 44; in diffusion experiment, **43**
Thoracic duct, 218
Thorax, of insects, 94
Thorndike, E. L., and behavior, **281**
Thoroughbred, horse, **434**
Throwback, def., 415
"Thunder lizard," 474
Thymus gland, 243, 251, 252
Thyroid gland, 230, **243,** 244–247, **244, 245, 246,** 252
Thyroxin, 244–246, **245, 246,** 252
Ticks, 105
Time clock, for man, **495**
Tissues, 49–55, **49;** culture of, 328; def., 50; lab study of, 55; origin in embryo, 53; plant, 53; relation to lymph, 218, **218;** stomach, 196; summary, 53–54; table of animal, 54; types, 49, **49,** 51, 54
Toads, 110–111, **110;** midwife and eggs, **393**
Toadstools, 63
Tobacco, 532; and health, 354; mammoth mutation of, 441, **441;** mosaic disease of, 328
Tomato, dusting of plants, **525;** irrigated field, **537**

Tongue, man, 193, 272
Tonsils, 229, **230**; and infection, 353
Topsoil, 528, 529–530, **530**, 536, 539
Touch corpuscle, 238
Tourniquet, 214
Toxin-antitoxin, and diphtheria, 318
Toxins, 311; bacterial, 311; diphtheria, 317; malaria, 338; specific, 311; tetanus, 319
Toxoid, for diphtheria, 318; for tetanus, 319
Trace elements, 36
Tracer atoms, 247
Trachea, **195**, **225**, 229–230, **230**, **244**
Tracheids, 156
Trailing arbutus, 551
Transfusions, and blood banks, 208–210, 211
Transpiration, 161–162
Transplantation, of bacteria, 304; of plants, 161
Transportation system, human, 204–224; plant, 153–162
Trapdoor spider, 105
Trees, 70, **72**, **153**, **155**, **158**; and allergies, 351; as crop, 538, 539–540; cross-section, **157**; leaves, **71**; live, 515–516; and lumber, 537–538; nurseries, 540, **540**; petrified, **463**
Trial and error learning (see Activity and success learning)
Triceratops, 475
Trichina, 88, 341, 342–343, **342**
Trilobite, 472, **472**, 473
Tropisms, animal, **263**, 264; plant, 264, **265**, 266, **266**, 267
Trudeau, E. L., and tuberculosis, 306
Trunk, cross-section of, **157**
Trypsin, 198
Tsetse fly, 337–338
Tube feet, of starfish, 90
Tuber, 162; def., 163, 379
Tuberculosis, 306, 347; death rate graph, **305**; and milk supply, 333; vaccine for, 317; and x-ray, **306**
Tubes, in roots, 158–159; in stems, 156–157, **156**
Tulips, 71; vegetative reproduction of, 379, **379**
Tumor, 347–349, **348**; benign, 347; malignant, 347–348
Tuna fish, 108
Turgidity, and plant behavior, 164
Turkey, wild, 545
Turtles, 111, **112**; babies hatching, **394**

Twig, horse chestnut, 151–154, **152**
Twins, fraternal, 455; identical, **454**, 454–455
Tyndall, John, and spontaneous generation, 362
Typhoid, 314, **315**, 332; bacteria, **301**; and carriers, 337; statistics, 314, **315**; and water supply, 332
Typhus, 328, 337; vaccine preparation, **317**
Tyrannosaurus, 474, **475**

Ultraviolet light, and sunburn, 240; and vitamin D, 180
Ulva, 61
Umbilical cord, **396**, 396
Undulant fever, and milk supply, 333
Unequal division, in yeast, 364, **365**
Unit characters, law, 415–416, **416**, 417
United States, Department of Agriculture, 436, 533, 537, 542; Fish and Wildlife Service, 549–550; Forest Service, 543–545, 548; National Park Service, 548; Public Health Service, 332, 349; Soil Conservation Service, 533, 537
Unlearned behavior, 256–269
Uranium, 33–34, 460
Urea, 201; and diabetes, 247–248; as waste, 235, **235**, 240
Ureter, 235–237, **236**; of frog, 392
Uric acid, 235, **235**, 240
Urine, **236**, 237; and diabetes, 247; and pregnancy, 397
"Use and disuse" theory of evolution, 490–492
Uterus, 395–396, **396**, 397

Vaccination, 313–314, **315**; reasons for, 314; smallpox, 313–314 (see Inoculation, Immunity)
Vaccine, influenza, 317; measles, 317; polio, 316–317; preparation of, **315**, **317**; scarlet fever, 317; smallpox, 314; tuberculosis, 317; typhus, **317**; whooping cough, 317
Vacuoles, in ameba, **45**, 46; cell, 32, 161; food, **45**, 46; in paramecium, **82**, 83, 84; root hair, 161, **161**
Vagina, 396, 397
Valves, 217–218, **217**; heart, 217–218, **217**; leaking, 218; lymphatic, 218; vein, 217, **217**
Van Helmont, Jan, plant experiment, 140, 146

Variation, in bean length, 427–428, **428**; environmental, 426–428, **430**, 431–432; in evening primrose, 490; and evolution, 489; hereditary, 411–421; in man, **430**, 431–432, 503; measurement of, 427–428; partly explained, 416–417; in pig, **429**
Varieties, in classification, 130
Vascular bundles, 164–165; in corn, **115**; in sunflower, **164**
Vascular tissues, 155
Vegetables, seedless, 380
Vegetative propagation (see Vegetative reproduction)
Vegetative reproduction, 377–379, 383; in African violet, 379; in Bryophyllum, 379, **379**; and mutation, 423–424, **424**; and plant breeding, 442–443, **443**; in potato, 378–379, **378**; in strawberry, 378, **378**; in sweet potato, 379; in tulip, 379, **379**
Veins, **204**, 205, **214**, 215, 217, **217**; leaf, 159; of leaves, 159; structure of, 215, **215**; valves, 217, **217**
Vena cava, inferior, 220; superior, **211**, 220
Venereal disease, 327
Ventilation, 240
Ventricles, **211**, 212–213, **212**, 217
Venus's flytrap, 265, **267**
Vertebrae, 272, 277
Vertebral column, 107, 272
Vertebrates, 107–122; behavior, 263, **263**; brain, 270, **271**, 481; classes, 107–122, 134–135; def., 107; examples of, **107**; kinds, 107–122; reproduction, 386–401; structural resemblances, 480–482, **480**, **481**
Vestigial structures, 483; in porpoise, **483**
Vestigial wing, in fruit fly, 418, **418**, 422; and temperature, 426
Villus, 199–200, **200**
Vines, 70
Virulence, of germs, 312
Virus, 40, 327–328, **328**; common virus diseases, 327; influenza, **328**; measles, 317; and polio, 298, 314–317; and rabies, 312; smallpox, 313–314; tobacco mosaic, 328
Vision, and cerebrum, 270
Visual purple, and vitamin A, 179
Vital statistics, 331
Vitamins, 176–184, 187; A, 178, 179; B_1, 178, 180–181; B_2, formula, 36; B complex, 178, 180–182; C, 178, 180; and cooking, 182; D, 179–180; E, 182;

INDEX

607

experiments, **177, 178**; in common foods, table, 186–187; K, 182; pills, 182
Voicebox, 229, **230, 244**
Voluntary muscle (see Muscle)
Von Behring, Emil, 317–318
Von Mohl, Hugo, 47
Vorticella, 83
Vultures, 115

Waksman, Selman, 326
Walking stick, and protective adaptation, **492**
Wallace, Alfred Russell, and evolution, 488
Warm-blooded, 117
Wassermann test, for syphilis, 327
Wastes, def., 235; diagram, **235**; and kidney, 235–237; removal, 235–241; and sweat glands, 238–239; table of, 240
Water, 34, 36; absorption by plants, 161; in diet, 175; in diffusion, 43–45, **43**; distilled, in exp., **44**; excretion, 235–241, **235**; formula, 34; ground, 534–535; movement in plants, 153, 155, 157, 161–162; in oxidation, 41; in photosynthesis, 143, 145; plants, **24**; in protoplasm, 36; in soil, 161; table, 534–535; test for, 37; and tropisms, 266; as waste, 235–241, **235**
Water lily, 141
Water-living animals, 80–88, **82, 83, 84, 85, 86, 87, 88,** 89–92, **89, 90, 91,** 107–111, **108, 109, 110, 111;** plants, 59–63, **59, 60, 61, 62**
Watermelon, 439
Water moccasin, 113
Watershed, 333; after fire, **541**
Water supply, conservation of, 534–537; conservation agencies, 536–537; how lost, 535; need for, 534; and public health, 333, **333**; and typhoid, 314
Web, spinning of, 105, 260, 262, **262**
Web of life, 515–527
Wedgwood-Darwin pedigree, 452–453, **453**
Weight, and calories, 173–174, 175; reducing, 174; relation to diet, 174
Weller, Thomas H., and polio, 316
Whale, 118; flipper bones, 480, **480**
Wheat, 75; Kanred, 439; stems, 164–165
"White ant" (termite), 102, 103, 104
White corpuscles (blood cells), **206,** 207, **207**; of lymph nodes, 219
Whitefish, mitosis, **407**
White matter, of brain, 270, **271**
"White plague" (see Tuberculosis)
Whooping cough, immunity, 317
Whooping crane, 545–546
Wildlife, conservation of, 545–552; importance of, 545; laws, 547; vanishing, 545–546
Willow, 370
Windpipe, of man, 229–230, **230**
Wine, and Pasteur, 307
Wings, birds, 116, **116;** insect, 94, 96–97, 98, 99
Wisdom teeth, 194
Wood, 73, 77, 153–158, 538; heart, 157–158, **157;** need for, 538; sap, 157–158, **157**; uses of, 538
Woodpecker, bill, 115; ivory-billed, 545–546

Work, 42, **42**
Worker, ants, 101, **101**; bees, 102, **103**
Worms, 87–89, **88, 89**; sperm, **387**
Wounds, and sulfa drugs, 327; and tetanus, 320
Wren, Carolina, 114
Wriggler, of mosquito, **340,** 341
Wyoming fossils, 466

X-rays, and barley, **425;** and cancer, 349; and fruit flies, 424, **424;** of lily, 371; and mutation, 424, **424;** of snake, **113;** and tuberculosis, 306, **306**
Xylem, of root, 158–159, **159;** of stem, 153, **154,** 155, 156–157, **156, 157**

Yale University, study of behavior, 285–286
Yeast, 64, 307; reproduction, 364, **365**
Yellow fever ("Yellow Jack"), 340
Yerkes, Dr. Robert, and behavior, 285–286
Yolk, 389–390, **390**
Yolk sac, of fish, 389–390, **390;** of mammal, **396**
Young (see Offspring)

Zinc, 36
Zoologist, 80
Zygospore, of bread mold, **367;** def., 366; of spirogyra, 366–367, **367**
Zygote, 386; of animal, 386, 388–389, 391, 394, 395, 397; def., 367; of flowering plant, 374–375, **374**